H. A. Goldsmith
P.O. #158

TREATISE

ON

HYDRAULICS

BY

MANSFIELD MERRIMAN
MEMBER OF AMERICAN SOCIETY OF CIVIL ENGINEERS

TENTH EDITION, REVISED

WITH THE ASSISTANCE OF

THADDEUS MERRIMAN
MEMBER OF AMERICAN SOCIETY OF CIVIL ENGINEERS

TOTAL ISSUE, FIFTY THOUSAND

NEW YORK
JOHN WILEY & SONS, INC.
LONDON: CHAPMAN & HALL, LIMITED

First Edition, published February, 1889
Second Edition, published February, 1890
Third Edition, published March, 1891
Fourth Edition, published March, 1892; reprinted 1893 (twice), 1894 (twice)
Fifth Edition, enlarged, published March, 1895; reprinted 1895, 1896, 1897, 1898
Sixth Edition, published July, 1898; reprinted 1899
Seventh Edition, published July, 1900; reprinted 1901, 1902 (twice)
Eighth Edition, rewritten and enlarged, published May, 1903;
reprinted 1903, 1904, 1905, 1906, 1907, 1908, 1909, 1910
Ninth Edition, revised and reset, published December, 1911;
reprinted, 1912, 1914
Tenth Edition, revised, published October, 1916

7/20

PRESS OF
BRAUNWORTH & CO.
BOOK MANUFACTURERS
BROOKLYN, N. Y.

PREFACE TO EIGHTH EDITION

Since the publication of the first edition of this treatise, in 1889, many advances have been made in Hydraulics. Some of these have been briefly noted in later editions, but to properly record and correlate them it has now become necessary to rewrite and reset the book. In so doing the author has endeavored to incorporate other features that have been suggested to him by teachers and engineers, to whom he here expresses his thanks. All of these suggestions could not be followed, for thereby the work would have been expanded to two volumes. Indeed the question as to what should be left out has often been a more difficult one than that as to what should be inserted, and the author has made the decision from the point of view of the probable benefit that may accrue to students in engineering colleges and to engineers in ordinary conditions of practise.

The same plan of arrangement as in former editions has been followed, but two new chapters have been added, one on Hydraulic Instruments and Observations, which treats of the methods of measuring pressures and velocities, and another on Pumps and Pumping, in which the various machines for raising water are discussed from a hydraulic point of view. Among the new topics introduced in the other chapters may be noted the vortex whirl that occurs in emptying a vessel, new coefficients for dams and for steel and wood pipes, the loss of head in pipes due to curvature, branched circuits or diversions in pipe systems, the influence of piers in producing backwater, canals for water-power plants, discharge curves for rivers, the tidal and the land bore, water-supply estimates, water hammer in pipes, the stability of a ship, and hydraulic-electric analogies. Many new examples and problems are given and in these the author has endeavored not only to exemplify the theory of the subject, but also to illustrate the conditions of actual practise.

Historical notes and references to hydraulic literature are presented with greater fullness than before. . . . Many letters from foreign countries have urged the author to introduce the metric system of measures into the book. To meet this demand the most important data, coefficients, and formulas are given in both English and metric measures, the latter being placed at the end of each chapter; the student who follows these will have no occasion to transform English units, but may learn to think in metric units and to use them without hesitation. . . . The most important tables are presented both in the English and in the metric system, the latter not being a mere transformation of the former but being arranged to be used with metric arguments.

In former editions of this work, as in most other books, the numbers of the articles, formulas, cuts, and problems were consecutive and independent. In this edition, however, only the articles are numbered consecutively, while the number of any formula, cut, or problem agrees with that of the article, and this is placed at the top of the right-hand page. While the main purpose in rewriting the book has been to keep it abreast with modern progress, the attempt has also been made to present the subject more concisely and clearly than before in order to advance the interests of thorough education and to promote sound engineering practise.

NOTE TO NINTH EDITION

During 1903–1910 the eighth edition of this book was reprinted eight times, each impression containing some changes and corrections. It has now become necessary to revise and reset the entire book in order to more fully include the advances of the last decade. New matter will be found on hydraulic instruments, methods of measuring water, oblique weirs, submerged tubes, regulating devices for pipes, conduits, dams, backwater, rainfall, evaporation, and runoff. The tables of coefficients for orifices, weirs, pipes, conduits, and channels have been revised and extended so as to include the results of recent experiments. Some old matter has been omitted or condensed, and a few changes in arrangement have been made. About one-fifth of the text is put in smaller type, so as to aid teachers in selecting shorter courses for their classes. The hydraulic tables are placed in the text in connection with the matter explaining them instead of being collected at the end of the book as before.

In this edition all tables, figures, formulas, and problems bear the number of the article in which they are located, this number being given in heavy type on the headline of each right-hand page. While the amount of matter is about six percent greater than that in the eighth edition, it occupies twenty pages less, owing to the smaller type and longer page. A subject index will be found at the end of the volume. The authors have everywhere endeavored to unify the presentation of the subject in a manner advantageous alike to the technical student and the practising engineer.

NOTE TO TENTH EDITION

In this edition over forty pages have been rewritten and reset, and minor changes have been made on about fifty other pages. This has been done so as to keep the book abreast with modern progress, and thus render it more valuable than the preceding edition for the use of both students and engineers.

The new Articles $72\frac{1}{2}$, $124\frac{1}{2}$, and $136\frac{1}{2}$ treat of proportional weirs, of Biel's formula for flow in pipes and channels, and of backwater due to bridge piers. In Art. 118 Horton's extended table of values of Kutter's n is given, and in Art. 121 new coefficients for riveted steel pipes will be found. In Art. 129 there is new matter regarding the vertical and horizontal curves for open channels, and Art. 157, on water hammer and the surge tank, has been mostly rewritten. Arts. 177–182 have been entirely revised, so as to include modern turbines and the methods for their discussion, while old Art. 202 has been replaced by a new one on hydraulic machinery.

The authors are indebted to Prof. Lewis F. Moody of Rensselaer Polytechnic Institute, to W. M. White, Chief Engineer of Allis-Chalmers Manufacturing Company, to Robert E. Horton, Consulting Engineer, and to other professors and hydraulic engineers for valuable suggestions and kind assistance.

New York, July, 1916.

CONTENTS

CHAPTER 10. THE FLOW OF RIVERS

CHAPTER 11. WATER SUPPLY AND WATER POWER

CHAPTER 12. DYNAMIC PRESSURE OF WATER

CHAPTER 13. WATER WHEELS

CHAPTER 14. TURBINES

CHAPTER 15. NAVAL HYDROMECHANICS

Chapter 16. Pumps and Pumping

Appendix

Mathematical Tables

Hydraulic Tables (In text)

The number of the Table is also the number of the Article

TREATISE ON HYDRAULICS

CHAPTER 1

FUNDAMENTAL DATA

Article 1. Units of Measure

The unit of linear measure universally used in English and American hydraulic literature is the foot, which is defined as one-third of the standard yard. For some minor purposes, such as the designation of the diameters of orifices and pipes, the inch is employed, but inches should always be reduced to feet for use in hydraulic formulas. The unit of superficial measure is usually the square foot, except for the expression of the intensity of pressures, when the square inch is more commonly employed.

Table 1*a*. Inches Reduced to Feet

Inches	Feet	Inches	Feet	Square Inches	Square Feet	Cubic Inches	Cubic Feet
⅛	0.0104	3	0.2500	10	0.6944	1000	0.5787
¼	.0208	4	.3333	20	1.3889	2000	1.1574
⅜	.0313	5	.4167	30	2.0833	3000	1.7361
½	.0417	6	.5000	40	2.6777	4000	2.3148
⅝	.0521	7	.5833	50	3.4722	5000	2.8935
¾	.0625	8	.6667	60	4.1667	6000	3.4722
⅞	.0729	9	.7500	70	4.5500	7000	4.0509
1	.0833	10	.8333	80	5.3555	8000	4.6296
2	.1667	11	.9167	90	6.2500	9000	5.2083

The units of volume employed in measuring water are the cubic foot and the gallon, but the latter must always be reduced to cubic feet for use in hydraulic formulas. In Great Britain and its colonies the Imperial gallon is used, but in the United States the old English gallon has continued to be employed, and the former is 20 percent larger than the latter. The following are the relations between the cubic foot and the two gallons:

1 cubic foot = 6.2288 Imp. gallons = 7.481 U. S. gallons
1 Imp. gallon = 0.1605 cubic feet = 1.201 U. S. gallons
1 U. S. gallon = 0.1337 cubic feet = 0.832 Imp. gallons

In this book the word "gallon" will always mean the United States gallon of 231 cubic inches, unless otherwise stated.

TABLE 1*b*. GALLONS AND CUBIC FEET

Cubic Feet	U. S. Gallons	U. S. Gallons	Cubic Feet	Cubic Feet	Imperial Gallons	Imperial Gallons	Cubic Feet
1	7.481	1	0.1337	1	6.229	1	0.1605
2	14.961	2	0.2674	2	12.458	2	0.3211
3	22.442	3	0.4010	3	18.686	3	0.4816
4	28.922	4	0.5347	4	24.915	4	0.6422
5	37.403	5	0.6684	5	31.144	5	0.8027
6	44.883	6	0.8021	6	37.373	6	0.9633
7	52.364	7	0.9358	7	43.602	7	1.1238
8	59.844	8	1.0695	8	49.830	8	1.2844
9	67.325	9	1.2031	9	56.059	9	1.4490
10	74.805	10	1.3368	10	62.288	10	1.6054

The unit of force is the pound, or the force exerted by gravity at the surface of the earth on a mass of matter called the avoirdupois pound. This unit is also used in measuring weights and pressures of water. The intensity of pressure is measured in pounds per square foot or in pounds per square inch, as may be most convenient, and sometimes in atmospheres. Gages for recording the pressure of water are usually graduated to read pounds per square inch.

The unit of time to be used in all hydraulic formulas is the second, although in numerical problems the time is often stated in minutes, hours, or days. Velocity or speed is defined as the space passed over by a body in one second, under the condition of uniform motion, so that velocities are to be always expressed in feet per second, or are to be reduced to these units if stated in miles per hour or otherwise. Acceleration is the velocity gained in one second, and it is measured in feet per second per second.

The unit of work is the foot-pound; that is, one pound lifted through a vertical distance of one foot. Energy is work which can be done; for example, a moving body has the ability to do a certain amount of work by virtue of its quantity of matter and its velocity, and this is called kinetic energy. Again, water at the top of a fall has the ability to do a certain amount of work by virtue of its quantity and its height above the foot of the fall, and this is called potential energy. Potential energy changes into kinetic energy as the water drops, and kinetic energy is either changed into heat or may be transformed, by means of a water motor, into useful work. Power is work done, or energy capable of being transformed into work, in a specified time, and the unit for its measure is the horse-power, which is 550 foot-pounds per second.

In French and German literature the metric system of measures is employed, and this is far more convenient than the English one in hydraulic computations. This system is understood and more or less used in all countries, and its universal adoption will probably occur during the present century, but the time has not yet come when an American engineering book can be prepared wholly in metric measures. This treatise will, therefore, mainly use the English units described above, but at the close of most of the chapters hydraulic data, tables, and empirical formulas will be given in metric measures. At the end of the volume will be found tables giving fundamental hydraulic constants and equivalents in each system of the principal units in the other system.

Problem 1. When one cubic foot of water, weighing $62\frac{1}{2}$ pounds, falls each second through a vertical height of 11 feet, what horse-power can be developed by a hydraulic motor which utilizes 80 percent of the energy?

Art. 2. Physical Properties of Water

At ordinary temperatures pure water is a colorless liquid which possesses almost perfect fluidity; that is, its particles have the capacity of moving over each other, so that the slightest disturbance of equilibrium causes a flow. It is a consequence of this property that the surface of still water is always level; also, if several vessels or tubes be connected, as in Fig. 2, and water be poured into one of them, it rises in the others until, when equilibrium ensues, the free surfaces are in the same level plane.

The free surface of water is in a different molecular condition from the other portions, its particles being drawn together by stronger attractive forces, so as to form what may be called the "skin of the water," upon which insects may walk or a needle be caused to float. The skin is not immediately pierced by a sharp point which moves slowly upward toward it, but a slight elevation occurs, and this property enables precise determinations of the level of still water to be made by the hook gage (Art. 35).

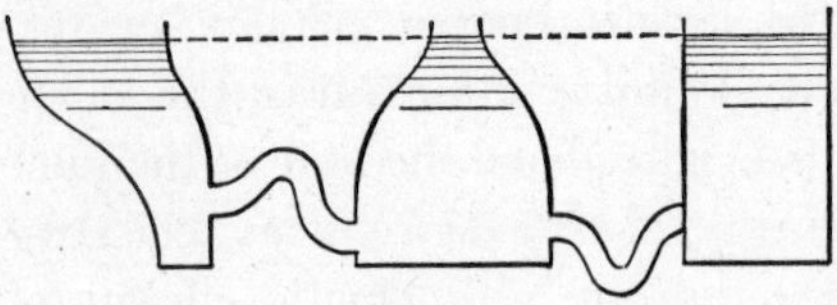

Fig. 2.

At about 32° Fahrenheit a great alteration in the molecular constitution of water occurs, and ice is formed. If a quantity of water be kept in a perfectly quiet condition, it is found that its temperature can be reduced to 20° or even to 15° Fahrenheit, before congelation takes place, but at the moment when this occurs the temperature rises to 32°. The freezing-point is hence not constant, but the melting-point of ice is always at the same temperature of 32° Fahrenheit or 0° centigrade.

While water freezes at 32° Fahrenheit, yet its maximum density is reached at 39°.3 Fahrenheit. At this latter temperature its specific gravity is 1.0 while at 32° it is 0.99987. As the temperature rises above that of maximum density the specific gravity of water steadily grows smaller until the boiling-point is reached at 212° Fahrenheit when its specific gravity is 0.95865. To the occurrence of the maximum density at a temperature above the freezing-point is to be attributed the fortunate circumstance that ponds and streams do not freeze solid from the bottom up.

Ice, as a rule, forms upon the surface of the water in a solid sheet. The rapidity with which such ice forms is dependent on the temperature and decreases with the thickness of the ice-sheet.

The coefficient of linear expansion of ice varies from 0.0000408 to 0.0000197 as the temperature varies from + 30° Fahrenheit to − 30° Fahrenheit.* Under certain conditions a rise in temperature may cause a considerable expansion, and if the sheet is a heavy one and expansion is prevented, the pressure brought to bear on any resisting surface becomes very great. A second variety of ice called frazil or slush ice is formed in rapidly flowing water when the temperature of the air is materially below the freezing-point. This ice is formed in the shape of small needles which are carried along and deposited in quiet water below. Accumulations of frazil to a depth of 80 feet have been known.* A third variety, known as anchor ice, may of itself be formed directly on the bed and sides of a rapidly flowing stream or be increased in volume by accretions of frazil. In cold countries the design of hydraulic structures must take into account all of these three kinds of ice.

Water is a solvent of high efficiency, and is therefore never found pure in nature. Descending in the form of rain, it absorbs dust and gaseous impurities from the atmosphere; flowing over the surface of the earth it absorbs organic and mineral substances. These affect its weight only slightly as long as it remains fresh, but when it has reached the sea and becomes salt, its weight is increased more than 2 percent. The flow of water through orifices is only in a very slight degree affected by the impurities held in solution, but in the flow through pipes they often cause incrustation or corrosion which increases the roughness of the surface and diminishes the velocity.

The capacity of water for heat, the latent heat evolved when it freezes, and that absorbed when it is transformed into steam need not be considered for the purposes of hydraulic investigations. Other physical properties, such as its variation in volume with the temperature, its compressibility, and its capacity for transmitting pressures, are discussed in the following pages. The laws which govern its pressure, flow, and energy under various circumstances belong to the science of Hydraulics and form the subject-matter of this volume.

Prob. 2. How many degrees centigrade are equivalent to − 20° Fahrenheit? How many degrees Fahrenheit are equivalent to − 20° centigrade and how many to + 20° centigrade?

* Barnes's Ice Formation (New York, 1906), pp. 106, 226.

Art. 3. The Weight of Water

The weight of water per unit of volume depends upon the temperature and upon its degree of purity. The following approximate values are, however, those generally employed except when great precision is required:

1 cubic foot of water weighs 62.5 pounds
1 U. S. gallon of water weighs 8.355 pounds

These values will be used in this book, unless otherwise stated, in the solution of the examples and problems.

The weight per unit of volume of pure distilled water is the greatest at the temperature of its maximum density, 39°.3 Fahrenheit, and least at the boiling-point. For ordinary computations the variation in weight due to temperature is not considered, but in tests of the efficiency of hydraulic motors and of pumps it should be regarded. The following table contains the weights of one cubic foot of pure water at different temperatures as deduced by Hamilton Smith from the experiments of Rosetti.*

Table 3. Weight of Distilled Water

Temperature Fahrenheit	Pounds per Cubic Foot	Temperature Fahrenheit	Pounds per Cubic Foot	Temperature Fahrenheit	Pounds per Cubic Foot
32°	62.42	95°	62.06	160°	61.01
35	62.42	100	62.00	165	60.90
39.3	62.424	105	61.93	170	60.80
45	62.42	110	61.86	175	60.69
50	62.41	115	61.79	180	60.59
55	62.39	120	61.72	185	60.48
60	62.37	125	61.64	190	60.36
65	62.34	130	61.55	195	60.25
70	62.30	135	61.47	200	60.14
75	62.26	140	61.39	205	60.02
80	62.22	145	61.30	210	59.89
85	62.17	150	61.20	212	59.84
90	62.12	155	61.11		

* Hamilton Smith, Jr., Hydraulics: The Flow of Water through Orifices, over Weirs, and through Open Conduits and Pipes (London and New York, 1886), p. 14.

Waters of rivers, springs, and lakes hold in suspension and solution inorganic matters which cause the weight per unit of volume to be slightly greater than for pure water. River waters are usually between 62.3 and 62.6 pounds per cubic foot, depending upon the amount of impurities and on the temperature, while the water of some mineral springs has been found to be as high as 62.7. It appears that, in the absence of specific information regarding a particular water, the weight 62.5 pounds per cubic foot is a fair approximate value to use. It also has the advantage of being a convenient number in computations, for 62.5 pounds is 1000 ounces, or $\frac{1000}{16}$ is the equivalent of 62.5.

Brackish and salt waters are always much heavier than fresh water. For the Gulf of Mexico the weight per cubic foot is about 63.9, for the oceans about 64.1, while for the Dead Sea there is stated the value 73 pounds per cubic foot. For Great Salt Lake the weight of water varies from 69 to 76 pounds per cubic foot.* The weight of ice per cubic foot varies from 57.2 to 57.5 pounds. The sewage of American cities is impure water which weighs from 62.4 to 62.7 pounds per cubic foot, but the sewage of European cities is somewhat heavier on account of the smaller amount of water that is turned into the sewers.

Prob. 3. How many gallons of water are contained in a pipe 4 inches in diameter and 12 feet long? How many pounds of water are contained in a pipe 8 inches in diameter and 12 feet long?

Art. 4. Atmospheric Pressure

Torricelli in 1643 discovered that the atmospheric pressure would cause mercury to rise in a tube from which the air had been exhausted. This instrument is called the mercury barometer, and owing to the great density of mercury the height of the column required to balance the atmospheric pressure is only about 30 inches. When water is used in the vacuum tube, the height of the column is about 34 feet. In both cases the weight of the barometric column is equal to the weight of a column of air of the same cross-section as that of the tube, both columns being measured upward from the common surface of contact.

* Science, Oct. 21, 1910.

The atmosphere exerts its pressure with varying intensity as indicated by the readings of the mercury barometer. At and near the sea level the average reading is 30 inches, and as mercury weighs 0.49 pounds per cubic inch at common temperatures, the average atmospheric pressure is taken to be 30 × 0.49 or 14.7 pounds per square inch. The pressure of one atmosphere is therefore defined to be a pressure of 14.7 pounds per square inch. Then a pressure of two atmospheres is 29.4 pounds per square inch. And conversely, a pressure of 100 pounds per square inch may be expressed as a pressure of 6.8 atmospheres.

Pascal in 1646 carried a mercury barometer to the top of a mountain and found that the height of the mercury column decreased as he ascended. It was thus definitely proved that the cause of the ascent of the liquid in the vacuum tube was due to the pressure of the air. Since mercury is 13.6 times heavier than water, a column of water should rise to a height of 30 × 13.6 = 408 inches = 34 feet under the pressure of one atmosphere, and this was also found to be the case. A water barometer is impracticable for use in measuring atmospheric pressures, but it is convenient to know its approximate height corresponding to a given height of the mercury barometer. Table 4 shows heights of the mercury and water barometers, with the corresponding pres-

TABLE 4. ATMOSPHERIC PRESSURE

Mercury Barometer Inches	Pressure Pounds per Square Inch	Pressure Atmospheres	Water Barometer Feet	Elevations Feet	Boiling-point of Water Fahrenheit
31	15.2	1.03	35.1	− 890	213°.9
30	14.7	1.00	34.0	0	212 .2
29	14.2	0.97	32.9	+ 920	210 .4
28	13.7	0.93	31.7	1880	208 .7
27	13.2	0.90	30.6	2870	206 .9
26	12.7	0.86	29.5	3900	205 .0
25	12.2	0.83	28.3	4970	203 .1
24	11.7	0.80	27.2	6080	201 .1
23	11.3	0.76	26.1	7240	199 .0
22	10.8	0.72	24.9	8455	196 .9
21	10.3	0.69	23.8	9720	194 .7
20	9.8	0.67	22.7	11050	192 .4

sures in pounds per square inch and in atmospheres. It also gives, in the fifth column, values from the vertical scale of altitudes used in barometric leveling which show approximate elevations above sea level corresponding to barometer readings, provided that the reading at sea level is 30 inches. In the last column are approximate boiling-points of water corresponding to the readings of the mercury barometer.

The atmospheric pressure must be taken into account in many computations on the flow of water in tubes and pipes. It is this pressure that causes water to flow in syphons and to rise in tubes from which the air has been exhausted. By virtue of this pressure the suction pump is rendered possible, and all forms of injector pumps depend upon it to a certain degree. On a planet without an atmosphere many of the phenomena of hydraulics would be quite different from those observed on this earth.

Prob. 4. A mercury barometer reads 30.25 inches at the foot of a hill, and at the same time another barometer reads 29.56 inches at the top of the hill. What is the difference in height between the two stations?

Art. 5. Compressibility of Water

The popular opinion that water is incompressible is not justified by experiments, which show in fact that it is more compressible than iron or even timber within the elastic limit. These experiments indicate that the amount of compression is directly proportional to the applied pressure, and that water is perfectly elastic, recovering its original form on the removal of the pressure. The decrease in the unit of volume caused by a pressure of one atmosphere varies, according to the experiments of Grassi, from 0.000051 at 35° Fahrenheit to 0.000045 at 80° Fahrenheit.* As a mean 0.00005 may be taken for this cubical unit-compression.

A vertical column of water accordingly increases in density from the surface downward. If its weight at the surface be 62.5 pounds per cubic foot, at a depth of 34 feet the weight of a cubic foot will be

$$62.5(1+0.00005) = 62.503 \text{ pounds,}$$

* Grassi, Annales de chemie et physique, 1851, vol. 31, p. 437.

and at a depth of 340 feet a cubic foot will weigh

$$62.5(1+0.0005) = 62.53 \text{ pounds.}$$

The variation in weight, due to compressibility, is hence too small to be regarded in hydrostatic computations.

The modulus of elasticity of volume for water is the ratio of the unit-stress to the cubical unit-compression, or

$$E = \frac{14.7}{0.00005} = 294\,000 \text{ pounds per square inch.}$$

The modulus of elasticity of volume for steel, when subjected to uniform hydrostatic pressure, is the same as the common modulus due to stress in one direction only, or $E = 30\,000\,000$ pounds per square inch. Hence water is about 100 times more compressible than steel.

The velocity of sound or stress in any substance is given by the formula $u = \sqrt{Eg/w}$, where w is the weight of a cubic unit of the material weighed by a spring balance at the place where the acceleration of gravity is g (Art. 6). For water having $w = 62.4$ pounds per cubic foot at a place where $g = 32.2$ feet per second per second, and $E = 42\,300\,000$ pounds per square foot, this formula gives $u = 4670$ feet per second for the velocity of sound, which agrees well with the results of experiments.

In order to deduce the above formula for the velocity of stress it is necessary to use some of the fundamental principles of elementary mechanics and of the mechanics of elastic bodies. Let a free rigid body of weight W be acted upon for one second by a constant force F and let f be the velocity of the body at the end of one second. Let g be the velocity gained in one second by W when falling under the action of the constant force of gravity. Then, since forces are proportional to their accelerations, $F = W \,.\, f/g$, and during the second of time the body has moved the distance $\frac{1}{2}f$. Now, consider a long elastic bar of the length u, so that a force applied at one end will be felt at the other end in one second, it being propagated by virtue of the elasticity of the material. Let A be the area of the cross-section of the bar and E the modulus of elasticity of the material. When a constant compressive force F is applied to the bar, the shortening ultimately produced is $2\,Fu/AE$,* but if this be done for one second only the elongation is only half this amount, since the first increment of stress is just reaching the other end of the bar at the end of the second. The center of gravity of the bar has then moved through the distance $\frac{1}{2}\,Fu/AE$, and its velocity v is Fu/AE. If w is this weight of a cubic unit of the material, the weight W is wAu. Inserting these values of v and W in the above equation, there is found

$$\frac{F}{wAu} = \frac{Fu}{AEg} \qquad \text{whence} \qquad u = \sqrt{\frac{Eg}{w}} \tag{5}$$

which is the formula for the propagation of sound or stress in elastic materials first established by Newton.

Prob. 5. Compute the velocity of sound in distilled water at 35° and also at 90° Fahrenheit.

Art. 6. Acceleration Due to Gravity

The motion of water in river channels, and its flow through orifices and pipes, is produced by the force of gravity. This force is proportional to the acceleration of the velocity of a body falling freely in a vacuum; that is, to the increase in velocity in one second. Acceleration is measured in feet per second per second, so that its numerical value represents the number of feet per second which have been gained in one second. The letter g is used to denote the acceleration of a falling body near the surface of the earth. In pure mechanics g is found in all formulas relating to falling bodies; for instance, if a body falls from rest through the height h, it attains in a vacuum a velocity equal to $\sqrt{2gh}$. In hydraulics g is found in all formulas which express the laws of flow of water under the influence of gravity.

The quantity 32.2 feet per second per second is an approximate value of g which is often used in hydraulic formulas. It is, however, well known that the force of gravity is not of constant intensity over the earth's surface, but is greater at the poles than at the equator, and also greater at the sea level than on high mountains. The following formula of Peirce, which is partly theoretical and partly empirical, gives g in feet per second per

* Merriman's Mechanics of Material (New York, 1911), pp. 25, 325.

second for any latitude l, and any elevation e above the sea level, e being in feet:

$$g = 32.0894(1 + 0.0052375 \sin^2 l)(1 - 0.0000000957e) \quad (6)_1$$

and from this its value may be computed for any locality.

The greatest value of g is at the sea level at the pole, and for this locality $l = 90°$, $e = 0$, whence $g = 32.258$. The least value of g is on high mountains at the equator; for this there may be taken $l = 0°$, $e = 10\,000$ feet, whence $g = 32.059$. The mean of these is the value of the acceleration used in this book, unless otherwise stated, namely,

$$g = 32.16 \text{ feet per second per second,}$$

and from this the mean values of the frequently occurring quantities $\sqrt{2g}$ and $1/2g$ are found to be

$$\sqrt{2g} = 8.020, \qquad 1/2g = 0.01555. \quad (6)_2$$

If greater precision be required, which will sometimes be the case, g can be computed from the above formula for the particular latitude and elevation. Table 6 gives multiples of the quantities g, $2g$, $1/2g$, and $\sqrt{2g}$ which will often be useful in numerical computations.

TABLE 6. ACCELERATION OF GRAVITY

No.	Multiples of g	Multiples of $2g$	Multiples of $1/2g$	Multiples of $\sqrt{2g}$	No
1	32.16	64.32	0.01555	8.02	1
2	64.32	128.6	0.03109	16.04	2
3	96.48	193.0	0.04664	24.06	3
4	128.6	257.3	0.06219	32.08	4
5	160.8	321.6	0.07774	40.10	5
6	193.0	385.9	0.09328	48.12	6
7	225.1	450.2	0.1088	56.14	7
8	257.3	514.5	0.1244	64.16	8
9	289.4	578.9	0.1399	72.18	9
10	321.6	643.2	0.1555	80.20	10

Prob. 6. Compute to four significant figures the values of g and $\sqrt{2g}$ for the latitude of $40°36'$ and the elevation 400 feet. Also for the same latitude and the elevation 4000 feet.

Art. 7. Historical Notes

Hydraulics is that branch of the mechanics of fluids which treats of water in motion, while Hydrostatics treats of water at rest. These two branches are sometimes regarded as a part of Hydromechanics, the name of the mechanics of fluids and gases. While the main purpose of this book is to treat of water in motion, the most important principles of hydrostatics will also be discussed, since these are necessary for a complete development of the laws of flow. The word "Hydraulics" is hence here used as closely synonymous with the hydromechanics of water.

Hydraulics is a modern science which is still far from perfect. Archimedes, about 250 B.C., established a few of the principles of hydrostatics and showed that the weight of an immersed body is less than its weight in air by the weight of the water that it displaces. Chain and bucket pumps were used at this period by the Egyptians, and the force pump was invented by Ctesibius about 120 B.C. The Romans built aqueducts as early as 300 B.C., and later used earthen and lead pipes to convey water from them to their houses. They knew that water would rise in a lead pipe to the same level as in the aqueduct and that a slope was necessary to cause flow in the latter, but had no conception of such a simple quantity as a cubic foot per minute. Even this slight knowledge was lost after the destruction of Rome, 475 A.D., and Europe, for a thousand years sunk in barbarism, made no scientific inquiries until the Renaissance period began.

Galileo, in 1630, studied the subject of the flotation of bodies in water, and a little later his pupils Castelli and Torricelli made notable discoveries, the former on the flow of water in rivers and the latter on the height of a jet issuing from an orifice. Pascal, about 1650, extended Torricelli's researches on the influence of atmospheric pressure in causing liquids to rise in a vacuum. Mariotte, about 1680, considered the influence of friction in retarding the flow in pipes and channels; and Newton, in 1685, observed the contraction of a jet issuing from an orifice.

During the eighteenth century notable advances were made. Daniel and John Bernoulli extended the theory of the equilibrium and motion of fluids, and this theory was much improved and generalized by D'Alembert. Bossut and Dubuat made experiments on the flow of water in pipes and deduced practical coefficients, while Chezy and Prony, near the close of the century, established general formulas for computing velocity and discharge.

During the nineteenth century progress in every branch of hydraulics was great and rapid. Eytelwein, Weisbach, and Hagen stood high among German experimenters; Venturi and Bidone among those of Italy; Poncelet, Darcy, and Bazin among those of France; while Kutter in Switzerland, Rankine in England, and James B. Francis and Hamilton Smith in America also took high rank for either practical or theoretical investigations. By the experiments and discussions of these and many other engineers the necessary coefficients for the discussion of orifices, weirs, jets, pipes, conduits, and rivers have been determined and the theory of the flow of water has been much extended and perfected. The invention of the turbine by Fourneyron in 1827 exerted much influence upon the development of water power, while the studies necessary for the construction of canals and for the improvement of rivers and harbors have greatly promoted hydraulic science. In this advance the engineers of the United States did much good work during the latter part of the nineteenth and are continuing it during the present part of the twentieth century, as is shown by the numerous valuable papers published in the Transactions of the American engineering societies and in the scientific press, many of which will be cited in this book.

Galileo said in 1630 that the laws controlling the motion of the planets in their celestial orbits were better understood than those governing the motion of water on the surface of the earth. This is true today, for the theory of the flow of water in pipes and channels has not yet been perfected. Experiment is now in advance of theory, but it is intended to present both in this volume as far as practicable, for each is necessary to a satisfactory understanding of the other.

Prob. 7. Who was the author of a book called Lowell Hydraulic Experiments? When and where was it published? What influence has it exerted upon hydraulic science?

Art. 8. Numerical Computations

The numerical work of computation should not be carried to a greater degree of refinement than the data of the problem warrant. For instance, in questions relating to pressures, the data are uncertain in the third significant figure, and hence more figures than three in the final result must be delusive. Thus let it be required to compute the number of pounds of water in a box containing 307.37 cubic feet. Taking the mean value 62.5 pounds as the weight of one cubic foot, the multiplication gives the result 19 210.625 pounds, but evidently the decimals here have no precision, since the last figure in 62.5 is not accurate, and is likely to be less than 5, depending upon the impurity of the water and its temperature. The proper answer to this problem is 19 200 pounds, or perhaps 19 210 pounds, and this is to be regarded as a probable average result rather than an exact quantity.

Three significant figures are usually sufficient in the answer to any hydraulic problem, but in order that the last one may be correct four significant figures should be used in the computations. Thus, 307.37 has five significant figures and this should be written 307.4 before multiplying it by 62.5. The zeros following a decimal point of a decimal are not counted significant figures; thus, 0.0019 has two and 0.0003742 has four significant figures.

The use of logarithms is to be recommended in hydraulic computations, as thereby both mental labor and time are saved. Four-figure tables are sufficient for common problems, and their use is particularly advantageous in all cases where the data are not precise, as thus the number of significant figures in final results is kept at about three, and hence statements implying great precision, when none really exists, are prevented. The four-place logarithmic table at the end of this volume will be found very convenient in solving numerical problems. As an example, let it be required to find the weight of a column of water 2.66

inches square and 28.7 feet long. The computation, both by common arithmetic and by logarithms, is as follows, and it will be found, by trying similar problems, that in general the use of

By Arithmetic		By Logarithms	
2.66	0.04914	2.66	0.4249
2.66	28.7		2
5.32	9828		0.8498
1 596	39312	144	2.1584
160 | 144	3439		$\bar{2}$.6914
7.076(0.04914	1.410	28.7	1.4579
576	62.5	62.5	1.7959
1316	846	Ans. 88.1	1.9452
1296	282		
20	70		
14	Ans. 88.1 pounds.		
6			

logarithms effects a saving of time and labor. The common slide rule, which is constructed on the logarithmic principle, will also be found very useful in the numerical work of many hydraulic problems.

The tables of constants, squares, and areas of circles at the end of this volume will also be advantageous in abridging computations. For instance, it is seen at once from Table E that the square of 2.66 to four significant figures is 7.076, while Table F shows that the area of a circle having a diameter of 0.543 inch is 0.2316 square inch. Logarithms of hydraulic and mathematical constants are given in Tables A, C, and K. Tables 1*a*, 1*b*, and 6 of this chapter and others in the next chapter give multiples of constants which may be advantageously used when it is necessary to multiply several numbers by the same constant. For example, when it is required to reduce 333.4, 318.7, and 98.6 cubic feet to U. S. gallons, the book is opened at Table 1*b*, where the multiples of 7.481 are given, and the work is as follows:

333.4	318.7	98.6
2244.2	2244.2	673.2
224.4	74.8	59.8
22.4	59.8	4.5
3.0	5.2	737.5
2494.0	2384.0	

These results are more accurate than can be obtained with four-place logarithmic tables. The logarithmic work for this case would be the following:

333.4	318.7	98.6
2.5229	2.5034	1.9939
0.8740	0.8740	0.8740
3.3969	3.3774	2.8679
2494	2384	737.7

As this book is mainly intended for the use of students in technical schools, a word of advice directed especially to them may not be inappropriate. It will be necessary for students, in order to gain a clear understanding of hydraulic science, or of any other engineering subject, to solve many numerical problems, and in this a neat and systematic method should be cultivated. The practice of performing computations on any loose scraps of paper that may happen to be at hand should be at once discontinued by every student who has followed it, and he should hereafter solve his problems in a special book provided for that purpose, and accompany them by such explanatory remarks as may seem necessary in order to render the solutions clear. Such a note-book, written in ink, and containing the fully worked out solutions of the examples and problems given in these pages, will prove of great value to every student who makes it. Before beginning the solution of a problem a diagram should be drawn whenever it is possible, for a diagram helps the student to clearly understand the problem, and a problem thoroughly understood is half solved. Before commencing the numerical work, it is also well to make a mental estimate of the final result.

In this volume Greek letters are used only for signs of operation and for angles. The letter δ is employed as the symbol of differentiation and it should be called "differential." Following are names of some Greek letters:

α Alpha	η Eta	ν Nu	ϕ Phi
β Beta	θ Theta	π Pi	ψ Psi
γ Gamma	κ Kappa	ρ Rho	ξ Zeta
δ Delta	λ Lambda	σ Sigma	ω Omega
ϵ Epsilon	μ Mu	τ Tau	

In every rational algebraic equation it is necessary that all the terms should be of the same dimension, for it is impossible to add together quantities of different kinds. This principle will be of great assistance to the student in checking the correctness of algebraic work. For example, let a and b represent areas and l a length; then such an equation as $al-l^2=b$ is impossible, because al is a volume, while l^2 and b are areas. Again, let V represent velocity, Q cubic feet per second, and a area; then the equation $Q=aV$ is correct dimensionally, for the dimension of V is length per second and hence aV is of the same dimension as Q. The equation $Q/a=V^2$ is, however, impossible, for Q/a is of the same dimension as the first power of V, and this cannot also be equal to its second power.

Prob. 8. When the height of the water barometer is 33.5 feet, what is the height of the mercury barometer, and what is the atmospheric pressure in pounds per square inch?

Art. 9. Data in the Metric System

When the metric system is used for hydraulic computations, the meter is taken as the unit of length, the cubic meter as the unit of volume, and the kilogram as the unit of force and weight. Lengths are sometimes expressed in centimeters and volumes in liters, but these should be reduced to meters and cubic meters for use in the formulas. The unit of time is the second, the unit of velocity is one meter per second, and accelerations are measured in meters per second per second. Pressures are usually expressed in kilograms per square centimeter and densities in kilograms per cubic meter. The metric horse-power is 75 kilogram-meters of work per second, and this is about $1\frac{1}{2}$ per cent less than the English horse-power. Tables at the end of this book give the equivalents in each system of the units of the other system, but the student will rarely need to use such tables. He should, on the other hand, exclusively employ the metric system when using it, and learn to think readily in it. The following matter is supplementary to the corresponding articles of the preceding pages.

(Art. 2) At about 0° centigrade ice is generally formed. When water is kept perfectly quiet, however, it is found that its temperature can be reduced to $-7°$ or $-9°$ before freezing begins, but at this instant the temperature of the water rises to 0° centigrade.

(Art. 3) In the metric system the following approximate values are used for the weight of water:

1 liter of water weighs 1 kilogram
1 cubic meter weighs 1000 kilograms

It may be noted that the constants for the weight of water differ slightly in the two systems. Thus, the equivalent of 62.5 pounds per cubic foot is about 1001 kilograms per cubic meter. The weight per unit of volume of pure distilled water is greatest at the temperature of maximum density, 4°.1 centigrade, and least at the boiling-point. Table 9*a* gives weights of distilled water at different temperatures in kilograms per cubic meter, as determined by Rossetti.* River

TABLE 9*a*. WEIGHT OF DISTILLED WATER

Metric Measures

Temperature Centigrade	Kilograms per Cubic Meter	Temperature Centigrade	Kilograms per Cubic Meter	Temperature Centigrade	Kilograms per Cubic Meter
− 3°	999.59	16°	999.00	55°	985.85
0	999.87	18	998.65	60	983.38
+ 3	999.99	20	998.26	65	980.74
4	1000.00	22	997.83	70	977.94
5	999.99	25	997.12	75	974.98
6	999.97	30	995.76	80	971.94
8	999.89	35	994.13	85	968.79
10	999.75	40	992.35	90	965.56
12	999.55	45	990.37	95	962.19
14	999.30	50	988.20	100	958.65

waters are usually between 998 and 1001 kilograms per cubic meter, depending upon the amount of impurities and the temperature, while the water of some mineral springs has been found as high as 1004. It appears then that 1000 kilograms per cubic meter is a fair average value to use in hydraulic work for the weight of fresh water. Brackish and salt waters are heavier. For the Gulf of Mexico the weight per cubic meter is about 1023, for the oceans, about 1027, while for the Dead Sea there is stated the value of 1169 kilograms per cubic meter. For Great Salt Lake the weight of water varies from 1105 to 1227 kilograms per cubic meter. The weight of ice per cubic meter varies from 916 to 921 kilograms.

* Annales de chemie et de physique, 1869, vol. 17, p. 370.

(Art. 4) Near the sea level the average reading of the mercury barometer is 76 centimeters, and since mercury weighs 13.6 grams per cubic centimeter, the average atmospheric pressure is taken to be $76 + 0.0136 = 1.0333$ kilograms per square centimeter. One atmosphere of pressure is therefore slightly greater than a pressure of one kilogram per square centimeter. Conversely, a pressure of one kilogram per square centimeter may be expressed as a pressure of 0.968 atmosphere. In a perfect vacuum water will rise to a height of about $10\frac{1}{3}$ meters under a mean pressure of one atmosphere, for the average specific gravity of mercury is 13.6, and $13.6 \times 0.76 = 10.33$ meters. Table 9*b* shows atmospheric pressures, altitudes, and boiling-points of water corresponding to heights of the mercury and water barometers.

TABLE 9*b*. ATMOSPHERIC PRESSURE

Metric Measures

Mercury Barometer Millimeters	Pressure Kilograms per Square Centimeter	Pressure Atmospheres	Water Barometer Meters	Elevations Meters	Boiling-point of Water Centigrade
790	1.074	1.04	10.74	− 325	101°.1
760	1.033	1.00	10.33	0	100 .0
730	0.992	0.96	9.92	+ 340	98 .9
700	.952	.92	9.52	690	97 .8
670	.911	.88	9.11	1045	96 .6
640	.870	.84	8.70	1420	95 .4
610	.829	.80	8.29	1820	94 .1
580	.788	.76	7.88	2240	92 .8
550	.748	.72	7.48	2680	91 .5
520	.707	.68	7.07	3140	90 .1

(Art. 5) If the weight of a cubic meter of water is 1000 kilograms at the surface of a pond, the weight of a cubic meter at a depth of $10\frac{1}{3}$ meters will be

$$1000\,(1 + 0.00005) = 1000.05 \text{ kilograms},$$

and at a depth of $103\frac{1}{3}$ meters a cubic meter will weigh

$$1000\,(1 + 0.0005) = 1000.5 \text{ kilograms}.$$

Hence the variation due to compression is too small to be generally taken into account. The modulus of elasticity of volume for water is

$$E = \frac{1.033}{0.00005} = 20\,700 \text{ kilograms per square centimeter},$$

while that of steel is about 2 100 000. Using $g = 9.8$ meters per second per second, the mean velocity of sound in water is

$$v = \sqrt{Eg/w} = 1420 \text{ meters per second.}$$

(Art. 6) The formula of Peirce for the acceleration of gravity on the earth's surface is

$$g = 9.78085\,(1 + 0.0052375 \sin^2 l)(1 - 0.000000314\,e) \qquad (9)_1$$

in which g is the acceleration in meters per second per second at a place whose latitude is l degrees and whose elevation is e meters above the sea level. The greatest value of g is at the sea level at the pole; here $l = 90°$ and $e = 0$, whence $g = 9.8322$. The least value of g in hydraulic practice is found on high lands at the equator; here $l = 0°$ and $e = 4000$ meters, whence $g = 9.7683$. The mean of these is 9.800, which closely agrees with that found in Art. 6, since 32.16 feet equals 9.802 meters; accordingly

$$g = 9.800 \text{ meters per second per second}$$

is the value of the acceleration that will be used in the metric work of this book. From this are found

$$\sqrt{2g} = 4.427 \qquad\qquad 1/2g = 0.05102 \qquad (9)_2$$

Table 9*c* gives multiples of these values which will often be of use in numerical computations.

TABLE 9*c*. ACCELERATION DUE TO GRAVITY

Metric Measures

No.	Multiples of g	Multiples of $2g$	Multiples of $1/2g$	Multiples of $\sqrt{2g}$	No.
1	9.800	19.60	0.05102	4.427	1
2	19.60	39.20	0.1020	8.854	2
3	29.40	58.80	0.1531	13.282	3
4	39.20	78.40	0.2041	17.71	4
5	49.00	98.00	0.2551	22.14	5
6	58.80	117.60	0.3061	26.56	6
7	68.60	137.2	0.3571	30.99	7
8	78.40	156.8	0.4082	35.42	8
9	88.20	176.4	0.4592	39.84	9
10	98.00	196.0	0.5102	44.27	10

(Art. 8) The remarks as to precision of numerical computation also apply here. Thus, if it be required to find the weight of water in a pipe 38 centimeters in diameter and 6 meters long, Table F gives 0.1134 square meter for the sectional area, the volume is then 0.6804 cubic meter, and the weight is 680 kilograms, the fourth figure being omitted because nothing is known about the temperature or purity of the water. In general, hydraulic computations are much easier in the metric than in the English system.

Prob. 9*a*. Compute the acceleration of gravity at Quito, Ecuador, which is in latitude $-0^\circ\ 13'$ and at an elevation of 2850 meters above sea level.

Prob. 9*b*. What is the pressure in kilograms per square centimeter at the base of a column of water 95.4 meters high?

Prob. 9*c*. Compute the velocity of sound in fresh distilled water at the temperature of 12° centigrade, and also its mean velocity in salt water.

Prob. 9*d*. How many cubic meters of water are contained in a pipe 415 meters long and 15 centimeters in diameter? How many kilograms? How many metric tons?

Prob. 9*e*. What is the boiling-point of water when the mercury barometer reads 735 millimeters? How high will water rise in a vacuum tube at a place where the boiling-point of water is 92° centigrade?

CHAPTER 2

HYDROSTATICS

Art. 10. Transmission of Pressure

One of the most remarkable properties of a fluid is its capacity of transmitting a pressure, applied at one point of the surface of a closed vessel, unchanged in intensity, in all directions, so that the effect of the applied pressure is to cause an equal force per square inch upon all parts of the enclosing surface. Pascal, in 1646, was the first to note that great forces could be produced in this manner; he saw that the total pressure increased proportionally with the area of the surface. Taking a closed barrel filled with water, he inserted a small vertical tube of considerable length tightly into it, and on filling the tube the barrel burst under the great pressure thus produced on its sides, although the weight of the water in the tube was quite small. The first diagram in Fig. 10*a* represents Pascal's barrel, and it is seen that the unit-pressure in the water at *B* is due to the head *AB* and independent of the size of the tube *AC*.

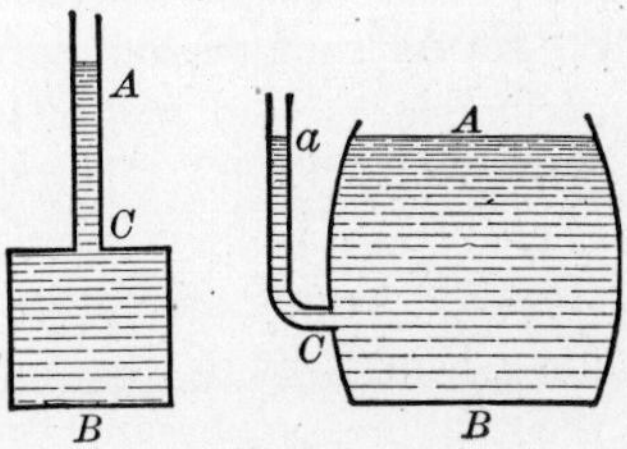

Fig. 10*a*.

Pascal clearly saw that this property of water could be employed in a useful manner in mechanics, but it was not until 1796 that Bramah built the first successful hydraulic press. This machine has two pistons of different sizes, and a force applied to the small piston is transmitted through the fluid and produces an equal unit-pressure at every point on the large piston. The applied force is here multiplied to any required extent, but the work performed by the large piston cannot exceed that imparted to the fluid by the small one. Let *a* and *A* be the areas of the small and large pistons, and p the pressure in pounds per square unit applied to a; then the unit-pressure in the fluid is p, and the total pressure on the small piston is pa, while that on the large piston is pA. Let the distances through which the pistons move during one stroke be d and D. Then the imparted work is pad, and the performed work, neglecting frictional resistances, is pAD. Consequently $ad = AD$, and since a is small as compared with A, the distance D must be small compared with d. Here is found an illustration of the popular maxim "What is lost in velocity is gained in force."

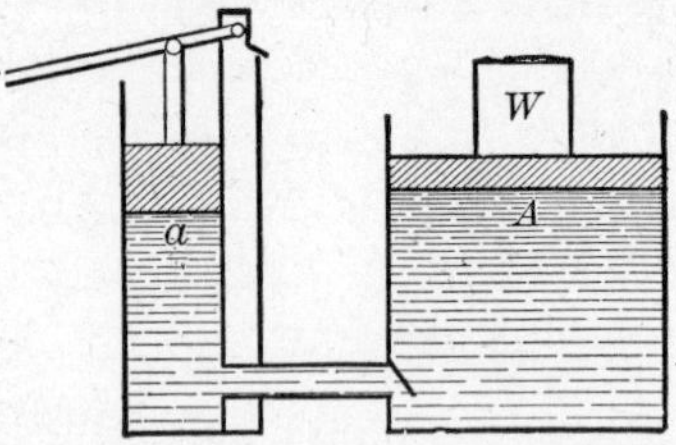

Fig. 10*b*.

Numerous applications of this principle are made in hydraulic presses for compressing materials and forging steel, as also in jacks, accumulators, and hydraulic cranes; some of these are briefly described in Art. 202. The famous Keely motor is said to have employed this principle to produce some of its effects; very small pipes, supposed by the spectators to be wires conveying some mysterious force, being used to transmit the pressure of water to a receiver where the total pressure became very great in consequence of greater area.

In consequence of its fluidity the pressure existing at any point in a body of water is exerted in all directions with equal intensity. When water is confined by a bounding surface, as in a vessel, its pressure against that surface must be normal at every point, for if it were inclined, the water would move along the surface. When water has a free surface, the unit-pressure at any depth depends only on that depth and not on the shape of the vessel. Thus in the second diagram of Fig. 10*a* the unit-pressure at C produced by the smaller column of water aC is the same as that caused by the larger column AC, and the total vertical pressure on the upper side of the base B is the product of its area into the unit-pressure caused by the depth AB.

Prob. 10. What is the upward pressure on the lower side of the base B in Fig. 10*a*? Explain why this is less than the downward pressure on the upper side of the base B.

Art. 11. Head and Pressure

The free surface of water at rest is perpendicular to the direction of the force of gravity, and for bodies of water of small extent this surface may be regarded as a plane. Any depth below this plane is called a "head," or the head upon any point is its vertical depth below the level surface. In Art. 10 it was seen that the unit-pressure at any depth depends only on the head and not on the shape of the vessel. Let h be the head and w the weight of a cubic unit of water; then at the depth h one horizontal square unit bears a pressure equal to the weight of a column of water whose height is h, and whose cross-section is one square unit, or wh. But the pressure at this point is exerted in all directions with equal intensity. The unit-pressure p at the depth h then is wh, and the depth, or head, for a unit-pressure p is p/w, or

$$p = wh \qquad h = p/w \qquad (11)_1$$

If h be expressed in feet and p in pounds per square foot, these formulas become, using the mean value of w,

$$p = 62.5h \qquad h = 0.016p$$

Thus pressure and head are mutually convertible, and in fact one is often used as synonymous with the other, although really each is proportional to the other. Any unit-pressure p can be regarded as produced by a head h, which is frequently called the "pressure head."

In engineering work p is usually taken in pounds per square inch, while h is expressed in feet. Thus the pressure in pounds per square foot is $62.5h$, and the pressure in pounds per square inch is $\frac{1}{144}$ of this, or

$$p = 0.4340h \qquad h = 2.304p \qquad (11)_2$$

These rules may be stated in words as follows:

1 foot head corresponds to 0.434 pounds per square inch;
1 pound per square inch corresponds to 2.304 feet head.

These values, be it remembered, depend upon the assumption that 62.5 pounds is the weight of a cubic foot of water, and hence are liable to variation in the third significant figure (Art. 4). The extent of these variations for fresh water may be seen in Table 11, which gives multiples of the above values, and also the corresponding quantities when the cubic foot is taken as 62.3 pounds.

TABLE 11. HEADS AND PRESSURES

Head in Feet	Pressure in Pounds per Square Inch		Pressure in Pounds per Square Inch	Head in Feet	
	$w = 62.5$	$w = 62.3$		$w = 62.5$	$w = 62.3$
1	0.434	0.433	1	2.304	2.311
2	0.868	0.865	2	4.608	4.623
3	1.302	1.298	3	6.912	6.934
4	1.736	1.731	4	9.216	9.246
5	2.170	2.163	5	11.520	11.557
6	2.604	2.596	6	13.824	13.868
7	3.038	3.028	7	16.128	16.180
8	3.472	3.461	8	18.432	18.491
9	3.906	3.894	9	20.736	20.803
10	4.340	4.326	10	23.040	23.114

The atmospheric pressure, which is about 14.7 pounds per square inch, is transmitted through water, and is to be added to the pressure due to the head whenever it is necessary to regard the absolute pressure. This is important in some investigations on the pumping of water, and in a few other cases where a partial or complete vacuum is produced on one side of a body of water. For example, if the air is exhausted from a small globe, so that its tension is only 6.5 pounds per square inch, and it is submerged in water to a depth of 250 feet, then the absolute pressure on the surface of the globe is

$$p = 0.434 \times 250 + 14.7 = 123.2 \text{ pounds per square inch,}$$

and the resultant effective pressure on that surface is

$$p' = 123.2 - 6.5 = 116.7 \text{ pounds per square inch.}$$

Unless otherwise stated, however, the atmospheric pressure need not be regarded, since under ordinary conditions it acts with equal intensity upon both sides of a submerged surface.

Prob. 11. How many pounds per square inch correspond to a head of 230 feet? How many feet head correspond to a pressure of 100 pounds per square inch?

Art. 12. Loss of Weight in Water

It is a familiar fact that bodies submerged in water lose part of their weight; a man can carry under water a large stone which would be difficult to lift in air, and timber when submerged has a negative weight or tends to rise to the surface. The following is the law of loss which was discovered by Archimedes, about 250 B.C., when considering the problem of King Hiero's crown:

> The weight of a body submerged in water is less than its weight in air by the weight of a volume of water which is equal to the volume of the body.

To demonstrate this, consider that the submerged body is acted upon by the water pressure in all directions, and that the horizontal components of these pressures must balance. Any vertical elementary prism is subjected to an upward pressure upon its base which is greater than the downward pressure upon its top, since these pressures are due to the heads. Let h_1 be the head on the top of the elementary prism and h_2 that on its base, and a the cross-section of the prism; then the downward pressure is wah_1 and the upward pressure is wah_2. The difference of these, $wa(h_2-h_1)$ is the resultant upward water pressure, and this is equal to the weight of a column of water whose cross-section is a and whose height is that of the elementary prism. Extending this theorem to all the elementary prisms, it is concluded that the weight of the body in water is less than its weight in air by the weight of an equal volume of water.

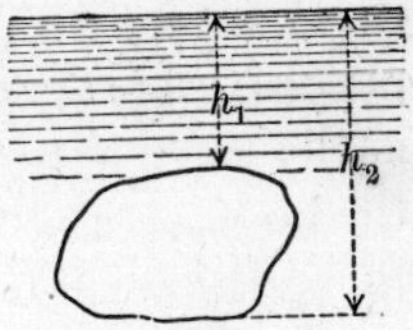

Fig. 12.

It is important to regard this loss of weight in constructions under water. If, for example, a dam of loose stones allows the water to percolate through it, its weight per cubic foot is less than its weight in air, so that it can be more easily moved by horizontal forces. As stone weighs about 150 pounds per cubic foot in air, its weight in water is only about $150-62=88$ pounds per cubic foot. If a cubic foot of sand, having voids amounting to 40 per cent of its volume, weighs 110 pounds, its loss of weight in water is $0.60 \times 62.5 = 37.5$ pounds, so that its weight in water is $110 - 37.5 = 72.5$ pounds.

The ratio of the weight of a substance to that of an equal volume of water is called the specific gravity of the substance, and this is easily computed from the law of Archimedes after weighing a piece of it in air and then in water; or, if w be the weight of a cubic unit of water and w' the weight of a cubic unit of any substance, the ratio w'/w is the specific gravity of the substance.

Prob. 12. A box containing 1.17 cubic feet weighs 19.3 pounds when empty and 133.5 when filled with sand. It is then found that 29.7 pounds of water can be poured in before overflow occurs. Find the percentage of voids in the sand, the specific gravity of the sand mass, and the specific gravity of a grain of sand.

Art. 13. Depth of Flotation

When a body floats upon water, it is sustained by an upward pressure of the water equal to its own weight, and this pressure is the same as the weight of the volume of water displaced by the body. Let W' be the weight of the floating body in air, and W be the weight of the displaced water; then $W' = W$. Now let z be the depth of flotation of the body; then to find its value for any particular case W' is to be expressed in terms of the linear dimensions of the body, and W in terms of the depth of flotation z. For example, a timber box caisson is $20 \times 10\frac{1}{2}$ feet in outside dimensions and weighs 33 400 pounds. The weight of displaced water in pounds is $62\frac{1}{2} \times 20 \times 10\frac{1}{2} \times z$, and equating this to 33 400 gives $z = 2.54$ feet for the depth of flotation.

To find the depth of flotation for a cylinder lying horizontally, let w' be its weight per cubic unit, l its length, and r the radius of its cross-section. The depth of flotation is DE, or letting θ be the angle ACE, then $z = (1 - \cos\theta)r$. The weight of the cylinder is $W' = \pi r^2 l \cdot w'$, and that of the displaced water is

$$W = (r^2 \operatorname{arc}\theta - r^2 \sin\theta \cos\theta) l \cdot w$$

Equating the values of W and W', and substituting for $\sin\theta \cos\theta$ its equivalent $\frac{1}{2} \sin 2\theta$, there results

$$2 \text{ arc}\theta - \sin 2\theta = 2 \pi s$$

in which s represents the ratio w'/w or the specific gravity of the material of the cylinder. From this equation θ is to be found by trial for any particular case, and then z is computed. For example, if $w' = 26.5$ pounds per cubic foot, then s is 0.424, and

$$2 \text{ arc}\theta - \sin 2\theta - 2.664 = 0$$

To solve this equation, values are to be assumed for θ, until one is found that satisfies it; thus from Table G,

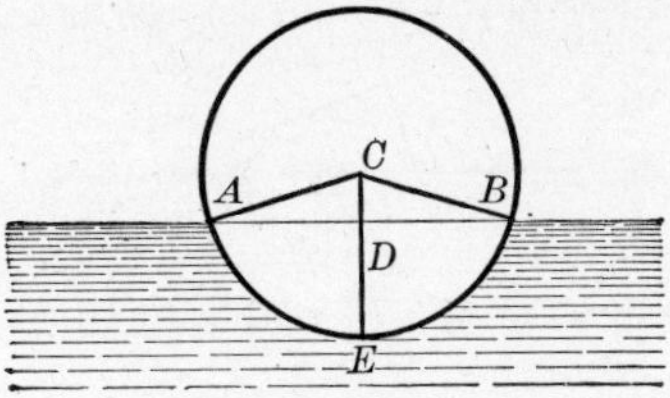

Fig. 13.

for $\theta = 83°$ $\quad 2.897 - 0.242 - 2.664 = -0.009$

for $\theta = 83\frac{1}{4}$ $\quad 2.906 - 0.234 - 2.664 = +0.008$

Therefore θ lies between 83° and 83° 15′, and is probably about 83° 8′. Hence the depth of flotation is $z = (1 - 0.120)r = 0.88r$, or if the diameter is one foot, the depth of flotation is 0.44 feet.

In a similar way it may be shown that the depth of flotation of a sphere of radius r and specific gravity s is given by the cubic equation $z^3 - 3rz^2 + 4r^3s = 0$. When $r = 4$ feet and $s = 0.65$, it may be found by trial that $z = 1.21$ feet.

Prob. 13. A wooden stick $1\frac{1}{4}$ inches square and 12 feet long is to be used for a velocity float which is to stand vertically in the water. How many square inches of sheet lead $\frac{1}{32}$ inch thick must be tacked on the sides of this stick so that only 4 inches will project above the water surface? The wood weighs 31.25 and the lead 710 pounds per cubic foot.

Art. 14. Stability of Flotation

The equilibrium of a floating body is stable when it returns to its primitive position after having been slightly moved therefrom by extraneous forces; it is indifferent when it floats in any position, and it is unstable when the slightest force causes it to leave its position of flotation. For instance, a short cylinder with its axis vertical floats in stable equilibrium, but a long cylinder in this position is unstable, and a slight force causes it to fall over and float with its axis horizontal in indifferent equilibrium. It is evident that the equilibrium is the more stable the lower the center of gravity of the body.

The stability depends in any case upon the relative position of the center of gravity of the body and its center of buoyancy, the latter being the center of gravity of the displaced water. Thus in Fig. 14 let G be the center of gravity of the body and let C be its center of buoyancy when in an upright position. Now if an extraneous force causes the body to tip into the position shown, the center of gravity remains at G, but the center of buoyancy moves to D. In this new position of the body it is acted upon by the forces W' and W, which are equal and parallel but opposite in direction. These forces form a couple which tends either to restore the body to the upright position or to cause it to deviate farther from that position. Let the vertical through D be produced to meet the center line CG in M. If M is above G, the equilibrium is stable, as the forces W and W' tend to restore it to its primitive position; if M coincides with G, the equilibrium is indifferent; and if M be below G, the equilibrium is unstable.

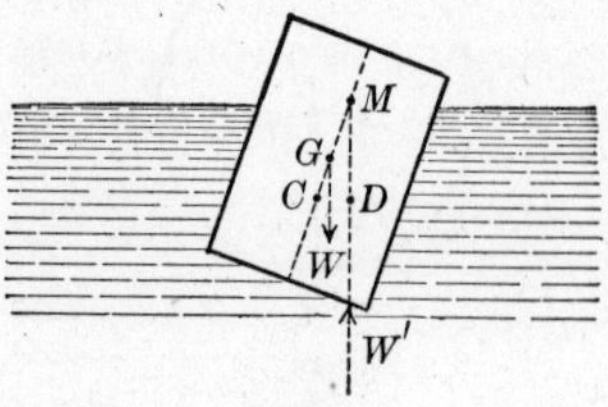

Fig. 14.

The point M is called the "metacenter," and the theorem may be stated that the equilibrium is stable, indifferent, or unstable according as the metacenter is above, coincident with, or below the center of gravity of the body. The measure of the stability of a stable floating body is the moment of the couple formed by the forces W and W'. But GM is proportional to the lever arm of the couple, and hence the quantity $W \times GM$ may be taken as a measure of stability. The stability, therefore, increases with the weight of the body, and with the distance of the metacenter above the center of gravity. (See Art. 189.)

The most important application of these principles is in the design of ships, and usually the problems are of a complex character which can only be solved by tentative methods. The rolling of the ship due to lateral wave action must also receive attention, and for this reason the center of gravity should not be put too low.

Prob. 14. A square prism of uniform specific gravity s has the length h and the cross-section b^2. When this prism is placed in water with its axis vertical, it may be shown that it is in stable, indifferent, or unstable equilibrium according as b^2 is greater, equal to, or less than $6\,h^2s\,(1 - s)$.

Art. 15. Normal Pressure

The total normal pressure on any immersed surface may be found by the following theorem:

> The total normal pressure is equal to the product of the weight of a cubic unit of water, the area of the surface, and the head on its center of gravity.

To prove this let A be the area of the surface, and imagine it to be composed of elementary areas, a_1, a_2, a_3, etc., each of which is so small that the unit-pressure over it may be taken as uniform; let h_1, h_2, h_3, etc., be the heads on these elementary areas, and let w denote the weight of a cubic unit of water. The unit-pressures at the depths h_1, h_2, h_3, etc., are wh_1, wh_2, wh_3, etc. (Art. 11), and hence the normal pressures on the elementary areas, a_1, a_2, a_3, etc., are wa_1h_1, wa_2h_2, wa_3h_3, etc. The total normal pressure P on the entire surface then is

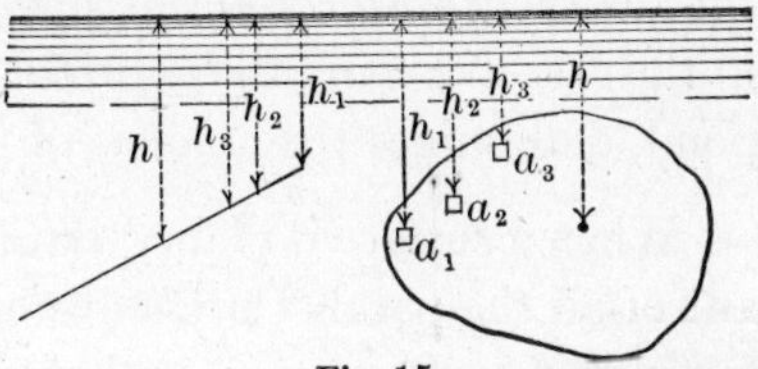

Fig. 15.

$$P = w(a_1h_1 + a_2h_2 + a_3h_3 + \text{etc.})$$

Now let h be the head on the center of gravity of the surface; then, from the definition of the center of gravity,

$$a_1h_1 + a_2h_2 + a_3h_3 + \text{etc.} = Ah$$

Therefore the normal pressure is

$$P = wAh \tag{15}$$

which proves the theorem as stated.

This rule applies to all surfaces, whether plane, curved, or warped, and however they be situated with reference to the water surface. Thus the total normal pressure upon the surface of an immersed cylinder remains the same whatever be its position, provided the depth of the center of gravity of that surface be kept constant. It is best to take h in feet, A in square feet, and w as 62.5 pounds per cubic foot; then P will be in pounds. In case surfaces are given whose centers of gravity are difficult to determine, they should be divided into simpler surfaces, and then the total normal pressure is the sum of the normal pressures on the separate surfaces.

The normal pressure on the base of a vessel filled with water is equal to the weight of a cylinder of water whose base is the base of the vessel, and whose height is the depth of water. Only in the case of a vertical cylinder does this become equal to the weight of the water, for the pressure on the base of a vessel depends upon the depth of water and not upon the shape of the vessel. Also in the case of a dam, the depth of the water and not the size of the pond, determines the amount of pressure.

When a surface is plane, the total normal pressure is the resultant of all the parallel pressures acting upon it. This is not true for curved surfaces; for, as the pressures have different directions, their resultant is not equal to their numerical sum, but must be obtained by the rules for the composition of forces. For example, when a sphere of diameter d is filled with water, the total normal pressure as found by the formula (15) is

$$P = w \cdot \pi d^2 \cdot \tfrac{1}{2} d = \tfrac{1}{2} w \pi d^3$$

but the resultant pressure is nothing, for the elementary normal pressures act in all directions so that no tendency to motion exists. The weight of water in this sphere is $\frac{1}{6} w \pi d^3$, or one-third of the total normal pressure, and the direction of this is vertical.

Prob. 15. An ellipse, with major and minor axes equal to 12 and 8 feet, is submerged so that one extremity of the major axis is 2.5 and the other 9.5 feet below the water surface. Find the normal pressure on one side.

Art. 16. Pressure in a Given Direction

The pressure against an immersed plane surface in a given direction may be found by obtaining the normal pressure by Art. 15 and computing its component in the required direction, or by means of the following theorem:

The horizontal pressure on any plane surface is equal to the normal pressure on its vertical projection; the vertical pressure is equal to the normal pressure on its horizontal projection; and the pressure in any direction is equal to the normal pressure on a projection perpendicular to that direction.

To prove this let A be the area of the given surface, represented by AA in Fig. 16a, and P the normal pressure upon it, or $P = wAh$. Now let it be required to find the pressure P' in a direction making an angle θ with the normal to the given plane. Draw $A'A'$ perpendicular to the direction of P', and let A' be the area of the projection of A upon it. The value of P' then is

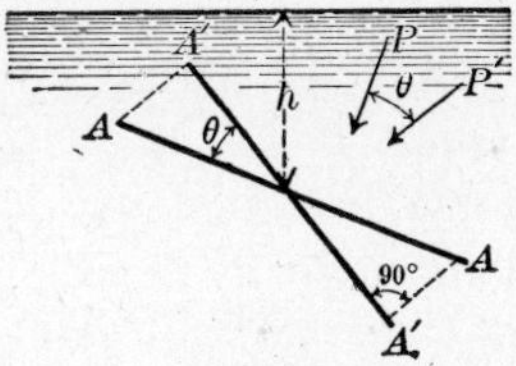

Fig. 16a.

$$P' = P\cos\theta = wAh\cos\theta$$

But $A\cos\theta$ is the value of A' by the construction. Hence

$$P' = wA'h \qquad (16)$$

and the theorem is thus demonstrated.

This theorem does not in general apply to curved surfaces. But in cases where the head of water is so great that the pressure may be regarded as uniform it is also true for curved surfaces. For instance, consider a cylinder or sphere subjected on every elementary area to the unit-pressure p due to the high head h, and let it be required to find the pressure in the direction shown by q_1, q_2, and q_3 in Fig. 16b. The pressures p_1, p_2, p_3, etc., on the elementary areas a_1, a_2, a_3, etc., have the values

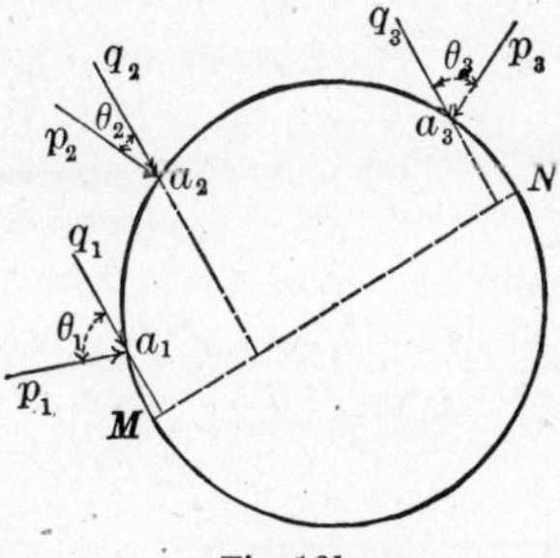

Fig. 16b.

$$p_1 = pa_1, \qquad p_2 = pa_2, \qquad p_3 = pa_3, \text{ etc.,}$$

and the components of these in the given direction are

$$q_1 = pa_1\cos\theta_1, \qquad q_2 = pa_2\cos\theta_2, \qquad q_3 = pa_3\cos\theta_3, \text{ etc.,}$$

whence the total pressure P' in the given direction is

$$P' = p(a_1 \cos\theta_1 + a_2 \cos\theta_2 + a_3 \cos\theta_3 + \text{etc.})$$

But the quantity in the parenthesis is the projection of the given surface upon a plane perpendicular to the given direction, or MN. Hence there results

$$P' = p \times \text{area } MN$$

which is the same rule as for plane surfaces.

For the case of a water pipe let p be the interior pressure per square inch, t its thickness, and d its diameter in inches. Then for a length of one inch the force tending to rupture the pipe longitudinally is pd. The tensile unit-stress S in the walls of the pipe acting over the area $2t$ constitutes the resisting force $2tS$. Since these forces are equal, it follows that $2St = pd$ is the fundamental equation for the discussion of the strength of water pipes under static water pressure. For example, when the tensile strength of cast iron is 20 000 pounds per square inch, the unit-pressure p required to burst a pipe 24 inches in diameter and 0.75 inches thick is 1250 pounds per square inch, which corresponds to a head of 2880 feet.

Prob. 16. A circular plate 5 feet in diameter is immersed so that the head on its center is 18 feet, its plane making an angle of 30° with the vertical. Compute the horizontal and vertical pressures upon one side of it.

Art. 17. Center of Pressure on Rectangles

The center of pressure on a surface immersed in water is the point of application of the resultant of all the normal pressures upon it. The simplest case is the following:

> When a rectangle is placed with one end in the water surface, the center of pressure is distant from that end two-thirds of the length of the rectangle.

This theorem will be proved by the help of the graphical illustration shown in Fig. 17*a*. The rectangle, which in practice might be a board, is placed with its breadth perpendicular to the plane of the drawing, so that AB represents its edge. It is required to find the center of pressure C. For any head h the unit-pressure is wh (Art. 15), and hence the unit-pressures on one side of AB may be graphically represented by arrows which form a triangle. Now when a force P equal to the total pressure is applied on the other side of the rectangle to balance these unit-pressures, it must be placed opposite to the center of gravity of the triangle. Therefore AC equals two-thirds of AB, and the rule is proved. The head on C is evidently also two-thirds of the head on B.

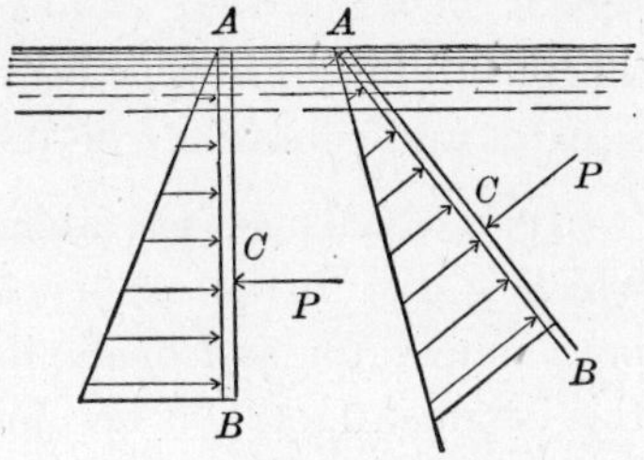

Fig. 17a.

Another case is that shown in Fig. 17b, where the rectangle, whose length is B_1B_2, is wholly immersed, the head on B_1 being h_1, and on B_2 being h_2. Let $AB_1 = b_1$, $AC = y$, and $AB_2 = b_2$. Now the normal pressure P_1, on AB_1 is applied at the distance $\frac{2}{3}b_1$ from A, and the normal pressure P_2 on AB_2 is applied at the distance $\frac{2}{3}b_2$ from A. The normal pressure P on B_1B_2 is the difference of P_1 and P_2, or $P = P_2 - P_1$. Also by taking moments about A as an axis,

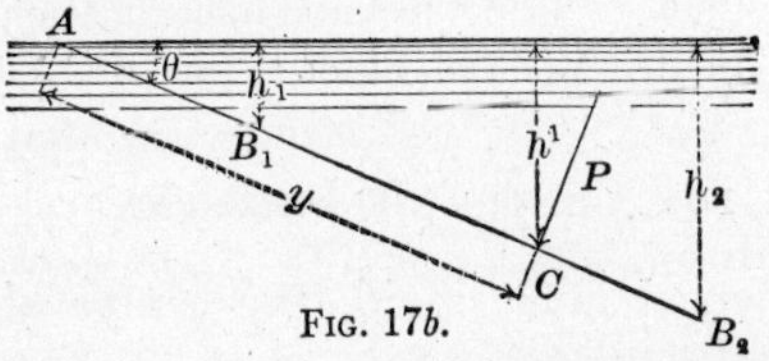

FIG. 17b.

$$P \times y = P_2 \times \tfrac{2}{3} b_2 - P_1 \times \tfrac{2}{3} b_1$$

Now, by Art. 15, the normal pressures P_2 and P_1 for a rectangle one unit in breadth are $P_2 = \frac{1}{2}wb_2h_2$ and $P_1 = \frac{1}{2}wb_1h_1$, whence the total normal pressure is $P = \frac{1}{2}w(b_2h_2 - b_1h_1)$, and accordingly the center of pressure is given by

$$y = \tfrac{2}{3} \cdot \frac{b_2^2h_2 - b_1^2h_1}{b_2h_2 - b_1h_1}$$

When θ is the angle of inclination of the plane to the water surface, the values of h_2 and h_1 are $b_2 \sin\theta$ and $b_1 \sin\theta$. Accordingly the expression becomes

$$y = \tfrac{2}{3} \cdot \frac{b_2^3 - b_1^3}{b_2^2 - b_1^2} \qquad (17)_1$$

Again, if h' is the head on the center of pressure, $y = h' \operatorname{cosec}\theta$, $b_2 = h_2 \operatorname{cosec}\theta$, and $b_1 = h_1 \operatorname{cosec}\theta$. These inserted in the last equation give

$$h' = \tfrac{2}{3} \cdot \frac{h_2^3 - h_1^3}{h_2^2 - h_1^2} \qquad (17)_2$$

These formulas are very convenient for computation, since the squares and cubes may be taken from tables.

If h_1 equals h_2, the above formula becomes indeterminate, which is due to the existence of the common factor $h_2 - h_1$ in both numerator and denominator of the fraction; dividing out this common factor, it becomes

$$h' = \tfrac{2}{3} \cdot \frac{h_2^2 + h_2 h_1 + h_1^2}{h_2 + h_1}$$

from which, if $h_2 = h_1 = h$, there is found the result $h' = h$.

Prob. 17. In Fig. 17*a* let the length of AB be 8.5 feet and its inclination to the vertical be 45 degrees. Find the depth of the center of pressure.

Art. 18. General Rule for Center of Pressure

For any plane surface immersed in a liquid, the center of pressure may be found by the following rule:

> Find the moment of inertia of the surface and its statical moment, both with reference to an axis situated at the intersection of the plane of the surface with the water level. Divide the former by the latter and the quotient is the perpendicular distance from that axis to the center of pressure.

The demonstration is analogous to that in the last article. Let B_1B_2 in Fig. 17*b* be the trace of the plane surface, which itself is perpendicular to the plane of the drawing, and C be the center of pressure, at a distance y from A where the plane of the surface intersects the water level. Let a_1, a_2, a_3, etc., be elementary areas of the surface, and h_1, h_2, h_3, etc., the heads upon them, which produce the normal elementary pressures, wa_1h_1, wa_2h_2, wa_3h_3, etc. Let y_1, y_2, y_3, etc., be the distances from A to these elementary areas. Then taking the point A as a center of moments, the definition of center of pressure gives the equation

$$(wa_1h_1 + wa_2h_2 + wa_3h_3 + \text{etc.})\, y = wa_1h_1y_1 + wa_2h_2y_2 + wa_3h_3y_3 + \text{etc.}$$

Now let θ be the angle of inclination of the surface to the water level; then $h_1 = y_1 \sin\theta$, $h_2 = y_2 \sin\theta$, $h_3 = y_3 \sin\theta$, etc. Hence, inserting these values, the expression for y is

$$y = \frac{a_1y_1^2 + a_2y_2^2 + a_3y_3^2 + \text{etc.}}{a_1y_1 + a_2y_2 + a_3y_3 + \text{etc.}}$$

The numerator of this fraction is the sum of the products obtained by multiplying each element of the surface by the square of its distance from the axis, which is called the moment of inertia of the surface. The denominator is the sum of the products obtained by multiplying each element of the surface by its distance from the axis, which is called the statical moment of the surface. Therefore

$$y = \frac{\text{moment of inertia}}{\text{statical moment}} = \frac{I'}{S} \tag{18}$$

is the general rule for finding the position of the center of pressure of an immersed plane surface.

The statical moment of a surface is simply its area multiplied by the distance of its center of gravity from the given axis. The moments of inertia of plane surfaces with reference to an axis through the center of gravity are deduced in works on theoretical mechanics; the following are a few values, the axis being parallel to the base of the rectangle or triangle:

for a rectangle of base b and depth d, $I = \frac{1}{12} bd^3$
for a triangle of base b and altitude d, $I = \frac{1}{36} bd^3$
for a circle with diameter d, $I = \frac{1}{64} \pi d^4$

To find from these the moment of inertia with reference to a parallel axis, the well-known formula $I' = I + Ak^2$ is to be used, where A is the area of the surface, k the distance from the given axis to the center of gravity of the surface, and I' the moment of inertia required.

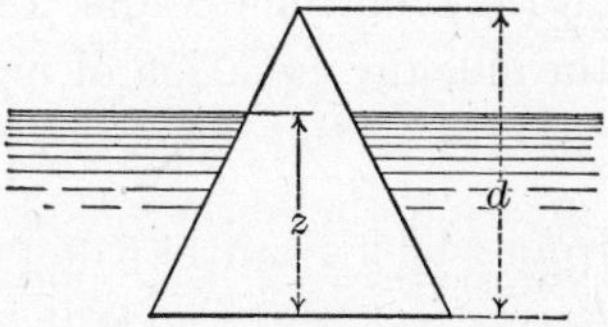

Fig. 18.

For example, let it be required to find the center of pressure of a vertical circle immersed so that the head on its center is equal to its radius. The area of the circle is $\frac{1}{4} \pi d^2$, and its statical moment with reference to the upper edge is $\frac{1}{4}\pi d^2 \times \frac{1}{2} d$. Then from (18)

$$y = \frac{\frac{1}{64}\pi d^4 + \frac{1}{4}\pi d^2 \cdot \frac{1}{4} d^2}{\frac{1}{4}\pi d^2 \cdot \frac{1}{2} d} = \frac{5}{8} d$$

or the center of pressure is at a distance $\frac{1}{8} d$ below the center of the circle.

Prob. 18. Find the depth of flotation for the triangle in Fig. 18. Also find the position of the center of pressure upon it in terms of z.

Art. 19. Pressures on Gates and Dams

In the case of an immersed plane the water presses equally upon both sides so that no disturbance of the equilibrium results from the pressure. But in case the water is at different levels on opposite sides of the surface the opposing pressures are unequal. For example, the cross-section of a self-acting tide-gate, built to drain a salt marsh, is shown in Fig. 19a. On the ocean side there is a head of h_1 above the sill, which gives for every linear foot of the gate the horizontal pressure

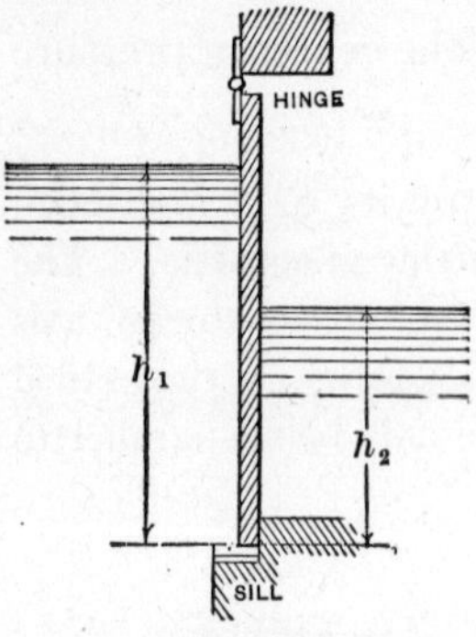

Fig. 19a.

$$P_1 = w \times h_1 \times \frac{1}{2} h_1 = \frac{1}{2} w h_1^2$$

which is applied at the distance $\frac{1}{3} h_1$ above the sill. On the other side the head on the sill is h_2, which gives the horizontal pressure $P_2 = \frac{1}{2} w h_2^2$ acting in the opposite direction to that of P_1. The resultant horizontal pressure is

$$P = P_1 - P_2 = \frac{1}{2} w (h_1^2 - h_2^2)$$

and if z be the distance of the point of application of P above the sill, the equation of moments is

$$Pz = P_1 \times \frac{1}{3} h_1 - P_2 \times \frac{1}{3} h_2$$

from which z can be computed. For example, if h_1 is 7 feet and h_2 is 4 feet, the resultant pressure on one linear foot of the gate is found to be 1031 pounds and its point of application to be 2.82 feet above the sill. The action of this gate in resisting the water pressure is like that of a beam under its load, the two points of support being at the sill and the hinge. If h is the height of the gate, the reaction at the hinge is Pz/h, and from the above expression for Pz it is seen that this reaction has its greatest value when h_1 becomes equal to h and h_2 is zero. In the case of the vertical gate of a canal lock, which swings horizontally like a door, a similar problem arises and a similar conclusion results.

When the water level behind a masonry dam is lower than its top, as in Fig. 19*b*, the water pressure on the back is normal to the plane AB and for computations this may be resolved into

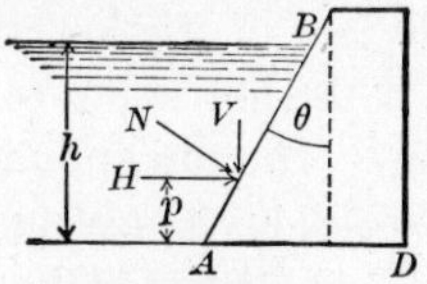

Fig. 19*b*.

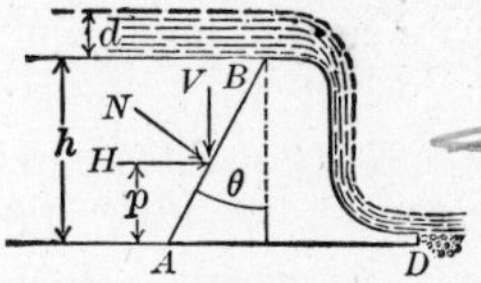

Fig. 19*c*.

horizontal and vertical components. Let h be the height of water above the base, θ the angle which the back makes with the vertical, then from Arts. 15–16 the values of these pressures, for one linear unit of the dam, are

$$\text{Normal Pressure } N = w \cdot h \sec\theta \cdot \tfrac{1}{2}h = \tfrac{1}{2}wh^2 \sec\theta$$
$$\text{Horizontal Component } H = N\cos\theta = \tfrac{1}{2}wh^2$$
$$\text{Vertical Component } V = N\sin\theta = \tfrac{1}{2}wh^2 \tan\theta$$

and from Art. 17 the point of application of these pressures is at a distance $\frac{1}{3}h$ above the base. Except in the case of hollow dams only the horizontal component H need usually be considered, since the neglect of V is on the side of safety.

When the water runs over the top of a dam, as in Fig. 19*c*, let h be the height of the dam and d the depth of water on its crest. Then

$$\text{Normal Pressure } N = w \cdot h\sec\theta \cdot (d + \tfrac{1}{2}h) = \tfrac{1}{2}wh(h+2d)\sec\theta$$
$$\text{Horizontal Component } H = N\cos\theta = \tfrac{1}{2}wh(h+2d)$$
$$\text{Vertical Component } V = N\sin\theta = \tfrac{1}{2}wh(h+2d)\tan\theta$$

and, from Art. 17, the point of application above the base AD is

$$p = \frac{h+3d}{h+2d} \cdot \tfrac{1}{3}h$$

when $d = 0$, these expressions for H and p become $\frac{1}{2}wh^2$ and $\frac{1}{3}h$. If d is infinite, the value of p reduces to $\frac{1}{2}h$ and hence in no case can the pressure N be applied as high as the middle of the height of the dam. Unless the dam be hollow or θ be greater than 30° it will usually be proper to neglect V and to consider only H.

It is not the place here to enter into the discussion of the subject of the design of masonry dams, but two ways in which they are liable to fail may be noted. The first is that of sliding along a horizontal joint, as AD; here the horizontal component of the thrust overcomes the resisting force of friction acting along the joint. If W is the weight of masonry above the joint, and f the coefficient of friction, the resisting friction is fW, and the dam will slide if the horizontal component of the pressure is equal to or greater than this. The condition for failure by sliding then is $H=fW$. For example, consider a masonry dam of rectangular cross-section which is 4 feet wide and h feet high, the water being level with its top. Let its weight per cubic foot be 140 pounds, and let it be required to find the height h for which it would fail by sliding along the base, the coefficient of friction being 0.70. The horizontal water pressure is $\frac{1}{2} \times 62.5 \times h^2$ and the resisting friction is $0.7 \times 140 \times 4 \times h$. Placing these equal, there is found for the height of the dam $h = 12.5$ feet.

The second method of failure of a masonry dam is by overturning, or by rotating about the toe D. This occurs when the moment of H equals the moment of W with respect to D, or if p and q are the lever arms dropped from D upon the directions of H and W, the condition for failure by rotation is $Hp=Wq$. For example, when it is required to find the height of the above rectangular dam so that it will fail by rotation, the lever arms p and q are $\frac{1}{3}h$ and 2 feet, and the equation of moments with respect to the toe of the dam is

$$\frac{1}{2} \times 62.5 \times h^2 \times \frac{1}{3}h = 140 \times 4 \times h \times 2$$

from which there is found $h=10.4$ feet. The horizontal water pressure for one linear foot of the dam at the instant of failure is $\frac{1}{2}wh^2=3380$ pounds.

In the case of an overfall dam, as in Fig. 19c, the falling sheet of water produces a partial vacuum when air cannot freely enter behind it, and thus the force H, tending to produce sliding, is increased. In the design of a dam consideration must also be given to the upward pressure of that water which gains access either beneath its foundation or directly into its mass. This upward pressure is equivalent to a loss of weight due to percolating water, as was described in Art. 12.

Prob. 19. A water pipe passing through a masonry dam is closed by a cast-iron circular valve AB, which is hinged at A, and which can be raised by a vertical chain BC. The diameter of the valve is 3 feet, its plane makes an angle of 27° with the vertical, and the depth of its center below the water level is 12.5 feet. Compute the normal water pressure P, and the distance of the center of pressure from the hinge A. Disregarding the weight of the valve and chain, compute the force F required to open the valve. When the weight of the chain is 23 pounds and that of the valve 180 pounds, compute the force F.

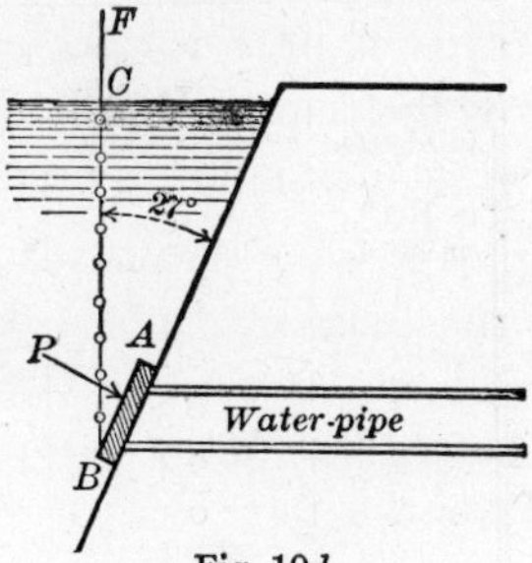

Fig. 19*d*.

Art. 20. Hydrostatics in Metric Measures

(Art. 11) When the head h is in meters and the unit-pressure p is in kilograms per square meter, the formulas $(11)_1$ become

$$p = 1000h \qquad h = 0.001p$$

In engineering practice p is usually taken in kilograms per square centimeter, while h is expressed in meters. Then

$$p = 0.1h \qquad h = 10p \tag{20}$$

Stated in words these practical rules are:

1 meter head corresponds to 0.1 kilogram per square centimeter
1 kilogram per square centimeter corresponds to 10 meters head

These values depend upon the assumption that 1000 kilograms is the weight of a cubic meter of water, and hence results derived from them are liable to an uncertainty in the third or fourth significant figure, as Table 20 shows.

The atmospheric pressure of 1.033 kilograms per square centimeter is to be added to the pressure due to the head whenever it is necessary to regard the absolute pressure. For example, if the air is exhausted from a small globe so that its pressure is only 0.32 kilogram per square centimeter and it be submerged in water to a depth of 86 meters, the absolute pressure per square centimeter on the globe is $0.1 \times 86 + 1.033 = 9.633$ kilograms, and the resultant effective pressure per square centimeter is $9.633 - 0.32 = 9.313$ kilograms.

TABLE 20. HEADS AND PRESSURES

Metric Measures

Head in Meters	Pressure in Kilograms per Square Centimeter		Pressure in Kilograms per Square Centimeter	Head in Meters	
	$w = 1000$	$w = 997$		$w = 1000$	$w = 997$
1	0.1	0.0997	1	10	10.03
2	0.2	0.1994	2	20	20.06
3	0.3	0.2991	3	30	30.09
4	0.4	0.3988	4	40	40.12
5	0.5	0.4985	5	50	50.15
6	0.6	0.5982	6	60	60.18
7	0.7	0.6979	7	70	70.21
8	0.8	0.7976	8	80	80.24
9	0.9	0.8973	9	90	90.27
10	1.0	0.9970	10	100	100.30

(Art. 12) The specific gravity of a substance is expressed by the same number as the weight of a cubic centimeter in grams, or the weight of a cubic decimeter in kilograms, or the weight of a cubic meter in metric tons. Thus, if the specific gravity of stone is 2.4, a cubic meter weighs 2.4 metric tons or 2400 kilograms. A bar one square centimeter in cross-section and one meter long contains 100 cubic centimeters; hence if such a bar be of steel having a specific gravity of 7.9, it weighs 790 grams or 0.79 kilogram in air, while in water it weighs 690 grams or 0.69 kilogram.

(Art. 15) Here h is to be taken in meters, A in square meters, and w as 1000 kilograms per cubic meter; then P will be in kilograms.

(Art. 16) For a water pipe let p be the interior pressure in kilograms per square centimeter and d its diameter in centimeters. Then for a length of one centimeter the force tending to rupture the pipe longitudinally is pd. Let S be the stress in kilograms per square centimeter in the walls of the pipe; this acts over the area $2t$, if t be the thickness. As these forces are equal, the equation $2St = pd$ is to be used for the investigation of water pipes. For example, let it be required to find what head will burst a cast-iron pipe 60 centimeters in diameter and 2 centimeters thick; the tensile strength of the material being 1400 kilograms per square centimeter. Using the equation, the value of p is found to be 93.3 kilograms per square centimeter and then, from Art. 9, the required head h is 933 meters.

(Art. 19) Consider a rectangular masonry dam which weighs 2400 kilograms per cubic meter and which is 1.4 meters thick. First, let it be required to find the height of water for which it would fail by sliding, the coefficient of friction being 0.75. The horizontal water-pressure is $\frac{1}{2} \times 1000 \times h^2$, and the resisting friction is $0.75 \times 2400 \times 1.4 \times h$; placing these equal, there is found $h = 5.04$ meters. Secondly, to find the height for which failure will occur by rotation, the equation of moments is

$$\tfrac{1}{2} \times 1000 \times h^2 \times \tfrac{1}{3} h = 2400 \times 1.4 \times h \times 0.75$$

from which there is found $h = 3.89$ meters. The horizontal water-pressure for one linear meter of this dam is $\frac{1}{2} wh^2 = 7560$ kilograms.

Prob. 20*a*. In a hydrostatic press one-half of a metric horse-power is applied to the small piston. The diameter of the large piston is 50 centimeters and it moves 2 centimeters per minute. Compute the pressure in the liquid.

Prob. 20*b*. What is the specific gravity of dry hydraulic cement of which 20.6 cubic centimeters weigh 63.2 grams? If a cube of stone 12.4 centimeters on each edge weighs 4.88 kilograms, what is its specific gravity?

Prob. 20*c*. In Fig. 19*a* let the head on one side of the gate be 2.5 and on the other side 0.6 meters above the sill. Find the resultant pressure for one linear meter of the gate and the distance of its point of application above the sill.

CHAPTER 3

THEORETICAL HYDRAULICS

ART. 21. LAWS OF FALLING BODIES

Theoretical Hydraulics treats of the flow of water when unretarded by opposing forces of friction. In a perfectly smooth inclined trough water would flow with accelerated velocity and be governed by the same laws as those for a body sliding down a frictionless inclined plane. Such a flow is, however, never found in practice, for all surfaces over which water moves are more or less rough. Friction retards the motions caused by gravity so that the theoretic velocities deduced in this chapter constitute limits which cannot be exceeded by the actual velocities. Many of the laws governing the free fall of bodies in a vacuum are similar to those of both theoretical and practical hydraulics, and hence they will here be briefly discussed.

A body at rest above the surface of the earth immediately falls when its support is removed. When the fall occurs in a vacuum, its velocity at the end of one second is g feet, the mean value of g being 32.16 feet per second per second, and at the end of t seconds its velocity is $V = gt$. The distance passed through in the time t is the product of the mean velocity $\frac{1}{2} V$ by the number of seconds, or $h = \frac{1}{2} gt^2$. Eliminating t from these two equations gives

$$V = \sqrt{2gh} \qquad \text{or} \qquad h = V^2/2g \qquad (21)_1$$

which show that the velocity varies with the square root of the height and that the height varies as the square of the velocity.

When a falling body has the initial velocity u at the beginning of the time t, its velocity at the end of this time is $V = u + gt$ and the distance passed over in that time is $h = ut + \frac{1}{2} gt^2$. Eliminating t from these equations gives

$$V = \sqrt{2gh + u^2} \qquad \text{or} \qquad h = (V^2 - u^2)/2g \qquad (21)_2$$

as the relations between V and h for this case. These formulas are also true whatever be the direction of the initial velocity u.

When a body of weight W is at the height h above a given horizontal plane, its potential energy with respect to this plane is Wh. When it falls from rest to this plane, the potential energy is changed into the kinetic energy $WV^2/2g$ if no work has been done against frictional resistance, and therefore $V^2 = 2gh$. When it has a velocity u in any direction at the height h above the plane, its energy there is partly potential and partly kinetic, the sum of these being $Wh + W \cdot u^2/2g$; on reaching the plane it has the kinetic energy $WV^2/2g$. Placing these equal, there results $V^2 = 2gh + u^2$, as found above by another method. In general, reasoning from the standpoint of energy is more satisfactory than that in which the element of time is employed.

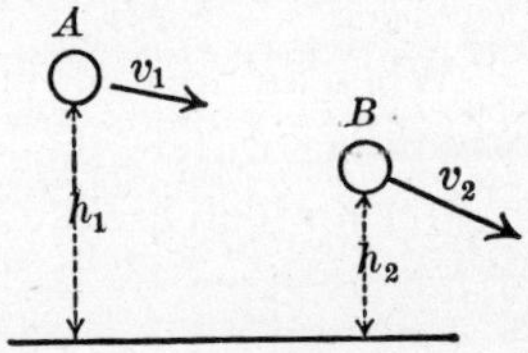

Fig. 21.

The general case of a body moving toward the earth is represented in Fig. 21. When the body is at A, it is at a height h_1 above a certain horizontal plane and has the velocity v_1. When it has arrived at B, its height above the plane is h_2 and its velocity is v_2. In the first position the sum of its potential and kinetic energy with respect to the given horizontal plane is

$$W\left(h_1 + \frac{v_1^2}{2g}\right)$$

and in the second position the sum of these energies is

$$W\left(h_2 + \frac{v_2^2}{2g}\right)$$

If no energy has been lost between the two positions, these two expressions are equal, and hence

$$h_1 + \frac{v_1^2}{2g} = h_2 + \frac{v_2^2}{2g} \qquad (21)_3$$

This equation is the simplest form of Bernouilli's theorem (Art. 31). It contains two heights and two velocities, and when three of these quantities are given, the fourth can be found; thus, if v_1, h_1, and h_2 are given, the value of v_2 is

$$v_2 = \sqrt{2g(h_1 - h_2) + v_1^2}$$

where $h_1 - h_2$ is the vertical height of A above B. With proper changes in notation this expression reduces to $(21)_2$, which is for the case where the horizontal plane passes through B, and to $(21)_1$, which is the case where there is no initial velocity.

Prob. 21. A body enters a room through the ceiling with a velocity of 47 feet per second, and in a direction making an angle of 27° with the vertical. If the height of the room is 16 feet, find the velocity of the body as it strikes the floor, resistances of the air being neglected.

Art. 22. Velocity of Flow from Orifices

When an orifice is opened, either in the base or side of a vessel containing water, the water flows out with a velocity which is greater for high heads than for low heads. The theoretic velocity of flow is given by the theorem established by Torricelli in 1644:

> The theoretic velocity of flow from the orifice is the same as that acquired by a body after having fallen from rest in a vacuum through a height equal to the head of water on the orifice.

One proof of this theorem is by experience. When a vessel is arranged, as in the first diagram of Fig. 22, so that a jet of water from an orifice is directed vertically upward, it is known that it never attains to the height of the level of the water in the vessel, although under favorable conditions it nearly reaches that level. It may hence be inferred that the jet would actually rise to that height were it not for the resistance of the air and the friction of the edges of the orifice. Now, since the velocity required to raise a body vertically to a certain height is the same as that acquired by it in falling from rest through that height, it is re-

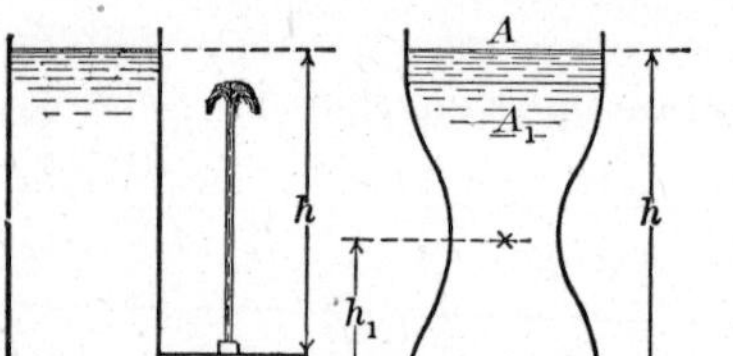

Fig. 22.

garded as established that the velocity at the orifice is that stated in the theorem.

The following proof rests on the law of conservation of energy. Let, as in the second diagram of Fig. 22, the water surface in a vessel be at A and let the flow through the orifice occur for a very short interval of time during which the water surface descends to A_1. Let W be the weight of water between the planes A and A_1, which is evidently the same as that which flows from the orifice during the short time considered. Let W_1 be the weight of water between the planes A_1 and B, and h_1 the height of its center of gravity above the orifice. Let h be the height of A above the orifice, and δh the small distance between A and A_1. At the beginning of the flow the water in the vessel has the potential energy $W_1 h_1 + W(h - \frac{1}{2}\delta h)$ with respect to B. V being the velocity at the orifice, the same water at the end of the short interval of time has the energy $W_1 h_1 + W \cdot V^2/2g$. By the law of conservation these are equal if no energy has been expended in overcoming frictional resistances; thus $h - \frac{1}{2}\delta h = V^2/2g$. Here δh is very small if the area A is large compared with the area of the orifice, and thus $V^2 = 2gh$, which is the same as for a body falling from rest through the height h. Or $h - \frac{1}{2}\delta h$ may be regarded as an average head corresponding to an average velocity V, so that in general $V^2/2g$ is equal to the average head on the orifice.

For any orifice, therefore, whether its plane is horizontal, vertical, or inclined, provided the head h is so large that it has practically the same value for all parts of the orifice, the relation between V and h is

$$V = \sqrt{2gh} \qquad \text{or} \qquad h = V^2/2g \qquad (22)_1$$

the first of which gives the theoretic velocity of flow due to a given head, while the second gives the theoretic head that will produce a given velocity. The term "velocity-head" will generally be used to designate the expression $V^2/2g$, this being the height to which the jet would rise if it were directed vertically upward and there were no frictional resistances. Using for g the mean value 32.16 feet per second per second (Art. 7), these formulas become

$$V = 8.020\sqrt{h} \qquad h = 0.01555\,V^2 \qquad (22)_2$$

in which h must be in feet and V in feet per second. The following table gives values of the velocity V corresponding to a given head h and also values of the velocity-head h corresponding to a given velocity V. It is seen that small heads produce high theoretic velocities. The relation between h and V is the same as that between the ordinate and abscissa of the common parabola when the origin is at the vertex. It may also be noted that the discussion here given applies not only to water but to any liquid; thus $V^2 = 2gh$ is theoretically true for alcohol and mercury as well as for water.

TABLE 22. VELOCITIES AND VELOCITY-HEADS

$V = \sqrt{2gh} = 8.020\sqrt{h}$				$h = V^2/2g = 0.01555\,V^2$			
Head in Feet	Velocity in Feet per Second	Head in Feet	Velocity in Feet per Second	Velocity in Feet per Second	Head in Feet	Velocity in Feet per Second	Head in Feet
0.1	2.537	1	8.02	1	0.016	10	1.56
0.2	3.587	2	11.33	2	0.062	20	6.22
0.3	4.393	3	13.89	3	0.140	30	13.99
0.4	5.072	4	16.04	4	0.249	40	24.88
0.5	5.671	5	17.93	5	0.389	50	38.87
0.6	6.212	6	19.64	6	0.560	60	55.97
0.7	6.710	7	21.22	7	0.762	70	76.19
0.8	7.171	8	22.68	8	0.995	80	99.51
0.9	7.608	9	24.06	9	1.260	90	125.95
1.0	8.020	10	25.36	10	1.555	100	155.50

When a Pitot tube (Art. 41) is placed with its mouth in the plane of the horizontal orifice in Fig. 22, and at the contracted section of the jet (Art. 45), it will be found that the water in it stands practically at the level of the water in the vessel.* In this manner the frictional resistance of the air is eliminated, and a valuable experimental demonstration of the theorem which connects the velocity and the velocity-head is obtained.

Prob. 22. Find from Table 22 the velocity due to a head of 0.085 feet, and the velocity-head corresponding to a velocity of 65.5 feet per second.

* Engineering Record, Feb. 15, 1902.

Art. 23. Flow under Pressure

The level of water in the reservoir and the orifice of outflow have been thus far regarded as subjected to no pressure, or at least only to the pressure of the atmosphere which acts upon both with the same mean force of 14.7 pounds per square inch, since the head h is rarely or never so great that a sensible variation in atmospheric pressure can be detected between the orifice and the water level. But the upper level of the water may be subject to the pressure of steam or to the pressure due to a heavy weight or to a piston. The orifice may also be under a pressure greater or less than that of the atmosphere. It is required to determine the velocity of flow from the orifice under these conditions.

First, suppose that the surface of the water in the vessel or reservoir is subjected to the uniform pressure of p_0 pounds per square unit above the atmospheric pressure, while the pressure at the orifice is the same as that of the atmosphere. Let h be the depth of water on the orifice. The velocity of flow V is greater than $\sqrt{2gh}$ on account of the pressure p_0, and it is evidently the same as that from a column of water whose height is such as to produce the same pressure at the orifice. If w is the weight of a cubic unit of water, the unit-pressure at the orifice due to the head is wh, and the total unit-pressure at the depth of the orifice is $p = wh + p_0$, and from formula $(11)_1$ the head of water which would produce this total unit-pressure is

$$\frac{p}{w} = h + \frac{p_0}{w}$$

Accordingly the theoretic velocity of flow from the orifice is

$$V = \sqrt{2g(h + p_0/w)}$$

or, if h_0 denote the head corresponding to the pressure p_0,

$$V = \sqrt{2g(h + h_0)}$$

The general formula $(22)_1$ thus applies to any small orifice if H be the head corresponding to the static pressure at the orifice.

Secondly, suppose that the surface of the water in the vessel is subjected to the unit-pressure p_0, while the orifice is under the external unit-pressure p_1. Let h be the head of actual water on the orifice, h_0 the head of water which will produce the pressure p_0, and h_1 the head which will produce p_1. The theoretic velocity of flow at the orifice is then the same as if the orifice were under a head $h + h_0 - h_1$, or

$$V = \sqrt{2g(h + h_0 - h_1)} \qquad (23)_1$$

in which the values of h_0 and h_1 are

$$h_0 = p_0/w \quad \text{and} \quad h_1 = p_1/w$$

Usually p_0 and p_1 are given in pounds per square inch, while h_0 and h_1 are required in feet; then (Art. 11)

$$h_0 = 2.304 p_0 \qquad h_1 = 2.304 p_1$$

The values of p_0 and p_1 may be absolute pressures, or merely pressures above the atmosphere. In the latter case p_1 may sometimes be negative, as in the discharge of water into a condenser.

As an illustration of these principles let the cylindrical tank in Fig. 23 be 2 feet in diameter, and upon the surface of the water let there be a tightly fitting piston which with the load W weighs 3000 pounds. At the depth 8 feet below the water level are three small orifices: one at A, upon which there is an exterior head of water of 3 feet; one not shown in the figure, which discharges directly into the atmosphere; and one at C, where the discharge is into a vessel in which the air pressure is only 10 pounds per square inch. It is required to determine the velocity of efflux from each orifice. The head h_0 corresponding to the pressure on the upper water surface is

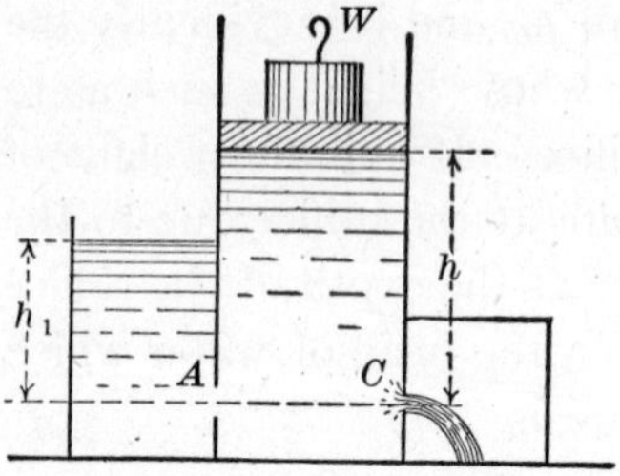

Fig. 23.

$$h_0 = \frac{p_0}{w} = \frac{3000}{3.142 \times 62.5} = 15.28 \text{ feet}$$

The head h_1 is 3 feet for the first orifice, 0 for the second, and $-2.304(14.7 - 10) = -10.83$ feet for the third. The three theoretic velocities of outflow then are:

$$V = 8.02\sqrt{8 + 15.28 - 3} = 30.1 \text{ feet per second,}$$
$$V = 8.02\sqrt{8 + 15.28 + 0} = 38.7 \text{ feet per second,}$$
$$V = 8.02\sqrt{8 + 15.28 + 10.83} = 46.8 \text{ feet per second.}$$

In the case of discharge from an orifice under water, as at A in Fig. 23, the value of $h - h_1$ is the same wherever the orifice be placed below the lower level, and hence the velocity depends upon the difference of level of the two water surfaces, and not upon the depth of the orifice.

The velocity of flow of oil or mercury under pressure is to be determined in the same manner as water by finding the heads which will produce the given pressure. Thus in the preceding numerical example, if the liquid is mercury whose weight per cubic foot is 850 pounds the head of mercury corresponding to the pressure of the piston is

$$h_0 = \frac{3000}{3.142 \times 850} = 1.12 \text{ feet,}$$

and, accordingly, for discharge into the atmosphere at the depth $h = 8$ feet the velocity is

$$V = 8.02\sqrt{8 + 1.12} = 24.2 \text{ feet per second,}$$

while for water the velocity was 38.7 feet per second. The general formula $(22)_1$ is applicable to all cases of the flow of liquids from a small orifice if for h its value p/w be substituted where p is the resultant unit-pressure at the depth of the orifice and w the weight of a cubic unit of the liquid. Thus for any liquid

$$V = \sqrt{2gp/w} \qquad (23)_2$$

is the theoretic velocity of flow from the orifice. Accordingly for the same unit-pressure p the velocities are inversely proportional to the square roots of the densities of the liquids.

Prob. 23. What is the theoretic velocity of flow from a small orifice in a boiler 2 feet below the water level when the steam-gage reads 75 pounds per square inch? What is the theoretic velocity when the gage reads 0?

Art. 24. Influence of Velocity of Approach

Thus far in the determination of the theoretic velocity and discharge from an orifice, the head upon it has been regarded as constant. But if the cross-section of the vessel is not large, the head can only be kept constant by an inflow of water, and this will modify the previous formulas. In this case the water approaches the orifice with an initial velocity. Let a be the area of the orifice and A the area of the horizontal cross-section of the vessel. Let V be the velocity of flow through a and v be the vertical velocity of inflow through A. Let W be the weight of water flowing from the orifice in one second; then an equal weight must enter at A in one second in order to maintain a constant head h.

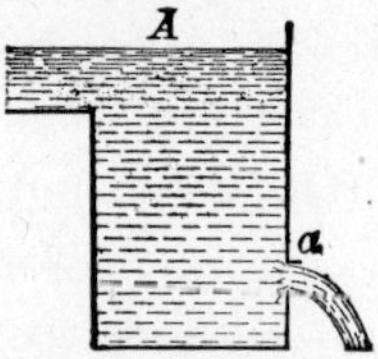

Fig. 24₁.

The kinetic energy of the outflowing water is $W \cdot V^2/2g$, and this is equal, if there be no loss of energy, to the potential energy Wh of the inflowing water plus its kinetic energy $W \cdot v^2/2g$,

or
$$W\frac{V^2}{2g} = Wh + W\frac{v^2}{2g}$$

Now since the same quantity of water Q passes through the two areas in one second, $Q = aV = Av$, whence $v = V \cdot a/A$. Inserting this value of v in the equation of energy, there is found

$$V = \sqrt{\frac{2gh}{1-(a/A)^2}} \qquad (24)_1$$

which is always greater than the value $\sqrt{2gh}$.

The influence of the velocity of approach on the velocity of flow at the orifice can now be ascertained by assigning values to the ratio a/A. Thus, if $a = A$, the velocity V must be infinite in order that the water may fill the entire section of the vessel and orifice. Further,

for $a = \frac{2}{3}A$ $\qquad V = 1.342\sqrt{2gh}$

for $a = \frac{1}{2}A$ $\qquad V = 1.154\sqrt{2gh}$

for $a = \frac{1}{3}A$ $\qquad V = 1.061\sqrt{2gh}$

for $a = \frac{1}{5}A$ $\qquad V = 1.021\sqrt{2gh}$

for $a = \frac{1}{10}A$ $\qquad V = 1.005\sqrt{2gh}$

It is here seen that the common formula $(22)_1$ is in error 2.1 percent when $a = \frac{1}{5}A$, if the head be maintained constant by a uniform vertical inflow at the water surface, and 0.5 percent when $a = \frac{1}{10} A$. Practically, if the area of the orifice be less than one-twentieth of the cross-section of the vessel, the error in using the formula $V = \sqrt{2gh}$ is too small to be noticed, even in the most precise experiments, and fortunately most orifices are smaller in relative size than this.

A more common case is that where the reservoir is of large horizontal and small vertical cross-section, and where the water approaches the orifice with velocity in a horizontal direction, as in Fig. 24*b*. Here let A be the area of the vertical cross-section of the trough or pipe, a the area of the orifice, and h the head on its center. Then if h be large compared with the depth of the

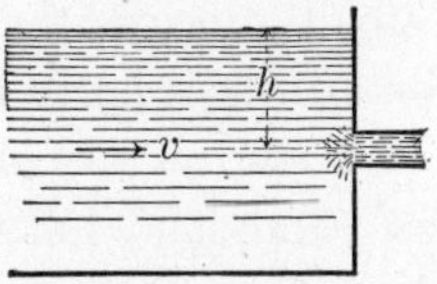

Fig. 24*b*.

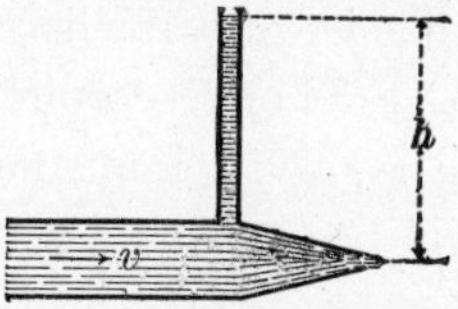

Fig. 24*c*.

orifice, exactly the same reasoning applies as before, and the theoretic velocity at the orifice is given by the above formula $(24)_1$. The same is also true for the case shown in Fig. 24*c*, where water is forced through a hose with the velocity v and issues from a nozzle with the velocity V, the head h being that due to the pressure at the entrance of the nozzle.

The "effective head" on an orifice is the head that will produce the theoretic velocity V. If H is this effective head, then $H = V^2/2g$, and from the first equation of this article

$$H = h + \frac{v^2}{2g} \qquad (24)_2$$

The effective head on an orifice is, therefore, the sum of the pressure and velocity heads which exist behind it. Another expression for the effective head can be obtained from $(24)_1$, or

$$H = \frac{h}{1 - (a/A)^2}$$

When H has been found from either of these formulas, the theoretic velocity and discharge are given by

$$V = \sqrt{2gH} \quad \text{and} \quad Q = aV = a\sqrt{2gH}$$

for all instances where h is sufficiently large so that its value is sensibly constant for all parts of the orifice. But if this is not the case, the value of Q is to be found by the methods of Arts. 47 and 48.

Prob. 24. In Fig. 24c let the head h be 60 feet, the diameter of the nozzle $1\frac{1}{2}$ inches, and the diameter of the hose 3 inches. Compute the effective head H, and also the discharge Q in cubic feet per second.

Art. 25. The Path of a Jet

When a jet of water issues from a small orifice in the vertical side of a vessel or reservoir, its direction at first is horizontal, but the force of gravity immediately causes the jet to move in a curve which will be shown to be the common parabola. Let x be the abscissa and y the ordinate of any point of the curve, measured from the orifice as an origin, as seen in Fig. 25a. The effect of the impulse at the orifice is to cause the space x to be described uniformly in a certain time t, or, if v be the velocity of flow, $x = vt$. The effect of the force of gravity is to cause the space y to be described in accordance with the laws of falling bodies (Art. 21), or $y = \frac{1}{2}gt^2$. Eliminating t from these two equations, and replacing v^2 by its theoretic value $2gh$, gives

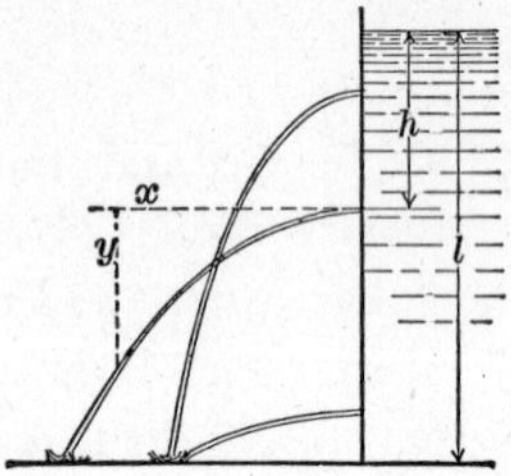

Fig. 25a.

$$y = gx^2/2v^2 = x^2/4h$$

which is the equation of a parabola whose axis is vertical and whose vertex is at the orifice.

The horizontal range of the jet for any given ordinate y is found from the equation $x^2 = 4hy$. If the height of the vessel be l, the horizontal range on the plane of the base is

$$x = 2\sqrt{h(l-h)}$$

This value is o when $h = o$ and also when $h = l$, and it is a maximum when $h = \frac{1}{2} l$. Hence the greatest range is from an orifice at the mid-height of the vessel.

A more general case is that where the side of the vessel is inclined to the vertical at the angle θ, as in Fig. 25*b*. Here the jet at first issues perpendicularly to the side with a velocity v, having the theoretic value $\sqrt{2gh}$, and under the action of the impulsive force a particle of water would describe the distance AB in a certain time t with the uniform velocity v. But in that same time the force of gravity causes it to descend through the distance BC. Now let x be the horizontal abscissa and y the vertical ordinate of the point C measured from the origin A. Then $AB = x \sec\theta$, and $BC = x \tan\theta - y$. Hence

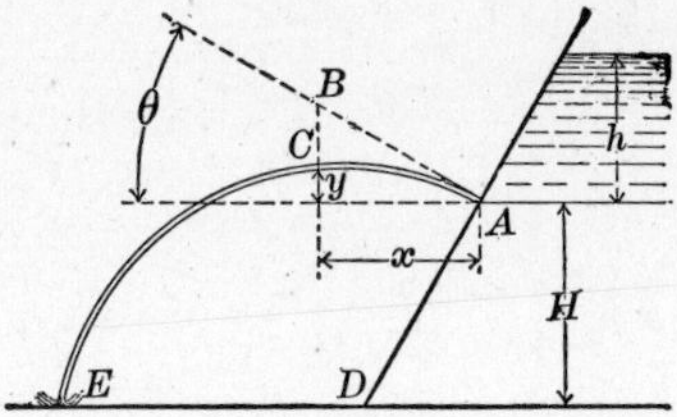

FIG. 25*b*.

$$x \sec\theta = vt \qquad x \tan\theta - y = \tfrac{1}{2} gt^2$$

The elimination of t from these expressions gives, after replacing v^2 by its value $2gh$,

$$y = x \tan\theta - x^2 \sec^2\theta / 4h \qquad (25)$$

which is also the equation of a common parabola.

To find the horizontal range in the level of the orifice take $y = o$ in the last equation; then

$$x = 4h \tan\theta / \sec^2\theta = 2h \sin 2\theta$$

This is o when $\theta = 0°$ or $\theta = 90°$; it is a maximum and equal to $2h$ when $\theta = 45°$. To find the highest point of the jet the first derivative of y with reference to x is to be equated to zero in order to obtain the maximum ordinate, and there results

$$x = h \sin 2\theta \qquad y = h \sin^2\theta$$

which are the coordinates of the highest point with respect to the origin A. In these if $\theta = 90°$, x is o and y is h; that is, if a jet be directed vertically upward, it will, theoretically, rise to the height of the water level in the reservoir.

As a numerical example let a vessel whose height is 16 feet stand upon a horizontal plane *DE*, Fig. 25*b*, the side of the vessel being inclined to the vertical at the angle $\theta = 30°$. Let a jet issue from a small orifice at *A* under a head of 10 feet. The jet rises to its maximum height, $y = \frac{1}{4} \times 10 = 2.5$ feet, at the distance $x = \frac{1}{2}\sqrt{3} \times 10 = 8.66$ feet from *A*. At $x = 17.32$ feet the jet crosses the horizontal plane through the orifice. To locate the point where it strikes the plane *DE*, the value of *y* is made -6 feet; then, from the equation of the curve, *x* is found to be 24.6 feet, whence the distance *DE* is 21.2 feet.

In practice the above equations are modified by the frictional resistance of the edges of the orifice which renders *v* less than the theoretic value $\sqrt{2gh}$, and also by the resistance of the air. They are, indeed, extreme limits which may be approached but not reached by equations that take these resistances into account.

Prob. 25. A jet issues from a vessel under a head of 6 feet, one side of the vessel being inclined to the vertical at an angle of 45° and its depth being 16 feet. Find the maximum height to which the jet rises, the point where it strikes the horizontal plane of the base, and its theoretic velocity as it strikes that plane.

Art. 26. The Energy of a Jet

Let a jet or stream of water have the velocity *v*, and let *W* be the weight of water per second passing any given cross-section. The kinetic energy of this moving water is the same as that stored up by a body of weight *W* falling freely under the action of gravity through a height *h* and thereby acquiring the velocity *v*. Thus, if *K* represents kinetic energy per second,

$$K = Wh = W \cdot v^2/2g \qquad (26)_1$$

Now if *a* be the area of the cross-section and *w* the weight of a cubic unit of water, *W* is the weight of a prism of water of length *v* and cross-section *a*, or $W = wav$, whence

$$K = wav^3/2g \qquad (26)_2$$

and accordingly the energy which a jet can yield in one second is directly proportional to its cross-section and to the cube of its velocity. The term "power" is often used to express energy per second, and when K is in foot-pounds per second, the horse-power that a jet can yield is ascertained by dividing K by 550. Hence the horse-powers of jets of the same cross-section vary as the cubes of their velocities. For example, if the velocity of a jet be doubled, the cross-section remaining the same, the horse-power is made eight times as great. The term "energy of a jet" is often used in hydraulics for brevity, but it always means energy per second of the jet; that is, the power of the jet.

The expressions just deduced give the theoretic energy of the jet, that is, the maximum work which can be obtained from it in one second, but this, in practice, can never be fully utilized. The actual work realized when a jet strikes a moving surface, like the vane of a water-motor, depends upon a number of circumstances which will be explained in a later chapter, and it is the constant aim of inventors so to arrange the conditions that the work realized may be as near the theoretic energy as possible. The "efficiency" of an apparatus for utilizing the power of moving water is the ratio of the work k actually utilized to the theoretic energy, or the efficiency e is

$$e = k/K \qquad (26)_3$$

The greatest possible value of e is unity, but this can never be attained, owing to the imperfections of the apparatus and the frictional resistances. Values greater than 0.90 have, however, been obtained; that is, 90 percent or more of the theoretic power of the water has been utilized in some of the best forms of hydraulic motors.

For example, let water issue from a pipe 2 inches in diameter with a velocity of 10 feet per second. The cross-section in square feet is 3.142/144, and the kinetic energy of the jet in foot-pounds per second is

$$K = 0.01555 \times 62.5 \times 0.0218 \times 10^3 = 21.2$$

which is 0.0385 horse-power. If the velocity is 100 feet per second, the theoretic horse-power will be 38.5; if this jet operates a motor yielding 27.7 effective horse-powers, the efficiency of the apparatus is 27.7/38.5 = 0.72, or 72 percent of the theoretic energy is utilized.

The energy of a jet is the same whether its direction of motion be vertical, horizontal, or inclined, and per second it is always Wh, where h is the velocity-head corresponding to actual velocity v, and W is the weight of water delivered per second. The energy should not be computed from the theoretical velocity V, as this is usually greater than the actual velocity.

Prob. 26. When water issues from a pipe with a velocity of 3 feet per second, its kinetic energy is sufficient to generate 1.3 horse-powers. What is the horse-power when the velocity becomes 6 feet per second?

ART. 27. IMPULSE AND REACTION OF A JET

When a stream or jet is in motion, delivering W pounds of water per second with the uniform velocity v, that motion may be regarded as produced by a constant force F, which has acted upon W for one second and then ceased. In this second the velocity of W has increased from 0 to v, and the space $\frac{1}{2}v$ has been described. Consequently the work $F \times \frac{1}{2}v$ has been imparted to the water by the force F. But the kinetic energy of the moving water is $W \cdot v^2/2g$, and hence by the law of conservation of energy $F \times \frac{1}{2} v = W \times v^2/2g$, from which the constant force is

$$F = W \cdot v/g \qquad (27)_1$$

This value of F is called the "impulse" of the jet. As W is in pounds per second, v in feet per second, and g in feet per second per second, the value of F is in pounds.

In theoretical mechanics, the term "impulse" is used in a slightly different sense, namely, as force multiplied by time. In hydraulics, however, W is not pounds, but pounds per second, and thus the impulse is simply pounds. The force F is to be regarded as a continuous impulsive pressure acting at the origin of the jet in the direction of the motion. For, by the definition, F acts for one second upon the W pounds of water which pass a given section; but in the next second W pounds also pass, and the same is the case for each second following. This impulse will be exerted as a pressure upon any surface which is placed in the path of the jet.

The reaction of a jet upon a vessel occurs when water flows from an orifice. This reaction must be equal in value and opposite in direction to the impulse, as in all cases of stress action and reaction are equal. In the direction of the jet the impulse produces motion, in the opposite direction it produces an equal pressure which tends to move the vessel backward. The force of reaction of a jet is hence equal to the impulse but opposite in direction. For example (Fig. 27), let a vessel containing water be suspended at A so that it can swing freely, and let an orifice be opened in its side at B. The head of water at B causes a pressure which acts toward the left and causes W pounds of water to move during every second with the velocity of v feet per second, and which also acts toward the right and causes the vessel to swing out of the vertical; the first of these forces is the impulse, and the second is the reaction of the jet. If a force R be applied on the right of a vessel so as to prevent the swinging, its value is

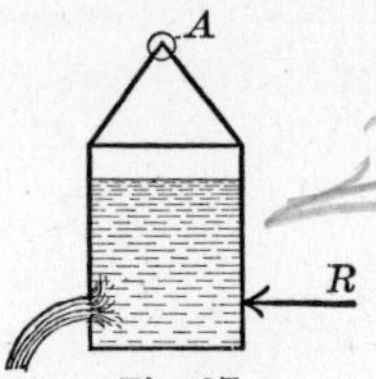

Fig. 27.

$$R = F = W \cdot v/g \qquad (27)_2$$

and this is the formula for the reaction of the jet.

The impulse or reaction of a jet issuing from an orifice is double the hydrostatic pressure on the area of the orifice. Let h be the head of water, a the area of the orifice, and w the weight of a cubic unit of water; then, by Art. 15, the normal pressure when the orifice is closed is wah. When the orifice is opened, the weight of water issuing per second is $W = wav$, and hence the impulse or reaction of the jet is

$$R = F = wav \cdot v/g = 2wa \cdot v^2/2g = 2wah$$

which is double the hydrostatic pressure. This theoretic conclusion has been verified by many experiments (Art. 153).

When a jet impinges normally on a plane, it produces a dynamic pressure on that plane equal to the impulse F, since the force required to stop W pounds of water in one second is the same as that required to put it in motion. Again, if a stream moving with the velocity v_1 is retarded so that its velocity becomes v_2, the impulse in the first instant is $W \cdot v_1/g$, and in the second $W \cdot v_2/g$. The difference of these, or

$$F_1 - F_2 = W(v_1 - v_2)/g \qquad (27)_3$$

is a measure of the dynamic pressure which has been developed. It is by virtue of the pressure due to change of velocity that turbine wheels and other hydraulic motors transform the kinetic energy of moving water into useful work.

Prob. 27. If a stream of water 3 inches in diameter issues from an orifice in a direction inclined downward 26° to the horizon with a velocity of 15 feet per second, find its horizontal reaction on the vessel.

Art. 28. Absolute and Relative Velocities

Absolute velocity is defined in this book as that with respect to the surface of the earth, and relative velocity as that with respect to a body moving on the earth. Thus absolute velocity is that seen by a spectator who is on the earth, and relative velocity is that seen by one who is on the moving body. For instance, if a body is dropped by a person who is on a moving railroad car, it appears to a person standing outside to move obliquely, but to one on the car it appears to move vertically. On a car in uniform motion all the laws of mechanics prevail exactly as if it were at rest; hence if a body of weight W is dropped through a height h, it acquires a theoretic vertical velocity of $\sqrt{2gh}$ with respect to the car. But if the horizontal velocity of the car is u, the kinetic energy of the body at the moment of letting it fall is $W \cdot u^2/2g$ and its potential energy is Wh, so that, neglecting frictional resistances, its total energy after falling through the height h is the sum of these, and accordingly its absolute velocity with respect to the earth is $\sqrt{2gh + u^2}$.

When a vessel containing water with a free surface, as in Fig. 28a, has an orifice under the head h and is in motion in a straight line with the uniform absolute velocity u, the theoretic velocity of flow relative to the vessel is $V = \sqrt{2gh}$, or the same as its absolute velocity if the vessel were at rest, for no accelerating forces exist to change the direction or the value of g. The absolute velocity of flow, however, may be greater or less than V, depending upon the value of u and its direction. To illustrate, take the case of a vessel in uniform horizontal motion from which water is flowing through three orifices. At A the direction of V is horizontal, and as the vessel is moving in the opposite direction with the velocity u, the absolute velocity of the water as it leaves the orifice is $v = V - u$. It is also plain, if the orifice is in front of the vessel and the direction of V is horizontal, that the absolute velocity of the water as it leaves the orifice is $v = V + u$.

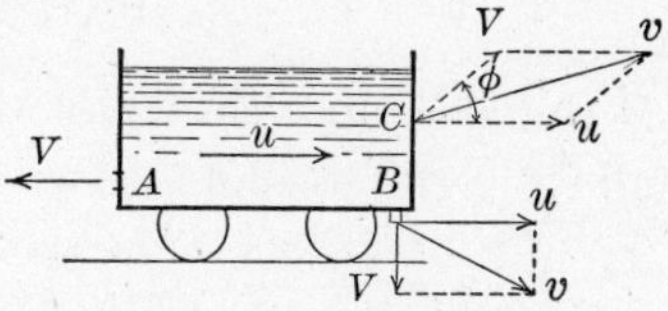

Fig. 28a.

Again, at B is an orifice from which the water issues vertically with respect to the vessel with the relative velocity V, while at the same time the orifice moves horizontally with the absolute velocity u. Forming the parallelogram, the absolute velocity v is seen to be the resultant of the velocities V and u, or

$$v = \sqrt{V^2 + u^2}$$

Lastly, at C is shown an orifice in the front of the vessel so arranged that the direction of the relative velocity V makes an angle ϕ with the horizontal. From C draw Cu to represent the velocity u, and CV to represent V, and complete the parallelogram as shown; then Cv, the resultant of u and V, is the absolute velocity with which the water leaves the orifice. From the triangle Cuv

$$v = \sqrt{V^2 + u^2 + 2\,uV \cos \phi} \qquad (28)$$

In this, if $\phi = 0$, the absolute velocity v becomes $V + u$, as before shown for an orifice in the front; if $\phi = 90°$, it becomes the same as when the water issues vertically from the orifice in the base; and if $\phi = 180°$, the value of v is $V - u$ as before found for an orifice in the rear end.

Another case is that of a revolving vessel having an opening from which the water issues horizontally with the relative velocity V, while the orifice is moving horizontally with the absolute velocity u. Fig. 28b shows this case, β being the angle which V makes with the reverse direction of u, and here also

$$v = \sqrt{V^2 + u^2 - 2uV \cos\beta}$$

is the absolute velocity of the water as it leaves the vessel. In all cases the absolute velocity of a body leaving a moving surface is the diagonal of a parallelogram, one side of which is the velocity of the body relative to the surface and the other side is the absolute velocity of that surface.

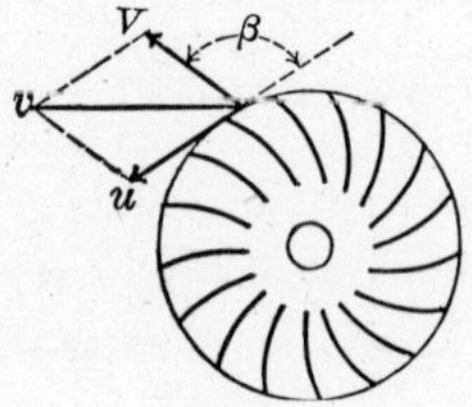

Fig. 28b.

When a vessel moves with a motion which is accelerated or retarded, this affects the value of g, and the reasoning of the preceding articles does not give the correct value of V. For instance, when a vessel moves vertically upward with an acceleration f, the relative velocity of flow from an orifice in it is $V = \sqrt{2(g+f)h}$, and if u be the velocity of the vessel at any instant, the absolute downward velocity of flow is $V - u$. Again, when it moves downward with the acceleration f, the relative velocity of flow is $V = \sqrt{2(g-f)h}$ and the absolute is $V + u$. If the downward acceleration is g, the vessel is freely falling and V will be zero, since both vessel and water are alike accelerated and there is then no pressure on the base.

Prob. 28. In Fig. 28a let the orifice at A be under a head of 5.5 feet and its height above the earth be 7.5 feet, while the car moves with a velocity of 60 miles per hour. Compute the relative velocity V, the absolute velocity v, and the absolute velocity of the jet as it strikes the earth.

Art. 29. Flow from a Revolving Vessel

Water in a vessel at rest on the surface of the earth is acted upon only by the vertical force of gravity, and hence its surface is a horizontal plane. Water in a revolving vessel is acted upon by centrifugal force as well as by gravity, and it is observed that its surface assumes a curved shape. The simplest case is that of a cylindrical vessel rotating with uniform velocity about its vertical axis, and it will be shown that here the water surface is that of a paraboloid.

Let BC be the vertical axis of the vessel, h the depth of water in it when at rest, and h_1 and h_2 the least and greatest depths of water in it when in motion. Let G be any point on the surface of the water at the horizontal distance x from the axis, and let y be the vertical distance of G above the lowest point C. The head of water on any point E in the base is EG or $h_1 + y$. Now this head y is caused by the velocity u with which the point G revolves around the axis, or, in other words, the position of G above C is due to the energy of rotation. Thus if W is the weight of a particle of water at G, the potential energy Wy equals the kinetic energy $Wu^2/2g$, and hence $y = u^2/2g$.

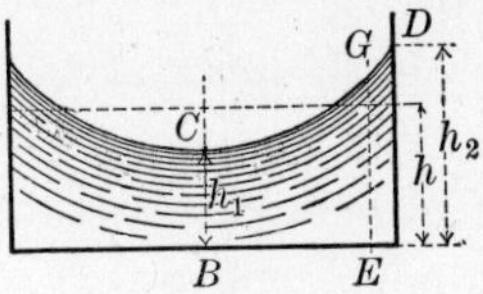

Fig. 29*a*.

Let n be the number of revolutions made by the vessel and water in one second. Then $u = 2\pi x \cdot n$, and hence

$$y = u^2/2g = 2\,\pi^2 n^2 x^2/g$$

which is the equation of a common parabola with respect to rectangular axes having an origin at its vertex C. The surface of revolution is hence a paraboloid.

Since the volume of a paraboloid is one-half that of its circumscribing cylinder, and since the same quantity of water is in the vessel when in motion as when at rest, it is plain that in the figure $\frac{1}{2}(h_2 - h_1)$ equals $h - h_1$. Consequently $h - h_1$ equals $h_2 - h$, or the elevation of the water surface at D above its original level is equal to its depression at C. If r be the radius of the vessel, the height $h_2 - h_1$ is, from the above equation, $2\,\pi^2 n^2 r^2/g$, and hence the distances $h - h_1$ and $h_2 - h$ are each equal to $\pi^2 n^2 r^2/g$. The head at the middle of the base of the vessel during the motion is now $h_1 = h - \pi^2 n^2 r^2/g$ and the head at any point E is $h_1 + y = h + (2x^2 - r^2)\pi^2 n^2/g$.

The theoretic velocity of flow from the small orifice in the base is that due to the head $h_1 + y$, or

$$V = \sqrt{2g(h_1 + y)} = \sqrt{2gh + 2\pi^2 n^2 (2x^2 - r^2)}$$

which is less than $\sqrt{2gh}$ when x^2 is less than $\frac{1}{2}r^2$, and greater when x^2 is greater than $\frac{1}{2}r^2$. For example, let $r = 1$ foot and $h = 3$ feet, then $V = 13.9$ feet per second when the vessel is at rest. But if it is rotating three times per second around its axis with uniform speed, the velocity from an orifice in the center of the base, where $x = 0$, is 3.9 feet per second, while the velocity from an orifice at the circumference of the base, where $x = 1$ foot, is 19.2 feet per second. At this speed the water is depressed 2.76 feet below its original level at the center and elevated the same amount above that level around the sides of the vessel.

In the case of a closed vessel where the paraboloid cannot form, the velocity of flow from all orifices, except one at the axis, is increased by the rotation. Thus in Fig. 29*b*, if the vessel is at rest and the head on the base is h, the velocity of flow from all small orifices in the base is $\sqrt{2gh}$. But if the vessel is revolved about the vertical axis BC, so that an orifice at E has the velocity u around that axis, then the pressure-head at E is $h + u^2/2g$, and accordingly

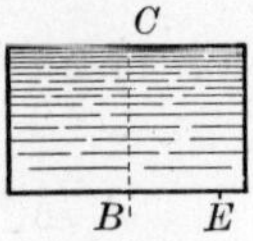

Fig. 29*b*.

$$V = \sqrt{2gh + u^2} \tag{29}$$

is the theoretic velocity of flow from an orifice at E. This formula is an important one in the discussion of hydraulic motors. Here, as before, the value of u may be expressed as $2\pi xn$, when x is the distance of E from the axis and n is the number of revolutions per second. As an example, let a closed vessel full of water be revolved about an axis 120 times per minute, and let it be required to find the theoretic velocity of flow from an orifice $1\frac{1}{2}$ feet from the axis, the head on which is 4 feet when the vessel is at rest. The velocity u is found to be 18.85 feet per second, and then the theoretic velocity of flow from the orifice is 24.8 feet per second, whereas it is only 16 feet per second when the vessel is at rest.

The velocity V in both these cases is a relative velocity, for the pressure at the moving orifice produces a velocity with respect to the vessel. The absolute velocity, or that with respect to the earth, is greater than the relative velocity when the stream issues from an orifice in the base, for the orifice moves horizontally with the absolute velocity u and the stream moves downward with the relative velocity V, and hence the absolute velocity of the stream is $\sqrt{V^2+u^2}$. When the stream issues from an orifice in the side of the vessel upon which the head is h, formula (29) gives its relative velocity, and then the absolute velocity is found by (28).

Prob. 29. A cylindrical vessel 2 feet in diameter and 3 feet deep is three-fourths full of water, and is revolved about its vertical axis so that the water is just on the point of overflowing around the upper edge. Find the number of revolutions per minute. Find the relative velocity of flow from an orifice in the base at a distance of 0.75 foot from the axis. Show that the velocity from all orifices within 0.707 foot of the axis is less than if the vessel were at rest.

Art. 30. Theoretic Discharge

The term "discharge" means the volume of water flowing in one second from a pipe or orifice, and the letter Q will designate the theoretic discharge; that is, the discharge as computed without considering the losses due to frictional resistances. When all the filaments of water issue from the pipe or orifice with the same velocity, the quantity of water issuing in one second is equal to the volume of a prism having a base equal to the cross-section of the stream and a length equal to the velocity. If this area is a and the theoretic velocity is V, then $Q = aV$ is the theoretic discharge. Taking a in square feet and V in feet per second, the discharge Q is in cubic feet per second.

For a small orifice on which the head h has the same value for all parts of the opening, the theoretic discharge is

$$Q = aV = a\sqrt{2gh} \qquad (30)$$

and in English measures $Q = 8.02a\sqrt{h}$. For example, let a circular orifice 3 inches in diameter be under a head of 10.5 feet, and let it be required to compute Q. Here 3 inches = 0.25 foot and from Table F the area of the circle is 0.04909 square foot. From Art. 22 the theoretic velocity V is $8.02 \times \sqrt{10.5} = 25.99$ feet per second. Accordingly the theoretic discharge is $0.04909 \times 25.99 = 1.28$ cubic feet per second.

The above formula for Q applies strictly only to horizontal orifices upon which the head h is constant, but it will be seen later that its error for vertical orifices is less than one-half of one percent when h is greater than double the depth of the orifice. Horizontal orifices are but little used, as it is more convenient in practice to arrange an opening in the side of a vessel than in its base. In applying the above formula to a vertical orifice, h is taken as the vertical distance from its center to the free-water surface. Vertical orifices where the head h is small are discussed in Arts. 47 and 48.

Since the theoretic velocity is always greater than the actual velocity, the theoretic discharge is a limit which can never be reached under actual conditions. Theoretically the discharge is independent of the shape of the orifice, so that a square orifice of area a gives the same theoretic discharge as a circular orifice of area a; it will be seen in Chap. 5 that this is not quite true for the actual discharge.

In this chapter it is supposed that the velocity of a jet is the same in all parts of the cross-section, as this would be the case if h has the same value throughout the section were it not for the retarding influence of friction. Actually, however, the filaments of water near the edges of the orifice move slower than those near the center. If q be the actual discharge from any orifice and v the mean velocity in the area a, then $q = av$, or the equation $v = q/a$ may be regarded as a definition of the term "mean velocity." The theoretic mean velocity is $\sqrt{2gh}$, but the actual mean velocity is slightly smaller, as will be seen in Chap. 5.

Formula (30) may be used for computing h when Q and a are given, and it shows that the theoretic head required to deliver a given discharge varies inversely as the square of the area of the orifice.

Prob. 30*a*. Compute the theoretic head required to deliver 300 gallons of water per minute through an orifice 3 inches in diameter.

Prob. 30*b*. A vessel one foot square has a small orifice in the base. What is the theoretic velocity of flow from this orifice when the vessel contains 125 pounds of mercury? Also when it contains 250 pounds of water?

Art. 31. Steady Flow in Smooth Pipes

When water flows through a pipe of varying cross-section and all sections are filled with water, the same quantity of water passes each section in one second. This is called the case of steady flow. Let q be this quantity of water and let v_1, v_2, v_3 be the mean velocities in three sections whose areas are a_1, a_2, a_3. Then

$$q = a_1v_1 = a_2v_2 = a_3v_3 \qquad (31)_1$$

This is called the condition for steady flow or the equation of continuity, and it shows that the velocities at different sections vary inversely as the areas of those sections. If v be the velocity at the end of the pipe where the area is a, then also $q = av$. When the discharge q and the areas of the cross-sections have been measured, the mean velocities may be computed.

When a pipe is filled with water at rest, the pressure at any point depends only upon the head of water above that point. But when the water is in motion, it is a fact of observation that the pressure becomes less than that due to the head. The unit-pressure in any case may be measured by the height of a column of water. Thus if water be at rest in the case shown in Fig. 31a, and small tubes be inserted at the sections whose areas are a_1 and a_2, the water will rise in each tube to the same level as that of the water surface in the reservoir, and the pressures in the sections will be those due to the hydrostatic heads H_1 and H_2. But if the valve at the right be opened, the water levels in the small tubes will sink and the mean pressures in the two sections will be those due to the pressure-heads h_1 and h_2.

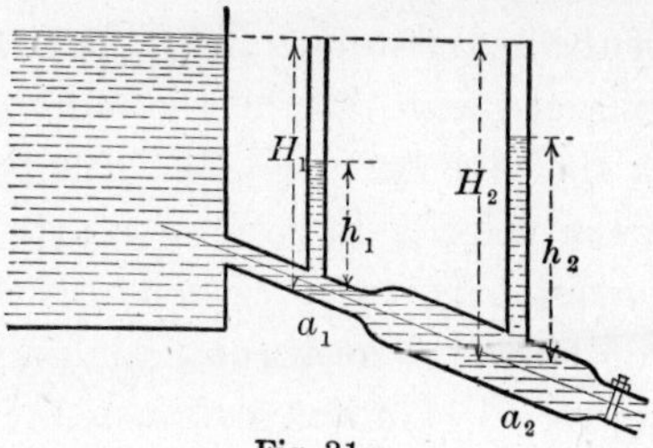

Fig. 31a.

Let W be the weight of water flowing in each second through each section of the pipe, and let v_1 and v_2 be the mean velocity in the section a_1 and a_2. When this water was at rest, the potential energy of pressure in the section a_1 was WH_1; when it is in motion, the energy in the section is the pressure energy Wh_1 plus the kinetic energy $W \cdot v_1^2/2g$. If no losses of energy due to friction or impact have occurred, the energy in the two cases must be equal. The same reasoning applies to the section a_2, and hence

$$H_1 = h_1 + \frac{v_1^2}{2g} \qquad \text{and} \qquad H_2 = h_2 + \frac{v_2^2}{2g} \qquad (31)_2$$

These equations exhibit the law of steady flow first deduced by Daniel Bernouilli in 1738, and hence often called Bernouilli's theorem; it may be stated in words as follows:

> At any section of a tube or pipe, under steady flow without friction, the pressure-head plus the velocity-head is equal to the hydrostatic head that obtains when there is no flow.

This theorem of theoretical hydraulics is of great importance in practice, although it has been deduced for mean velocities and mean pressure-heads, while actually the velocity and the pressure are not the same for all points of the cross-section.

The pressure-head at any section hence decreases when the velocity of the water increases. To illustrate, let the depths of the centers of a_1 and a_2 be 6 and 8 feet below the water level, and let their areas be 1.2 and 2.4 square feet. Let the discharge of the pipe be 14.4 cubic feet per second. Then from $(31)_1$ the mean velocity in a_1 is $v_1 = 14.4/1.2 = 12$ feet per second, which corresponds to a velocity head of $0.01555v^2 = 2.24$ feet, and consequently from $(31)_2$ the pressure-head in a_1 is $6.0 - 2.24 = 3.76$ feet. For the section a_2 the velocity is 6 feet per second and the velocity head is 0.56 feet, so that the pressure-head there is $8.0 - 0.56 = 7.44$ feet.

The theorem of $(31)_2$ may be also applied to the jet issuing from the end of the pipe. Outside the pipe there can be no pressure, and if h be the hydrostatic head and V the velocity, the equation gives $h = V^2/2g$, or $V = \sqrt{2gh}$; that is, if frictional resistances be not considered, the theoretic velocity of flow from the end of a pipe is that due to the hydrostatic head upon it. In Chap. 8 it will be seen that the actual velocity is much smaller than this, for a large part of the head h is expended in overcoming friction in the pipe.

A negative pressure may occur if the velocity-head becomes greater than the hydrostatic head, for $(31)_2$ shows that h_1 is negative when $v_1^2/2g$ exceeds H_1. A case of this kind is given in Fig. 31*b*, where the section at A is so small that the velocity is greater than that due to the head H_1, so that if a tube be inserted at A, no water runs out; but if the tube be carried downward into a vessel of water, there will be lifted a column CD whose height is that of the negative pressure-head h_1. For example, let the cross-section of A be 0.4 square feet, and its head H_1 be 4.1 feet, while 8 cubic feet per second are discharged from the orifice below. Then the velocity at A is 20 feet per second, and the corresponding velocity-head is 6.22 feet. The pressure head at A then is, from the theorem of formula $(31)_2$,

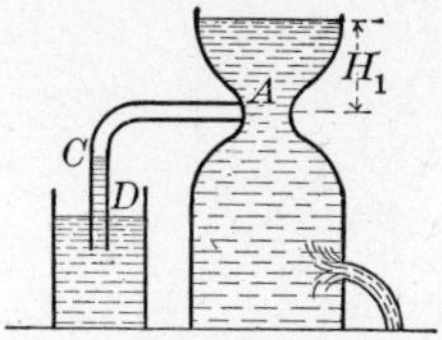

Fig. 31*b*.

$$h_1 = 4.1 - 6.22 = -2.12 \text{ feet}$$

and accordingly there exists at A an inward pressure

$$p_1 = -2.12 \times 0.434 = -0.92 \text{ pounds per square inch}$$

This negative pressure will sustain a column of water CD whose height is 2.12 feet. When the small vessel is placed so that its water level is less than 2.12 feet below A, water will be constantly drawn from the smaller to the larger vessel. This is the principle of the action of the injector-pump.

Prob. 31. In a horizontal tube there are two sections of diameters 1.0 and 1.5 feet. The velocity in the first section is 6.32 feet per second, and the pressure-head is 21.57 feet. Find the pressure-head for the second section if no energy is lost between the sections.

Art. 32. Emptying a Vessel

Let the depth of water in a vessel be H; it is required to determine the theoretic time of emptying it through an orifice in the base whose area is a. Let Y be the area of the water surface when the depth of water is y; let δt be the time during which the water level falls the distance δy. During this time the quantity of water $Y \cdot \delta y$ passes through the orifice. But the discharge in one second under the constant head y is $a\sqrt{2gy}$, and hence the discharge in the time δt is $a\delta t\sqrt{2gy}$. Equating these two expressions, there is found the general formula which gives the time for the water surface to drop the distance δy,

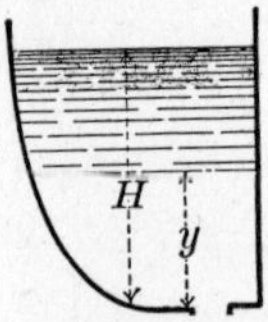

Fig. 32a.

$$\delta t = \frac{Y\delta y}{a\sqrt{2gy}} \qquad (32)_1$$

The time of emptying any vessel is now determined by inserting for Y its value in terms of y, and then integrating between the limits H and o.

For a cylinder or prism the cross-section Y has the constant value A, and the formula becomes

$$\delta t = \frac{Ay^{-\frac{1}{2}}\,\delta y}{a\sqrt{2g}}$$

the integration of which, between limits H and h, gives

$$t = \frac{2A}{a\sqrt{2g}}(\sqrt{H} - \sqrt{h})$$

as the theoretic time for the head H to fall to h. If h = o, this formula gives the time of emptying the vessel. If the head were maintained constant, the uniform discharge per second would be $a\sqrt{2gH}$, and the time of discharging a quantity equal to the capacity of the vessel is AH divided by $a\sqrt{2gH}$, which is one-half of the time required to empty it.

To find the time of emptying a hemispherical bowl of radius r through a small orifice at its lowest point, let x be the radius of the cross-section Y; then $x^2 + (r - y)^2 = r^2$ is the equation of the circle, from which the area Y is $\pi(2ry - y^2)$. Then

$$\delta t = \frac{\pi}{a\sqrt{2g}}(2ry^{\frac{1}{2}} - y^{\frac{3}{2}})\,\delta y$$

and by integration between the limits r and o

$$t = 14\pi r^{\frac{5}{2}}/15\,a\sqrt{2g}$$

which is the theoretic time required to empty the bowl.

The most important application of these principles is in the case of the right prism or cylinder, and here the formula for the time is modified in practice by introducing a coefficient, as may be seen in Art. 58. The theoretic time found by the above formula is always too small, since frictional resistances have not been considered. Moreover, the formula does not strictly apply when the head is very small, owing to a whirling motion that occurs and which tends to increase the theoretic time.

Venturi, in 1798, first described the phenomena of this whirl.* When the head becomes less than about three diameters of the orifice, the water is observed in whirling motion, the velocity being greatest near the vertical axis through the center of the orifice, and as the head decreases a funnel is formed through the middle of the issuing stream. The direction of this whirl, as seen from above, may be either clockwise or contraclockwise, depending on initial motions in the water or on irregularities in the vessel or orifice, but under ideal conditions it should be clockwise in the southern hemisphere of the earth and contraclockwise in the northern hemisphere, this being the effect of the earth's rotation. Fig. 32*b* represents a vertical section of this funnel, on which A is any point having the coördinates x and y with respect to the rectangular axes OX and OY. The axis OY is drawn through the center of the orifice, and OX is tangent to the level water surface at a distance H above the bottom of the vessel. Let r be the radius of the funnel in the plane of the orifice. It is required to find the relation between x, y, H, and r, or the equation of the curve shown in the figure.

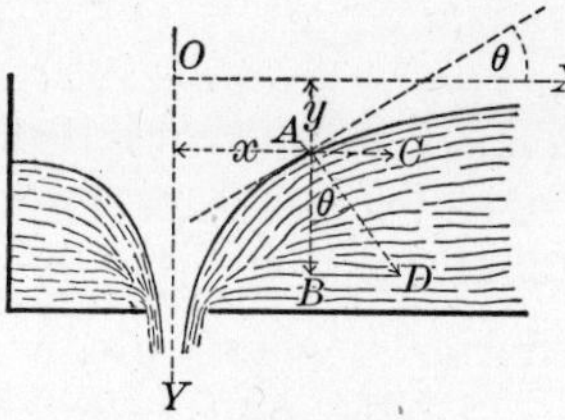

Fig. 32*b*.

An approximate solution may be made by supposing that the particle of water at A is moving nearly horizontally around the axis OY with the velocity v; this velocity must be due to the head y, whence $v^2 = 2gy$. This particle is acted upon by the downward force AB, due to gravity, and by the horizontal force AC, due to centrifugal action, and they are proportional to g and v^2/x, these being the

* Tredgold's Tracts on Hydraulics (London, 1799 and 1826) gives a translation of the memoir of Venturi.

accelerations due to gravity and centrifugal force. The ratio AC/AB is the tangent of the angle θ which the water surface at A makes with the axis OX, for this surface must be normal to the resultant AD of the two forces AB and AC. When the ordinate y is increased to $y+\delta y$, the abscissa x is decreased to $x-\delta x$, and hence the value of $\tan\theta$ must be the same as $-\delta y/\delta x$. Accordingly

$$\tan\theta = \frac{AC}{AB} = \frac{v^2}{gx} = 2\frac{y}{x} = -\frac{\delta y}{\delta x}$$

and the integration of this differential equation gives $y = C/x^2$, in which C is the constant of integration. When y equals H, the value of x is r, and hence $C = Hr^2$, and thus

$$y = Hr^2/x^2 \qquad (32)_2$$

is the equation of the curve, which may be called a quadratic hyperbola, the surface of the funnel being then a quadratic hyperboloid. This equation represents the curve at one instant only, for H continually decreases as the water flows out, since the direction of v is not quite horizontal as the investigation assumes. The general phenomena are, however, well explained by this discussion.

Prob. 32. A prismatic vessel has a cross-section of 18 square feet and an orifice in its base has an area of 0.18 square foot. Find the theoretic time for the water level to drop 7 feet, when the head upon the orifice at the beginning is 16 feet.

Art. 33. Computations in Metric Measures

(Art. 22) Using for the acceleration of the mean value 9.80 meters per second per second, formulas $(22)_2$ become

$$V = 4.427\sqrt{h} \qquad h = 0.05102\, V^2 \qquad (33)$$

in which h is in meters and V in meters per second. Table 33 shows values of the velocity for given heads, and values of the velocity-head for given velocities.

(Art. 23) For Fig. 23 let the reservoir be one meter in diameter, the load W be 2000 kilograms, and the orifices be 3 meters below the piston. Let the exterior head on A be 1.5 meters, the orifice B be open to the atmosphere, and the orifice C be in air whose pressure is 0.7 kilograms per square centimeter. The area of the piston is 0.7854

TABLE 33. VELOCITIES AND VELOCITY-HEADS

Metric Measures

$V = \sqrt{2gh} = 4.427\sqrt{h}$				$h = V^2/2g = 0.05102\,V^2$			
Head in Meters	Velocity in Meters per Second	Head in Meters	Velocity in Meters per Second	Velocity in Meters per Second	Head in Meters	Velocity in Meters per Second	Head in Meters
0.1	1.432	1	4.427	0.1	0.0005	1	0.0510
0.2	1.980	2	6.262	0.2	0.0020	2	0.2041
0.3	2.425	3	7.668	0.3	0.0046	3	0.4592
0.4	2.799	4	8.854	0.4	0.0082	4	0.8163
0.5	3.131	5	9.900	0.5	0.0123	5	1.276
0.6	3.429	6	10.84	0.6	0.0184	6	1.837
0.7	3.704	7	11.71	0.7	0.0250	7	2.500
0.8	3.960	8	12.52	0.8	0.0327	8	3.265
0.9	4.200	9	13.28	0.9	0.0413	9	4.133
1.0	4.427	10	14.00	1.0	0.0510	10	5.102

square meters, and the head corresponding to the pressure on the upper water surface is

$$h_0 = \frac{p_0}{w} = \frac{2000}{0.7854 \times 1000} = 2.546 \text{ meters.}$$

The head h_1 is 3 meters for the first orifice, 0 for the second, and $-10(1.033-0.7) = -3.33$ meters for the third. The three theoretic velocities of outflow then are

$$V = 4.427\sqrt{3 + 2.546 - 1.5} = 8.91 \text{ meters per second,}$$

$$V = 4.427\sqrt{3 + 2.546 - 0} = 10.43 \text{ meters per second,}$$

$$V = 4.427\sqrt{3 + .546 + 3.33} = 13.19 \text{ meters per second.}$$

If in this example the liquid be alcohol which weighs 800 kilograms per cubic meter, the head of alcohol corresponding to the pressure of the piston is

$$h_0 = \frac{2000}{0.7854 \times 800} = 3.183 \text{ meters,}$$

and accordingly for discharge into the atmosphere at the depth $h_1 = 3$ meters the velocity is

$$V = 4.427\sqrt{3 + 3.18} = 11.01 \text{ meters per second,}$$

while for water the velocity was 10.43 meters per second.

(Art. 26) As an illustration of $(26)_2$ let water issue from a pipe 6 centimeters in diameter with a velocity of 4 meters per second. The cross-section is found from Table F to be 0.002827 square meters, and then the theoretic work in kilogram-meters per second is

$$K = 0.05102 \times 1000 \times 0.002827 \times 4^3 = 9.23$$

which is 0.123 metric horse-power. If the velocity is 16 meters per second, the stream will furnish 7.87 horse-powers.

(Art. 30) The area a is in square meters, the velocity V in meters per second, and the discharge Q in cubic meters per second. Thus if a pipe 20 centimeters in diameter discharges 0.15 cubic meters per second, the area of the cross-section is 0.03142 square meters and the mean velocity is $0.15/0.03142 = 4.77$ meters per second.

(Art. 31) In Fig. 31a, suppose the sections a_1 and a_2 to be 0.06 and 0.12 square meters, and the depths of their centers below the water level of the reservoir to be 4.5 and 5.5 meters. Let 0.24 cubic meters per second be discharged from the pipe, then from $(31)_1$ the mean velocities in a_1 and a_2 are 4.0 and 2.0 meters per second. The velocity-heads are then 0.82 meters for a_1 and 0.20 meters for a_2, so that during the flow the pressure-head at A is $4.5 - 0.82 = 3.68$ meters and that at B is $5.5 - 0.20 = 5.30$ meters.

Prob. 33a. What theoretic velocities are produced by heads of 0.1, 0.01, and 0.001 meter? What is the velocity-head of a jet, 7.5 centimeters in diameter, which discharges 500 liters per second?

Prob. 33b. A prismatic vessel has a cross-section of 1.5 square meters and an orifice in its base has an area of 150 square centimeters. Compute the theoretic time for the water level to drop 3 meters when the head at the beginning is 4 meters.

Prob. 33c. A small turbine wheel using 3 cubic meters of water per minute under a head of $10\frac{1}{2}$ meters is found to deliver 5.1 metric horse-powers. Compute the efficiency of the wheel.

Prob. 33d. In an inclined tube there are two sections of diameters 10 and 20 centimeters, the second section being 1.536 meters higher than the first. The velocity in the first section is 6 meters per second and the pressure-head is 7.045 meters. Find the pressure-head for the second section.

CHAPTER 4

INSTRUMENTS AND OBSERVATIONS

Art. 34. General Considerations

Some of the most important practical problems of Hydraulics are those involving the measurement of the amount of water discharged in one second from an orifice, pipe, or conduit under given conditions. The theoretic formulas of the last chapter furnish the basis of most of these methods, and in the chapters following this one are given coefficients derived from experience which enable those formulas to be applied to practical conditions. These coefficients have been determined by measuring heads, pressures, or velocities with certain instruments, and also the amount of water actually discharged, and then comparing the theoretic results with the actual ones. It is the main object of this chapter to describe the instruments used for this purpose, and a few remarks concerning advantageous methods for the discussion of the observations will also be made.

The engineer's steel tape, level, and transit are indispensable tools in many practical hydraulic problems. For example, two reservoirs M and N, connected by a pipe line, may be several miles apart. To ascertain the difference in elevation of their water surfaces lines of levels may be run and bench marks established near each reservoir, as also at other points along the pipe line. From the bench marks at the reservoirs there can be set up simple board gages, so that simultaneous readings can be taken at any time to find the difference in elevation. From the bench marks along the pipe line a profile of the same can be plotted for use in the discussion. With the transit

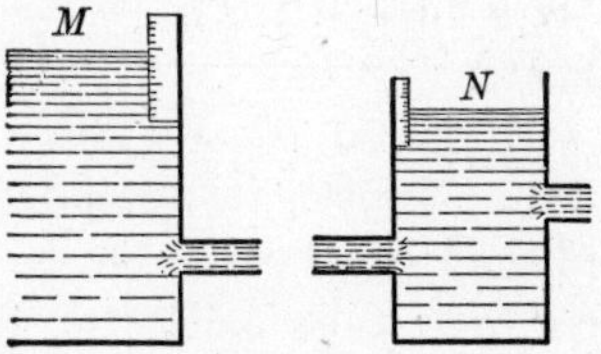

Fig. 34*a*.

and tape the alignment of the pipe line and the lengths of its curves and tangents can also be taken and mapped. All of these records, in fact, are necessary in order to determine the amount of water delivered through the pipe.

For work on a smaller scale, like that of the discharge from an orifice in a tank, the steel tape may be used to mark points from which a glass gage tube may be set and upon which the height of the water surface above the orifice can be read at any time during the experiment. Another method is to have a float on the water surface, the vertical motion of which is communicated to a cord passing over a pulley, so that readings can be taken on a scale as the weight at the lower end of the cord moves up or down. When the head is very small, however, these methods are not sufficiently precise, and the hook gage described in Art. 35 must be used.

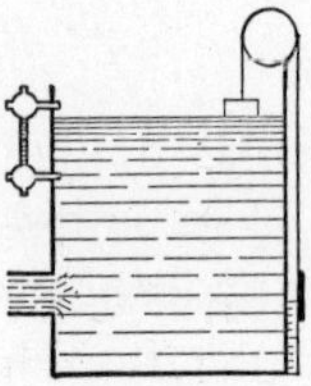

Fig. 34*b*.

It is often desirable for many purposes to keep a continuous record of the level of a water surface. This can be accom-

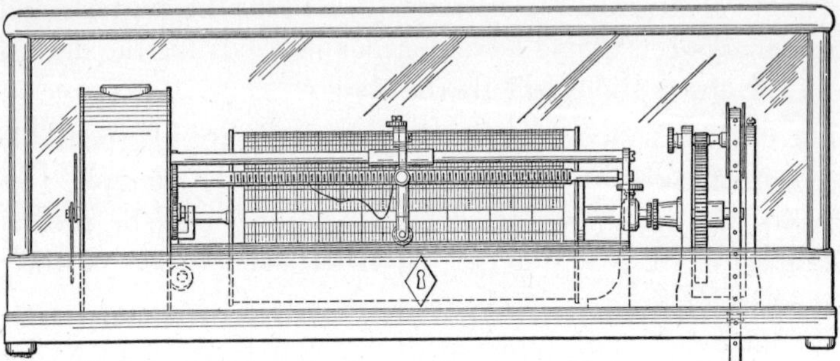

Fig. 34*c*.

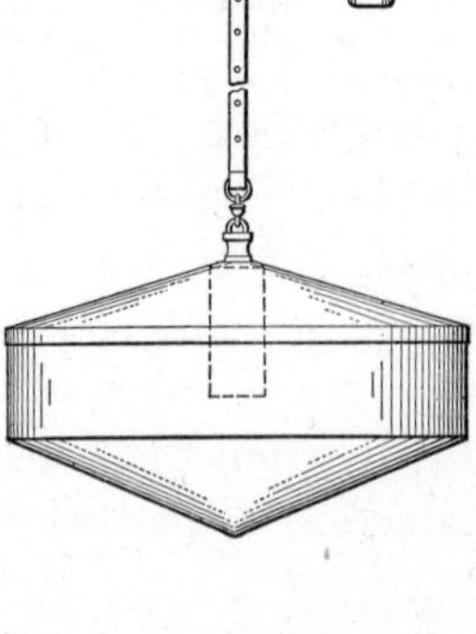

plished by the use of an automatic recording gage such as that shown in Fig. 34*c*. This apparatus, as made by Freiz, consists essentially of a float connected to a flat perforated copper band which passes over a sprocket wheel and which carries at its other end a counterweight. The sprocket wheel is directly connected to a drum the circumference of which is exactly one foot and on which a sheet of ruled paper can be clamped. A clockwork moves a pen at a constant and uniform rate in a direction parallel to the axis of the cylinder, and if the latter remains stationary, the pen will draw a straight line on the paper. If, however, the cylinder is caused to revolve by the rising or falling of the float, the pen will draw a curve, and each revolution of the cylinder will represent a change of one foot in the water level. Each sheet or chart, depending on the gear of the clock, will give a record either 24 hours or 7 days long before a new chart must be put on by an attendant. By the interposition of suitable gears between the sprocket wheel and the cylinder the ratio of the number of revolutions between the sprocket and the drum can be fixed at any desired number. With all forms of apparatus of this kind it is desirable that the float should be of large horizontal diameter in order that its lifting power may be sufficient to overcome the friction in the bearings of the machine and so cause it to easily and quickly respond to small fluctuations in the water surface.

The Bristol recording water level gage operates on the principle of the aneroid barometer. A bronze cylindrical box encloses air, the pressure of which is communicated through a flexible tube to the recording apparatus whenever that pressure exceeds the exterior atmospheric pressure. When this box is placed under water, the head of water acts on a diaphragm and increases the air pressure an amount proportional to the head on the diaphragm. In the recording apparatus is a pen which draws a curve on a sheet of paper moved by clockwork and thus gives a continuous record of the water level. This apparatus has been used for recording the heights of tides and of water levels in reservoirs. Of course the adjustment of the instrument must be made by experiment, its record being compared by one made by direct methods. The closest reliable reading of a gage of this kind appears to be about one-eighth of an inch.

A small quantity of water flowing from an orifice may be measured by allowing it to run into a barrel set upon a platform weighing scale. The weight of water discharged in a given time is thus ascertained, the time being noted by a stop-watch, and the volume is then computed by the help of Table 3. If the flow is uniform, the discharge in one second is then found by dividing the volume by the number of seconds. A larger quantity of water may be measured in a rectangular tank, the cross-section of which is accurately known; here the water surface is noted at the beginning and end of the experiment, and the volume is then computed by multiplying the area by the differences of the two elevations. For example, a square tank was 4 feet 2 inches inside dimensions, and the gage read 3.17 feet at the beginning and 4.62 feet at the end of the experiment, which lasted 304 seconds; then the flow, if uniform, was 0.0828 cubic feet per second.

Larger quantities of water still are sometimes measured in the reservoir of a city supply. The engineer, by the use of his level, transit, and tape, makes a precise contour map of the reservoir, determines with the planimeter the area enclosed by each contour curve, and computes the volume included between successive contour planes. For instance, if the area of the contour curve AB is 84 320 square feet and that of CD is 79 624 square feet and the vertical distance between the contour planes is 5 feet, the volume included is 409 860 cubic feet by the method of mean areas. A more precise determination, however, may be made by measuring the area of a contour curve halfway between AB and AC; if this is found to be 82 150 square feet, the volume included between AB and AC is computed by the prismoidal formula and found to be 410 450 cubic feet.

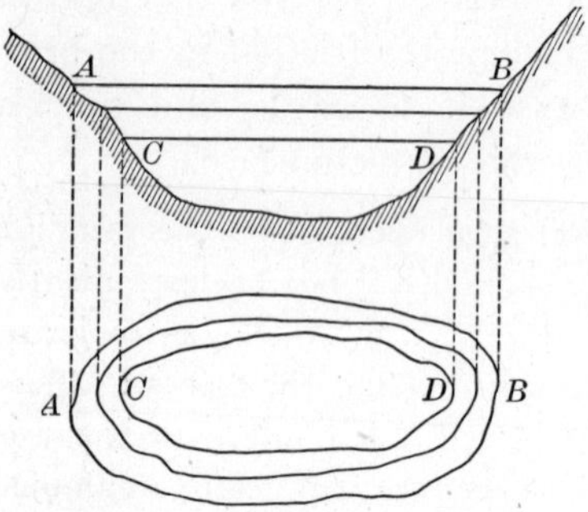

Fig. 34*d*.

These direct methods of water measurement form the basis of all hydraulic practice. In this manner water meters are rated, and the coefficients determined by which practical formulas for flow through orifices, weirs, and pipes are established. These coefficients being known, indirect methods may be used for water measurement; namely, the discharge can be computed from the formulas after area and heads have been ascertained. There are also methods of indirect measurement from observed velocities which will be described later, and which are especially valuable in finding the discharge of conduits and streams.

Prob. 34. Water flows from an orifice uniformly for 69.3 seconds and falls into a barrel on a platform weighing scale. The weight of the empty barrel is 27 pounds and that of the barrel and water is 276 pounds. What is the discharge of the orifice in gallons per minute, when the temperature of the water is 62° Fahrenheit?

Art. 35. The Hook Gage

The hook gage, invented by Boyden about 1840, consists of a graduated metallic rod sliding vertically in fixed supports, upon which is a vernier by which readings can be taken to thousandths of a foot. At the lower end of the rod is a sharp-pointed hook, which is raised or lowered until its point is at the water level. Fig. 35*a* represents the form of hook gage made by Gurley, the graduation on the rod being to feet and hundredths. The graduation has a length of 2.2 feet, so that variations in the water level of less than this amount can be measured, by using the vernier, to thousandths of a foot. To take a reading on a water surface, the point of the hook is lowered below the surface and then slowly raised by the screw at the top of the instrument. Just before the point of the hook pierces the skin of the water (Art. 2) a pimple or protuberance is seen to rise above it; the hook is then depressed until the pimple is barely visible and the vernier is read. The most precise hook gages read to ten-thousandths of a foot, and it has been stated that an experienced observer can, in a favorable light and on a water surface perfectly quiet, detect differences of level as small as 0.0002 feet.

Fig. 35*a*.

A cheaper form of hook gage, and one sufficiently precise for many classes of work, can be made by screwing a hook into the foot of an engineer's leveling rod. The back part of the rod is then held in a vertical position by two clamps on fixed supports, while the front part is free to slide. It is easy to arrange a slow-motion movement so that the point of the hook may be precisely placed at the water level. The reading of the vernier is determined when the point of the hook is at a known elevation above an orifice or the crest of a weir, and by subtracting from this the subsequent readings the heads of water are known. A New York leveling rod, reading to thousandths of a foot on its vernier, is to be preferred for this work.

Hook gages are principally used for determining the elevations of the water surface above the crest of a weir, as the heads of water are small and must be known with precision. In Fig. 35*b*, the crest of the weir is seen and the hook gage is erected at some distance back from it, where the water surface is level. In this case great care should be taken to determine the reading corresponding to the level of the crest. In the larger forms of hooks this may be done by taking elevations of the crest and of the point of the hook by means of an engineer's level and a light rod. With smaller hooks it may be done by having a stiff permanent hook, the elevation of whose point with respect to the crest is determined by precise levels; the water is then allowed to rise slowly until it reaches the point of this stiff hook, when readings of the vernier of the lighter hook are taken. Another method is to allow a small depth of water to flow over the crest and to take readings of the hook, while at the same time the depth on the crest is measured by a finely graduated scale. Still another way is to allow the water to rise slowly, and to set the hook at the water level when the first filaments pass over the crest; this method is not a very precise one on account of capillary attraction along the crest. As the error in setting the hook is a constant one which affects all the subsequent observations, especial care should be taken to reduce it to a minimum by taking a number of observations in order to obtain a precise mean result.

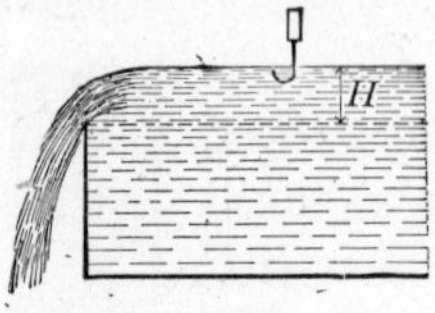

Fig. 35*b*.

The hook gage is also used to find the difference of the water levels in tanks for experiments for the determination of hydraulic coefficients, and in wells along pipe lines when experiments are made to investigate frictional resistances. In general its use is confined to cases where the head is small, as for high heads so great a degree of precision is not required (Art. 54).

Prob. 35. A wooden tank, 4.52 by 5.78 feet in inside dimensions, has leakage near its base. The hook gage reads 2.047 feet at 11.57 A.M., 1.470 feet at 12.05 P.M., and 0.938 foot at 12.13 P.M. Compute the probable leakage in the first and last minutes.

Art. 36. Pressure Gages

A pressure gage, often called a piezometer, is an instrument for measuring the pressure of water in a pipe. The form most commonly found in the market has a dial and movable pointer, the dial being graduated to read pounds per square inch. The principle on which this gage acts is the same as that of the Richard aneroid barometer and the Bourdon steam gage. Within the case is a small coiled tube closed at one end, while the other end is attached to the opening through which the water is admitted. This tube has a tendency to straighten when under pressure, and thus its closed end moves and the motion is communicated to the pointer; when the pressure is relieved, the tube assumes its original position and the pointer returns to zero. There is no theoretical method of determining the motion of the pointer due to a given pressure, and this is done by tests in which known pressures are employed, and accordingly the divisions on the graduated scale are usually unequal. These gages are liable to error after having been in use for some time, especially so at high pressures, and hence should be tested before and after any important series of experiments.

In most hydraulic work the head of water causing the pressure is required to be known. When p is the gage reading in pounds per square inch, the head of water in feet is $h = 2.304p$, or when p is the gage reading in kilograms per square centimeter, the head of water in meters is $h = 10p$. The graduation of the gage dial may be made to read heads directly, so as to avoid the necessity of numerical reduction.

The pressure at any point of a pipe may be measured by the height of a column of water in an open tube, as seen at A in Fig. 36a. The upper portion of the tube may be of glass, so that the position of the water level may be noted on a scale held alongside. It is not necessary that the water column should be vertical, and a hose is often used, as seen at B, with a glass tube at its top. At C is shown a dial pressure gage. When the head h is directly read in feet, the pressure in pounds per square inch may be computed from $p = 0.434h$. In order to secure precise results when the water in the pipe is in motion, it is necessary that a piezometer tube be inserted into the pipe at right angles; when inclined toward or against the current, the head h is greater or less than that due to the actual pressure at its mouth.

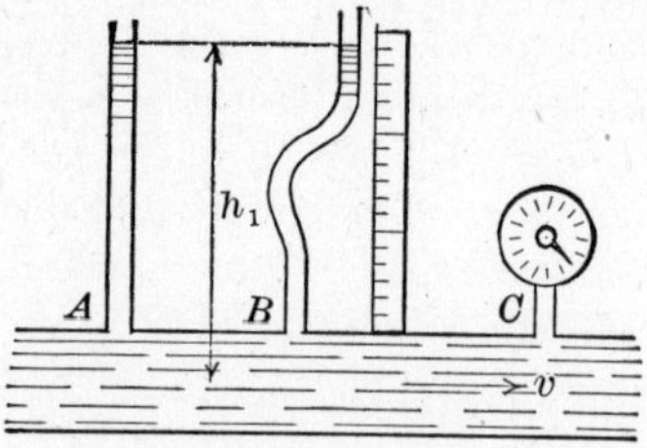

Fig. 36a.

For high pressures a water column is impracticable on account of its great height, and hence mercury gages are used. Fig. 36b shows the principle of construction, a bent tube ABC with both ends open, having mercury in its lower portion, and the water column of height h being balanced by the mercury column of height z. If the atmospheric pressures at A and C are the same, it is evident, from Art. 4, that the height h is about 13.6 times the height z, since the specific gravity of mercury is about 13.6. Now z can be read on a scale placed between the legs of the tube, and thus h is known, as also the water pressure at the point B. If the atmospheric pressures at A and C are different, as will be the case when h is very large, let b_1 be the barometer reading at A and b_2 that at C, both being in the same linear unit as h and z. The absolute pressure at B is that due to the height $sh + s'b_1$, where s and s' are the specific gravities of water and mercury, and the absolute

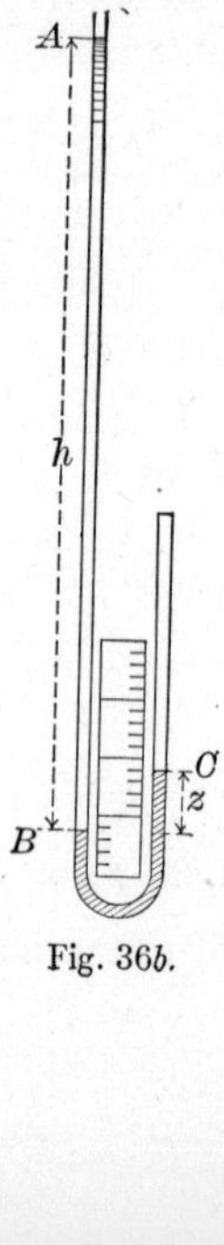

Fig. 36b.

pressure at the same elevation in the other leg is that due to the height $s'(z + b_2)$. Since these pressures are equal,

$$h = (s'/s)(z + b_2 - b_1)$$

is the head corresponding to the distance z on the scale. The ratio s'/s is 13.6 approximately, its actual value depending on the purity of the water and mercury and on the temperature.

Fig. 36*c* shows the mercury gage as arranged for measuring the pressure-head at a point A in a water pipe. The top is open to the air and through it the mercury may be poured in, the cock E being closed and F open; the mercury then stands at the same height in each tube. The cock F being closed and E opened, the water enters the left-hand tube, depressing the mercury to

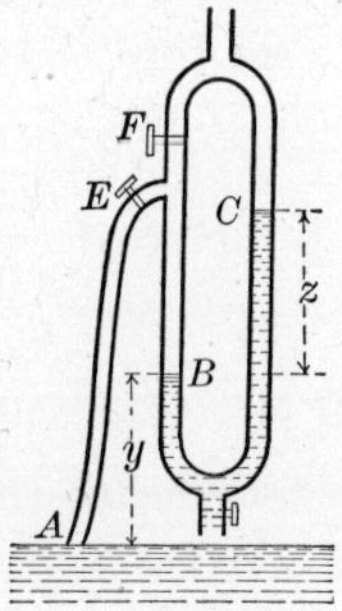

Fig. 36*c*.

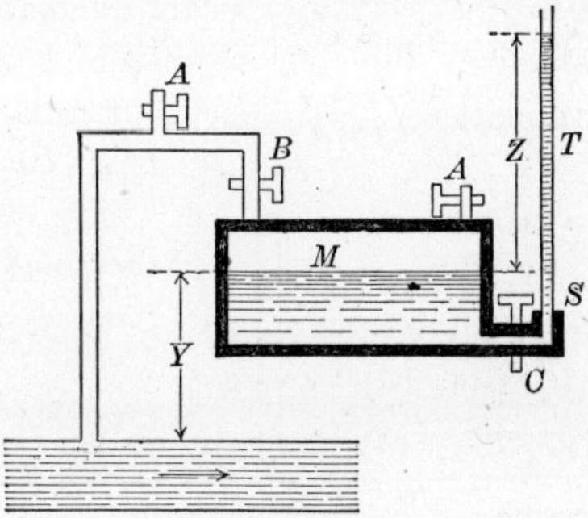

Fig. 36*d*.

B, causing it to rise to C on the other side. The distance z is then read on a scale between the two tubes, and the height of B above A by another scale. The pressure of the water at B is that due to the head $13.6z$, and the pressure at A is that due to the head $y + 13.6z$. In precise work it is necessary to determine the exact specific gravity of the mercury and water at different temperatures, so that precise values of the ratio s'/s may be known. The value of s' depends upon the purity of the mercury and is sometimes lower than 13.56.

A better form of mercury gage for use under most conditions is shown in Fig. 36*d*. It consists essentially of a heavy cast-iron reservoir having a large horizontal cross-section as compared with that of the glass tube *T*. The surface of the mercury *M* in this reservoir therefore remains at a practically constant level, and this level can be seen through a small glass window provided for that purpose. The glass tube is inserted through a stuffing box at *S* and the flow of mercury into it is controlled by a valve at *C*. Cocks at *A* permit of drawing off and preventing the entrainment of air, and the water pressure is admitted to the gage through the valve *B*. In case observations are to be made on a pressure which is constantly fluctuating the resulting oscillations in the tube can be dampened by partially closing the valves at either or both *B* and *C*.

For very high pressures, such as are used in operating heavy forging-presses, the mercury column of the above gage would be so long as to render it impracticable, and accordingly other methods must be employed. Fig. 36*e* represents a mercury gage constructed on the principle of the hydraulic press (Art. 10). *W* is a small cylinder into which the water is admitted through the small pipe at the top, and *M* is a large cylinder containing mercury to which a glass tube is attached. Before the water is admitted into *W* the mercury stands at the level of *B* in both the glass tube and large cylinder, if the piston does not rest on the mercury. When the water is admitted,

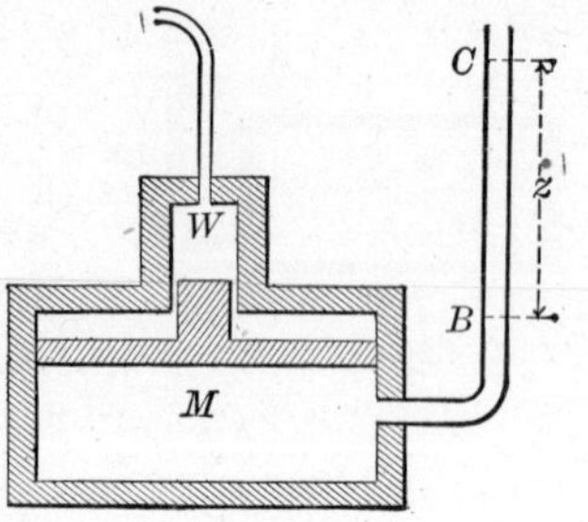

Fig. 36*e*.

its pressure on the upper end of the piston is pa, if p is the unit-pressure and a the area of the upper end. If A is the area of the lower end of the piston, the total pressure upon it is also pa, and hence the unit-pressure on the mercury surface is $p \cdot a/A$, and this is balanced by the column of height z in the glass tube. For example, suppose that $A = 200a$, then the unit-pressure on the mercury surface is $0.005p$; further, if z be 60 inches, the unit-pressure at B is about $2 \times 14.7 = 29.4$ pounds per square inch (Art. 4), and accordingly the pressure in W is $p = 200 \times 29.4 = 5880$ pounds per square inch, which corresponds to a head of water of about 13 550 feet.

Prob. 36. The diameter of the large end of the piston in the last figure is 15 inches, and the diameter of the mercury column is $\frac{1}{4}$ inch. Find the distance the piston is depressed when the mercury rises 60 inches.

Art. 37. Differential Pressure Gages

A differential gage is an instrument for measuring differences of heads or pressures, and this must be frequently done in hydraulic work. One of the simplest forms is that seen in Fig. 37*a*, where two water columns from *A* and *D* are brought to the sides of a common scale upon which the difference of height *BC* is directly read. A better form is one having two glass tubes

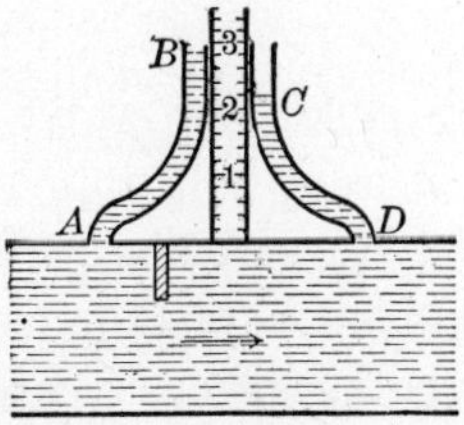

Fig. 37*a*.

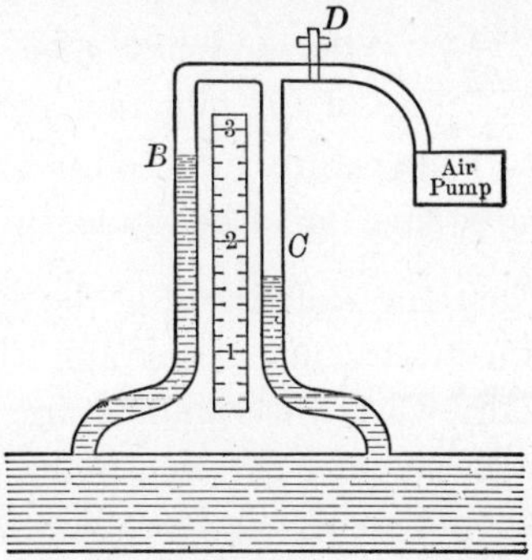

Fig. 37*b*.

fastened to a scale, these tubes being provided with attachments upon which can be screwed the hose leading from the pipe. Where it is desired to measure the difference between two large heads, provided that this difference is not greater than can be read on the scale board, this can be done by connecting the tubes across their tops, as in Fig. 37*b*, and by means of an air pump imposing a pressure sufficient to bring the water columns within visible range. After this pressure has been imposed the valve at *D* is closed and the difference in the heads read on the scale.

Fig. 37*c* shows the principle of the mercury differential gage.* Two parallel tubes are open at the top, and here the mercury is poured in, the cocks *E* and *F* being open and *A* and *C* closed; the mercury then stands at the same height in each tube. The cocks *E* and *F* being now closed and *A* and *C* opened, the water

* For the details of construction see paper by Kuichling in Transactions American Society of Civil Engineers, 1892, vol. 26, p. 439.

enters at A and C, and the mercury is depressed in one tube and elevated in the other. Let the pressure at B be that due to the head h_1, and the pressure at C be that due to the head h_2, and let h_1 be greater than h_2; also let the distance read on the scale between the two tubes be z. Then $h_1 = h_2 + 13.6z$, or the difference of the heads of water on B and C is $h_1 - h_2 = 13.6z$. Thus if z be 1.405 feet, the difference of the heads is 19.1 feet. Here, as for the mercury gage of Art. 36, the specific gravity of the mercury and water must be known for different temperatures, or comparisons of the instrument with a standard gage must be made.

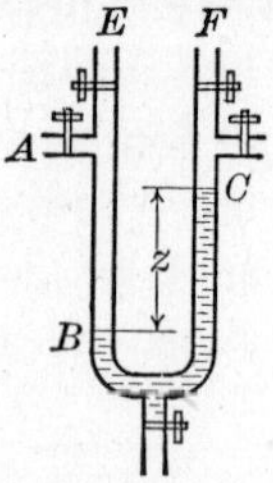

Fig. 37c.

When the difference of the heads is small, the water gage, explained in the first paragraph, cannot measure it with precision, especially when the columns are subject to oscillations. To increase the distance between B and C and at the same time decrease the amount of oscillation, the oil differential gage, invented by Flad in 1885, may be used. Fig. 37d shows the principle of construction.* The cocks A and D being closed and F open, sufficient oil is poured in at F to partially fill the two tubes. Then F is closed and the water admitted at A and D, when it rises to B in one tube and to C in the other, the oil filling the tubes above the water. Let s be the specific gravity of the water and s' that of the oil, let h_1 be the head of water on B and h_2 that on C, then $sh_2 = sh_1 + s'z$, whence $h_2 - h_1 = (s'/s)z$. Kerosene oil having a specific gravity of about 0.79 is generally used, and if the specific gravity of the water be unity, the difference of the heads is $0.79z$. Thus z is greater than $h_2 - h_1$, and hence an error in reading z produces a smaller error in $h_2 - h_1$. The specific gravities of the oil and water must be determined, however, so that s'/s can be

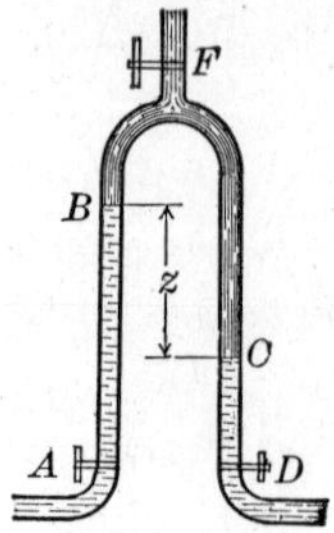

Fig. 37d.

*For the details see paper by Williams, Hubbell, and Fenkell in Transactions of American Society of Civil Engineers, 1902, vol. 47, pp. 72–83.

expressed to four significant figures when precise work on low heads is to be done.

The difference of head $h_1 - h_2$, determined by these differential gages, is the difference of the heads due to the pressure at the water levels B and C. The difference of the actual heads at the points of connection with the pipe under test is next to be determined. Fig. 37*e* shows a mercury gage set over a water pipe for the purpose of determining the loss of head due to a

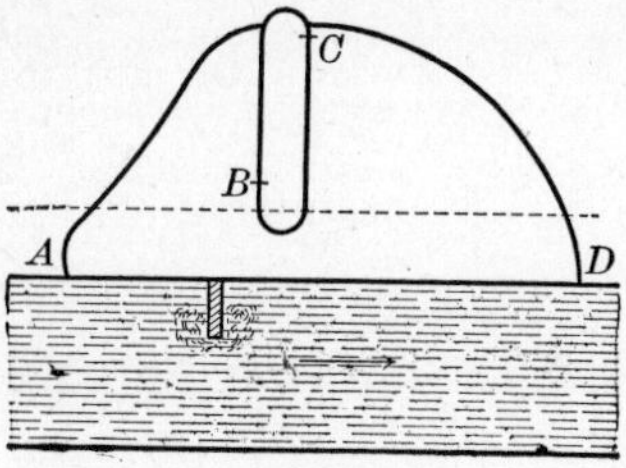

Fig. 37*e*.

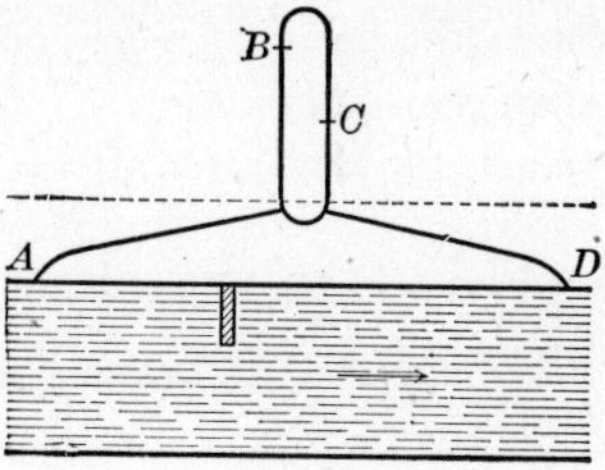

Fig. 37*f*.

valve, the velocity of the water being high, so that the difference of pressure at A and D is large. Fig. 37*f* shows an oil gage set over a similar pipe, the velocity being low, so that the difference of pressure is small. Let a horizontal plane, represented by the broken line, be drawn through the zero of the scale of the gage, and let d be the distance of this plane above the horizontal pipe. Let b and c be the readings of this scale at the water levels B and C in the gage tubes, the difference of these readings being z. Let h_1 and h_2 be the pressure-heads on B and C, and H_1 and H_2 those on A and D. Then $H_1 = h_1 + b + d$ and $H_2 = h_2 + c + d$, and the difference of these heads is

$$H_1 - H_2 = h_1 - h_2 + b - c$$

which is applicable to both kinds of differential gages. For the mercury gage the head $h_1 - h_2$ equals $13.6z$, while the value of $b - c$ is $-z$; hence

$$H_1 - H_2 = 13.6z - z = 12.6z$$

For the oil gage $h_1 - h_2$ is $-0.79z$, while $b - c$ is z, hence

$$H_1 - H_2 = -0.79z + z = 0.21z$$

In general, if s' is the ratio of the specific gravity of the mercury or oil to that of the water, the difference of the pressure-heads at A and D, which is the loss of head due to the valve, is $(s' - 1)z$ for the mercury gage and $(1 - s')z$ for the oil gage.

The principle of the mercury gage can also be applied to the measurement of small differences of head by using a liquid having a specific gravity but little heavier than water. Thus Cole, in 1897,* employed a mixture of carbon tetrachloride and gasoline which had a specific gravity of 1.25; for this mixture $H_1 - H_2$ equals $0.25z$, or z is four times the head $H_1 - H_2$, and accordingly when $H_1 - H_2$ is small, the error in determining it by the reading z is greatly diminished. It may be also noted that when the tube or pipe is not horizontal, the expressions $(s' - 1)z$ and $(1 - s')z$ give the loss of head between the two points A and D, although the difference of the actual pressure-heads may be greater or less according as A is lower or higher than D (Art. 85).

Prob. 37. In the case of Fig. 37*e* let the point D be lower than A by 0.45 foot, and let the reading z be 0.127 foot. How much greater is the pressure-head at A than that at D?

Art. 38. Water Meters

Exam

Meters used for measuring the quantity of water supplied to a house or factory are of the displacement type; that is, as the water passes through the meter it displaces or moves a piston, a wheel, or a valve, the motion of which is communicated through a train of clock wheels to dials where the quantity that has passed since a certain time is registered. There is no theoretical way of determining whether or not the readings of the dial hands are correct, but each meter must be rated by measuring the discharge in a tank. Several meters may be placed on the same pipe line in this operation, the same discharge then passing through each of them. When impure water passes through a meter for any length of time, deposits are liable to impair the accuracy of its readings, and hence it should be rerated at intervals.

The piston meter is one in which the motion of the water causes two pistons to move in opposite directions, the water

* Transactions American Society of Civil Engineers, 1902, vol. 47, p. 276.

leaving and entering the cylinder by ports which are opened and closed by slide valves somewhat similar to those used in the steam-engine. The rotary meter has a wheel enclosed in a case so that it is caused to revolve as the water passes through. The screw meter has an encased helical surface that revolves on its axis as the water enters at one end and passes out at the other. The disk meter has a wabbling disk so arranged that its motion is communicated to a pin which moves in a circle. In all these, and in many other forms, it is intended that the motion given to the pointers on the dials shall be proportional to the volume of water passing through the meter. The dials may be arranged to read either cubic feet or gallons, as may be required by the consumers. These meters are of different sizes according to the quantity of water to be registered. They all occasion considerable loss of head in the pipe on which they are installed and are of varying degrees of sensitiveness for small flows. The quantity of water registered by a meter of these types varies on account of wear both with its age and with the quality of the water it measures. For these reasons frequent ratings are desirable.*

The Venturi meter, named after the distinguished hydraulician who first experimented on the principle by which it operates, was invented by Herschel in 1887.† Fig. 38*a* shows a horizontal pipe having an area a_1 at each end, and the central part contracted to the area a_2, with two small piezometer tubes into which the water rises. When there is no flow, the water stands at the same level in these two columns, but when it is in motion, the heights of these columns above the axis of the pipe are h_1 and h_2. Let v_1 and v_2 be the mean velocities in the two cross-sections. Then by Art. 24 the effective head in the upper section is $h_1 + v_1^2/2g$, and that in

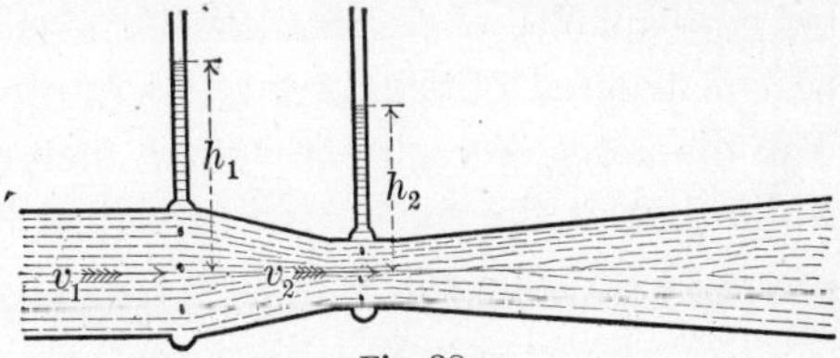

Fig. 38*a*.

* Transactions American Society of Civil Engineers, 1899, vol. 41, and Proceedings American Water Works Association, 1910.

† Transactions American Society of Civil Engineers, 1887, vol. 17, p. 228.

the small section is $h_2 + v_2^2/2g$; if there be no losses caused by friction, these two expressions must be equal, and hence by the theorem of (31)₂,

$$v_2^2 - v_1^2 = 2g(h_1 - h_2)$$

Now let Q be the discharge through the pipe, or $Q = a_1v_1$ and also $Q = a_2v_2$. Taking the values of v_1 and v_2 from these expressions, inserting them in the above equation, and solving for Q, gives

$$Q = \frac{a_1a_2}{\sqrt{a_1^2 - a_2^2}}\sqrt{2g(h_1 - h_2)} \qquad (38)$$

which may be called the theoretic discharge. Owing to frictional losses which occur between the two cross-sections, the actual discharge q is always less than Q, or $q = cQ$, in which c is a coefficient whose value generally lies between 0.97 and 0.99. To determine q, when the coefficient is known, it is hence only necessary to measure the difference $h_1 - h_2$, and then compute Q by formula (38).

The Venturi meter is used for measuring the discharge through pipes two inches or more in diameter, the largest meters of this type yet undertaken being those for the new Catskill Water System of the city of New York. Each of these meters will have a capacity of 650 000 000 U. S. gallons per day. They will be constructed of reinforced concrete with bronze throat pieces. The diameter of each end of the meter tube will be 210 inches, while that at the contracted section will be 93 inches.

The contracted section or throat of the meter is usually made from one-quarter to one-ninth of the area of the pipe, and hence the velocity through it is from four to nine times that in the pipe. The throat area used in any particular case is determined from considerations of the various rates of flow to be measured and the resulting throat velocities which should not, in order that the quantity may be well recorded on the automatic recording apparatus, fall much below 3 feet or far exceed 40 feet per second.

In practice the two water columns shown on Fig. 38a may be led to a mercury gage, Art. 37, where the difference between the pressure heads h_1 and h_2 is shown by the difference in level of the two mercury columns. A scale graduated so that $h_1 - h_2$ varies very nearly as q^2 will then enable the rate of flow in the pipe to be directly read (38). This meter is extensively used for the measurement of water and other liquids, and its capacity and accuracy are greater than that of any other form yet devised.

In Fig. 38*b* is shown a type of continuous recording apparatus as constructed by the Builders Iron Foundry of Providence, R. I., for use with the Venturi meter. On the upper dial, which is driven by a clock, a pen makes on a chart a continuous autographic record of the rate of flow through the meter. By means of this chart and a special planimeter the quantity of water which has passed the meter may be determined for any desired period. Depending on the gear of the clock, these charts are changed every 24 hours, every week, or at any other desired interval. On the central dial the mechanism automatically records the total quantity of water which has passed through the meter from the time it was set to the time any reading of

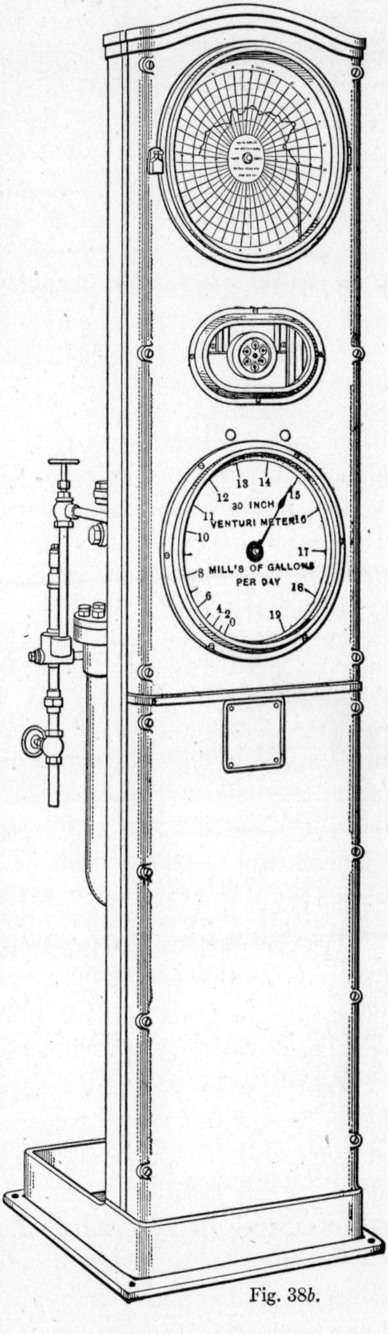

Fig. 38*b*.

the face is taken. On the lower dial the pointer continuously indicates the rate of flow, and, depending on the graduations of the scale, may indicate in millions of gallons per day, in cubic meters per second, or in any other desired unit.

A brief description of the operation of this apparatus is as follows. The two pressure pipes from the meter tube, Fig. 38*a*, are led to two mercury chambers connected near their bottoms and so forming a differential gage. In each of these chambers is a cast-iron float, and each float carries a toothed rack. Each rack meshes with a spur gear, both gears being attached to a single shaft which carries the pointer on the lower dial. The angular movement of this pointer is therefore exactly proportional to any change in the difference of the two mercury levels. Attached to this shaft is a cam, the curve of whose face is proportional to $\sqrt{h_1 - h_2}$. As the shaft rotates the cam presses against and moves a long vertical lever which carries at its top the pen which makes the record on the chart on the upper dial. It is evident therefore (38) that the movement of the pen is proportional to q. The lever which carries the pen is also connected to a clock-driven integrating mechanism in a manner such that the speed of the counter increases directly as the angular movement of the vertical lever increases from its starting position. The speed of the counter is at all times therefore proportional to the rate of flow through the meter, and thus the quantity passing is continuously integrated. The accuracy of this recording mechanism can be tested at any time by comparing the rate of flow indicated by it with the difference between h_1 and h_2 as shown by a differential gage connected to the two pressure tubes leading from the meter. A known difference in pressure may also be imposed upon the pipes leading to the recording mechanism by means of two water columns and the registration of the apparatus observed and compared with this known difference. In this way the apparatus can be tested through greater ranges than those usually to be obtained under service conditions.

Another form of recording apparatus for use with the Venturi meter is made by the Simplex Valve and Meter Company of Philadelphia, Pa.* This apparatus performs all of the functions of that above described. Its operation is also based on a cam but details of its mechanism are materially different.

* Proceedings American Water Works Association, 1906.

The Premier meter * manufactured by The National Meter Company makes use of the Venturi principle though in a manner entirely different from the others above described. It consists essentially of a Venturi tube with a by-pass leading from its upstream end to its throat. On this by-pass, which is materially smaller than the main tube, there is put a displacement meter of the piston type which records that proportion of the entire flow which passes through it. The ratio between the total flow and that indicated by the small meter being determined by experiment, the entire arrangement becomes an instrument for the measurement of water or other liquids. This type of meter is strictly of the proportional type, and as such, is open to all of the objections which hold against the class. It gives best results for throat velocities in excess of 10 feet per second at which the friction in the small recording meter becomes relatively small and consequently has less effect on the strict proportionality of flow through the two branches. This type of meter is adapted to locations close to the hydraulic gradient, where the styles of recording apparatus hereinbefore described could not be used in connection with a simple Venturi tube on account of insufficient submergence of the throat. For the proper operation of these recording mechanisms it is always necessary that the pressure-head at the throat be a positive quantity.

Still another instrument adapted for making a continuous record of the flow of water in a pipe is the Pitotmeter as perfected by Cole.† This apparatus consists essentially of a pair of Pitot tubes, Art. 41, which can be inserted through a corporation cock to any position within the pipe. One of these tubes looks upstream and the other downstream. From them connection is made to the branches of a differential gage in which is placed a mixture of carbon tetrachloride and gasoline (Art. 37). The difference in level between the columns is photographically recorded on a strip of sensitized paper by means of suitable apparatus, and from this

* Proceedings American Water Works Association, 1908; Engineering News, June 16, 1904.

† Journal New England Water Works Association, 1906; Proceedings American Water Works Association, 1907.

recorded difference the quantity of water which has passed through the pipe can be computed. With this apparatus the usual procedure is to first rate the Pitot tubes (Art. 41), and then after inserting them into the pipe, making a traverse in order to determine the ratio between the average and maximum velocities. This ratio usually varies from 0.80 to 0.86 (Art. 83). Thereafter the tubes are set so as to record the maximum velocity, and by means of the ratio the average velocity is computed. In order to insure correct results the tubes must be carefully rated and care be taken to see that they are kept clean of materials deposited from the water about their mouths. The Pitotmeter has the advantage of causing little or no loss of head. It is a very portable instrument, and is particularly adapted for application to water waste investigations, pump slippage, and other allied subjects.

All meters cause a loss in pressure, so that the pressure-head in the pipe beyond the meter is less than in the pipe where it enters the meter. This is due to the energy lost in overcoming friction. For a Venturi tube having a throat area of one-ninth that of the pipe the loss of head in feet is about $0.0021 V^2$, where V is the velocity in the contracted section in feet per second. Thus, when the velocity in a water main is 3 feet per second, the velocity in the contracted section will be 27 feet per second, and the loss of pressure-head due to the meter tube about 1.53 feet.

Prob. 38. A 12-inch pipe delivers 810 gallons per minute through a Venturi meter, a_2 being one-ninth of a_1. Compute the mean velocities in the sections a_1 and a_2. If the pressure-head in a_1 is 21.4 feet, compute the pressure-head in a_2.

Art. 39. Mean Velocity and Discharge

In Chap. 3 the velocity of water flowing from an orifice, or through a tube or pipe, was regarded as uniform over the cross-section. If a is that area, and v the uniform velocity, the discharge is $q = av$; hence, if a and v can be found by measurement, q is known. In fact, however, the velocity varies in different parts of a cross-section, so that the determination of v cannot be directly made. Yet there always is a certain value for

v, which multiplied into a will give the actual discharge q, and this value is called the mean velocity.

In the case of a stream or open channel the velocity is much less along the sides and bottom than near the middle. A rough determination of the mean velocity may be made, however, by observing the greatest surface velocity by a float, and taking eight-tenths of this for the approximate mean velocity. Thus, if the float requires 50 seconds to run 120 feet, the mean velocity is about 1.9 feet per second; then if the cross-section be 820 square feet, the discharge is 1560 cubic feet per second.

The practical object of determining the mean velocity is, in nearly all cases, to determine the discharge, but as a rule the mean velocity cannot be directly observed. A knowledge of its value, however, is necessary in all branches of hydraulics, since hydraulic coefficients and formulas are based upon it. Accordingly, many experiments have been made upon small orifices and pipes by catching the flow in tanks and thus determining q, then the mean velocity has been computed from $v = q/a$. This process has been extended, by indirect methods, to large orifices and pipes, and finally to canals and rivers.

A common method of finding the discharge of a stream is to subdivide the cross-section into parts and determine their areas a_1, a_2, etc., the sum of which is the total area a. Then, if v_1, v_2, etc., are the mean velocities in these areas, and if these are determined by observations, the discharge is

$$q = a_1v_1 + a_2v_2 + a_3v_3 + \text{etc.} \qquad (39)$$

Here the mean velocities may be roughly found by observing the passage of a surface float at the middle of each subdivision and multiplying this surface velocity by 0.9. There are, however, more precise methods, one of which will be explained in Art. 40,

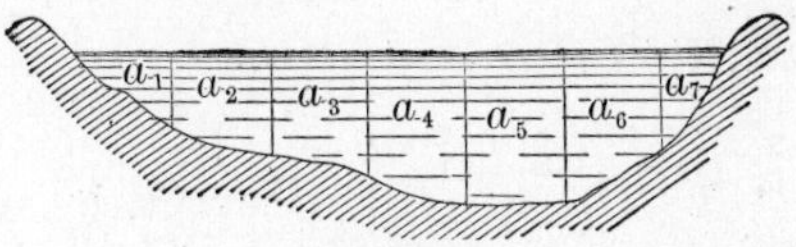

Fig. 39*a*.

while others will be described in Chap. 10. When q has been found in this manner, the mean velocity of the stream may be computed, if desired, by $v = q/a$.

Formula (39) applies also to a cross-section of any kind. Thus, let the pipe of Fig. 39*b* be divided by concentric circles into the areas, a_1, a_2, a_3, a_4, and let the mean velocities v_1, v_2, v_3, v_4, be determined by observation for each of these areas; the discharge q is then given by (39). Again, in the conduit of Fig. 126*a*, let a velocity observation be taken at each of the 97 points marked by a dot, these points being uniformly spaced over the cross-section, so that each of the areas a_1, a_2, etc., may be regarded as $\frac{1}{97}a$. Then from (39) the discharge is

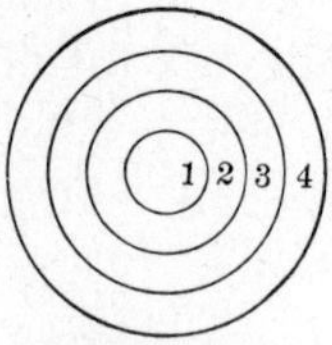

Fig. 39*b*.

$$q = \tfrac{1}{97}a(v_1 + v_2 + v_3 + \cdots + v_{97}) = av$$

or v is the sum of the individual velocities divided by 97. In general, if a cross-section be divided into n equal parts, the mean velocity is the average of the n observed velocities. This result is the more accurate the greater the number of parts into which the cross-section is divided. If the number of parts be infinite and the water passing through each be called a filament, the mean velocity in the cross-section may be defined as the average of the velocities of all the filaments.

Prob. 39. A water pipe, 3 inches in diameter, is divided into three parts by concentric circles whose diameters are 1, 2, and 3 inches. The mean velocities in these parts are found to be 6.6, 4.8, and 3.0 feet per second. Compute the discharge and mean velocity for the pipe.

Art. 40. The Current Meter

In 1790 the German hydraulic engineer Woltmann invented an apparatus for measuring the velocity of flowing water which was later improved by Darcy and others, and is now extensively used for gaging streams and other open channels. This meter is like a windmill, having three or more vanes mounted on a spindle and so arranged that the face of the wheel always stands normal to the direction of the current, the pressure of which causes it to revolve. The number of revolutions of the wheel is approximately proportional to the velocity of the current. In the best forms of this instrument the number of revolutions made in a given time is determined and recorded by an apparatus placed near the observer on a bridge, in a boat, or elsewhere. In these forms an electric connection is made and broken at every fifth revolution and a dial on the recording apparatus affected. By means of a telephone receiver the making and breaking of the circuit can be made audible to the observer, who in such case simply keeps count of the number of clicks and observes on a stop-watch the time elapsed for a given number of revolutions.

The meter may be operated by placing it on a rod on which its position may be changed at will or by suspending it from a chain or rope. The former of these methods is applicable only to small streams and to cases where the velocity is low. Under the second method the meter can best be operated from a bridge, and in some cases at permanent gaging stations in lieu of a bridge a wire cable may be stretched across the stream and at a sufficient height above it, so that the operator, when seated in a cage which travels on the cable, will have room for operation. On very large streams or where the expense of a cable is not warranted the gagings may be made from a boat. At times of low water, in shal low streams the meter is carried and held di-

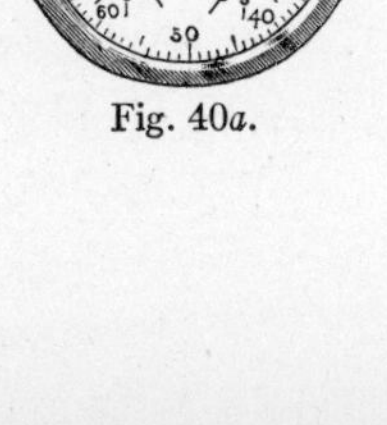

Fig. 40*a*.

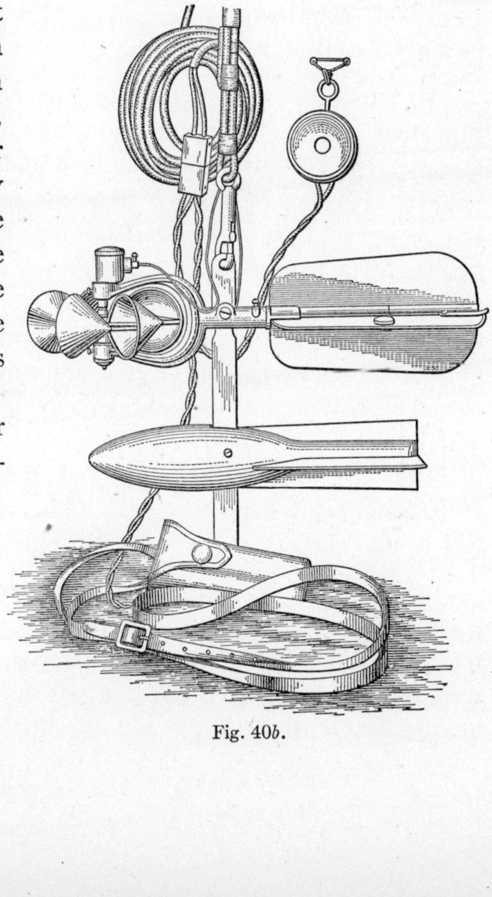
Fig. 40*b*.

rectly in position by the observer who wades out into the stream. In such cases care must be taken to hold the meter clear of the disturbing influence of the observer's presence.

Figure 40*a* shows the recording dial of an electrically operated device for counting the revolutions of a meter, and in Fig. 40*b* is shown the Price current meter, a form extensively used in the United States. The cups or vanes are kept facing the current by means of the cross-shaped rudder immediately behind them. At the lower end of the standard is a heavy torpedo-shaped lead weight also equipped with rudder vanes. The supporting cable is shown connected to the upper end of the standard by a snap, and the electric connection wires are shown extending from the battery in the leather case through the meter and thence to the telephone receiver. Both the battery and the receiver are carried by the observer. In order to assist in keeping the meter more nearly vertical in swiftly flowing streams a line may be attached to the supporting cable a short distance above the meter and carried to some point upstream, so that a pull on it will help to make the meter better maintain its position.

A current meter cannot be used for determining the velocity in a small trough or channel, since the introduction of it into the cross-section would contract the area and cause a change in the velocity of the flowing water. In large conduits, canals, and rivers it is, however, a convenient and accurate instrument. By simply holding it at a fixed position below the surface the velocity at that point is found; by causing it to descend at a uniform rate from surface to bottom the mean velocity in that vertical is obtained; and by passing it at a uniform rate over all parts of the cross-section of a channel the mean velocity v can be directly determined. This latter procedure is one which can be put into practice only in small channels and under unusual conditions. It is mentioned here simply to illustrate the various uses to which the current meter may be put.

In operation the current meter is generally suspended from a cable which is graduated so that the distance of the center of the meter below the surface of the water can be directly read by the observer. The current meter, like every other instrument, must be used and handled with care to produce the best results. Hoyt * has well summarized recent current meter practice and the results which have been obtained.

To derive the velocity of the water from the number of recorded revolutions per second the meter must first be rated by pushing it at a known velocity through still water. The best place for doing this is in a pond or navigation canal, where the water has no sensible velocity. A track is built along the bank on which a small car can be moved at a known velocity. From this car the meter is suspended into the water either from a rod or a cable, and the method of suspension used should be the same as that to be employed in actual service. The lowest velocity of the car should be that at which the meter will just start and continue revolving; this velocity is from 0.1 to 0.2 feet per second. The highest velocity should be somewhat in excess of the actual velocities to be observed, and ratings are usually carried up to velocities of from 10 to 15 feet per second. It is always found that the number of revolutions per minute is not exactly proportional to the velocity of the car, and hence when the meter is held stationary in running water, the velocity of the water is not proportional to the number of revolutions.

From the observations made at the different known velocities there is prepared a rating table showing the velocity of the water in feet per second corresponding to the number of meter revolutions. This form of table is best, since in making observations best results are obtained by noting the number of seconds required to complete a certain number of revolutions. To make such a table the known velocities of the car are taken as abscissas on cross-section paper and the number of revolutions as ordinates, and a point corresponding to each observation is plotted. A mean curve may then be drawn to agree as closely as possible with the plotted points, and from this curve the velocity corresponding to any number of revolutions can be taken off. This curve may be expressed by an equation of the form $V = a + bn$ or $V = a + bn + cn^2$, in which V is the velocity of the car in feet per second and n in the number of revolutions of the meter per second. By the

* Transactions American Society of Civil Engineers, 1910, vol. 66, p. 70.

aid of the Method of Least Squares the constants of the equation may then be computed and the curve determined (Art. 42). In the case of the small Price meter it has been found that the curve is very closely approximated by two straight lines *AB* and *BC*, as shown in Fig. 40*c*, which is a typical rating curve for this

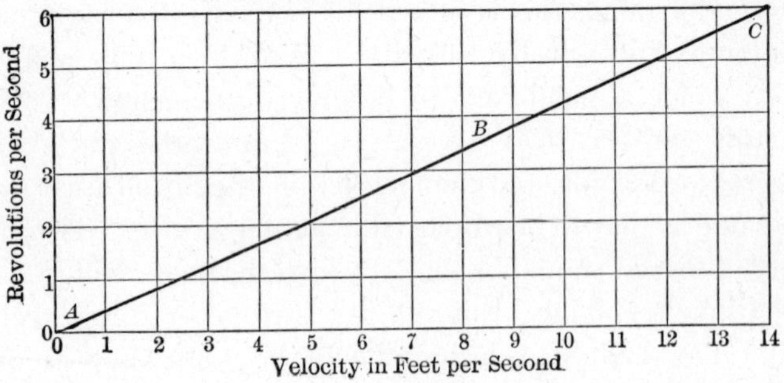

Fig. 40*c*.

type of meter.* This curve was based on thirty-five observations at different velocities, and practically all of them fell on the line *ABC* which is also very nearly a straight line.

An examination† of the rating tables of a number of meters has shown that possible errors due to differences in rating are quite small, and that a Price meter in good condition can be used with a standard rating table without serious error for all velocities greater than 0.5 foot per second and then generally within about 2 percent.

While the current meter is an extensively used instrument, there are, as in most other hydraulic work, certain features which are not yet fully understood. These are the differences shown in the results of the ratings of the same meter when held on a rod and when suspended by a cable.‡ It has also been found that the rating of a meter made in still water differs somewhat from that made in running water,‡ but no successful means for making direct running water ratings have as yet been devised. Many good comparisons between current meter gagings and weir measurements have been made, but the current meter

* Transactions American Society of Civil Engineers, 1910, vol. 66, p. 83.
† Transactions American Society of Civil Engineers, 1910, vol. 66, p. 83.
‡ Water Supply and Irrigation Paper, No. 95, U. S. Geological Survey.

velocities in all of them have been relatively low, so that no complete comparison has up to the present been possible.

Prob. 40. In order to rate a certain current meter, three observations were taken in still water, as follows:

Velocity of the car =	2.0	3.8	7.4 feet per second
Revolutions per minute =	30	60	120

Plot these observations on cross-section paper and deduce, without using the Method of Least Squares, the relation between V and n in the equation $V = a + bn$.

Art. 41. The Pitot Tube

About 1750 the French hydraulic engineer Pitot invented a device for measuring the velocity in a stream by means of the velocity-head which it will produce. In its simplest form it consists of a bent tube, the mouth of which is placed so as to directly face the current. The water then rises in the vertical part of the tube to a height h above the surface of the flowing stream, and this height is equal to the velocity-head $v^2/2g$, so that the actual velocity v is in practice approximately equal to $\sqrt{2gh}$. As constructed for use in streams, Pitot's apparatus consists of two tubes placed side by side with their submerged mouths at right angles, so that when one is opposed to the current, as seen in Fig. 41b, the other stands normal to it, and the water surface in the latter tube hence is at the same level as that of the stream. Both tubes are provided with cocks which may be closed while the instrument is immersed, and it can be then lifted from the water and the head h be read at leisure. It is found that the actual velocity is always less than $\sqrt{2gh}$, and that a coefficient must be deduced for each instrument by moving it in still water at known velocities. Pitot's tube has the advantage that no time observation is needed to determine the velocity, but it has the disadvantage that the distance h is

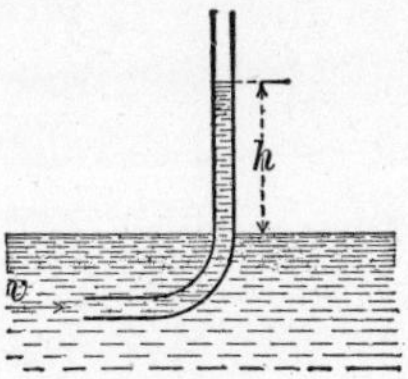

Fig. 41a.

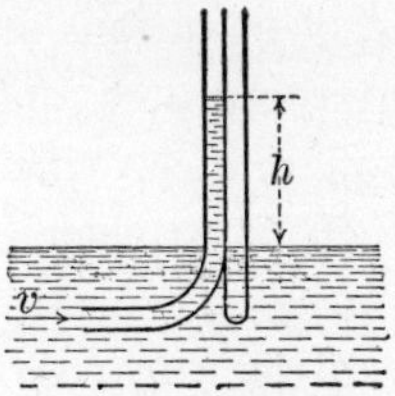

Fig. 41b.

usually very small, so that an error in reading it has a large influence. Although the instrument was improved by Darcy in 1856 and used by him for some stream measurements, it was for a long time regarded as having a low degree of precision.

When using a Pitot tube for measuring the velocity in a stream, the two columns may be raised above the level of the water in the stream and brought to a height convenient for observation by partly exhausting the air from the tubes above the columns. This procedure is analogous to the imposing of an air pressure above the water columns in the case of high heads, as was described in Art. 37.

In 1888 Freeman made experiments on the distribution of velocities in jets from nozzles, in which an improved form of Pitot tube was used.* The point of the tube facing the current was the tip of a stylographic pen, the diameter of the opening being about 0.006 inch. This point was introduced into different parts of the jet and the pressure caused in the tube was measured by a Bourdon pressure gage reading to single pounds. The velocities of the jets were high; for example, in one series of observations on a jet from a $1\frac{1}{8}$-inch nozzle, the gage pressures at the center and near the edge were 51.2 and 18.2 pounds per square inch, which correspond to velocity-heads of 118.2 and 42.0 feet, or to velocities of 87.2 and 52.0 feet per second. By computing the mean velocity of the jet from measurements in concentric rings (Art. 39) and also from the measured discharge, Freeman concluded that any velocity as determined by the tube was smaller than that computed from $v = \sqrt{2gh}$ by less than one percent. This investigation established the fact that the Pitot tube is an instrument of great precision for the measurement of high velocities.

Experiments on the flow of water in pipes, in which Pitot tubes were successfully used, were made in 1897 by Cole at Terre Haute, and in 1898 by Williams, Hubbell, and Fenkell at Detroit.† In the Detroit experiments the tube was introduced into the pipe

* Transactions American Society of Civil Engineers, 1889, vol. 21, p. 413.

† Transactions American Society of Civil Engineers, 1902, vol. 47, pp. 12, 275.

through an opening provided with a stuffing-box, so that the point of the tube might be placed at any desired position. The tubes had openings at their points $\frac{1}{32}$ inch in diameter and other openings of the same size on their sides to admit the static pressure of the water. These latter openings led to a common channel parallel to that leading from the point, and each of these was connected to a rubber hose running to a differential gage, consisting of two parallel glass tubes open at the top, where the difference of head was read on a scale. In order to be able to deduce the velocities in the pipe from the readings of the gage, the Pitot tubes were rated by moving them in still water at known velocities as for the current meter (Art. 40). Thus a coefficient c_v was derived for each tube for use in the formula $v = c_v\sqrt{2gh}$. This coefficient was found to range from 0.86 to 0.95 for different tubes, and it varied but little with v.

Many different forms of Pitot tubes have been made and experimented upon. Each of these forms has, in common with the others, the pressure opening which faces the current, though the shape and dimensions of this opening differ materially in the various types. In some of them the static pressure is admitted through a hole in the side of the apparatus, while in others it is admitted through a number of such holes. In another type the tube is made symmetrical with an opening looking downstream. In this case the water column connected with the upstream opening will indicate the velocity head, while that connected with the opening which faces downstream will indicate a pressure less than the static head on account of the negative head induced by the arrangement. The difference between the two columns is thus increased and its reading on the scale rendered more easy, while the proportional error of any reading is also reduced. In Fig. 41*c* is shown a form of tube used by the U.S. Geological Survey* for the measurement of velocity in small and shallow streams in connection with experiments on the transporting capacity of currents, while in Fig. 41*d* is shown the type used in connection with the Pitotmeter (Art. 38). In this figure is shown also the method of introducing the tubes into a pipe where the velocity is to be measured.

Some recent comparisons * between the still and moving water ratings of Pitot tubes indicate that there may be a difference between

* Engineering News, Aug. 12, 1909.

the results obtained by these two methods. It is desirable, of course, that every instrument should be rated under conditions similar to those in which it is to be used. One of the ways of rating a Pitot tube

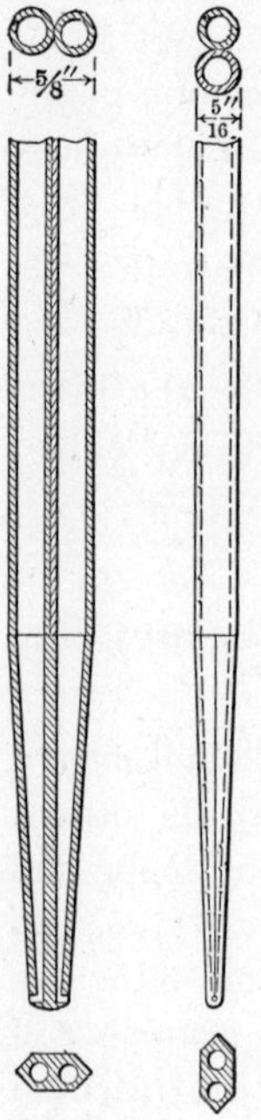

Fig. 41*c*.

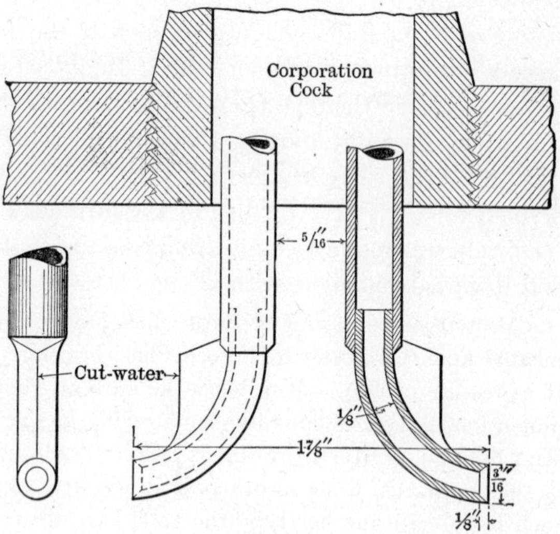

Fig. 41*d*.

in running water is that suggested and used by Judd and King* who placed the tube used by them at the contracted section of a jet and concluded that its coefficient was 1.00.

Prob. 41. Explain how a well-rated Pitot tube may be used to measure the speed of a boat or ship.

Art. 42. Discussion of Observations

An observation is the recorded result of a measurement. All measurements are affected with errors due to imperfections of the instrument and lack of skill of the observers, and the recorded results contain these errors. Thus, if 6.05, 6.02, 6.01, and 6.04 inches be four observations on the diameter of an orifice, all of

* Engineering News, Sept. 27, 1906.

these cannot be correct, and probably each is in error. The best that can be done is to take the average of these observations, or 6.03 inches, as the most probable result, and to use this in the computations.

An observer is often tempted to reject a measurement when it differs from others, but this can only be allowed when he is convinced that a mistake has been made. A mistake is a large error, due generally to carelessness, and must not be confounded with the small accidental errors of measurement. When a series of observations is placed before a computer, he should never be permitted to reject one of them, unless there is some remark in the note-book which casts doubt upon it.

Graphical methods of discussing and adjusting observations, like that mentioned in Art. 40, are of great value in hydraulic work. As another example, the following observations made by Darcy and Bazin on the flow of water in a rectangular trough, 1.812 meters wide and having the uniform slope 0.049, may be noted. Water was allowed to run through it with varying depths, and for each depth the mean velocity (Art. 39) and the hydraulic mean depth (Art. 112) was determined by measurement. Let v be the mean velocity and r the hydraulic mean depth; then five measurements gave the following observations, v being in meters per second and r in centimeters. Let it be assumed that the

No. =	1	2	3	4	5
v =	1.73	1.98	2.17	2.33	2.46
r =	11.4	14.4	17.0	19.2	21.2

relation between v and r is of the form $v = mr^n$, and let it be required to determine the most probable values of m and n.

For each of these observations a point may be plotted on cross-section paper, taking the values of v as ordinates and those of r as abscissas, and a smooth curve may then be drawn so as to agree as nearly as possible with the points. Such a curve, however, is of little assistance in determining the values of m and n, unless the curve should be a straight line drawn through the origin, in which case it is plain that n is unity and that m is the tangent of the angle that the line makes with axis of abscissas. In this case no straight line can be drawn approximating to the points and passing through the origin, but the plot gives the curve shown in Fig. 42*a*. If, however, the logarithm of each side of the assumed formula be taken, it becomes

$$\log v = n \log r + \log m$$

which represents a straight line if log v be considered as the variable ordinate and log r as the variable abscissa, log m being

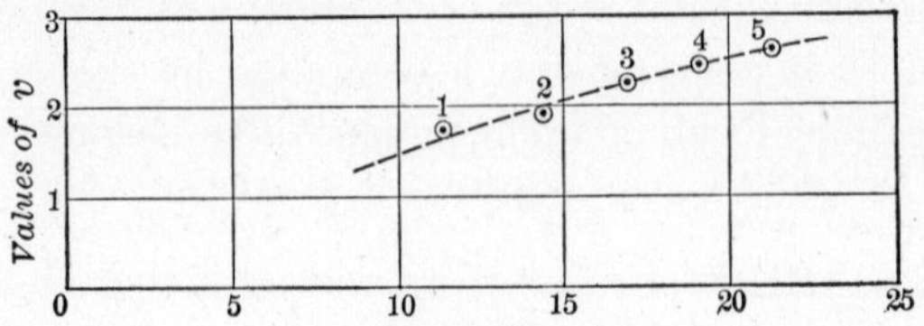

Fig. 42*a*.

the intercept on the axis of ordinates and n the tangent of the angle which the line makes with the axis of abscissas. On plotting the points corresponding to the values of log v and log r, it is seen that a straight line can be drawn closely agreeing with the

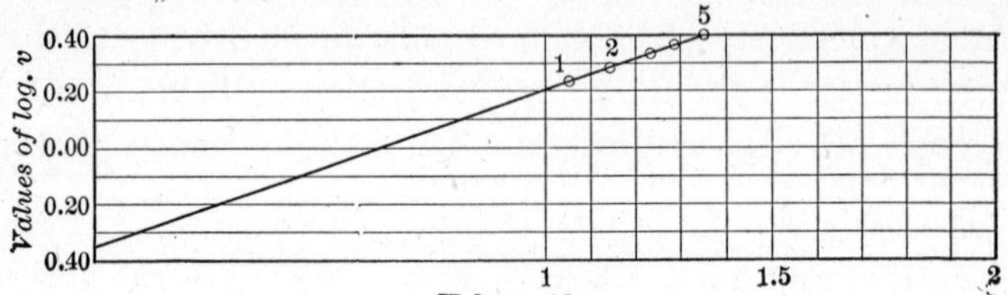

Fig. 42*b*.

points, that this line cuts the axis of ordinates at a distance of about 0.35 below the origin, and that the tangent of the angle made by it with the axis of abscissas is about 0.55. Hence (Fig. 42*b*) $n = 0.55$, $\log m = -0.35 = \bar{1}.65$, or $m = 0.446$; then

$$\log v = 0.55 \log r - 0.35 \quad \text{or} \quad v = 0.446 r^{0.55}$$

is an empirical formula for computing the mean velocity in this trough. Using the above values of r and computing those of v, it is found that the computed and observed results agree fairly, the former being generally a little smaller, which is due to the fact that only two significant figures are found from the plot.

Whenever a series of plotted points can be closely represented by a straight line on logarithmic section paper, the equation between the variables is an exponential one. Numerous exponential formulas for the flow of water in pipes and channels rest upon the judgment of the investigator in deciding that the plotted points are sufficiently well represented by a straight line.

There is a process, known as the Method of Least Squares, by which the constants of an empirical formula may be obtained from observations with a higher degree of precision than by any graphic method. Its application to the above case will here be given. Let the simultaneous values of log v and log r for each experiment be placed in the logarithmic formula as follows:

$$
\begin{array}{ll}
\text{for No. 1,} & 0.238 = 1.057n + \log m \\
\text{for No. 2,} & 0.297 = 1.158n + \log m \\
\text{for No. 3,} & 0.336 = 1.230n + \log m \\
\text{for No. 4,} & 0.367 = 1.283n + \log m \\
\text{for No. 5,} & 0.391 = 1.326n + \log m
\end{array}
$$

These five equations contain two unknown quantities, n and log m, but no values of these can be found that will exactly satisfy all the equations. The best that can be done is to find the values that have the greatest degree of probability, and these will satisfy the equations with the smallest discrepancies. To do this, let each equation be multiplied by the coefficient of n in that equation and the results be added; also let each equation be multiplied by the coefficient of log m in that equation and the results be added. Thus are found the two normal equations containing the two unknown quantities:

$$1.998 = 7.375n + 6.054 \log m$$
$$1.629 = 6.054n + 5.000 \log m$$

and the solution of these gives $n = 0.571$ and log $m = -0.366$. Since -0.366 equals $\bar{1}.634$, the value of m is 0.431, and then

$$\log v = 0.571 \log r - 0.366 \quad \text{or} \quad v = 0.431 r^{0.571}$$

is the empirical formula for this particular case.

The Method of Least Squares is usually more laborious than the graphical method, but it has the great advantage that its results are the most probable ones that can be derived from the given data. It has the further advantage that all computors will derive the same results, whereas in the graphic method the results will usually differ, because the position of the line drawn on the plot is affected by the different degrees of judgment and experience of the draftsmen. It will be seen from Fig. 42*b* that it is not very easy to determine close values of log *m* since the plotted points are so far away from the origin.

Prob. 42*a*. In order to rate a certain current meter four observations were taken in still water as follows:

Velocity of the car	0.7	2.4	4.7	9.3 feet per second
Revolutions of meter	18	60	120	240 per minute

Find the values of a and b in the formula $v = a + bn$, both by plotting and by the method of least squares.

Prob. 42*b*. Three observations of horizontal angles are made at the station O, which give $AOB = 62°17'$, $BOC = 20°35'$, $AOC = 82°55'$. Adjust these observations by the method of least squares so that the large angle may be equal to the sum of its parts.

CHAPTER 5

FLOW OF WATER THROUGH ORIFICES

Art. 43. Standard Orifices

Orifices for the measurement of water are usually placed in the vertical side of a vessel or reservoir, but may also be placed in the base. In the former case it is understood that the upper edge of the opening is completely covered with water; and generally the head of water on an orifice is at least three or four times its vertical height. The term "standard orifice" is here used to signify that the opening is so arranged that the water in flowing from it touches only a line, as would be the case in a plate of no thickness. To secure this result the inner part of the opening is a definite edge, which alone is touched by the water. In precise experiments the orifice may be in a metallic plate whose thickness is really small, as at *A* in the figure, but more commonly it is cut in a board or plank, care being taken that the inner edge is sharp and definite. It is usual to bevel the outer part of the orifice, as at *C*, so that the escaping jet may by no possibility touch the same except at the inner edges. The term "orifice in a thin plate" is often used to express the condition that the water shall only touch the edges of the opening along a line. This arrangement may be regarded as a kind of standard apparatus for the measurement of water; for, as will be seen later, the discharge is modified when the inner edges are rounded, and different degrees of rounding give different discharges. The standard arrangements shown in Fig. 43*a* are accordingly always used when water is to be measured by the use of orifices.

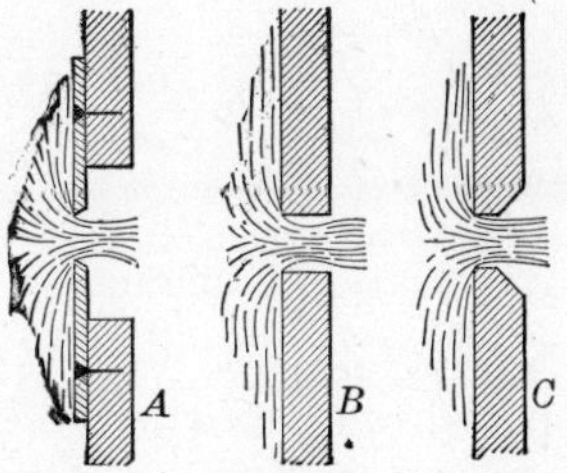

Fig. 43*a*.

The contraction of the jet which is always observed when water issues from a standard orifice, as described above, is a most interesting and important phenomenon. It is due to the circumstance that the particles of water as they approach the orifice move in converging directions, and that these directions continue to converge for a short distance beyond the plane of the orifice. It is this contraction of the jet that causes only the inner corner of the orifice to be touched by the escaping water. The appearance of such a jet under steady flow, issuing from a circular orifice, is that of a clear crystal bar whose beauty claims the admiration of every observer. The convergence due to this cause ceases at a distance from the plane of the orifice of about one-half its diameter. Beyond this section the jet enlarges in size if it be directed upward, but decreases in size if it be directed downward or horizontally.

The contraction of the jet is also observed in the case of rectangular and triangular orifices, its cross-section being similar to that of the orifice until the place of greatest contraction is passed. Fig. 43*b* shows in the top row cross-sections of a jet from a square orifice, in the middle row those from a triangular one, and in the third row those from an elliptical orifice. The left-hand diagram in each case is the cross-section of the jet near the place of greatest contraction, while the following ones are cross-sections at greater distances from the orifice, and the jets are supposed to be moving horizontally or nearly so.

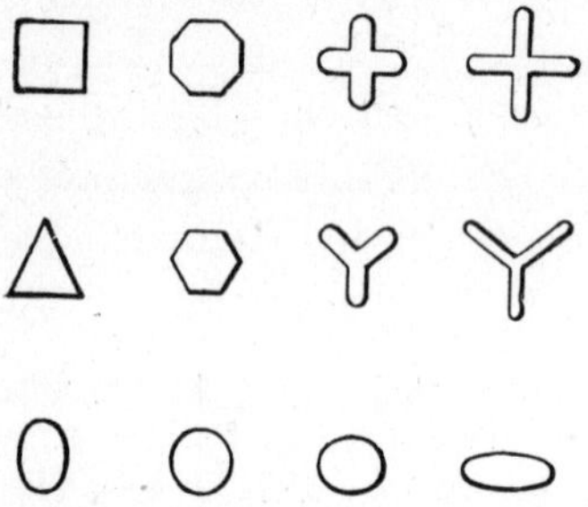

Fig. 43*b*.

Owing to this contraction, the discharge from a standard orifice is always less than the theoretic discharge, which, from Arts. 22 and 30, would be expressed by

$$Q = a\sqrt{2gh} \qquad (43)$$

where a is the area of the orifice and h the head above its center. It is evident that the quantity of water passing the plane of the orifice and that passing the plane of the contracted section in any unit of time are the same, and since there probably can be no appreciable change in the density of the water, there must therefore be an increase in velocity between these two planes. The reasons for such an increase are not fully known. It is not probable that the velocity at the center of the jet changes materially, but rather that the increase occurs in its outer filaments, so that at the contracted section they are all traveling parallel with each other and at the same velocity.*

It is the object of this chapter to determine how the theoretic formulas for orifices given in Chap. 3 are to be modified so that they may be used for the practical purposes of the measurement of water. This is to be done by the discussion of the results of experiments. It will be supposed, unless otherwise stated, that the size of the orifice is small compared with the cross-section of the reservoir, so that the effect of velocity of approach may be neglected (Art. 24).

Prob. 43. At a distance from a circular orifice of one-half its diameter a jet has a diameter of 1 inch and a velocity of 16 feet per second. When it is directed vertically downward, what is the diameter of a section 5 feet lower? When it is directed vertically upward, what is the diameter of a section 5 feet higher?

Art. 44. Coefficient of Contraction

The coefficient of contraction is the number by which the area of the orifice is to be multiplied in order to give the area of the section of the jet at a distance from the plane of the orifice of about one-half its diameter. Thus, if c_c be the coefficient of contraction, a the area of the orifice, and a' the area of the contracted section of the jet, then

$$a' = c_c a \tag{44}$$

The coefficient of contraction for a standard orifice is evidently always less than unity.

The only direct method of finding the value of c_c is to measure by calipers the dimensions of the least cross-section of the jet. The size of the orifice can usually be determined with precision,

* Engineering News, Sept. 27, 1906.

and with care almost an equal precision in measuring the jet. To find c_c for a circular orifice let d and d' be the diameters of the sections a and a'; then

$$c_c = a'/a = (d'/d)^2$$

Therefore the coefficient of contraction is the square of the ratio of the diameter of the jet to that of the orifice. The first measurements were made by Newton * who found the ratio of d' to d to be 21/25, which gives for c_c the value 0.73. The experiments of Bossut gave from 0.66 to 0.67; and Michelotti found from 0.57 to 0.624 with a mean of 0.61. Eytelwein gave 0.64 as a mean value, and Weisbach mentions 0.63.

The following mean value will be used in this book, and it should be kept in mind by the student:

$$\text{Coefficient of contraction } c_c = 0.62$$

or, in other words, the minimum cross-section of the jet is 62 percent of that of the orifice. This value, however, undoubtedly varies for different forms of orifices and for the same orifice under different heads, but little is known regarding the extent of these variations or the laws that govern them. Probably c_c is slightly smaller for circles than for squares, and smaller for squares than for rectangles, particularly if the height of the rectangle is long compared with its width. Probably also c_c is larger for low heads than for high heads.

Judd and King in 1906,† using a specially constructed pair of calipers,‡ found the following values for the coefficient of contraction for standard orifices:

Orifice diameter, inches,	0.75	1.00	1.50	2.00	2.50
Coefficient of contraction,	0.6134	0.6115	0.6051	0.6082	0.5955

Prob. 44. The diameter of a circular orifice is 1.995 inches. Three measurements of the diameter of the contracted section of the jet gave 1.55, 1.56, and 1.59 inches. Find the mean coefficient of contraction.

* Philosophiæ Naturalis Principia Mathematica, 1687, Book II, prop. 36.
† Engineering News, Sept. 27, 1906. ‡ Science, March 4, 1904.

Art. 45. Coefficient of Velocity

The coefficient of velocity is the number by which the theoretic velocity of flow from the orifice is to be multiplied in order to give the actual velocity at the least cross-section of the jet. Thus, if c_v be the coefficient of velocity, V the theoretic velocity due to the head on the center of the orifice, and v the actual velocity at the contracted section, then

$$v = c_v V = c_v \sqrt{2gh} \qquad (45)$$

The coefficient of velocity must be less than unity, since the force of gravity cannot generate a greater velocity than that due to the head.

The velocity of flow at the contracted section of the jet cannot be directly measured. To obtain the value of the coefficient of velocity, indirect observations have been taken on the path of the jet. Referring to Art. 25, it will be seen that when a jet flows from an orifice in the vertical side of a vessel, it takes a path whose equation is $y = gx^2/2v^2$, in which x and y are the coordinates of any point of the path measured from vertical and horizontal axes, and v is the velocity at the origin. Now placing for v its value $c_v\sqrt{2gh}$, and solving for c_v, gives

$$c_v = x/2\sqrt{hy}$$

Therefore c_v becomes known by the measurement of the head h and the coordinates x and y. In making this experiment it would be well to have a ring, a little larger than the jet, supported by a stiff frame which can be moved until the jet passes through the ring. The flow of water can then be stopped, and the coordinates of the center of the ring determined. By placing the ring at different points of the path different sets of coordinates can be obtained. The value of x should be measured from the contracted section rather than from the orifice, since v is the velocity at the former point and not at the latter.

By this method of the jet Bossut in two experiments found for the coefficient of velocity the values 0.974 and 0.980, Michelotti in three experiments obtained 0.993, 0.998, and 0.983, and Weisbach deduced 0.978. Great precision cannot be obtained in these determinations, nor indeed is it necessary for the purposes of hydraulic investigation that c_v should be accurately known for standard orifices. As a mean value the following may be kept in the memory:

$$\text{Coefficient of velocity } c_v = 0.98$$

or, the actual velocity of flow at the contracted section is 98 percent of the theoretic velocity. The value of c_v for the standard orifice is greater for high than for low heads, and may probably often exceed 0.99.

Another method of finding the coefficient c_v is to place the orifice horizontal so that the jet will be directed vertically upward, as in Fig. 22. The height to which it rises is the velocity-head $h_0 = v^2/2g$, in which v is the actual velocity $c_v\sqrt{2gh}$. Accordingly, $h_0 = c_v^2 h$, from which c_v may be computed. For example if, under a head of 23 feet, a jet rises to a height of 22 feet, the coefficient of velocity is

$$c_v = \sqrt{h_0/h} = \sqrt{22/23} = 0.978$$

This method, however, fails to give good results for high velocities, owing to the resistance of the air, and moreover it is impossible to measure with precision the height h_0.

For a vertical orifice Poncelet and Lesbros found, in 1828, that the coefficient c_v was sometimes slightly greater than unity, and this was confirmed by Bazin in 1893. This is probably due to the fact that the head is greater for the lower part of the orifice than for the upper part, and hence $\sqrt{2gh}$ does not represent the true theoretic velocity. The same experimenters found no instance of a horizontal orifice where the coefficient exceeded unity.

Since the coefficient of velocity is the ratio between the coefficient of discharge (Art. 46) and the coefficient of contraction, it may be computed from observations on these quantities. Thus Judd and King,* using the average of the coefficients of contraction shown in Art. 44 and the average of the coefficients of discharge shown in Art. 46, found the following:

$$\text{coefficient of velocity} = \frac{\text{coefficient of discharge}}{\text{coefficient of contraction}} = \frac{0.60664}{0.60674} = 0.99983$$

* Engineering News, Sept. 27, 1906.

By traversing the jets with a Pitot tube they also determined the coefficient of velocity to be 0.99993 and showed that the velocity at the contracted area is uniform throughout its cross-section. From the results of these experiments they concluded that the coefficient of velocity is unity and hence adopted the term "frictionless orifice" as descriptive of the particular standard orifices used by them.

Prob. 45. The range of a jet is 13.5 feet on a horizontal plane 2.82 feet below the orifice which is under a head of 14.38 feet. Compute the coefficient of velocity.

Art. 46. Coefficient of Discharge

The coefficient of discharge is the number by which the theoretic discharge is to be multiplied in order to obtain the actual discharge. Thus, if c is the coefficient of discharge, Q the theoretical, and q the actual discharge per second, then

$$q = cQ \qquad (46)_1$$

Here also the coefficient c is a number less than unity.

The coefficient of discharge can be accurately found by allowing the flow from an orifice to fall into a vessel of constant cross-section and measuring the heights of water by the hook gage (Art. 35). Thus q is known, and Q having been computed,

$$c = q/Q \qquad (46)_2$$

For example, a circular orifice of 0.1 foot diameter was kept under a constant head of 4.677 feet; during 5 minutes and $32\frac{1}{5}$ seconds the jet flowed into a measuring vessel which was found to contain 27.28 cubic feet. Here the actual discharge was

$$q = 27.28/332.2 = 0.08212 \text{ cubic feet per second}$$

The theoretic discharge, from formula (30), is

$$Q = \pi \times 0.05^2 \times 8.02\sqrt{4.677} = 0.1361 \text{ cubic feet per second}$$

Then the coefficient of discharge is found to be

$$c = 0.08212/0.1361 = 0.604$$

In this manner thousands of experiments have been made upon different forms of orifices under different heads, for accurate knowledge regarding this coefficient is of great importance in practical hydraulic work.

The following articles contain values of the coefficient of discharge for different kinds of orifices, and it will be seen that in general c is greater for low heads than for high heads, greater for rectangles than for squares, and greater for squares than for circles. Its value ranges from 0.59 to 0.63 or higher, and as a mean to be kept in mind the following value may be stated:

$$\text{Coefficient of discharge } c = 0.61$$

or, the actual discharge from a standard orifice is, on the average, about 61 percent of the theoretic discharge.

The coefficient c may be expressed in terms of the coefficients c_c and c_v. Let a and a' be the areas of the orifice and the cross-section of the contracted jet, and Q and q the theoretic and actual discharge per second. Then, since $a'/a = c_c$,

$$c = \frac{q}{Q} = \frac{a' c_v \sqrt{2gh}}{a\sqrt{2gh}} = \frac{a'}{a} c_v = c_c c_v$$

and therefore the coefficient of discharge is the product of the coefficients of contraction and velocity.

The coefficient of discharge is of greater importance than the coefficients of contraction and velocity, since it is the quantity generally used in making measurements of water. Tabulations of its values for all practical cases are given below.

Prob. 46. The diameter of a contracted circular jet was found to be 0.79 inches, the diameter of the orifice being 1 inch. Under a head of 16 feet the actual discharge per minute was found to be 6.42 cubic feet. Find the coefficient of velocity.

ART. 47. CIRCULAR VERTICAL ORIFICES

Let a circular orifice of diameter d be in the side of a vessel and let h be the head of water on its center. Then, from Art. 22, the theoretic mean velocity is $\sqrt{2gh}$, and from Art. 30 the theoretic discharge is

$$Q = \tfrac{1}{4}\pi d^2 \sqrt{2gh}$$

which applies when h is large compared with d.

To deduce a more exact formula let the radius of the circle be r, and let an elementary strip be drawn at a distance y above

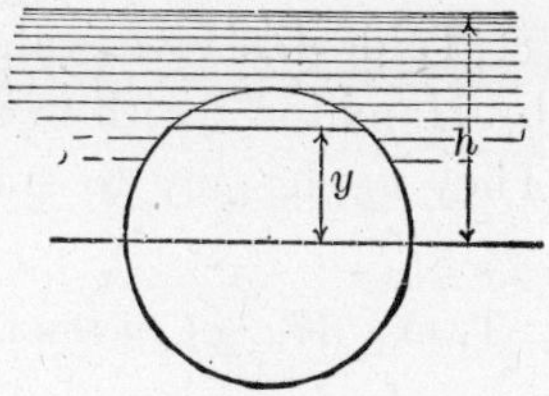

Fig. 47.

the center; the length of this is $2\sqrt{r^2-y^2}$, its area is $2\delta y\sqrt{r^2-y^2}$, and the head upon it is $h-y$. Then the theoretic discharge through this strip is

$$\delta Q = 2\delta y\sqrt{r^2-y^2}\sqrt{2g(h-y)}$$

To integrate this $(h-y)^{\frac{1}{2}}$ is to be expanded by the binomial formula. Then it may be written

$$\delta Q = 2\sqrt{2gh}\left[(r^2-y^2)^{\frac{1}{2}} - \frac{(r^2-y^2)^{\frac{1}{2}}y}{2h} - \frac{(r^2-y^2)^{\frac{1}{2}}y^2}{8h^2} - \text{etc.}\right]\delta y$$

Each term of this expression is now integrable, and taking the limits of y as $+r$ and $-r$ the entire circle is covered, and Q is found. Finally, replacing r by $\frac{1}{2}d$ there results

$$Q = \tfrac{1}{4}\pi d^2\sqrt{2gh}\left[1 - \frac{(d/h)^2}{128} - \frac{5(d/h)^4}{16384} - \text{etc.}\right]$$

which is the theoretic discharge from the circular orifice.

It is plain that this formula gives values which are always less than those found from the approximate formula of the first paragraph. Thus for $h = d$ the quantity in the parenthesis is 0.992 and for $h = 2d$ it is 0.998. Hence the error in using the approximate formula is less than three-tenths of one percent when the head on the center of the orifice is greater than twice its diameter.

For most cases, then, the actual discharge from a circular vertical orifice of area a may be computed from

$$q = c \cdot a\sqrt{2gh} = 8.02\, ca\sqrt{h} \qquad (47)_1$$

in which c is the coefficient of discharge. When h is smaller than two or three times the diameter of the orifice, and when precision is required, then

$$q = [1 - 0.007812(d/h)^2 - 0.000306(d/h)^4]\, 8.02\, ca\sqrt{h} \qquad (47)_2$$

is the formula to be used. Here a may be taken from Table F (Art. 205) for the given diameter expressed in feet, h is to be taken in feet, and then q will be in cubic feet per second.

Table 47*a* gives values of c for circular orifices as determined by Hamilton Smith in a discussion of all the best experiments.* They apply only to standard orifices with definite inner edges.

TABLE 47*a*. COEFFICIENTS FOR CIRCULAR VERTICAL ORIFICES

Head *h* in Feet	Diameter of Orifice in Feet						
	0.02	0.04	0.07	0.1	0.2	0.6	1.0
0.4		0.637	0.624	0.618			
0.6	0.655	.630	.618	.613	0.601	0.593	
0.8	.648	.626	.615	.610	.601	.594	0.590
1.0	.644	.623	.612	.608	.600	.595	.591
1.5	.637	.618	.608	.605	.600	.596	.593
2.0	.632	.614	.607	.604	.599	.597	.595
2.5	.629	.612	.605	.603	.599	.598	.596
3.0	.627	.611	.604	.603	.599	.598	.597
4.0	.623	.609	.603	.602	.599	.597	.596
6.0	.618	.607	.602	.600	.598	.597	.596
8.0	.614	.605	.601	.600	.598	.596	.596
10.0	.611	.603	.599	.598	.597	.596	.595
20.0	.601	.599	.597	.596	.596	.596	.594
50.0	.596	.595	.594	.594	.594	.594	.593
100.0	.593	.592	.592	.592	.592	.592	.592

The table shows that the coefficient of discharge decreases as the size of the orifice increases, and that in general it also decreases as the head increases. In this table the coefficients found above the horizontal lines in the last three columns are to be used in the exact formula $(47)_2$ and all others in the approximate formula $(47)_1$.

For example, let it be required to find the discharge through a standard circular orifice, 2 inches in diameter, under a head of 2.35 feet. First, 2 inches = 0.1667 feet, and by interpolation in Table 47*a* the coefficient c is found to be 0.602. Next, from Table F at the end of this book, the area a is 0.02182 square feet. Then formula $(47)_1$ gives the discharge q as 0.161 cubic feet per second. As the coefficient is probably liable to an error

* Hydraulics (London and New York, 1886), p. 59.

of one or two units in the last figure, the third figure of this value of q is subject to the same uncertainty.

Judd and King * determined in 1906 the following values of the coefficient of discharge for circular vertical orifices:

Orifice diameter, inches	0.75	1.00	1.50	2.00	2.50
Coefficient of discharge	0.611	0.6097	0.6085	0.6083	0.5956

The heads under which the observations were made ranged from 5 to 90 feet and the results showed no appreciable change in the coefficient of discharge due to increased head. For example the following are part of the results found for a 2-inch orifice:

Head in feet =	5.00	9.08	17.79	36.12	57.70	92.01
Coefficient c =	0.6084	0.6083	0.6080	0.6082	0.6081	0.6080

Bilton† in 1907 made a series of experiments on orifices, ranging from 0.025 to 0.75 inches in diameter and determined the following coefficients for varying heads.

TABLE 47*b*. COEFFICIENTS OF DISCHARGE FOR SMALL ORIFICES

Head h in Feet	Diameter of Orifice in Inches								
	0.025	0.05	0.10	0.20	0.30	0.40	0.50	0.60	0.75
0.50	0.748	0.722	0.690	0.673	0.665	0.652	0.645	0.644	0.632
1.00	.748	.717	.680	.659	.647	.636	.630	.627	.618
2.00	.748	.708	.666	.642	.630	.624	.621	.618	.613
4.00	.748	.697	.652	.630	.627	.624	.621	.618	.613
6.00	.748	.688	.647	.630	.627	.624	.621	.618	.613
8.00		.683	.645	.630	.627	.624	.621	.618	.613

Experiments made in 1908 by Strickland‡ on standard orifices 1 and 2 inches in diameter gave results for the coefficient of discharge very closely represented by the formula

$$c = 0.5925 + 0.018/h^{\frac{1}{2}}d^{\frac{2}{3}}$$

* Engineering News, Sept. 27, 1906.

† Proceedings Victorian Institute of Engineers, Australia, 1908.

‡ Transactions Canadian Society of Civil Engineers, 1909, vol. 23, p. 198.

where h is in feet and d in inches. Applying this formula to an orifice 2 inches in diameter under a head of 19 feet, c is found to be 0.5951 while the experiments indicated a value of 0.5947.

Prob. 47. Compute the probable actual discharge from a circular orifice 8 inches in diameter, under a head of 15 inches.

Art. 48. Square Vertical Orifices

If the size of an orifice in the side of a vessel is small compared with the head, the theoretic velocity of the outflowing water may be taken as $\sqrt{2gh}$, where h is the head on the center of the orifice. For a rectangular orifice under this condition the theoretic discharge is

$$Q = bd\sqrt{2gh}$$

where b is the width and d the depth of the orifice. When b is equal to d, the rectangle becomes a square.

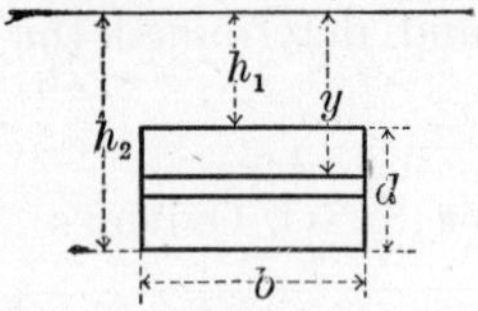

Fig. 48.

To deduce a more exact formula, let h_1 be the head on the upper edge of the orifice and h_2 that on the lower edge. Consider an elementary strip of area $b \cdot \delta y$ at a depth y below the water level. The velocity of flow through this elementary strip is $\sqrt{2gy}$, and the theoretic discharge per second through it is

$$\delta Q = b\delta y\sqrt{2gy}$$

Integrating this between the limits h_2 and h_1, there results

$$Q = \tfrac{2}{3} b\sqrt{2g}(h_2^{\frac{3}{2}} - h_1^{\frac{3}{2}})$$

which is the true theoretic discharge from the orifice.

To ascertain the error caused by using the approximate formula, let h be the head on the center of the rectangle; then $h_2 = h + \frac{1}{2}d$ and $h_1 = h - \frac{1}{2}d$. Developing by the binomial formula the values of $h_2^{\frac{3}{2}}$ and $h_1^{\frac{3}{2}}$, the last formula becomes

$$Q = bd\sqrt{2gh}\left[1 - \frac{(d/h)^2}{96} - \frac{(d/h)^4}{2048} - \text{etc.}\right]$$

and this shows that the discharge computed by using the approximate formula is always too great. For $h = d$, the quantity in the parenthesis is 0.989, and for $h = 2d$, it is 0.997. Accordingly, the error of the approximate formula is only three-tenths of one percent when the head on the center of the rectangle is twice the depth of the orifice.

For most cases, then, the actual discharge from a square vertical orifice may be very approximately found from

$$q = c \cdot b^2 \sqrt{2gh} = 8.02\, cb^2 \sqrt{h} \qquad (48)_1$$

where b is the side of the square and c is the coefficient of discharge. When h is smaller than two or three times the side of the orifice, and when precision is required,

$$q = 5.347\, cb(h_2^{\frac{3}{2}} - h_1^{\frac{3}{2}}) \qquad (48)_2$$

is the formula to be used. The linear quantities are to be taken in feet, and then q will be in cubic feet per second.

Table 48 gives values of the coefficient c for standard square orifices, taken from a more extended one formed by Hamilton

TABLE 48. COEFFICIENTS FOR SQUARE VERTICAL ORIFICES

Head h in Feet	Side of the Square in Feet						
	0.02	0.04	0.07	0.1	0.2	0.6	1.0
0.4		0.643	0.628	0.621			
0.6	0.660	.636	.623	.617	0.605	0.598	
0.8	.652	.631	.620	.615	.605	.600	0.597
1.0	.648	.628	.618	.613	.605	.601	.599
1.5	.641	.622	.614	.610	.605	.602	.601
2.0	.637	.619	.612	.608	.605	.604	.602
2.5	.634	.617	.610	.607	.605	.604	.602
3.0	.632	.616	.609	.607	.605	.604	.603
4.0	.628	.614	.608	.606	.605	.603	.602
6.0	.623	.612	.607	.605	.604	.603	.602
8.0	.619	.610	.606	.605	.604	.603	.602
10.0	.616	.608	.605	.604	.603	.602	.601
20.0	.606	.604	.602	.602	.602	.601	.600
50.0	.602	.601	.601	.600	.600	.599	.599
100.0	.599	.598	.598	.598	.598	.598	.598

Smith in 1886 by the discussion of all the best experiments. It is seen that the coefficient decreases as the size of the orifice increases and as the head increases. Comparing this table with Table 47a it is seen that the coefficient of discharge for a square is always slightly larger than that for a circle having a diameter equal to the side of the square. The values above the horizontal lines in the last three columns are to be used in the exact formula $(48)_2$ when precision is required, and all other values in the approximate formula $(48)_1$.

There are few recorded experiments on large square orifices. Ellis measured the discharge from a vertical orifice 2 feet square* and deduced the following coefficients for use in the approximate formula:

for $h = 2.07$ feet, $c = 0.611$
for $h = 3.05$ feet, $c = 0.597$
for $h = 3.54$ feet, $c = 0.604$

which indicate that a mean value of 0.60 may be used for large square orifices under low heads.

Prob. 48. Find from the table the coefficient for an orifice 3 inches square when the head on its center is 1.8 feet.

Art. 49. Rectangular Vertical Orifices

The theoretic formulas of Art. 48 apply to rectangles of width b and depth d, and the approximate formula for computing the actual discharge is

$$q = cbd\sqrt{2gh} = 8.02\, cbd\sqrt{h} \tag{49}$$

in which c is the coefficient of discharge, b the width and d the depth of the rectangular orifice, and h the head on its center.

Table 49 gives values of the coefficient c which have been compiled and rearranged from the discussion given by Fanning.† It is seen that the variation of c with the head follows the same law as for circles and squares. It is also seen that for a rectangle of constant breadth the coefficient increases as the depth decreases, from which it is to be inferred that for a rectangle of constant depth the coefficient increases with the breadth,

* Transactions American Society of Civil Engineers, 1876, vol. 5, p. 92.
† Treatise on Water Supply Engineering (New York, 1888), p. 205.

TABLE 49. COEFFICIENTS FOR RECTANGULAR ORIFICES
1 FOOT WIDE

Head h in Feet	Depth of Orifice in Feet						
	0.125	0.25	0.50	0.75	1.0	1.5	2.0
0.4	0.634	0.633	0.622				
0.6	.633	.633	.619	0.614			
0.8	.633	.633	.618	.612	0.608		
1.0	.632	.632	.618	.612	.606	0.626	
1.5	.630	.631	.618	.611	.605	.626	0.628
2.0	.629	.630	.617	.611	.605	.624	.630
2.5	.628	.628	.616	.611	.605	.616	.627
3.0	.627	.627	.615	.610	.605	.614	.619
4.0	.624	.624	.614	.609	.605	.612	.616
6.0	.615	.615	.609	.604	.602	.606	.610
8.0	.609	.607	.603	.602	.601	.602	.604
10.0	.606	.603	.601	.601	.601	.601	.602
20.0				.601	.601	.601	.602

and this is confirmed by other experiments. The value of c for a rectangular orifice is seen to be only slightly larger than that for a square whose side is equal to the depth of the rectangle. All the coefficients in this table are for the above approximate formula, since that formula was used in computing them.

A comparison of the values of c for the orifice one foot square with those in the last article shows that the two sets of coefficients disagree, these being about one percent greater. This is probably duc to the less precise character and smaller number of experiments from which they were deduced.

Prob. 49. What constant head is required to discharge 5 cubic feet of water per second through an orifice 3 inches deep and 12 inches long?

ART. 50. VELOCITY OF APPROACH

It was shown in Art. 24 that the theoretic velocity of flow from an orifice is greater then $\sqrt{2gh}$ when the ratio of the cross-section of the orifice to that of the vessel or tank is not small. The same is true for the actual velocity, but formula $(24)_1$ must be modified because it takes no account of the contraction of the jet. Let v be the velocity at the contracted section of the jet and a' the area of that section; let v_1 be the velocity through the horizontal cross-section A of the vessel; then $a'v = Av_1$. But if a be the area of the orifice and c_c the coefficient of contraction, then a' equals ac_c and hence $c_c av = Av_1$. Now the effective head on the orifice is

$$H = h + \frac{v_1^2}{2g}$$

and the velocity v is given by $c_v\sqrt{2gH}$ where c_v is the coefficient of velocity. Substituting in the last equation $v^2/2gc_v^2$ for H and $c_c va/A$ for v_1, and noting that $c_v c_c$ is equal to the coefficient of discharge c, it reduces to

$$v = c_v\sqrt{\frac{2gh}{1 - c^2(a/A)^2}} \qquad (50)_1$$

which is the velocity of the jet at a section distant from the orifice about one-half its diameter. The discharge q is found by multiplying this by the area $c_c a$ of that cross-section, whence

$$q = ca\sqrt{\frac{2gh}{1 - c^2(a/A)^2}} = a\sqrt{\frac{2gh}{(1/c)^2 - (a/A)^2}} \qquad (50)_2$$

is the formula for the actual discharge, and this includes no coefficient except that of discharge.

These formulas apply to orifices of any kind, and when c equals unity, they reduce to the theoretic expressions established in Art. 24. When a/A is less than $1/5$, as is almost always the case in practice, the last formula may be written, with sufficient precision,

$$q = (1 + \tfrac{1}{2}(ca/A)^2)ca\sqrt{2gh} \qquad (50)_3$$

For example, let a square tank, 4×4 feet in horizontal cross-section, have a standard square orifice one square foot in area, and let the head on its center be 16 feet. From Table 48 the coefficient of discharge is 0.60, and the formula gives

$$q = (1 + 0.0007) \times 0.60 \times 1 \times 8.02 \times 4 = 19.3 \text{ cubic feet per second}$$

For this case it is seen that the influence of velocity of approach is expressed by the addition of 0.0007 to unity, which is an increase of less than one-tenth of one percent. In general the increase in discharge due to velocity of approach is expressed, when a/A is not greater than $1/5$, by $\frac{1}{2}\, c^3 a(a/A)^2 \sqrt{2gh}$.

A common case is that where the vessel or tank is of large horizontal and small vertical cross-section, and where the water approaches the orifice with a horizontal velocity, as in a canal or conduit. Here let A be the area of the vertical cross-section of the vessel, a the area of the orifice, and h the head on its center. Then, if the head h be large compared with the depth of the orifice, the same reasoning applies as in Art. 24, the theoretic velocity is given by $(24)_1$ and the actual discharge by $(50)_2$.

When the head h is not large, let h_1 and h_2 be the heads on the upper and lower edges of the orifice, which is taken as rectangular and of the width b. Let v be the velocity of approach, which is regarded as uniform over the area A. Then by the same reasoning as that in Art. 24, the theoretic velocity in the plane of the orifice at the depth y below the water level is given by $V^2 = 2gy + v^2$.

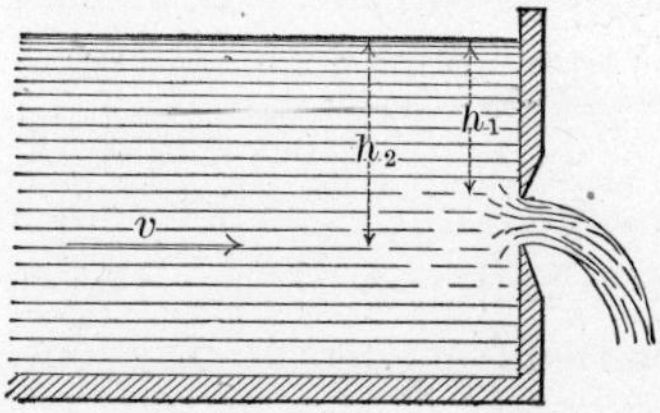

Fig. 50.

The theoretic discharge through an elementary strip of the length b and the depth δy now is

$$\delta Q = (2gy + v^2)^{\frac{1}{2}}\, b\delta y$$

and, by integration between the limits h_2 and h_1, the total theoretic discharge is found. If $v^2/2g$ be replaced by h_0, the head which would cause the velocity v, the theoretic discharge is

$$Q = \tfrac{2}{3}\, b \sqrt{2g}\, [(h_2 + h_0)^{\frac{3}{2}} - (h_1 + h_0)^{\frac{3}{2}}] \qquad (50)_4$$

and the actual discharge q is found by multiplying this by a coefficient of discharge. When there is no velocity of approach, the formula reduces to that found in Art. 49 for this case.

Prob. 50a. When n is a small quantity compared with unity, show that $(1 + n)^{\frac{1}{2}} = 1 + \frac{1}{2}\, n$, and that $1 \,/\, (1 + n) = 1 - n$. Deduce formula $(50)_3$ from $(50)_2$.

Prob. 50*b*. In the case of horizontal approach, as seen in Fig. 50, compute the discharge when $b = 4$ feet, $h_2 = 0.8$ feet, $h_1 = 0$, $v = 2.5$ feet per second, and $c = 0.6$.

Art. 51. Submerged Orifices

It is shown in Art. 23 that the effective head h which causes the flow from a submerged orifice is the difference in level between the two water surfaces. The discharge from such an orifice, its inner edge being a sharp definite one, as in Fig. 43*a*, has been found by experiment to be slightly less than when the flow occurs freely into the air, and hence the values of the coefficients of discharge are slightly smaller than those given in Tables 47*a*, 47*b*, 48, 49. For large orifices and large heads the difference is very small, and for orifices one inch square under six inches head it is about 2 percent. In all cases of submerged orifices the discharge is to be found from $q = ca\sqrt{2gh}$.

Table 51 gives values of the coefficient of discharge for submerged orifices as determined from experiments made by Hamilton Smith in 1884. The depth of submergence of the orifices varied from 0.57 to 0.73 foot. As a mean value of the coefficient of discharge for standard submerged orifices 0.6 is frequently used.

Table 51. Coefficients for Submerged Orifices

Effective Head in Feet	Size of Orifice in Feet				
	Circle 0.05	Square 0.05	Circle 0.1	Square 0.1	Rectangle 0.05 × 0.3
0.5	0.615	0.619	0.603	0.608	0.623
1.0	.610	.614	.602	.606	.622
1.5	.607	.612	.600	.605	.621
2.0	.605	.610	.599	.604	.620
2.5	.603	.608	.598	.604	.619
3.0	.602	.607	.598	.604	.618
4.0	.601	.606	.598	.604	

The theoretic discharge from a submerged orifice is the same for the same effective head h, whatever be its distance below water level. The theoretic velocity in all parts of the orifice is the same, as may be proved from Fig. 51, where the triangles *ACD* and *BCE* represent the distribution of pressure on *AC* and *BC* when the orifice is closed (Art. 17). Making *CF* equal to *CE* and drawing *BF*, the unit-pressure on *BC* is seen to have the constant value *DF*. Now when the orifice is opened, the velocity at any point depends on the unit-pressure there acting, as seen by $(23)_1$, and accordingly the theoretic velocity is uniform over the section. For this reason the coefficients of discharge probably vary less with the head than for the previous cases.

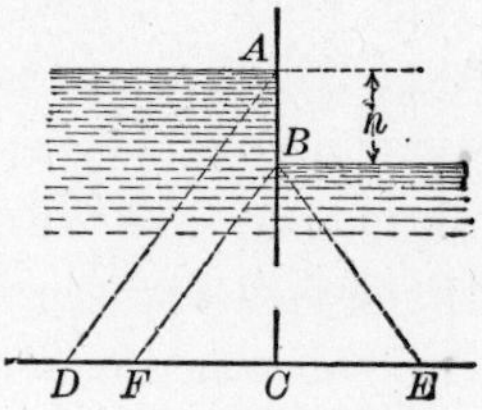

Fig. 51.

Submerged orifices are used for canal-locks, tide-gates, filter-beds, for the discharge of waste water through dams, and for the admission of water from a canal to a power-plant. The inner edges of such orifices are usually rounded, and the coefficient of discharge may then be higher than 0.9 (Art. 53).

Prob. 51. An orifice one inch square in a gate, such as shown in Fig. 19*a*, is 4.1 feet below the higher water level and 3.1 feet below the lower level. Compute the discharge in cubic feet per second, and also in gallons per minute.

Art. 52. Suppression of the Contraction

When a vertical orifice has its lower edge at the bottom of the reservoir, as shown at *A* in Fig. 52, the particles of water flowing through its lower portion move in lines nearly perpendicular to the plane of the orifice, or the contraction of the jet does not form on the lower side. This is called a case of suppressed or incomplete contraction. The same thing occurs, but in a lesser degree, when the lower edge of the orifice is near the bottom, as shown at *B*. In like manner, if an orifice be placed so that one of its vertical edges is at or near a side of the reservoir, as at *C*, the contraction of the jet is suppressed upon one side, and if it be placed at the lower corner of the reservoir suppression occurs both upon one side and the lower part of the jet.

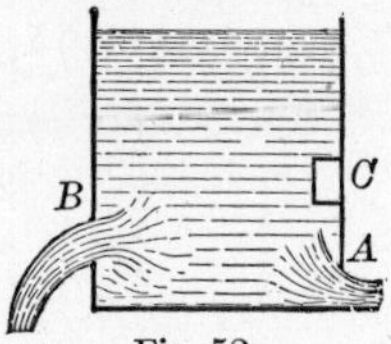

Fig. 52.

The effect of suppressing the contraction is, of course, to increase the cross-section of the jet at the place where full contraction would otherwise occur, and it is found by experiment that the discharge is likewise increased. Experiments also show that more or less suppression of the contraction will occur unless each edge of the orifice is at a distance at least equal to three times its least diameter from the sides or bottom of the reservoir.

The experiments of Lesbros and Bidone furnish the means of estimating the increased discharge caused by suppression of the contraction. They indicate that for square orifices with contraction suppressed on one side the coefficient of discharge is increased about 3.5 percent, and with contraction suppressed on two sides about 7.5 percent. For a rectangular orifice with the contraction suppressed on the bottom edge the percentages are larger, being about 6 or 7 percent when the length of the rectangle is four times its height, and from 8 to 12 percent when the length is twenty times the height. The percentage of increase, moreover, varies with the head, the lowest heads giving the lowest percentages.

It is apparent that suppression of the contraction should be avoided if accurate results are desired. The experiments from which the above conclusions are deduced were made upon small orifices with heads less than 6 feet, and it is not known how they will apply to large orifices under high heads. For a rectangular orifice of length about three times its height, with contraction suppressed on the ends and bottom, the coefficient of discharge is probably about 0.75.

Prob. 52. Compute the probable discharge from a vertical orifice one foot square when the head on its upper edge is 4 feet, the contraction being suppressed on the lower edge. Compute the discharge for the same data when contraction is suppressed on all sides.

Art. 53. Orifices with Rounded Edges

When the inner edge of the orifice is made rounded, as shown in Fig. 53, the contraction of the jet is modified, and the discharge is increased. With a slight degree of rounding, as at A, a partial contraction occurs; but with a more complete rounding, as at C, the particles of water issue perpendicular to the plane

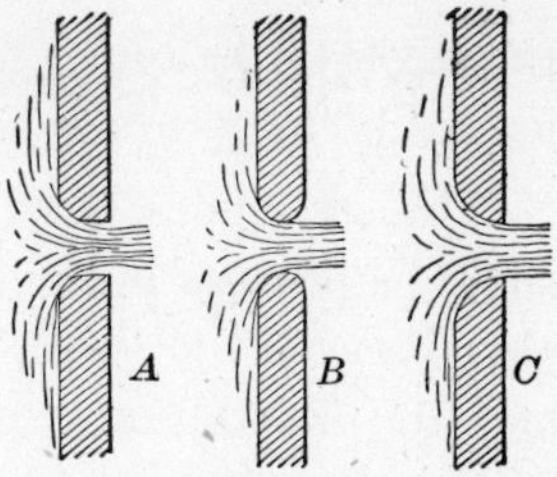

Fig. 53.

of the orifice and there is no contraction of the jet. If a be the area of the least cross-section of the orifice, and a' that of the jet, the coefficient of contraction as defined in Art. 44 is

$$c_c = a'/a \qquad (53)$$

For a standard orifice with sharp inner edges (Art. 43) the mean value of c_c is 0.62, but for an orifice with rounded edges c_c may have any value between 0.62 and 1.0, depending upon the degree of rounding.

The coefficient of discharge c for standard orifices has a mean value of about 0.61; this is increased with rounded edges and may have any value between 0.61 and 1.0. A rounded interior edge in an orifice is therefore always a source of error when the object of the orifice is the measurement of the discharge. If a contract provides that water shall be gaged by standard orifices, care should always be taken that the interior edges do not become rounded either by accident or by design.

Prob. 53. When an orifice with rounded edges has a coefficient of velocity of 0.88 and a coefficient of discharge of 0.75, find the coefficient of contraction of the jet.

Art. 54. Water Measurement by Orifices

In order that water may be accurately measured by the use of orifices many precautions must be taken, some of which have already been noted, but may here be briefly recapitulated. The area of the orifice should be small compared with the size of the reservoir in order that velocity of approach may not exist, or if this cannot be avoided, it should be taken into account by formula $(50)_1$. The inner edge of the orifice must have a definite right-angled corner, and its dimensions are to be accurately determined. If the orifice be in wood, care should be taken that the inner surface be smooth, and that it be kept free from the slime which often accompanies the flow of water, even when apparently clear. That no suppression of the contraction may occur, the edges of the orifice should not be nearer than three times its least dimension to a side of the reservoir.

Orifices under very low heads should be avoided, because slight variations in the head produce relatively large errors, and also because the coefficients of discharge vary more rapidly and are probably not so well determined as for cases where the head is greater than four times the depth. If the head be very low on an orifice, vortices will form which render any estimation of the discharge unreliable.

The measurement of the head, if required with precision, must be made with the hook gage described in Art. 35. For heads greater than two or three feet the readings of an ordinary glass gage placed upon the outside of the reservoir will usually prove sufficient, as this can be read to hundredths of a foot with accuracy. An error of 0.01 foot when the head is 3.00 feet produces an error in the computed discharge of less than two-tenths of one per cent; for, the discharges being proportional to the square roots of the heads, the square root of 3.01 divided by the square root of 3.00 equals 1.0017. For the rude measurements in connection with the miner's inch a common foot-rule will usually suffice.

The effect of temperature upon the discharge remains to be noticed; this is only appreciable with small orifices and under low heads and hence such orifices and heads are not desirable in precise measurements. Unwin found that the discharge was diminished one percent by a rise of 144° in temperature; his orifice was a circle 0.033 feet in diameter under heads ranging from 1.0 to 1.5 feet. Hamilton Smith found that the discharge was diminished one percent by a rise of 55° in temperature; his orifice was a circle 0.02 feet in diameter under heads ranging from 0.56 to 3.2 feet.

The coefficients given in the tables of this chapter may be supposed liable to a probable error of about two units in the third decimal place: thus a coefficient 0.615 should really be written 0.615 ± 0.002; that is, the actual value is as likely to be between 0.613 and 0.617 as to be outside of those limits. The probable error in computed discharges due to the coefficient is hence nearly one-half of one percent. To this are added the errors due to inaccuracy of observation, so that it is thought that the probable error of careful work with standard circular orifices is at least one percent. The computed discharges are hence liable to error in the third significant figure, so that it is useless to carry numerical results beyond three figures when based upon tabular coefficients. As a precise method of measuring small quantities of water, standard orifices take a high rank when the observations are conducted with care.

Prob. 54. If e is a small error in measuring the head h, show that the error in the computed discharge q due to this cause is $qe/2h$.

Art. 55. The Miner's Inch

The miner's inch may be roughly defined to be the quantity of water which will flow from a vertical standard orifice one inch square, when the head on the center of the orifice is $6\frac{1}{2}$ inches. From Table 48 the coefficient of discharge is seen to be about 0.623 and accordingly the actual discharge from the orifice in cubic feet per second is $q = \frac{1}{144} \times 0.623 \times 8.02 \sqrt{6.5/12} = 0.0255$ and the discharge in one minute is $60 \times 0.255 = 1.53$ cubic feet. The mean value of one miner's inch is therefore about 1.5 cubic feet per minute.

The actual value of the miner's inch, however, differs considerably in different localities. Bowie states that in different counties of California it ranges from 1.20 to 1.76 cubic feet per minute.* The reason for these variations is due to the fact that when water is bought for mining or irrigating purposes, a much larger quantity than one miner's inch is required, and hence larger orifices than one square inch are needed. Thus at Smartsville a vertical orifice or module 4 inches deep and 250 inches long, with a head of 7 inches above the top edge, is said to furnish 1000 miner's inches. Again, at Columbia Hill, a module 12 inches deep and $12\frac{3}{4}$ inches wide, with a head of 6 inches above the upper edge, is said to furnish 200 miner's inches. In Montana the customary method of measurement is through a vertical rectangle,

* Treatise on Hydraulic Mining (New York, 1885), p. 268.

1 inch deep, with a head on the center of the orifice of 4 inches, and the number of miner's inches is said to be the same as the number of linear inches in the rectangle; thus under the given head an orifice 1 inch deep and 60 inches long would furnish 60 miner's inches. The discharge of this is said to be about 1.25 cubic feet per minute, or 75 cubic feet per hour.

The following are the values of the miner's inch in different parts of the United States; in California and Montana it is established by law that 40 miner's inches shall be the equivalent of one cubic foot per second, and in Colorado 38.4 miner's inches is the equivalent. In other States and Territories there is no legal value, but by common agreement 50 miner's inches is the equivalent of one cubic foot per second in Arizona, Idaho, Nevada, and Utah; this makes the miner's inch equal to 1.2 cubic feet per minute.

A module is an orifice which is used in selling water, and which under a constant head is to furnish a given number of miner's inches, or a given quantity per second. The size and proportions of modules vary greatly in different localities, but in all cases the important feature to be observed is that the head should be maintained nearly constant in order that the consumer may receive the amount of water for which he bargains, and no more.

The simplest method of maintaining a constant head is by placing the module in a chamber which is provided with a gate that regulates the entrance of water from the main reservoir or canal. This gate is raised or lowered by an inspector once or twice a day so as to keep the surface of the water in the chamber at a given mark. This plan is a costly one, on account of the wages of the inspector, except in works where many modules are used and where a daily inspection is necessary in any event, and it is not well adapted to cases where there are frequent and considerable fluctuations in the water surface of the feeding canal.

Numerous methods have been devised to secure a constant head by automatic appliances; for instance, the gate which admits water into the chamber may be made to rise and fall by means of a float upon the surface; the module itself may be made to decrease in size when the water rises, and to increase when it falls, by a gate or by a tapering plug which moves in and out and whose motion is controlled by a float. In another variety the head on an orifice is kept constant by placing it in the side of a vessel which is movable and whose vertical movement is proportional to the rise or fall of the water in the feeding channel or reservoir. These self-acting contrivances, however, are liable to get out of order, and require to be inspected more or less frequently.* Another method is to have the water flow over the crest of a weir as soon as it reaches a certain height.†

The use of the miner's inch, or of a module, as a standard for selling water, is awkward and confusing, and for the sake of uniformity it is greatly to be desired that water should always be bought and sold by the cubic foot per second. Only in this way can comparisons readily be made, and the consumer be sure of obtaining exact value for his money.

Prob. 55. When a miner's inch is 1.57 cubic feet per minute, how many miner's inches will be furnished by a module 2 inches deep and 50 inches long with a head of 6 inches above the upper edge?

Art. 56. Loss of Energy or Head

A jet of water flowing from an orifice possesses by virtue of its velocity a certain kinetic energy, which is always less than the theoretic potential energy due to the head (Art. 26). Let h be the head and W the weight of water discharged per second, then the theoretic energy per second or the power of the jet, is

$$K = Wh$$

Let v be the actual velocity of the water at the contracted section of the jet; then the actual energy per second of the water as it passes that section is

$$k = W \cdot v^2/2g$$

Now let c_v be the coefficient of velocity (Art. 45); then

$$v^2 = c_v^2 \cdot 2gh$$

and accordingly the actual energy of the jet per second is

$$k = c_v^2 Wh$$

* For descriptions of several, see Engineering News, Dec. 17, 1908.

† Foote, Transactions American Society Civil Engineers, 1887, vol. 16, p. 134.

The efficiency of the jet, or the ratio of the actual to the theoretic energy, now is

$$e = k/K = c_v^2 \tag{56}$$

which is a number always less than unity.

For the standard orifice the mean value of c_v is 0.98, and hence a mean value of c_v^2 is 0.96. The actual energy of a jet from such an orifice is hence about 96 percent of the theoretic energy, and the loss of energy is about 4 percent. This loss is due to the frictional resistance of the edges of the orifice, whereby the energy of pressure or velocity is changed into heat.

In the plane of the standard orifice the velocity is slower than at the contracted section since the area there is greater. If v_1 be this velocity, a the area of the orifice, and a' that of the jet at the contracted section, it is clear that $av_1 = a'v$ or $v_1 = c_c v$, where c_c is the coefficient of contraction 0.62. The kinetic energy in the plane of the orifice is $W \cdot v_1^2/2g$, or $0.37\ Wv^2/2\ g$, or $0.37\ Wh$. Thus, in the plane of the orifice 4 percent of the theoretic energy is lost overcoming friction, 37 percent is in the form of kinetic energy, and the remaining 59 percent exists in the form of pressure energy. This 59 percent is transformed into kinetic energy when the water has reached the contracted section.

In hydraulics the terms "energy" and "head" are often used as synonymous, although really energy is proportional to head. Thus the pressure-head that causes the flow is h and the velocity-head of the issuing jet is $v^2/2g$, and these are proportional to the theoretic and effective energies. The lost head h' is the difference of these, or

$$h' = h - \frac{v^2}{2g}$$

and this applies not only to an orifice but to any tube or pipe. Inserting for v^2 its value, this becomes

$$h' = (1 - c_v^2)\,h$$

which gives the lost head in terms of the total head. Inserting for h its value in terms of v reduces this to

$$h' = \left(\frac{1}{c_v^2} - 1\right)\frac{v^2}{2g}$$

which gives the lost head in terms of the velocity-head. Thus, for an orifice whose coefficient of velocity is 0.97 the lost head h' is 0.060 h or 0.063 $v^2/2g$. For the standard orifice the lost head h' is 0.040 h or 0.041 $v^2/2g$. For the standard orifice h' can also be expressed as 0.11 $v_1^2/2g$, where v_1 is the velocity in the plane of the orifice.

Prob. 56. What is the loss of head in an orifice whose coefficient of velocity is unity?

Art. 57. Discharge under a Dropping Head

If a vessel or reservoir receives no inflow of water while an orifice is open, the head drops and the discharge decreases in each successive second. Let H be the head on the orifice at a certain instant, and h the head t seconds later; let A be the area of the uniform horizontal cross-section of the vessel, and a the area of the orifice. Then, the theoretic time t is given by the second formula in Art. 32. To determine the actual time the coefficient of discharge must be introduced. Referring to the demonstration, it is seen that $a\sqrt{2gy}\cdot\delta t$ is the theoretic discharge in the time δt; hence the actual discharge is $c \cdot a\sqrt{2gy}\delta t$, and accordingly a in the above-mentioned formula is to be replaced by ca, or

$$t = \frac{2A}{ca\sqrt{2g}}(\sqrt{H} - \sqrt{h}) \qquad (57)_1$$

is the practical formula for the time in which the water level drops from H to h. In using this formula c is to be taken from the tables of this chapter, an average value being selected corresponding to the average head.

Experiments have been made to determine the value of c by the help of this formula; the liquid being allowed to flow, A, a, H, h, and t being observed, whence c is computed. In this way c for mercury has been found to be about 0.62.* Only approximate mean values can be found in this manner, since c varies with the head, particularly for small orifices (Art. 47). For a large orifice the time of descent is usually so small that it

* Downing's Elements of Practical Hydraulics (London, 1875), p. 187.

cannot be noted with precision, and the friction of the liquid on the sides of the vessel may also introduce an element of uncertainty. Further, when h is small, a vortex forms which renders the formula unreliable. This experiment has therefore little value except as illustrating and confirming the truth of the theoretic formulas.

The discharge in one second when the head is H at the beginning of that second is found as follows: the above equation may be written in the form

$$\sqrt{H} - tca\sqrt{2g}/2A = \sqrt{h}$$

By squaring both members, transposing, and multiplying by A, this may be reduced to

$$A\,(H-h) = tca\sqrt{2g}\,(\sqrt{H} - tca\sqrt{2g}/4\,A)$$

But the first member of this equation is the quantity discharged in t seconds; therefore the discharge in the first second is

$$q = ca\sqrt{2g}\,(\sqrt{H} - ca\sqrt{2g}/4\,A)$$

If $A = \infty$, this becomes $ca\sqrt{2gh}$, which should be the case, for then H would remain constant. At the end of the first second the water level has fallen the amount q/A, so that the head at the beginning of the second second is $H - q/A$.

For example, let an orifice one foot square in a reservoir of 10 square feet section be under a head of 9 feet, and $c = 0.602$. Then the discharge in one second is 13.9 cubic feet, and the head drops to 7.61 feet. The discharge in the next second is 12.7 cubic feet, and the head drops to 6.34 feet.

Prob. 57. Find the time required to discharge 480 gallons of water from an orifice 2 inches in diameter at 8 feet below the water level when the cross-section of the tank is 4 × 4 feet.

Art. 58. Emptying and Filling a Canal Lock

A canal lock is emptied by opening one or more orifices in the lower gates. Let a be their area and H the head of water on them when the lock is full; let A be the area of the horizontal cross-section of the lock. Then in the first formula of the last article $h = 0$, and the time of emptying the lock is

$$t = 2A\sqrt{H}/ca\sqrt{2g} \tag{58}$$

If the discharge be free into the air, H is the distance from the center of the orifice to the level of the water in the lock when filled; but if, as is usually the case, the orifices be below the level of the water in the tail bay, H is the difference in height between the two water levels. The tail bay is regarded as so large compared with the lock that its water level remains constant during the time of emptying.

For example, let it be required to find the time of emptying a canal lock 80 feet long and 20 feet wide through two orifices each of 4 square feet area, the head upon which is 16 feet when the lock is filled. Using for c the value 0.6 for orifices with square inner edges, the formula gives

$$t = \frac{2 \times 80 \times 20 \times 4}{0.6 \times 8 \times 8.02} = 333 \text{ seconds} = 5\tfrac{1}{2} \text{ minutes}$$

If, however, the circumstances be such that c is 0.8, the time is about 250 seconds, or $4\frac{1}{6}$ minutes. It is therefore seen that it is important to arrange the orifices of discharge in canal locks with rounded inner edges.

The filling of the lock is the reverse operation. Here the water in the head bay remains at a constant level, and the discharge through the orifices in the upper gates decreases with the rising head in the lock. Let H be the effective head on the orifices when the lock is empty, and y the effective head at any time t after the beginning of the discharge. The area of the section of the lock being A, the quantity $A\delta y$ is discharged in the time δt, and this is equal to $ca\sqrt{2gy}\,\delta t$, if a be the area of the orifices and c the coefficient of discharge. Hence the same expression as (58) results, and the

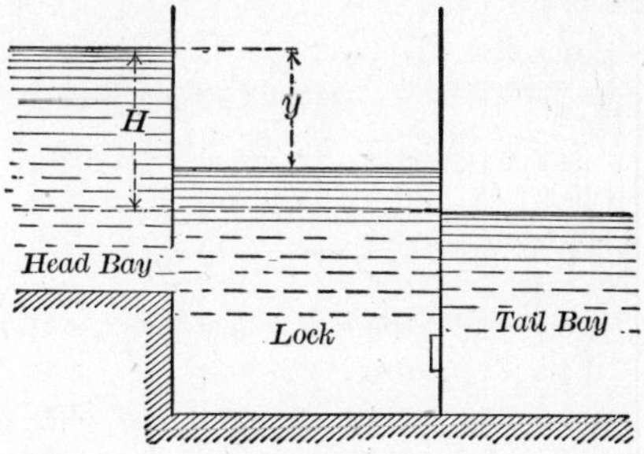

Fig. 58.

times of filling and emptying a lock are equal if the orifices are of the same dimensions and under the same heads. The area required for the orifices may be found for any case from (58) when A, H, t, and c are given.

Prob. 58. A lock 90 feet long and 20 feet wide, with a lift of 12 feet, contains a boat weighing 500 net tons. When the lock is emptied in order to lower the boat, how much water flows from the lower orifices? If the cross-section of these orifices is 12.3 square feet and $c = 0.7$, what is the time of emptying?

Art. 59. Computations in Metric Measures

Most of the formulas of this chapter are rational and may be used in all systems of measures. The coefficients of contraction, velocity, and discharge are abstract numbers, which are the same in all systems, like the constants of mathematics. In the metric system the area a is to be taken in square meters, the head h in meters, $\sqrt{2g}$ as 4.427, and then the discharge q will be in cubic meters per second.

(Art. 47) For standard circular vertical orifices the formulas $(47)_1$ and $(47)_2$ apply to the metric system if 8.02 be replaced by 4.427. In using these the coefficient c may be taken from Table 59a which has been adapted to metric arguments from Table 47. For example, if

Table 59a. Coefficients for Circular Vertical Orifices

Arguments in Metric Measures

Head h in Meters	Diameter of Orifice in Centimeters					
	1	2	3	6	18	30
0.1	0.642	0.626	0.619			
0.2	.639	.619	.613	0.601	0.593	
0.3	.634	.613	.608	.600	.595	0.591
0.5	.626	.609	.605	.600	.596	.593
0.7	.620	.607	.603	.599	.598	.596
1.	.619	.605	.602	.599	.598	.597
1.5	.614	.604	.601	.598	.597	.596
2.	.611	.603	.600	.597	.596	.596
3.	.607	.600	.598	.597	.596	.595
6.	.600	.597	.596	.596	.596	.594
15.	.596	.595	.594	.594	.594	.593
30.	.593	.592	.592	.592	.592	.592

the diameter of the orifice is 2.5 centimeters and the head on its center is 0.6 meters, interpolation in the table gives the value of c as 0.606.

(Art. 48) For standard square vertical orifices the formulas $(48)_1$ and $(48)_2$ are changed to the metric system by substituting 4.427 for 8.02 and 2.951 for 5.347. Table 59*b* gives values of the coefficient c for arguments in metric measures.

TABLE 59*b*. COEFFICIENTS FOR SQUARE VERTICAL ORIFICES

Arguments in Metric Measures

Head h in Meters	Side of the Square in Centimeters					
	1	2	3	6	12	30
0.1	0.652	0.632	0.622			
0.2	.648	.624	.617	0.605	0.598	
0.3	.636	.619	.613	.605	.601	0.599
0.5	.628	.618	.610	.605	.602	.601
0.7	.625	.612	.607	.605	.604	.602
1.0	.620	.610	.607	.605	.604	.603
1.5	.618	.609	.606	.604	.603	.602
2.	.614	.608	.605	.604	.603	.602
3.	.611	.606	.604	.603	.602	.601
6.	.605	.603	.602	.602	.601	.600
15.	.601	.601	.600	.600	.599	.599
30.	.598	.598	.598	.598	598	.598

(Art. 49) Table 49 has not been transformed into one with metric arguments, as it applies only to the special case where the rectangular orifice is one foot wide. If the heads in the first column are changed into meters, by writing 0.12 meters for 0.4 feet, 0.18 meters for 0.6 feet, etc., and the numbers at the top are changed into centimeters by writing 3.8 centimeters for 0.125 feet, 7.6 centimeters for 0.25 feet, etc., the table will be ready for use with metric arguments for rectangular orifices 30.5 centimeters wide.

(Art. 55) The miner's inch, when the head on the center of the orifice is 16.5 centimeters, is 0.0433 cubic meters or 43.3 liters per minute.

(Art. 58) In using (58) in the metric system, a and A are to be taken in square meters, H in meters, g as 9.80 meters per second per second, and $\sqrt{2g}$ as 4.427; q will then be found in cubic meters.

Prob. 59*a*. Michelotti found the range of a jet to be 6.25 meters on a horizontal plane 1.41 meters below the vertical orifice, which was under a head of 7.19 meters. Compute the coefficient of velocity.

Prob. 59*b*. An orifice 3 centimeters square was under a constant head of 4 meters, and during 230 seconds the jet flowed into a tank which was found to contain 1122 liters. Show that the coefficient of discharge was 0.612.

Prob. 59*c*. Find from the table the coefficient of discharge for a standard circular orifice 2.5 centimeters in diameter under a head of 2.5 meters.

Prob. 59*d*. Compute the discharge through a standard orifice 7.5 centimeters square under a head of 8 meters.

Prob. 59*e*. Compute the time required to empty a canal lock 7 meters wide and 32 meters long through an orifice of 0.9 square meters area, the head on the center of the orifice being 5.1 meters when the lock is filled.

CHAPTER 6

FLOW OF WATER OVER WEIRS

Art. 60. Standard Weirs

A weir is a notch in the top of the vertical side of a vessel or reservoir through which water flows. The notch is generally rectangular, and the word "weir" will be used to designate a rectangular notch unless otherwise specified, the lower edge of the rectangle being truly horizontal, and its sides vertical. The lower edge of the rectangle is called the "crest" of the weir. In

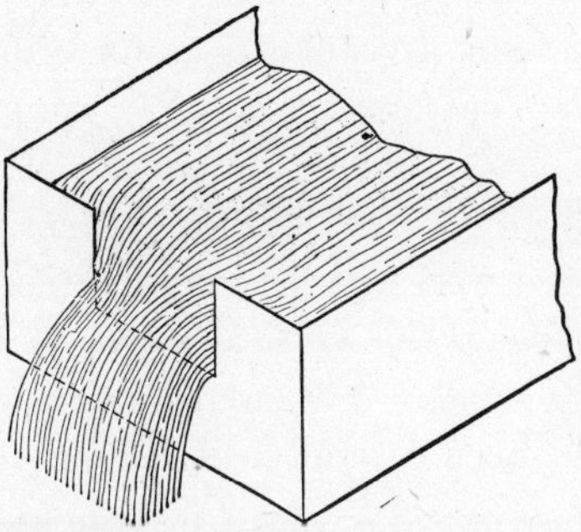

Fig. 60*a*.

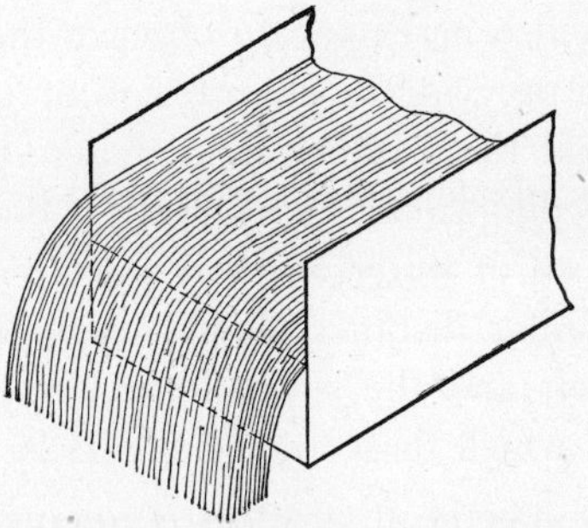

Fig. 60*b*.

Fig. 60*a* is shown the outline of the most usual form, where the vertical edges of the notch are sufficiently removed from the sides of the reservoir or feeding canal, so that the sides of the stream may be fully contracted; this is called a weir with end contractions. In the form of Fig. 60*b* the edges of the notch are coincident with the sides of the feeding canal, so that the filaments of water along the sides pass over without being deflected from the vertical planes in which they move; this is called a weir without end contractions, or with end contractions suppressed. Both kinds of weirs are extensively used for the measurement of water in engineering operations.

It is necessary in order to make accurate measurements of discharge by a weir that the same precaution should be taken as for orifices (Art. 54), namely, that the inner edge of the notch shall be a definite angular corner so that the water in flowing out may touch the crest only in a line, thus insuring complete contraction, as in Fig. 61. In precise observations a thin metal plate will be used for a crest, while in common work it may be sufficient to have the crest formed by a plank of smooth hard wood with its inner corner cut to a sharp right angle and its outer edge beveled. The vertical edges of the weir should be made in the same manner for weirs with end contractions, while for those without end contractions the sides of the feeding canal should be smooth and be prolonged a slight distance beyond the crest. It is also necessary to observe the same precautions as for orifices to prevent the suppression of the contraction (Art. 52), namely, that the distance from the crest of the weir to the bottom of the feeding canal, or reservoir, should be greater than three times the head of water on the crest. For a weir with end contractions a similar distance should exist between the vertical edges of the weir and the sides of the feeding canal. A standard weir is one in which these arrangements have been carefully carried out.

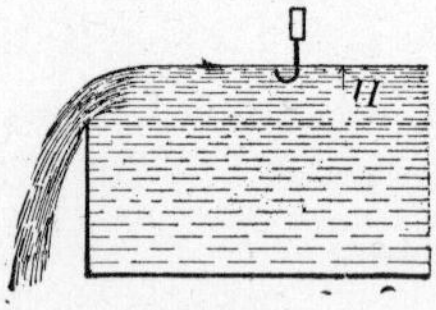

Fig. 60*c*.

The head of water H upon the crest of a weir is usually much less than the breadth of the crest b. The value of H should not be less than 0.1 feet, and it should not exceed 4.5 feet in order to keep within the range of experiments on the standard weir. The least value of b in practice is about 0.5 feet, and it does not often exceed 20 feet. Weirs are extensively used for measuring the discharge of small streams, and for determining the quantity of water supplied to hydraulic motors; the practical importance of the subject is so great that numerous experiments have been made to ascertain the laws of flow, and the coefficients of discharge.

Since the head on the crest of a weir is small, it must be determined with precision in order to avoid error in the computed discharge. The hook gage illustrated in Art. 35 is generally used for accurate work in connection with hydraulic motors, and the simpler form, consisting of a hook set into a leveling rod, is usually of sufficient precision for many cases. For rough gagings of streams the heads may be determined by setting a post a few feet upstream from the weir and on the same level as the crest, and measuring the depth of the water over the top of the post by a scale graduated to tenths and hundredths of a foot, the thousandths being either estimated or omitted entirely.

The head H on the crest of the weir is in all cases to be measured several feet upstream from the crest, as indicated in Fig. 60*c*. This is necessary because of the curve taken by the surface of the water in approaching the weir. The distance to which this curve extends back from the crest of the weir depends upon many circumstances (Art. 70), but it is generally considered that perfectly level water will be found at 2 or 3 feet back of the crest for small weirs, and at 6 or 8 feet for very large weirs. It is desirable that the hook should be placed at least one foot from the sides of the feeding canal, if possible. As this is apt to render the position of the observer uncomfortable, some experimenters have placed the hook in a pail a few feet away from the canal, the water being led to the pail by a pipe which joins the feeding canal several feet back from the crest, and the water should enter this pipe, not at its end, but through a number of holes drilled at intervals along its circumference. Piezometers (Art. 36) consisting of a glass tube and scale are also sometimes used for large heads, the water being led to the tube by such a pipe. A rough method of measuring the head is to hold a common foot rule on a post set with its top on the same level as the crest and upstream from it.

In a case where it is desired to obtain the highest degree of accuracy care should be taken to reproduce as nearly as possible the conditions which obtained under the experiments from which the coefficients to be used were obtained. This is particularly true of the manner in which the head is to be measured. Thus Poncelet and Lesbros, whose experimental results have been recomputed by Hamilton Smith, measured the head in a reservoir 11.48 feet upstream from the weir. Francis * in some of his experiments measured the head with a hook gage in a wooden stilling box, having a hole one inch in diameter in its bottom which was placed at a level of about four inches below the crest of the weir and about 6 feet upstream from it. Fteley and Stearns † measured the head with a hook gage in a pail placed below the weir, the pail being connected to the channel above the weir at a point 6 feet upstream from the crest. Bazin ‡ in his work on standard thin-edged weirs measured the head in pits 16.40 feet upstream from the weir. One pit was placed on each side of the channel of approach and connected with it through an opening 4 inches in diameter, the opening being exactly flush and at right angles to the channel.

A valuable discussion by Horton,§ in which he tabulates the results of many experiments made on weirs up to 1907, is strongly recommended for reference.

In cases where the flow of water to be measured is constant it is best that a number of observations of the head on the measuring weir should be taken and their mean used in computing the quantity. In most practical cases, however, the flow is constantly fluctuating, and, in order that the total quantity may be accurately determined, observations at frequent intervals must be taken. It may be best in some cases, for convenience or where a high degree of refinement is required, to install an instrument such as that described in Art. 34 for automatically and continuously recording the head. Where such a record has been obtained, it will not do to simply average the heads and use the resulting figure in the formula for the discharge. Since the discharges vary with the three-halves power of the head, it is necessary to compute them for various instants which are so selected that the computed discharges can be fairly averaged before multiplying by the total time between the beginning and end of the tests in order to obtain the total quantity which has passed over the weir. No definite rules can be laid down for this procedure, but every case

* Lowell Hydraulic Experiments (4th edition, New York, 1883).

† Transactions American Society of Civil Engineers, vol. 12.

‡ Translated in Proceedings of Engineers Club, Philadelphia, vols. 7, 9, 10.

§ Water Supply and Irrigation Paper No. 200, U. S. Geological Survey.

should be studied and a plan be adopted which will give the results desired with the required degree of accuracy.

Prob. 60. The trough of a weir, several feet back from the crest, is 6 feet wide, and the depth of water in it is 1.96 feet. What is the mean velocity in this trough when the flow over the weir is 4.24 cubic feet per second?

Art. 61. Formulas for Discharge

Referring to the demonstration of Art. 48 it is seen that a rectangular orifice becomes a weir when the head on its top is zero. Let b be the breadth of the notch, commonly called the length of the crest, and H the head of water on the crest. Then replacing h_1 by 0 and h_2 by H, the theoretic discharge per second is

$$Q = \tfrac{2}{3}\sqrt{2g} \cdot bH^{\frac{3}{2}} \qquad (61)_1$$

The head H is not the depth measured in the vertical plane of the crest, for since the deduction of the formula assumes nothing regarding the fall due to the surface curve, and regards the velocity at any point vertically over the crest as due to the head upon that point below the free water surface, it seems that H should be measured with reference to that surface, as is actually done by the hook gage. The above formula then gives the theoretic discharge per second, provided that there be no velocity at the point where H is measured, which can only be the case when the area of the weir opening is very small compared to that of the cross-section of the feeding canal. This condition would be fulfilled for a rectangular notch at the side of a large pond.

When there is an appreciable velocity of approach of the water at the point where H is measured by the hook gage, the above formula must be modified. Let v be the mean velocity in the feeding canal at this section; this velocity may be regarded as due to a fall, h, from the surface of still water at some distance upstream from the hook, as shown in

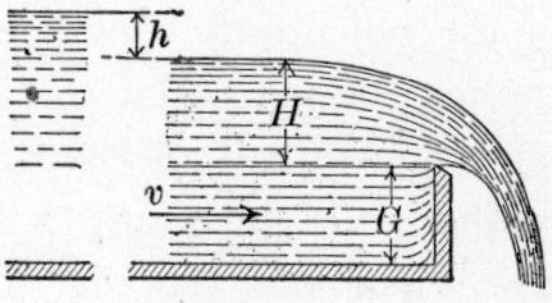

Fig. 61.

Fig. 61. Now the true head on the crest of the weir is $H + h$, since this would have been the reading of the hook gage had it been placed where the water had no velocity. Hence the theoretic discharge per second over the weir is

$$Q = \tfrac{2}{3}\sqrt{2g}\cdot b(H+h)^{\frac{3}{2}}$$

in which H is read by the hook and h is to be determined from the mean velocity v.

The actual discharge is always less than the theoretic discharge, due to the contraction of the stream and the resistances of the edges of the weir. To take account of these a coefficient is applied to the theoretic formulas in the same manner as for orifices; these coefficients being determined by experiment, the formulas may then be used for computing the actual discharge. It was also proposed by Hamilton Smith to modify the head h, owing to the fact that the velocity of approach is not constant throughout the section, but greater near the surface than near the bottom, as in conduits and streams (Art. 125). Accordingly the following is an expression for the actual discharge:

$$q = c\cdot\tfrac{2}{3}\sqrt{2g}\cdot b(H+nh)^{\frac{3}{2}} \qquad (61)_2$$

in which c is the coefficient of discharge whose value is always less than unity, and n is a number which lies between 1.0 and 1.5. For the English system of measures a mean value of $\sqrt{2g}$ is 8.020, but a more precise value can be found from $(6)_1$ for any locality.

The above formulas are not in all respects perfectly satisfactory, and indeed many others have been proposed, one of these being derived from $(50)_4$ by making $h_0 = h$, $h_2 = H$, and $h_1 = 0$. The actual discharge differs, however, so much from the theoretical that the final dependence must be upon the coefficients deduced from experiment, and hence any fairly reasonable formula may be used within the limits for which its coefficients have been established. In spite of the objections which may be raised against all forms of formulas, the fact remains that the measurement of water by weirs is one of the most convenient methods, and for many conditions the most precise method. If the quantity is so small as to pass through a circular orifice less than one foot in diameter, then the orifice is more precise than the weir. For the continuous measurement of water passing through large pipes the Venturi meter gives the best results. With proper precautions the probable error in measurements of discharge by weirs should be less than two or three percent.

Prob. 61. Show by using formula $(61)_1$ that an error of about one-half of one percent results in the computed discharge if an error of 0.001 feet is made in reading the head when $H = 0.3$ feet.

Art. 62. Velocity of Approach

The head h which produces the velocity v is expressed by $v^2/2g$, and in the case of a weir, the velocity of approach v is due to a fall from the height h; thus the velocity-head is

$$h = v^2/2g = 0.01555\, v^2$$

and when v is known, h can be computed. One way of finding v is to observe the time of passage of a float through a given distance; but this is not a precise method. The usual method is to compute v from an approximate value of the discharge, which is itself first computed by regarding v, and hence h, as zero. This determination is rendered possible by the fact that v is usually small, and hence that h is quite small as compared with H.

Let B be the breadth of the cross-section of the feeding canal at the place where the readings of the hook are taken, and let G be its depth below the crest (Fig. 61). The area of that cross-section then is

$$A = B(G + H)$$

The mean velocity in this section now is

$$v = q'/A$$

in which the discharge q' is found from the formula

$$q' = c\,\tfrac{2}{3}\sqrt{2g}\cdot bH^{\frac{3}{2}}$$

This value of q' is an approximation to the actual discharge; from it v is found, and then h, after which the discharge q can be computed. If thought necessary, h may be recomputed by using q instead of q'; but this will rarely be necessary.

For example, a small weir with end contractions, which was used in the hydraulic laboratory of Lehigh University prior to 1896, had $B = 7.82$ feet and $G = 2.5$ feet. The length of the weir b was adjustable according to the quantity of water delivered by the stream. On April 10, 1888, the value of b was 1.330 feet, and values of H ranged from 0.429 to 0.388 feet.

It is required to find the velocity v and the head h, when H = 0.429 feet. Here the coefficient c is 0.602 (Table 63); hence the approximate discharge per second is

$$q' = 0.602 \times \tfrac{2}{3} \times 8.02 \times 1.33 \times 0.429^{\frac{3}{2}}$$

or $$q' = 1.203 \text{ cubic feet per second.}$$

The mean velocity of approach then is

$$v = \frac{1.203}{(2.5+0.4)\,7.82} = 0.053 \text{ feet per second,}$$

and the head h producing this velocity is

$$h = 0.01555 \times 0.053^2 = 0.00004 \text{ feet,}$$

which is too small to be regarded, since the hook gage used determined the heads only to thousandths of a foot.

The head h may be directly expressed in terms of the discharge by substituting for v its value q/A; thus

$$h = 0.01555\,(q/A)^2 \qquad (62)_1$$

and when q is approximately known, this expression will be found a very convenient one for computing the value of the head corresponding to the velocity of approach.

The head h may be directly computed, when it is small compared with H, from the formula

$$h = H\left(\frac{2\,cHb}{3\,(H+G)B}\right)^2 \qquad (62)_2$$

To deduce this, let the above values of A and q' be inserted in the equation $v = q'/A$, and then v be placed in $h = v^2/2g$. This is a convenient expression for logarithmic computation.

With a weir opening of given size under a given head H, the velocity of approach is less the greater the area of the section of the feeding canal, and it is desirable in building a weir to make this area large so that the velocity v may be small. For large weirs, and particularly for those without end contractions, v is sometimes as large as one foot per second, giving h = 0.0155 feet, and these should be regarded as the highest values allowable if precision of measurement is required.

Prob. 62. Fteley and Stearns' large suppressed weir had the following dimensions: $b = B = 18.996$ feet, $G = 6.55$ feet, and the greatest measured head was 1.6038 feet. Taking $c = 0.622$, compute the velocity of approach and its velocity-head.

Art. 63. Weirs with End Contractions

Let b be the breadth of the notch or length of the weir, H the head above the crest measured by the hook gage, and c an experimental coefficient. Then, when there is no velocity of approach, the discharge per second is

$$q = c \cdot \tfrac{2}{3} \sqrt{2g} \cdot bH^{\frac{3}{2}} \qquad (63)_1$$

But when the mean velocity of approach at the section where the hook is placed is v, let h be the head which would produce this velocity as computed by $(62)_2$. Then the discharge is

$$q = c \cdot \tfrac{2}{3} \sqrt{2g} \cdot b(H + 1.4\,h)^{\frac{3}{2}} \qquad (63)_2$$

The quantity $H + 1.4\,h$ is called the effective head on the crest, and, as shown in the last article, the velocity-head h is usually small compared with the head H.

Table 63 contains values of the coefficient of discharge c as deduced by Hamilton Smith, from a discussion of the experiments made by Lesbros, Francis, Fteley and Stearns, and others on standard weirs.* In these experiments q was determined by actual measurement in a tank of large size, and the other quantities being observed, the coefficient c was computed. Values of c for different lengths of weir and for different heads were thus obtained, and after plotting them mean curves were drawn from which immediate values were taken. The heads in the first column are the effective heads $H + 1.4\,h$; but as h is small, little error can result in using H as the argument with which to enter the table in selecting a coefficient.

It is seen from the table that the coefficient c increases with the length of the weir, which is due to the fact that the end contractions are independent of the length. The coefficient also

* Hamilton Smith, Hydraulics, 1884, p. 132.

increases as the head on the crest diminishes. The table also shows that the greatest variation in the coefficients occurs under small heads, which are hence to be avoided in order to secure accurate measurements of discharge.

TABLE 63. COEFFICIENTS FOR CONTRACTED WEIRS

Effective Head in Feet	Length of Weir in Feet						
	0.66	1	2	3	5	10	19
0.1	0.632	0.639	0.646	0.652	0.653	0.655	0.656
0.15	.619	.625	.634	.638	.640	.641	.642
0.2	.611	.618	.626	.630	.631	.633	.634
0.25	.605	.612	.621	.624	.626	.628	.629
0.3	.601	.608	.616	.619	.621	.624	.625
0.4	.595	.601	.609	.613	.615	.618	.620
0.5	.590	.596	.605	.608	.611	.615	.617
0.6	.587	.593	.601	.605	.608	.613	.615
0.7		.590	.598	.603	.606	.612	.614
0.8			.595	.600	.604	.611	.613
0.9			.592	.598	.603	.609	.612
1.0			.590	.595	.601	.608	.611
1.2			.585	.591	.597	.605	.610
1.4			.580	.587	.594	.602	.609
1.6				.582	.591	.600	.607

Interpolation may be made in this table for heads and lengths of weirs intermediate between the values given, regarding the coefficient to vary uniformly between the values given. When coefficients are frequently required for a weir of given length, it will be best to make out a special table for that weir and to diagram the results to a large scale on cross-section paper, so that interpolation for different heads can be more readily made.

As an example of the use of the formulas and Table 63, let it be required to find the discharge per second over a weir 4 feet long when the head H is 0.457 feet, there being no velocity of approach. From the table the coefficient of discharge is 0.614 for $H = 0.4$ and 0.6095 for $H = 0.5$, which gives about 0.612 when $H = 0.457$. Then the discharge per second is

$$q = 0.612 \times \tfrac{2}{3} \times 8.02 \times 4 \times 0.457^{\frac{3}{2}} = 4.04 \text{ cubic feet.}$$

If the width of the feeding canal be 7 feet, and its depth below the crest be 1.5 feet, the velocity-head is

$$h = 0.01555\left(\frac{4.04}{7 \times 1.96}\right)^2 = 0.00134 \text{ feet.}$$

The effective head now becomes $H + 1.4\,h = 0.459$ feet, and the discharge per second over the weir is

$$q = 0.612 \times \tfrac{2}{3} \times 8.02 \times 4 \times 0.459^{\frac{3}{2}} = 4.07 \text{ cubic feet.}$$

It is to be observed that the reliability of these computed discharges depends upon the precision of the observed quantities and upon the coefficient c; this is probably liable to an error of one or two units in the third decimal place, which is equivalent to a probable error of about three-tenths of one per cent. On the whole, regarding the inaccuracies of observation, a probable error of one per cent should at least be inferred, so that the value $q = 4.07$ cubic feet per second should strictly be written $q = 4.07 \pm 0.04$; that is, the discharge per second has 4.07 cubic feet for its most probable value, and it is as likely to be between the values 4.03 and 4.11 as to be outside of those limits.

When velocity of approach is considered, an excellent method of computing the discharge is to expand the parenthesis of $(63)_2$ in a series and use only two terms of the expansion, thus

$$q = c \cdot \tfrac{2}{3}\sqrt{2g} \cdot bH^{\frac{3}{2}}\left(1 + 2.1\frac{h}{H}\right) \qquad (63)_3$$

in which h/H is computed from the expression $(2\,cIIb/3\,(H + G)\,B)^2$, where B is the breadth of the feeding canal and G is the distance of the bottom of the canal below the level of the crest (Fig. 61). For example, in the case of the last paragraph h/H is found from the numerical data to be 0.00297, whence the quantity in the parenthesis is 1.00624 and the discharge is $4.04 \times 1.00624 = 4.07$ cubic feet per second. It is seen that this method requires less numerical work than that of the one explained above.

In very precise work the value of the acceleration g should be computed from formula $(6)_1$ for the particular latitude and elevation above sea level where the weir is located.

Prob. 63. A weir in north latitude 40° 24′ and 395 feet above sea level has a length of 2.5 feet. Compute the discharges over it, the feeding canal having the width 6 feet and the depth below crest 1.6 feet, when the heads on the crest are 0.314, 0.315, and 0.316 feet.

Art. 64. Weirs without End Contractions

For weirs without end contractions, or suppressed weirs as they are often called, when there is no velocity of approach, the discharge per second is

$$q = c \cdot \tfrac{2}{3} \sqrt{2g} \cdot bH^{\frac{3}{2}} \qquad (64)_1$$

and when there is velocity of approach,

$$q = c \cdot \tfrac{2}{3} \sqrt{2g} \cdot b(H + 1\tfrac{1}{3}\, h)^{\frac{3}{2}} \qquad (64)_2$$

Here the notation is the same as in the last article, and c is to be taken from Table 64, which gives the coefficients of discharge as deduced by Smith, in 1888.

Table 64. Coefficients for Suppressed Weirs

Effective Head in Feet	Length of Weir in Feet						
	19	10	7	5	4	3	2
0.1	0.657	0.658	0.658	0.659			
0.15	.643	.644	.645	.645	0.647	0.649	0.652
0.2	.635	.637	.637	.638	.641	.642	.645
0.25	.630	.632	.633	.634	.636	.638	.641
0.3	.626	.628	.629	.631	.633	.636	.639
0.4	.621	.623	.625	.628	.630	.633	.636
0.5	.619	.621	.624	.627	.630	.633	.637
0.6	.618	.620	.623	.627	.630	.634	.638
0.7	.618	.620	.624	.628	.631	.635	.640
0.8	.618	.621	.625	.629	.633	.637	.643
0.9	.619	.622	.627	.631	.635	.639	.645
1.0	.619	.624	.628	.633	.637	.641	.648
1.2	.620	.626	.632	.636	.641	.646	
1.4	.622	.629	.634	.640	.644		
1.6	.623	.631	.637	.642	.647		

It is seen that the coefficients for suppressed weirs are greater than for those with end contractions; this of course should be the case, since contractions diminish the discharge. They decrease with the length of the weir, while those for contracted weirs increase with the length. Their greatest variation occurs under low heads, where they rapidly increase as the head diminishes. It should be observed that these coefficients are not reliable for lengths of weirs under 4 feet, owing to the few experiments which have been made for short suppressed weirs. Hence, for small quantities of water, weirs with end contractions should be built in preference to suppressed weirs. For a weir of infinite length it would be immaterial whether end contractions exist or not; hence for such a case the coefficients lie between the values for the 19-foot weir in Table 63 and those for the 19-foot weir in Table 64.

For a numerical illustration a suppressed weir having the same dimensions as in the example of the last article will be used, namely, $b = 4$ feet, $G = 1.5$ feet, and $H = 0.457$ feet. The coefficient is found from Table 64 to be 0.630; then for no velocity of approach the discharge per second is

$$q = 0.630 \times \tfrac{2}{3} \times 8.02 \times 4 \times 0.457^{\frac{3}{2}} = 4.16 \text{ cubic feet.}$$

Here the width B is also 4 feet; the head corresponding to the velocity of approach then is by $(62)_1$

$$h = 0.01555\left(\frac{4.16}{4 \times 1.96}\right)^2 = 0.0044 \text{ feet,}$$

and the effective head on the crest is

$$H + 1\tfrac{1}{3}\,h = 0.463 \text{ feet,}$$

from which the discharge per second is

$$q = 0.630 \times \tfrac{2}{3} \times 8.02 \times 4 \times 0.463^{\frac{3}{2}} = 4.24 \text{ cubic feet.}$$

This shows that the velocity of approach exerts a greater influence upon the discharge than in the case of a weir with end contractions.

When velocity of approach exists, a good method of computation is to expand the parenthesis of $(64)_2$ in a series and use only two terms of the expansion thus,

$$q = c \cdot \tfrac{2}{3}\sqrt{2g} \cdot bH^{\frac{3}{2}}\left(1 + 2.0\frac{h}{H}\right)$$

in which h/H can be computed from the equivalent expression $(2\,cH/3\,(H+G))^2$. For example, from the above data the value of h/H is 0.0095, whence the quantity in the parenthesis is 1.019 and $q = 4.16 \times 1.019 = 4.24$ cubic feet per second.

Prob. 64. Compute the discharge per second over a weir without end contractions when b = 0.995 feet, H = 0.7955 feet, G = 4.6 feet.

Art. 65. Francis' Formulas

The formulas most extensively used for computing the flow through weirs are those established by Francis in 1854* from the discussion of his numerous and carefully conducted experiments, but as they are stated without tabular coefficients they are to be regarded as giving only mean approximate results. The experiments were made on large weirs, most of them 10 feet long, and with heads ranging from 0.4 to 1.6 feet, so that the formulas apply particularly to such, rather than to short weirs and low heads. The shape and details of the crest of the weirs are shown in Fig. 65 and the head was measured as described in Art. 60. The length b and the head H being expressed in feet, the discharge per second, when there is no velocity of approach, is, for weirs without end contractions, or suppressed weirs,

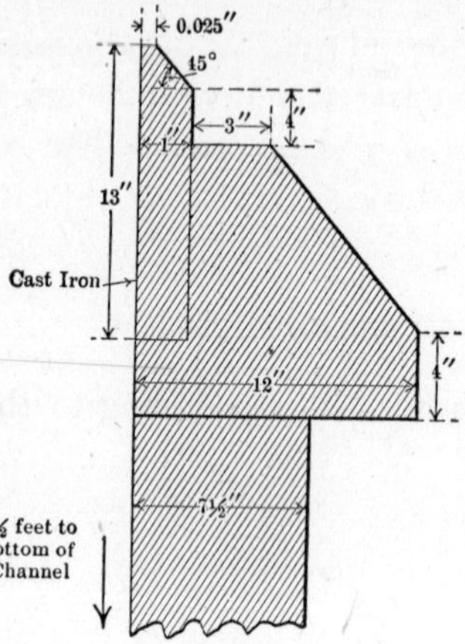

Fig. 65.

$$q = 3.33\,bH^{\frac{3}{2}} \qquad (65)_1$$

and for weirs with two end contractions,

$$q = 3.33\,(b - 0.2\,H)H^{\frac{3}{2}} \qquad (65)_2$$

Here it was considered by Francis that the effect of each end contraction is to diminish the effective length of the weir by

* Lowell Hydraulic Experiments (4th edition, New York, 1883), p. 133.

0.1 H. In these formulas b and H must be taken in feet and q will be found in cubic feet per second.

It is seen that the number 3.33 is $c \cdot \frac{2}{3}\sqrt{2g}$, where c is the true coefficient of discharge. The 88 experiments from which this mean value was deduced show that the coefficient 3.33 actually ranged from 3.30 to 3.36, so that by the use of the mean value an error of one per cent in the computed discharge may occur. When such an error is of no importance, the formula may be safely used for weirs longer than 4 feet and heads greater than 0.4 feet.

Francis' method of correcting for velocity of approach differs from that of Hamilton Smith, and is the same as that explained in Art. 50. The head h causing the velocity of approach is computed in the usual way, and then the formulas are written, for weirs without end contractions,

$$q = 3.33\, b\,[(H+h)^{\frac{3}{2}} - h^{\frac{3}{2}}]$$

and for weirs with end contractions,

$$q = 3.33\,(b - 0.2\,H)[(H+h)^{\frac{3}{2}} - h^{\frac{3}{2}}]$$

It is necessary that this method of introducing the velocity of approach should be strictly observed, since the mean number 3.33 was deduced for this form of expression.

Prob. 65. What modification would you introduce in $(65)_2$, if the weir has one end with and the other end without contraction?

Art. 66. Other Weir Formulas

Fteley and Stearns* in the discussion of their experiments on standard weirs proposed the formula

$$Q = 3.31\, bH^{\frac{3}{2}} + 0.007\, b \qquad (66)_1$$

in which correction for end contraction is made as in the Francis formula (Art. 65). They also proposed the following corrections for velocity of approach for use in the above formula $(66)_1$.

$$H + h = H + 1.50\frac{v^2}{2g} \qquad H + h = H + 2.05\frac{v^2}{2g}$$

* Transactions American Society of Civil Engineers, vol. 12.

the former of which is applicable to suppressed weirs and the latter to weirs having end contractions, v being the mean velocity of approach.

Among the most recent formulas for the flow over weirs are those of Bazin* who experimented on sharp crests varying in height from 0.79 to 3.72 feet and in length from 1.64 to 6.56 feet. From his discussion of his own results as well as those of Fteley and Stearns, he deduced the following formulas for weirs without end contractions

$$Q = \mu \sqrt{2g} \cdot bH^{\frac{3}{2}} \quad \text{and} \quad Q = m \sqrt{2g} \cdot bH^{\frac{3}{2}} \qquad (66)_2$$

The first of these formulas is applicable to cases where there is no velocity of approach, while the second, by means of the coefficient m, corrects for any approach velocity which may exist. The relations between m, μ, and H are

$$m = \mu\left[1 + 0.55\left(\frac{H}{G+H}\right)^2\right] \qquad \mu = 0.405 + \frac{0.00984}{H}$$

where G is the height of the weir crest above the bottom of the channel of approach. It is thus seen that m varies with the head and also with the height of the weir above the bottom of the channel, both of which factors influence the velocity of approach. On the other hand μ varies only with the head.

TABLE 66. BAZIN'S COEFFICIENTS m FOR SUPPRESSED WEIRS

Head in Feet	Height G of Weir Crest, in Feet				
	0.79	1.15	1.64	2.46	3.72
0.20	0.447	0.445	0.444	0.444	0.443
0.39	.447	.440	.435	.433	.431
0.59	.458	.446	.438	.432	.427
0.79	.470	.455	.443	.434	.426
0.98	.482	.464	.418	.437	.427
1.18	.495	.473	.454	.441	.428
1.38			.460	.444	.429

* Annales des ponts et chaussées, 1898; translated by Maichal and Trautwine in Proceedings Engineers' Club of Philadelphia, vols. 5, 7, and 9.

In the above table are given some of the values of the coefficient m determined by Bazin's experiments for varying heads and heights G of standard sharp-crested weirs. These coefficients are applicable only to weirs having suppressed end contractions. While these formulas give results agreeing well with many weir gagings under ordinary heads, the expression for μ cannot be regarded as a rational one since it becomes infinite when H is zero.

Prob. 66. What will be the value of m in the case of a weir 2.50 feet high when H is 1.25 feet?

Art. 67. Submerged Weirs

When the water on the downstream side of the weir is allowed to rise higher than the level of the crest, the weir is said to be submerged. In such cases an entire change of condition results, and the preceding formulas are inapplicable. Let H be the head above the crest measured upstream from the weir by the hook gage in the usual manner, and let H' be the head above the crest of the water downstream from the weir measured by a second hook gage. If H be constant, the discharge is uninfluenced until the lower water rises to the level of the crest, provided that free access of air is allowed beneath the descending sheet of water. But as soon as it rises slightly above the crest so that H' has small values, the contraction is suppressed and the discharge hence increased. As H' increases, however, the discharge diminishes until it becomes zero when H' equals H. Submerged weirs cannot be relied upon to give precise measurements of discharge on account of the lack of experimental knowledge regarding them, and should hence always be avoided if possible.

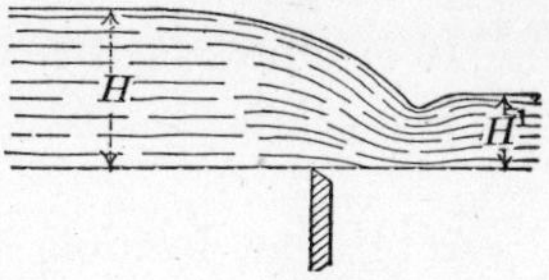

Fig. 67.

The following method for estimating the discharge over submerged weirs without end contractions is taken from the discussion given by Herschel* of the experiments made by Francis and by Fteley and Stearns. The observed head H is first multiplied

* Transactions American Society of Civil Engineers, 1885, vol. 14, p. 194.

by a number n, which depends upon the ratio of H' to H, and then the discharge is to be computed by using the modified Francis' formula

$$q = 3.33\, b\,(nH)^{\frac{3}{2}} \tag{67}_1$$

The values of n deduced by Herschel* are given in Table 67. They are liable to a probable error of about one unit in the second decimal place when H' is less than 0.2 H, and to greater errors in the remainder of the table, values of n less than 0.70 being in particular uncertain. It is seen that H' may be nearly one-fifth of H without affecting the discharge more than two percent.

TABLE 67. FACTORS FOR SUBMERGED WEIRS

$\frac{H'}{H}$	n	$\frac{H'}{H}$	n	$\frac{H'}{H}$	n	$\frac{H'}{H}$	n
0.00	1.000	0.18	0.989	0.38	0.935	0.58	0.856
.01	1.004	.20	0.985	.40	0.929	.60	0.846
.02	1.006	.22	0.980	.42	0.922	.62	0.836
.04	1.007	.24	0.975	.44	0.915	.64	0.824
.06	1.007	.26	0.970	.46	0.908	.66	0.813
.08	1.006	.28	0.964	.48	0.900	.70	0.787
.10	1.005	.30	0.959	.50	0.892	.75	0.750
.12	1.002	.32	0.953	.52	0.884	.80	0.703
.14	0.998	.34	0.947	.54	0.875	.90	0.574
.16	0.994	.36	0.941	.56	0.866	1.00	0.000

A rational formula for the discharge over submerged weirs may be deduced in the following manner. The theoretic discharge may be regarded as composed of two portions, one through the upper part $H - H'$, and the other through the lower part H'. The portion through the upper part is given by the usual weir formula, $H - H'$ being the head, or

$$Q_1 = \tfrac{2}{3}\sqrt{2g}\cdot b\,(H - H')^{\frac{3}{2}}$$

and that through the lower part is given by the formula for a submerged orifice (Art. 51), in which b is the breadth, H' the height, and $H - H'$ the effective head, or

$$Q_2 = bH'\sqrt{2g\,(H - H')}$$

* Transactions American Society of Civil Engineers, 1885, vol. 14, p. 194.

The addition of these gives the total theoretic discharge,

$$Q = \tfrac{2}{3}\sqrt{2g}\cdot b(H - H')^{\frac{3}{2}} + \sqrt{2g}\cdot bH'(H - H')^{\frac{1}{2}}$$

which may be put into the more convenient form,

$$Q = \tfrac{2}{3}\sqrt{2g}\cdot b(H + \tfrac{1}{2}H')(H - H')^{\frac{1}{2}}$$

The actual discharge per second may now be written,

$$q = c\cdot\tfrac{2}{3}\sqrt{2g}\cdot b(H + \tfrac{1}{2}H')(H - H')^{\frac{1}{2}}$$

in which c is the coefficient of discharge.

Fteley and Stearns adopted the above formula for the discharge, or placing M for $c\cdot\frac{2}{3}\sqrt{2g}$, they wrote,*

$$q = \text{M}b(H + \tfrac{1}{2}H')(H - H')^{\frac{1}{2}} \qquad (67)_2$$

and from their experiments deduced the following values of the coefficient M:

for	$H'/H =$	0.00	0.04	0.08	0.12	0.16	0.2	0.3
	M =	3.33	3.35	3.37	3.35	3.32	3.28	3.21
for	$H'/H =$	0.4	0.5	0.6	0.7	0.8	0.9	1.0
	M =	3.15	3.11	3.09	3.09	3.12	3.19	3.33

These are for suppressed weirs; for contracted weirs few or no experiments are on record.

Thus far in this article velocity of approach has not been considered. This may be taken into account in the usual way by determining the velocity-head h, and thus correcting H. But it is unnecessary, on account of the limited use of submerged weirs, and the consequent lack of experimental data, to develop this branch of the subject. What has been given above will enable an approximate probable estimate to be made of the discharge in cases where the water accidentally rises above the crest, and further than this the use of submerged weirs cannot be recommended.

Prob. 67. Compute by the two methods the discharge over a submerged weir when $b = 8$, $H = 0.46$, and $H' = 0.22$ feet.

* Transactions American Society of Civil Engineers, 1883, vol. 12, p. 103.

Art. 68. Rounded and Wide Crests

When the inner edge of the crest of a weir is rounded as at *A* in Fig. 68, the discharge is materially increased as in the case of orifices (Art. 53), or rather the coefficients of discharge become much larger than those given for the standard sharp crests. The degree of rounding influences so much the amount of increase that no definite values can be stated, and the subject is here merely mentioned in order to emphasize the fact that a rounded inner edge is always a source of error. If the radius of the rounded edge is small, the sheet of escaping water is at a point below the top (*a* in the figure), which has the practical effect of increasing the measured head by a constant quantity. The experiments of Fteley and Stearns show that when the radius is less than one-half an inch, the discharge can be computed from the usual weir formula, seven-tenths of the radius being first added to the measured head *H*.

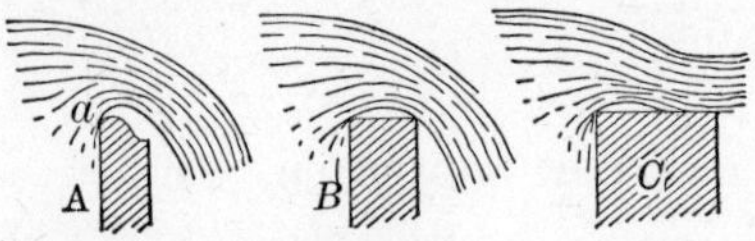

Fig. 68.

Two wide-crested weirs with square inner corners are shown in Fig. 68, the one at *B* being of sufficient width so that the descending sheet may just touch the outer edge, causing the flow to be more or less disturbed, while that at *C* has the sheet adhering to the crest for some distance. In both cases the crest contraction occurs, although water instead of air may fill the space above the inner corner. For *B* the discharge may be equal to or greater than that of the standard weir having the same head *H*, depending upon whether the air has or has not free access beneath the sheet in the space above the crest. For *C* the discharge is always less than that of the standard weir.

Table 68 is an abstract from the results obtained by Fteley and Stearns,* and gives the corrections in feet to be subtracted from the depths on a wide crest, like *C* in Fig. 68, in order to obtain the depths on a standard sharp-crested suppressed weir giving the same discharge.

* Transactions American Society of Civil Engineers, 1883, vol. 12, p. 96.

TABLE 68. CORRECTIONS FOR WIDE CRESTS

Head on Wide Crest Feet	Width of Crest in Inches						
	2	4	6	8	10	12	24
0.05	0.010	0.009	0.009	0.009	0.009	0.009	0.009
.10	.016	.018	.017	.017	.017	.017	.017
.20	.012	.029	.031	.032	.033	.033	.034
.30		.030	.041	.045	.047	.048	.050
.40		.022	.045	.055	.060	.062	.066
.50		.006	.041	.060	.069	.074	.082
.60			.031	.059	.075	.083	.097
.70			.017	.052	.075	.089	.112
.80			.000	.040	.071	.091	.125
.90				.027	.062	.089	.137
1.00				.011	.050	.082	.149
1.20					.021	.061	.168
1.40						.032	.180

The U. S. Geological Survey* during 1903 caused to be made at the laboratory of Cornell University a series of experiments on broad-crested weirs. These experiments covered crest widths of from 0.479 to 16.302 feet and heads from 0.2 to 5.0 feet. Without here going into detail, it was concluded from the results obtained that a coefficient of 2.64 may be used in the formula $q = cbH^{\frac{3}{2}}$ for all cases of broad-crested weirs exceeding 3.0 feet in breadth and under heads in excess of 2.0 feet. For heads of less than 2.0 feet the coefficients are variable and dependent on both the head and the width of the crest as well as on whether or not the nappe or water sheet remains attached to or becomes detached from the downstream face of the weir. For heads of less than 0.5 feet the sheet is very unstable and the coefficients fluctuate correspondingly. From 0.5 to 2.0 feet the coefficients are still somewhat variable and uncertain but become quite steady for higher heads and on crests exceeding 3.0 feet in width. In general when the sheet becomes detached, the coefficient becomes equal to that for a sharp-crested weir; when the sheet is adherent, the coefficient may drop to 2.60. The possible range

* Water Supply and Irrigation Paper, No. 200, U. S. Geological Survey.

in coefficients for such cases is hence seen to be from 2.60 to 3.33.

Prob. 68. Compute the discharge for a weir like C in Fig. 68 when the width of crest is 1.5 feet, the head 0.85 feet, and the length of weir 10 feet.

Art. 69. Waste Weirs and Dams

Waste weirs are constructed at the sides of reservoirs in order to allow the surplus water to escape. They are usually arranged so that the end contractions are suppressed. When the crest is narrow and the front vertical, so that the descending sheet of water has air upon its lower side, the discharge is approximately given by Francis' weir formula (Art. 65),

$$q = 3.33\, bH^{\frac{3}{2}}$$

in which b is the length of the crest, and H the head measured some distance back from the crest. When the crest is wide and the approach to it is inclined, as is often the case, the discharge is somewhat smaller. For a crest about three feet wide and level, with an inclined approach back of it, Francis deduced

$$q = 3.01\, bH^{1.53}$$

which, for a head of one foot, gives a discharge ten percent less than that of the first formula.

In constructing a waste weir the discharge q is generally known or assumed, and it is required to determine b and H. The latter being taken at 1, 2, or 3 feet, as may be judged safe and proper, b is found by one of these formulas. For example, let the crest be wide, q be 87 cubic feet per second, and H be 2.0 feet, then

$$\log b = \log 87 - \log 3.01 - 1.53 \log 2$$

from which $\log b = 1.0004$, whence $b = 10.0$ feet. When, however, the crest is narrow, the first formula gives $b = 9.2$ feet. Evidently no great precision is needed in computing the length of a waste weir, since it is difficult to determine the exact discharge which is to pass over it, and an ample factor of safety should be introduced to cover unusual floods.

The above formulas may be used for obtaining the approximate flow of a stream in which a dam with level crest has been built. The water, however, is often received upon an apron of timber or masonry, and the inclination of this, as well as the inclination of the approach to the crest, materially modifies the discharge. The formula,

$$q = c \cdot \tfrac{2}{3}\sqrt{2g} \cdot bH^{\frac{3}{2}} = \text{M}bH^{\frac{3}{2}} \qquad (69)_1$$

is usually employed for dams, and it is found that the value of M, for English measures, may range under different circumstances from 2.5 to 4.2. This formula is modified below for the influence of velocity of approach (Art. 62).

Experiments were made by Bazin in 1897* on dams from 1.6 to 2.5 feet high with heads of water on the crests ranging from 0.2

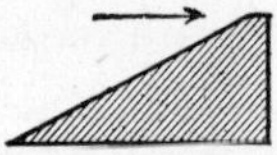

Fig. 69*a*.

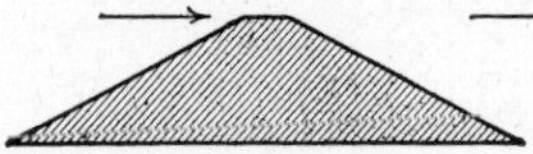

Fig. 69*b*.

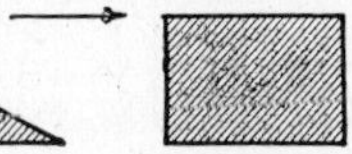

Fig. 69*c*.

to 1.4 feet. For the case of Fig. 69*a* the approach had an inclination of 1 on 2 and the front was vertical; when the width of the crest was 0.33 feet, the coefficient M varied from 3.24 to 4.12 as the head increased from 0.27 to 1.41 feet; when the width of the crest was 0.66 feet, M varied from 3.10 to 3.89 for similar heads. For the case of Fig. 69*b* both approach and apron had slopes of 1 on 2 and the crest was 0.66 feet wide; here M increased from 2.83 to 3.75 as the head ranged from 0.22 to 1.42 feet. For Fig. 69*c*, with a crest 2.62 feet wide, M ranged from 2.47 to 2.76, but when the upstream corner was rounded to a radius of 4 inches, it ranged from 2.71 to 3.12. Here it is seen that widening the crest decreases the discharge, as already noted in Art. 68, and that the apron produces a similar influence.

Experiments on a larger scale were made by Rafter in 1898, for the U. S. Deep Waterways Commission at the canal of the Cornell hydraulic laboratory, in which the flow over dams

* Annales des ponts et chaussées, 1898; translated by Rafter in Transactions American Society of Civil Engineers, 1900, vol. 44, p. 254.

was measured by a standard weir. The results of these experiments are given in Table 69*a*, the first five being for dams of the form shown in Fig. 69*a*, the next three for dams like Fig. 69*b*, and the next four for dams like Fig. 69*c*, those marked with an asterisk having the upstream corner rounded

TABLE 69*a*. COEFFICIENTS M FOR DAMS

Upstream Slope	Width of Crest Feet	Down-stream Slope	Head *H* on Crest in Feet						
			0.5	1.0	1.5	2.0	3.0	4.0	5.0
1 on 2	0.33	Vertical	3.35	3.68	3.82	3.77	3.68	3.70	3.71
1 on 2	0.66	Vertical	3.22	3.44	3.59	3.66	3.68	3.70	3.71
1 on 5	0.66	Vertical	3.31	3.33	3.34	3.35	3.38	3.39	3.39
1 on 4	0.66	Vertical		3.44	3.46	3.48	3.48	3.48	3.48
1 on 3	0.66	Vertical	3.64	3.82	3.83	3.69	3.55	3.55	3.55
1 on 2	0.00	1 on 1	4.21	4.24	4.09	3.97	3.83	3.74	3.68
1 on 2	0.66	1 on 2	3.14	3.42	3.45	3.61	3.66	3.66	3.64
1 on 2	0.33	1 on 5	3.30	3.57	3.60	3.51	3.47	3.54	3.57
Vertical	2.62	Vertical	2.60	2.67	2.75	2.84	3.01	3.21	3.39
Vertical	2.62 *	Vertical	2.96	3.01	3.03	3.08	3.25	3.38	3.47
Vertical	6.56	Vertical	2.50	2.60	2.54	2.48	2.51	2.61	2.70
Vertical	6.56 *	Vertical	2.71	2.83	2.84	2.84	2.86	2.90	2.94
1 on 1	Round	Vertical	2.95	3.17	3.31	3.45	3.56	3.61	3.65

to a radius of 4 inches. The last line of the table refers to a section whose top was 5 feet wide and rounded to a radius of 3.37 feet, the rounding beginning on the upstream side 1.00 foot below the crest. The height of these dams varied from 4.56 to 4.91 feet, and the length of the crest was in all cases 6.58 feet.*

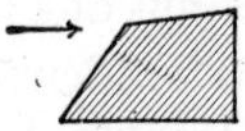
Fig. 69*d*.

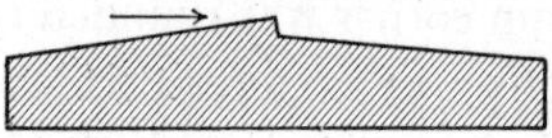
Fig. 69*e*.

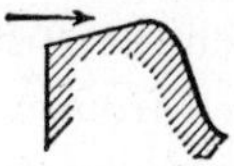
Fig. 69*f*.

Rafter also made experiments on some other forms of dams. The one shown in Fig. 69*d* had a vertical front 4.57 feet deep, and the two back slopes were 1 on 6 and 1 on $\frac{3}{4}$, the width of the former being 4.5 feet; the values of M for this case ranged from

* Transactions American Society of Civil Engineers, 1900, vol. 44, p. 266.

3.33 to 3.46 for heads ranging from 1.0 to 6.0 feet. The one shown in Fig. 69*e* had a total width of about 23 feet and a height of 4.53 feet, the slopes of the approach and apron being 1 on 6, and that just below the crest about 1 on $\frac{1}{4}$, the vertical depth of this being 0.75 feet; for this the mean values of M ranged from 3.07 to 3.27 for heads ranging from 1.0 to 6.0 feet, the smaller coefficients being due to the contact of the water with the apron.

For ogee dams similar in cross-section to Fig. 69*f*, experiments were made in 1903 * by the U. S. Geological Survey. The widths *a* of the various crests ranged from 3.0 to 6.0 feet, the radii *r* from 1.0 to 3.0 feet, and the rises *c* from 0.75 feet to 2.88 feet. From a discussion of these results it was concluded that the coefficient M has a value of $(3.78 - 0.16\, s)\, H^{\frac{1}{20}}$, where *s* is the ratio of *a* to *c* in Fig. 69*g*. For example, when $s = 3.0/1.5$ and $H = 4.0$ feet, then M = 3.70.

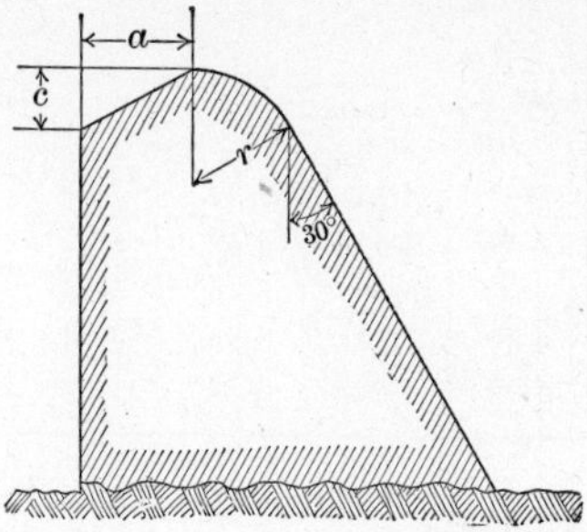

Fig. 69*g*.

In the table on the next page are shown the principal results of the above experiments on models of ogee dams:

The height of the crests above the bottom of the channel of approach of all the models was 11.25 feet and the heads were measured at two points, one 10.3 feet and the other 16.059 feet upstream from the weir crest. It was found that in general the reading of the gage nearest the weir was not affected by the surface curve for heads of less than three feet on the crest. The water which was used in these experiments was measured over a sharp-crested standard weir 6.65 feet high and having a crest 15.93 feet in length.

By the use of these coefficients the discharge of a stream over a dam may be computed with a good degree of precision. For-

* Water Supply and Irrigation Paper No. 200, p. 131.

TABLE 69b. COEFFICIENTS M FOR OGEE DAMS

	1	2	3	4	5	6	7	8
a, feet	3.00*	3.00†	3.00*	3.00†	3.00*	4.50*	‡4.83*	6.00*
c, feet	0.75	0.75	1.50	1.50	2.88	1.00	1.00	1.00
r, feet	3.00	3.00	3.00	3.00	3.00	2.00	2.00	1.00
Head in Feet	Value of Coefficient M							
0.50	3.31		3.21	3.27	3.15	3.18	3.23	3.28
1.00	3.44	3.29	3.48	3.37	3.45	3.30	3.34	3.49
2.00	3.42	3.36	3.67	3.51	3.75	3.42	3.52	3.42
3.00	3.46	3.43	3.72	3.57	3.87	3.49	3.64	3.31
4.00	3.52	3.53	3.74	3.67	3.88	3.53	3.70	3.30
5.00		3.72		3.82				

* Length of crest 15.969 feet, contractions suppressed.
† Length of crest 7.938 feet, with one end contraction.
‡ This model had upstream corner rounded to radius of 4 inches.

mula $(62)_1$ may be used to find the head corresponding to the velocity of approach, and then

$$q = \text{M}b(H+h)^{\frac{3}{2}} \qquad (69)_2$$

gives the discharge in cubic feet per second. For example, when M = 3.45, b = 15.0 feet, H = 1.25 feet, h = 0.02 feet, then q = 74.0 cubic feet per second. A fair estimate of the probable error of a coefficient M is from 3 to 4 percent.

The following formula has been found to give good results in automatically applying a correction for the velocity of approach for heads above 0.5 feet.

$$q = \frac{\text{M}bH^{\frac{3}{2}}}{1 - \frac{1}{3}H/(G+H)}$$

where G is the height of the weir crest above the bottom of the approach channel. It will be noted that in form the term $H/3\,(G+H)$ is similar to the correction for velocity of approach used by Bazin (Art. 66).

Prob. 69. Find the length of a waste weir which will be ample to discharge a rainfall of one inch per hour on a drainage area of 3.65 square miles the head on the crest of the weir being 2.12 feet. Also when the head is 4.24 feet.

Art. 70. The Surface Curve

The surface of the water above a weir or dam assumes a curve whose equation is a complex one, but some of the laws that govern the drop in the plane of the crest may be deduced. Let H be the head on the level of the crest measured in perfectly level water at some distance back of the weir, and let d be the depression or drop of the curve below this level in the plane of the weir (Fig. 70). Then the discharge per second q can be expressed in terms of H and d by formula $(50)_4$, placing H for h_2 and d for h_1, and making $h_0 = 0$. This formula becomes, after replacing $\frac{2}{3}\sqrt{2g}$ by M, and Q by q,

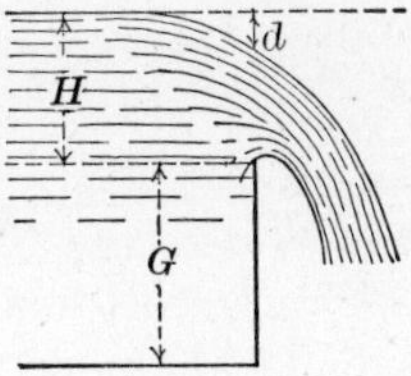

Fig. 70.

$$q = \mathrm{M} \cdot b\,(H^{\frac{3}{2}} - d^{\frac{3}{2}})$$

This expression, it may be remarked, is the true weir formula, and only the practical difficulties of measuring H and d prevent its use. This may be written

$$d^{\frac{3}{2}} = H^{\frac{3}{2}} - q/\mathrm{M}b$$

from which the drop d in the plane of crest of the weir can be found. Let B be the breadth of the feeding canal, G its depth below the crest, and v the mean velocity of approach; then also

$$q = B\,(G + H)v$$

and inserting this in the expression for $d^{\frac{3}{2}}$ it becomes

$$d^{\frac{3}{2}} = H^{\frac{3}{2}} - \frac{B}{\mathrm{M}b}(G + H)\,v \qquad (70)$$

which is an expression for the drop of the curve in terms of the dimensions of the weir, the total head, and the velocity of approach.

The approximate value of the coefficient M is about 5.3 for English measures, but precise values of d cannot be computed unless M and H are known with accuracy. The formula, however, serves to exemplify the laws which govern the drop of the curve in the plane of the weir. It shows that the drop increases with the head on the crest and with the length of a contracted weir, that it decreases with the breadth and depth of the feeding canal, and that it decreases with the velocity of approach. It also shows for suppressed weirs, where $B = b$, that the drop is independent of the length of the weir. All of these laws except the last have been previously deduced by the discussion of experiments.

The path of the stream after leaving the weir is closely that of a parabola. In the plane of the crest the mean velocity is

$$V = q/b(H - d)$$

and the direction of this may be taken as approximately horizontal. The range of a stream on a horizontal plane at the distance y below the middle of the weir notch is then readily found. For, if x be this range which is reached in the time t, then $x = Vt$, and also $y = \frac{1}{2} gt^2$; whence, by the elimination of t, there results $gx^2 = 2 V^2y$, and accordingly the horizontal range at the depth y is

$$x = \mathrm{M}\frac{H^{\frac{3}{2}} - d^{\frac{3}{2}}}{H - d}\sqrt{\frac{2y}{g}}$$

in which d is given by (70). For example, let $B = b$, also $H = 3$ feet, $G = 23$ feet, and $v = 0.67$ feet per second. From (70) the value of d is found to be 0.35 feet. Now, when $y = 50$ feet, the last formula gives $x = 11.7$ feet, which is the approximate distance of the middle of the stream from the vertical plane through the crest.

Prob. 70. In the above example what velocity of approach is necessary in order that there may be no drop in the plane of the crest? What is the range for this case?

ART. 71. TRIANGULAR WEIRS

Triangular weirs are sometimes used for the measurement of water, the arrangement being shown in Fig. 71. Let b be the width of the orifice at the water level, and H the head of water on the vertex. Let an elementary strip of the depth δy be drawn at a distance y below the water level. From similar triangles the length of this strip is $(H - y)b/H$ and the elementary discharge through it then is

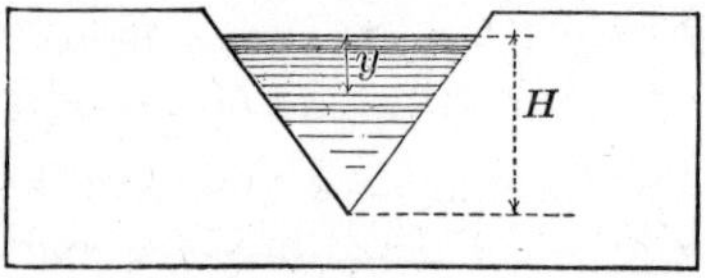

Fig. 71.

$$\delta Q = \frac{b}{H}(H - y)\,\delta y\sqrt{2gy} = \frac{b}{H}\sqrt{2g}\,(Hy^{\frac{1}{2}} - y^{\frac{3}{2}})\,\delta y$$

The integration of this between the limits H and 0 gives the theoretic discharge through the triangular weir, namely,

$$Q = \tfrac{4}{15} b \sqrt{2g} \cdot H^{\frac{3}{2}} \qquad (71)_1$$

If the sides of the triangle are equally inclined to the vertical, as should be the case in practice, and if this angle be α, the surface width b may be expressed in terms of α and H, so that the last formula becomes

$$Q = \tfrac{8}{15} \tan \alpha \cdot \sqrt{2g} \cdot H^{\frac{5}{2}} \qquad (71)_2$$

The discharge is thus equal to a constant multiplied by the $2\frac{1}{2}$ power of the measured depth.

Triangular weirs are used but little, as in general they are only convenient when the quantity of water to be measured is small. Such a weir must have sharp inner corners, so that the stream may be fully contracted, and the sides should have equal slopes. The angle at the lower vertex should be a right angle, as this is the only case for which coefficients are known with precision. The depth of water above this lower vertex is to be measured by a hook gage in the usual manner at a point several feet upstream from the notch. Making the angle at the vertex a right angle, and applying a coefficient, the actual discharge per second is given by the expression

$$q = c \cdot \tfrac{8}{15} \sqrt{2g}\, H^{\frac{5}{2}}$$

in which H is the head of water above the vertex. Experiments made by Thomson * indicate that the coefficient c varies less with the head than for ordinary weirs; this, in fact, was anticipated, since the sections of the stream are similar in a triangular notch for all values of H, and hence the influence of the contractions in diminishing the discharge should be approximately the same. As the result of his experiments the mean value of c for heads between 0.2 and 0.8 feet may be taken as 0.592, and hence the mean discharge in cubic feet per second through a right-angled triangular weir may be written

$$q = 2.53\, H^{\frac{5}{2}} \qquad (71)_3$$

* British Association Report, 1858, p. 133.

in which, as usual, H must be expressed in feet. About 4 feet is probably the greatest practicable value for H, and this gives a discharge of only 81 cubic feet per second. When velocity of approach exists, H in this formula should be replaced by $H + 1.4\,h$, as for rectangular weirs with end contractions.

Prob. 71. A triangular orifice in the side of a vessel has a horizontal base b and an altitude d, the head of water on the base being h and that on the vertex being $h + d$. Show that the theoretic discharge through the orifice is $\frac{1}{15}\sqrt{2g}(b/d)[4(h+d)^{\frac{5}{2}} - (4h+10d)h^{\frac{3}{2}}]$.

Art. 72. Trapezoidal Weirs

Trapezoidal weirs are sometimes used instead of rectangular ones, as the coefficients vary less in value. The theoretic discharge through a trapezoidal weir which has the length b on the crest, the head H, and the length $b + 2z$ on the water surface, as seen in Fig. 72, is the sum of the discharges through a rectangle of area bH and a triangle of area zH. Taking the former from $(61)_1$ and the latter from $(71)_2$, and replacing $\tan\alpha$ by z/H

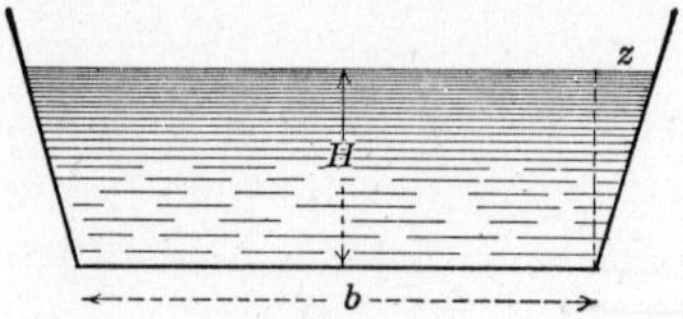

Fig. 72.

$$Q = \tfrac{2}{15}\sqrt{2g}(5b + 4z)H^{\frac{3}{2}}$$

is the theoretic discharge. Here z/H, which is the slope of the ends, may be any convenient number, and it is usually taken as $\frac{1}{4}$, as first recommended by Cippoletti.*

The reasoning from which this conclusion was derived is based upon Francis' rule that the two end contractions in a standard rectangular weir diminished the discharge by a mean amount $3.33 \times 0.2\,H^{\frac{5}{2}}$ (Art. 65), or in general by the amount $c \cdot \frac{2}{3}\sqrt{2\,g} \times 0.2\,H^{\frac{5}{2}}$. If the sides are sloped, however, the discharge through the two end triangles is $c \cdot \sqrt{2g} \times \frac{8}{15} z H^{\frac{3}{2}}$. If, now, the slope is just sufficient so that the extra discharge balances the effect of the end contractions, these two quantities are equal. Equating them, and supposing that c has the same value in each,

* Cippoletti, Canal Villoresi, 1887; see Engineering Record, Aug. 13, 1892.

there results $z = \frac{1}{4}H$. Hence for such a trapezoidal weir the discharge should be the same as that through a suppressed rectangular weir of length b, or according to Francis $q = 3.33bH^{\frac{3}{2}}$. Cippoletti, however, concluded from his experiments that the coefficient should be slightly larger, and he gave

$$q = 3.367bH^{\frac{3}{2}} \qquad (72)$$

as the formula for a trapezoidal weir when $z/H = \frac{1}{4}$. If h is the head due to velocity of approach H may be replaced by $H + 1.4$ h.

Prob. 72. Show that the Cippoletti formula may be written

$$q = c \cdot \tfrac{2}{3}\sqrt{2g}(b + 0.2H)H^{\frac{3}{2}}.$$

Art. $72\frac{1}{2}$. Proportional Weirs

A proportional weir is one so shaped that its theoretic discharge varies with the first power of the head or $Q = AH + B$ where A and B are constants. Let b be the length of the crest, as in Fig. $72\frac{1}{2}a$, where the lower part is a rectangle with the height a. Let the head on the upper part of this rectangle be k or $H = k + a$. Then the upper part of the weir is required to be so shaped that $Q = Ak + Aa + B$. The discharge consists of two parts, first that through the rectangle ab and second that through the part above the rectangle; writing expressions for these from Art. 48, and equating their sum to Q, gives

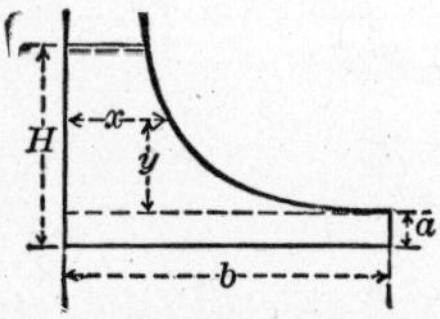

Fig. $72\frac{1}{2}a$.

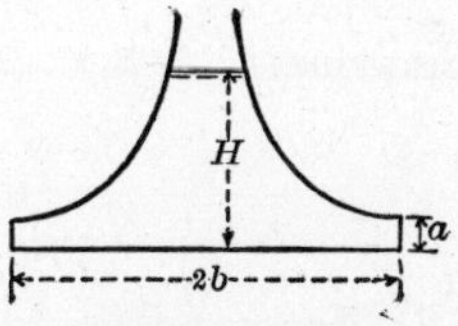

Fig. $72\frac{1}{2}b$.

$$Ak + Aa + B = \tfrac{2}{3}b\sqrt{2g}\left((a+k)^{\frac{3}{2}} - k^{\frac{3}{2}}\right) + \sqrt{2g}\int_0^k \sqrt{k - y}\cdot x\,dy$$

as the condition for finding the values of A and B and also the relation between the coordinates x and y of the curve. To do this expand $(a + k)^{\frac{3}{2}}$ according to integral powers of k, also assume

$$x = C + Dy^{\frac{1}{2}} + Ey^{\frac{3}{2}} + Fy^{\frac{5}{2}} + Gy^{\frac{7}{2}} + \ldots$$

then integrate and equate the coefficients of like powers of k; thus will be found $A = a^{\frac{1}{2}}b\sqrt{2g}$, $B = -\frac{1}{3}a^{\frac{3}{2}}b\sqrt{2g}$, $C = b$, $D = -2b/\pi a^{\frac{1}{2}}$, $E = 2b/3\pi a^{\frac{3}{2}}$, $F = -2b/5\pi a^{\frac{5}{2}}$, etc. Hence, if the curve is constructed from the equation

$$x = b - (2\pi/b)\left((y/a)^{\frac{1}{2}} - \tfrac{1}{3}(y/a)^{\frac{3}{2}} + \tfrac{1}{5}(y/a)^{\frac{5}{2}} - \tfrac{1}{7}(y/a)^{\frac{7}{2}} + \ldots\right)$$

$$\text{or } x = b(1 - (2/\pi)\tan^{-1}\sqrt{y/a}) \qquad (72\tfrac{1}{2})_1$$

then the theoretic discharge through the weir is

$$Q = a\sqrt{2g}\, a^{\frac{1}{2}} b(H - \tfrac{1}{3}a) \qquad (72\tfrac{1}{2})_2$$

This conclusion is true provided H be greater than a.

Values of x are readily computed from $(72\frac{1}{2})_1$ for assumed values of y; in this equation $2/\pi$ may be replaced by $\frac{1}{90}^\circ$ if $\tan^{-1}$ be taken in degrees; thus for $y = 2a$, $\tan^{-1}\sqrt{2} = 54^\circ 44' 8'' = 54^\circ.7355$ and $x = 0.392b$. A weir constructed in this shape is called a Sutro weir * and such have been used to measure chemical solutions for water-softening plants. Little is known about the coefficients and hence $(72\frac{1}{2})_2$ gives results too large. A Sutro weir used in 1915 at the University of California † was like Fig. $72\frac{1}{2}a$ and of dimensions $a = \frac{1}{48}$ feet, $b = 2$ feet; seventeen measurements when plotted gave the discharge formula as $q = 1.46H + 0.01$, while $(72\frac{1}{2})_2$ gives $Q = 2.32H - 0.016$. Of course a weir might be built as in Fig. $72\frac{1}{2}b$ and then the theoretic discharge would be double that of $(72\frac{1}{2})_2$.

Prob. $72\frac{1}{2}$. Perform the algebraic work above indicated and deduce the values of A, B, C, D, E, F, G.

Art. 73. Oblique Weirs

In certain cases weirs or dams are built obliquely across streams. When the velocity of the stream is small, so that the water approaches the crest in a direction sensibly at right angles to it, the discharge is proportional to the crest length and may be computed by the formulas already given. When, however, the velocity becomes so great that the water approaches the crest obliquely, the discharge tends to approximate that over a weir placed normal to the axis of the stream. This, however, is not strictly true in case the obliquity be large; in such a case the discharge is increased above that over the normal weir. An oblique weir is sometimes built to keep down the effect of backwater during floods, but it causes a loss of available head during medium and low water. The problem of the regulation of river heights is well exemplified by the conditions at the Chaudiere Dam, Ottawa.‡

Achiel § experimented on weirs inclined to the axis of the chan-

* Pratt, Engineering News, August 27, 1914, p. 462. † Moses, Engineering News, August 5, 1915, p. 277. ‡ Engineering News, June 30, 1910, p. 741. § Zeitschrift Verein Deutschen Ingenieure; see abstract in Engineering Record, July 3, 1909, p. 10.

nel at angles varying from 15 to 90°. These weirs were placed in channels 1.64 and 3.28 feet in width, the end contractions were suppressed, and the nappe was thoroughly aerated; their height was 0.82 feet and the heads ranged from 0.04 to 0.60 feet. From these experiments the formula $F_c = 1 - H/Gr$ was deduced. Here H is the measured head on the weir, G the height of the weir crest above the channel of approach, and r a number taken from the table below. F_c then is a correction factor by which the values of the coefficient for a vertical thin-edged weir are to be multiplied in order to obtain the coefficients for each unit of length of the oblique weir. This formula does

Angle of weir	=15°	30°	45°	60°	75°	90°
r for broad channels	= 1.4	2.8	5.0	9.1	26.3	∞
r for narrow channels	= 1.2	2.1	3.6	7.7	26.3	∞

not hold when the ratio H/G is greater than 0.62, and this ratio should be smaller as the obliquity of the weir increases. In general it can be said that outside the range of the few experiments which have been made but little is known on this subject.

Prob. **73.** What is the coefficient for an oblique sharp-edged weir with contractions suppressed, 19 feet long and two feet in height when the head is 0.6 feet and the obliquity of the weir 45 degrees?

Art. 74. Computations in the Metric System

The formulas for discharge in Arts. 61–64 are rational and may be used in all systems, the coefficients c being abstract numbers. In the metric system b and H are often expressed in centimeters, but they should be reduced to meters for use in the formulas, and then q will be in cubic meters per second. The mean value of $\sqrt{2g}$ is 4.427 and that of $1/2g$ is 0.05102.

(Art. 62) The head h in meters corresponding to the mean velocity of approach is to be computed from the formula

$$h = 0.05102\,(q/A)^2 \qquad (74)_1$$

in which A is in square meters. For example, take a weir where B = 200, G = 90, b = 45.1, H = 26.28 centimeters, and c = 0.620.

Then by $(63)_1$ the discharge q' is 0.1112 cubic meters per second, and from $(74)_1$ the head h is 0.0002 meters.

(Art. 63) Table 74*a* gives values of the coefficient c for weirs with end contractions, with arguments in the metric system. Thus, if $H = 5.45$ centimeters and $b = 0.45$ meters, there is found, by interpolation, $c = 0.626$, which is liable to a probable error of about two units in the third decimal place.

TABLE 74*a*. COEFFICIENTS c FOR CONTRACTED WEIRS

Arguments in Metric Measures

Effective Head in Centimeters	Length of Weir in Meters						
	0.2	0.3	0.6	0.9	1.5	3.0	5.8
3.	0.633	0.640	0.647	0.653	0.654	0.656	0.657
5.	.618	.624	.634	.638	.640	.641	.642
7.	.606	.613	.622	.625	.627	.629	.630
9.	.601	.608	.616	.619	.621	.624	.625
12.	.596	.602	.609	.613	.615	.618	.620
15.	.591	.597	.605	.608	.611	.615	.617
18.	.588	.593	.601	.605	.608	.613	.615
22.		.589	.597	.603	.606	.612	.614
26.			.594	.599	.604	.610	.613
30.			.590	.595	.601	.608	.611
35.			.586	.592	.597	.605	.610
45.				.585	.593	.601	.608

(Art. 64) Coefficients c for weirs without end contractions, with metric arguments, are given in Table 74*b*, which has been prepared by the help of Table 64.

(Art. 65) When b and H are in meters and q in cubic meters per second, Francis' formula for suppressed weirs takes the form

$$q = 1.84\, bH^{\frac{3}{2}} \tag*{$(74)_2$}$$

and for weirs with end contractions,

$$q = 1.84\,(b - 0.2\,H)\,H^{\frac{3}{2}} \tag*{$(74)_3$}$$

the number 1.84 being a mean value of $c \cdot \frac{2}{3}\sqrt{2g}$.

(Art. 67) Table 67 applies to any system of measures, and the formula $q = 1.84\, b(nH)^{\frac{3}{2}}$ then gives the discharge in cubic meters per

TABLE 74*b*. COEFFICIENTS *c* FOR SUPPRESSED WEIRS

Arguments in Metric Measures

Effective Head in Centimeters	Length of Weir in Meters						
	5.8	3.0	2.0	1.5	1.2	0.9	0.6
3.	0.658	0.659	0.659	0.660			
5.	.642	.643	.644	.645	0.647	0.649	0.652
7.	.632	.633	.634	.635	.637	.640	.643
9.	.626	.628	.629	.631	.633	.636	.639
12.	.621	.623	.625	.628	.630	.633	.636
15.	.619	.621	.624	.627	.630	.633	.637
18.	.618	.620	.623	.627	.630	.634	.638
22.	.618	.620	.624	.628	.632	.636	.640
26.	.619	.622	.627	.631	.635	.639	.645
30.	.619	.624	.628	.633	.637	.641	
35.	.620	.626	.631	.635	.640	.645	
45.	.622	.630	.635	.641	.645		

second, if b and H be in meters. The metric values of M for use in $(67)_2$ are found by multiplying those in the text by 0.5522.

(Art. 69) The formulas of the first paragraph are transformed into metric measures by replacing 3.33 by 1.84 and 3.01 by 1.72. For formula $(69)_1$ the value of M for dams may range from about 1.4 to 2.3. Table 74*c* gives metric values of M as deduced from the experiments made by Bazin in 1897, and by Rafter in 1898. The explanation of this table is in all respects like that of Table 69*a*. All values of M given in Art. 69 may be reduced to metric measures by multiplying by 0.5522, this being the ratio of the value of $\sqrt{2g}$ expressed in meters to that expressed in feet.

(Art. 71) The metric formula for discharge over the triangular weir is $q = 1.40\ H^{\frac{5}{2}}$.

(Art. 72) The metric formula for Cippoletti's trapezoidal weir takes the form $q = 1.86\ bH^{\frac{3}{2}}$.

Prob. 74*a*. Compute the head that produces a velocity of approach of 50.5 centimeters per second.

Prob. 74*b*. What are the discharges, in liters per minute, over a suppressed weir 2.35 meters long when the heads on the crest are 12.3, 12.4, and 12.5 centimeters?

Table 74c. Coefficients m for Dams

Metric Measures

Up-stream Slope	Width of Crest Meters	Down-stream Slope	Head H on Crest in Meters					
			0.15	0.30	0.60	0.91	1.22	1.52
1 on 2	0.10	Vertical	1.85	2.03	2.08	2.03	2.04	2.05
1 on 2	0.20	Vertical	1.78	1.90	2.02	2.03	2.04	2.05
1 on 5	0.20	Vertical	1.83	1.84	1.85	1.86	1.87	1.87
1 on 4	0.20	Vertical		1.90	1.92	1.92	1.92	1.92
1 on 3	0.20	Vertical	2.01	2.11	2.04	1.96	1.96	1.96
1 on 2	0.00	1 on 1	2.33	2.34	2.19	2.11	2.06	2.03
1 on 2	0.10	1 on 2	1.73	1.90	1.99	2.02	2.02	2.01
1 on 2	0.20	1 on 5	1.82	1.97	1.94	1.93	1.95	1.97
Vertical	0.80	Vertical	1.43	1.47	1.57	1.66	1.77	1.87
Vertical	0.80*	Vertical	1.63	1.66	1.70	1.79	1.87	1.92
Vertical	2.00	Vertical	1.38	1.43	1.37	1.39	1.44	1.49
Vertical	2.00*	Vertical	1.50	1.56	1.57	1.58	1.60	1.63
1 on 1	Round	Vertical	1.63	1.75	1.91	1.96	1.99	2.01

* For explanation see Art. 69.

Prob. 74*c*. Compute the discharge over a submerged weir when $b = 2.35$, $H = 0.123$, and $H' = 0.027$ meters.

Prob. 74*d*. Compute the discharge over a dam, like Fig. 68*b*, when the side slopes are 1 on 2, the length of the crest 4.25 meters, and the head on the crest 1.07 meters.

CHAPTER 7

FLOW OF WATER THROUGH TUBES

Art. 75. Loss of Energy or Head

A tube is a short pipe which may be attached to an orifice or be used for connecting two vessels. The most common form is a cylinder of uniform cross-section, but conical forms are also used, and in some cases a tube is made of cylinders with different diameters. The laws of flow through tubes are important as a starting-point for the theory of flow through pipes, for the discharge from nozzles, and for the discussion of many practical hydraulic problems. The theorem of Art. 31, that pressure-head plus velocity-head is a constant for a given section of a tube, is only true when there are no losses due to friction and impact. As a matter of fact such losses always exist and must be regarded in practical computations.

Energy in a tube filled with moving water exists in two forms, in potential energy of pressure and in kinetic energy of motion. Thus in the horizontal tube of Fig. 75*a* let two piezometers (Art. 37) be inserted at the sections a_1 and a_2 where the velocities are v_1 and v_2 and it is found that the water rises to the heights h_1 and h_2 above the middle of the tube. Let W be the weight of water that passes each section per second. Then in the first section the pressure energy per second is Wh_1 and the kinetic energy per second is $W \cdot v_1^2/2g$, so that the total energy of the water passing that section in one second is

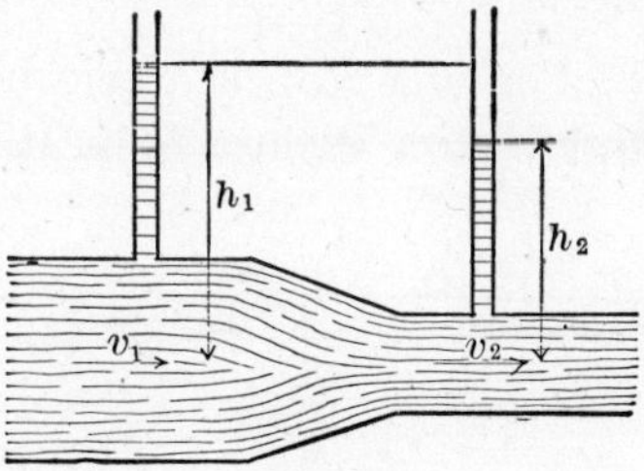

Fig. 75*a*.

$$Wh_1 + W \cdot v_1^2/2g$$

In the same manner the total energy of the water passing the second section in one second is

$$Wh_2 + W \cdot v_2^2/2g$$

but this is less than the former because some energy has been expended in friction and impact. Let Wh' be the amount of energy thus lost; then equating this to the difference of the energies in the two sections, the W cancels out and

$$h' = h_1 - h_2 + \frac{v_1^2}{2g} - \frac{v_2^2}{2g} \qquad (75)_1$$

The quantity h' is called the lost head, and the equation shows that it equals the difference of the pressure-heads plus the difference of the velocity-heads.

In hydraulics the terms "energy" and "head" are often used as equivalent, although really energy is proportional to head. In the general case, the lost head is not a loss of pressure-head only, but a loss of both pressure-head and velocity-head. When, however, the two sections are of equal area, the velocities v_1 and v_2 are equal, since the same quantity of water passes each section in one second; then the lost head h' is $h_1 - h_2$ or the loss occurs in pressure-head only. Here the loss is mainly due to the roughness of the interior surface of the tube or pipe. It should be noted that it is only necessary to measure the difference $h_1 - h_2$ and this can be done by the methods of Art. 37.

Formula $(75)_1$ is applicable to all horizontal tubes and pipes, and with a slight modification it is also applicable to inclined ones, as will be shown in Art. 85. It also applies to a flow from a standard orifice, or to the flow from an orifice to which a tube is attached.

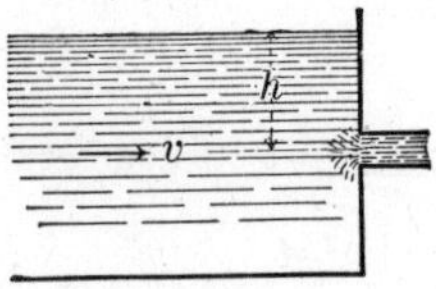

Fig. 75*b*.

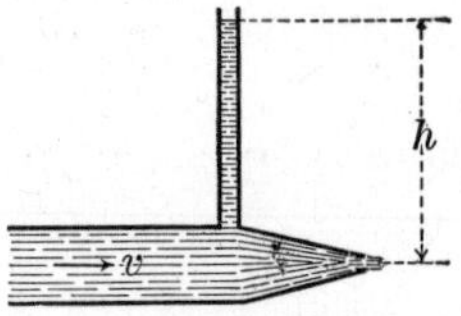

Fig. 75*c*.

Thus for the large vessel of Fig. 75*b* let the sections be taken through the vessel and through the stream as it leaves the tube. Then $h_1 = h$, and since there is no pressure outside the tube, $h_2 = 0$; also $v_1 = 0$ and $v_2 = v$; then $h' = h - v^2/2g$. For the case in Fig. 75*c*, where the stream approaches with the velocity v_1, the formula becomes $h' = h_1 + (v_1^2 - v^2)/2g$. In both cases, if h' is made zero, these equations reduce to those established in the chapter on theoretical hydraulics, where losses of energy were not considered; thus for the second case the theoretic effective head h is equal to $h_1 + v_1^2/2g$.

In order to use $(75)_1$ for numerical computations three quantities must be known, the difference $h_1 - h_2$, and the velocities v_1 and v_2. As a direct measurement of the velocities is usually impracticable, these are generally computed from the measured discharge q and the areas a_1 and a_2 of the cross-sections; thus $v_1 = q/a_1$ and $v_2 = q/a_2$. For example, let the cross-section be circular, having diameters of 18 and 6 inches, and let the discharge be 4.7 cubic feet per second; the areas are 1.767 and 0.196 square feet, and the velocities are 2.66 and 23.94 feet per second. If the difference of the pressure-heads is 8.85 feet, the lost head is

$$h' = 8.85 + 0.01555(2.66^2 - 23.94^2) = 0.05 \text{ feet}$$

The general formula $(75)_1$ may be expressed in terms of the areas of the sections and one of the velocities. Since $a_1 v_1 = a_2 v_2$ it may be written

$$h' = h_1 - h_2 + \left(1 - \frac{a_1^2}{a_2^2}\right)\frac{v_1^2}{2g} \qquad (75)_2$$

or

$$h' = h_1 - h_2 + \left(\frac{a_2^2}{a_1^2} - 1\right)\frac{v_2^2}{2g} \qquad (75)_3$$

which are often convenient forms for numerical computations.

Prob. 75. In Fig. 75*a* let the areas a_1 and a_2 be 1.0 and 0.5 square feet, $h_1 - h_2 = 0.697$ feet, and $v_1 = 3.5$ feet per second. What is the value of the lost head?

Art. 76. Loss Due to Expansion of Section

When a tube or pipe is filled with flowing water a loss of head is found to occur when the section is enlarged, so that the velocity is diminished. This case is shown in Fig. 76*a*, where v_1 and v_2 are the velocities in the smaller and larger sections and h_1 and h_2 the corresponding pressure-heads. The interior surface may be very smooth, so that friction has but little influence, and yet there will usually be more or less loss due to the fact that the velocity v_1 is changed to the smaller value v_2. Formula $(75)_1$ is here directly applicable and gives the loss of head. It is seen that $h_1 - h_2$ must be negative for this case and that its numerical value will be less than that of the difference of the velocity-heads. The general formula $(75)_1$ gives the loss of head due not only to expansion of section, but to all resistances between any two sections of a horizontal tube or pipe.

When there is a sudden enlargement of section, as in Fig. 76*b*, energy is lost in impact. In the section *AB* the pressure-

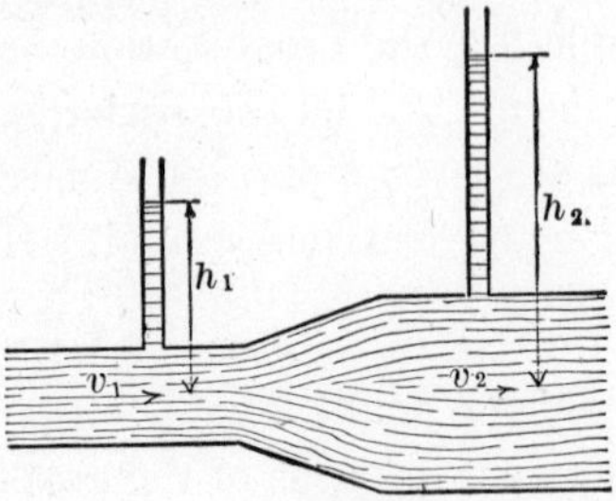

Fig. 76*a*.

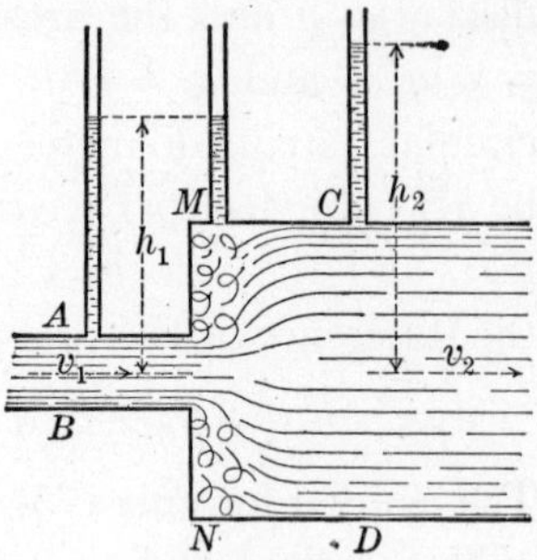

Fig. 76*b*.

head is h_1 and the velocity-head is $v_1^2/2g$, while in the section *CD* the pressure-head has the larger value h_2 and the velocity-head has the smaller value $v_2^2/2g$. At the section *MN*, near the place of sudden expansion, the pressure-head is also h_1, since the velocity v_1 is maintained for a short distance after leaving the small section; its direction, however, being changed so as to form whirls and foam. In this region the impact occurs, the velocity v_1 being finally decreased to v_2. Let a_2 be the area of the sections *MN* and *CD*, and w the weight of a cubic unit of water. Then by (15) the hydrostatic pressure normal to the section *CD* is wa_2h_2, and that normal to the section *MN* is wa_2h_1. The difference of these pressures is the force which causes the velocity v_1 to decrease to v_2, and by Art. 27, this force is equal to $W(v_1 - v_2)/g$, where W is the weight of water passing the section *CD* in one second. Hence

$$wa_2h_2 - wa_2h_1 = W\frac{v_1 - v_2}{g}$$

and, since W equals wa_2v_2, this equation becomes

$$h_2 - h_1 = \frac{v_2(v_1 - v_2)}{g}$$

Inserting this value of $h_2 - h_1$ in $(75)_1$, it reduces to

$$h' = \frac{(v_1 - v_2)^2}{2g} \qquad (76)_1$$

which is the loss of head due to sudden expansion of section, or rather due to the sudden diminution of velocity that is caused by such expansion.

When the expansion of section is made gradually and with smooth curves, the velocity v_1 will decrease without whirl and foam, so that no loss in impact occurs. In this case the kinetic energy $w \cdot v_1^2/2g$ is changed into pressure energy, as the velocity v_1 decreases to v_2. There is, however, no distinct line of demarcation between sudden and gradual expansion, so that in many practical cases it is necessary to make measurements of the discharge and of the head $h_2 - h_1$ in order to compute the lost head h' from $(75)_1$, which is a formula applicable to all cases.

Sudden enlargement of section should always be avoided in tubes and pipes owing to the loss of head that it causes, which may often be very great. For example, let there be no pressure-head in the section a_1 and let v_1 be due to a head h so that $v_1 = \sqrt{2gh}$; let the area a_2 be four times that of a_1 so that v_2 is one-fourth of v_1. The loss of head due to sudden expansion then is

$$h' = \frac{(v_1 - v_2)^2}{2g} = \tfrac{9}{16}\,h$$

so that more than one-half of the energy of the water in a_1 is lost in impact, having been changed into heat. In the section a_2 the effective head is $\frac{7}{16}\,h$, of which $\frac{1}{16}\,h$ is velocity-head and $\frac{6}{16}\,h$ is pressure-head.

Formula $(76)_1$ may be expressed in terms of the areas of the sections and one of the velocities, since $a_1v_1 = a_2v_2$. The value of h' takes the two forms

$$h' = \left(1 - \frac{a_1}{a_2}\right)^2 \frac{v_1^2}{2g} = \left(\frac{a_2}{a_1} - 1\right)^2 \frac{v_2^2}{2g} \qquad (76)_2$$

and these show that no loss of head occurs when $a_1 = a_2$.

Prob. 76. In a horizontal tube like Fig. 76*a* the diameters are 6 inches and 12 inches, and the heights of the pressure-columns or piezometers are 12.16 feet and 12.96 feet above the same bench-mark. Find the loss of head between the two sections when the discharge is 1.57 cubic feet per second, and also when it is 4.71 cubic feet per second.

Art. 77. Loss Due to Contraction of Section

When a sudden contraction of section in the direction of the flow occurs, as in Fig. 77, the water suffers a contraction similar to that in the standard orifice, and hence in its expansion to fill the second section a loss of head results. Let v_1 be the velocity in the larger section and v that in the smaller, while v' is the velocity in the contracted section of the flowing stream; and let a_1, a, and a' be the corresponding areas of the cross-sections. From the formula $(76)_2$ the loss of head due to the expansion of section from a' to a is

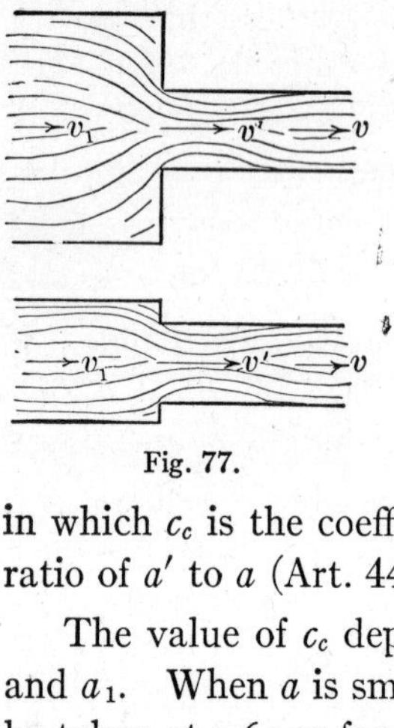

Fig. 77.

$$h' = \left(\frac{a}{a'} - 1\right)^2 \frac{v^2}{2g} = \left(\frac{1}{c'} - 1\right)^2 \frac{v^2}{2g} \qquad (77)_1$$

in which c_c is the coefficient of contraction of the stream or the ratio of a' to a (Art. 44).

The value of c_c depends upon the ratio between the areas a and a_1. When a is small compared with a_1, the value of c_c may be taken at 0.62 as for orifices (Art. 44). When a is equal to a_1, there is no contraction or expansion of the stream and c_c is unity. Let d and d_1 be the diameters corresponding to the areas a and a_1, and let r be the ratio of d to d_1. Then experiments seem to indicate that an expression of the form

$$c_c = m + \frac{n}{1.1 - r}$$

gives the law of variation of c' with r. Placing $c_c = 0.62$ and $r = 0$ gives one equation between m and n; placing $c_c = 1.00$ and $r = 1$ gives another equation; and the solution of these furnishes the values of m and n. Thus is found

$$c_c = 0.582 + \frac{0.0418}{1.1 - r} \qquad (77)_2$$

from which approximate values of c_c can be computed:

for	$r = 0.0$	0.4	0.6	0.7	0.8	0.9	0.95	1.0
	$c_c' = 0.62$	0.64	0.67	0.69	0.72	0.79	0.86	1.00

from which intermediate values may often be taken without the necessity of using the formula.

For a case of gradual contraction of section, such as shown in Fig. 75*a*, the loss of head is less than that given by formula $(77)_1$, and it can only be determined from three measured quantities by the help of the general formulas of Art. 75. If the change of section is made so that the stream has no subsequent enlargement, loss of head is avoided; for, as the above discussions show, it is the loss in velocity due to sudden expansion which causes the loss of head.

The loss due to sudden contraction of a tube or pipe is often much smaller than that due to sudden expansion. For instance, let the diameter of the large section be three times that of the smaller, and the velocity in the large section be 2 feet per second, then the loss of head which occurs when the flow passes from the small to the large section is, by Art. 76,

$$h' = 0.01555(18 - 2)^2 = 4.0 \text{ feet}$$

But if the flow occurs in the opposite direction, the ratio r is $\frac{1}{3}$, the coefficient c' is about 0.64, and the loss of head is

$$h' = 0.01555\left(\frac{1}{0.64} - 1\right)^2 18^2 = 1.6 \text{ feet}$$

When, however, the ratio r is higher than 0.77, the loss due to sudden contraction is greater than that due to sudden expansion. Thus, if the diameter of the small section be nine-tenths that of the large one and the velocity in the large section be 2 feet per second, the loss of head when the flow passes from the small to the large section is

$$h' = 0.01555\left(\frac{1}{0.81} - 1\right)^2 2^2 = 0.0034 \text{ feet}$$

But if the flow occurs in the opposite direction, the ratio r is 0.9, the coefficient c' is 0.79, and the loss of head is

$$h' = 0.01555\left(\frac{1}{0.79} - 1\right)^2 2.47^2 = 0.0066 \text{ feet}$$

As formula $(77)_2$ is an empirical one the results derived from it are to be regarded as approximate.

Prob. 77. Compute the loss of head when a pipe which discharges 1.57 cubic feet per second suddenly diminishes in section from 12 to 6 inches in diameter.

Art. 78. The Standard Short Tube

An adjutage is a tube inserted into an orifice, and the short-tube adjutage, consisting of a cylinder whose length is about three times its diameter, is the most common form. For convenience it will be called the standard short tube, because its theory and coefficients form a starting-point with which all other adjutages may be compared. This short tube is of little value for the measurement of water, since the coefficients for standard orifices are much more definitely known. The discussion here given is for the case where the inner edge is a sharp, definite corner like that of the standard orifice (Art. 43). When the tube is only two diameters in length, the stream passes through without touching it, as in Fig. 78a, and the discharge is the same as from the orifice. When it is lengthened sufficiently, the stream expands and fills the tube, as in Fig. 78b, and the discharge is much increased. By observations on glass tubes it is seen that the stream usually contracts after leaving the inner end of the tube and then expands. This contraction

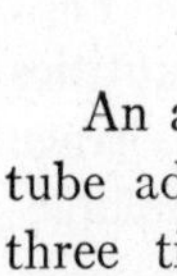

Fig. 78a.

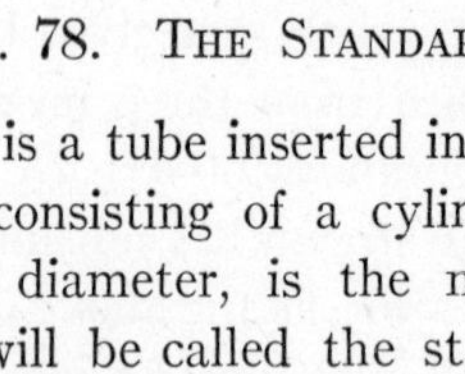

Fig. 78b.

may be apparently destroyed by agitating the water or by striking the tube, and the entire tube is then filled, yet if a hole is bored in the tube near its inner end, water does not flow out, but air enters, showing that a negative pressure exists.

An estimate of the velocity and discharge from this short-tube adjutage may be made as follows: Let h be the head on the inner end of the tube and v the velocity of the outflowing water. The head h equals the velocity-head $v^2/2g$ plus all the losses of head. At the inner edge a loss of $0.11\ v^2/2g$ occurs in entering the tube, as in the standard orifice (Art. 56), and then there is a loss of $(v' - v)^2/2g$ when the contracted stream suddenly expands so that its velocity v' is reduced to v (Art. 76). If a' and a are the areas of these two sections, their ratio a'/a is the coefficient of contraction c_c. Then

$$h = 0.11\frac{v^2}{2g} + \left(\frac{1}{c_c} - 1\right)^2\frac{v^2}{2g} + \frac{v^2}{2g}$$

Now, taking for c_c its mean value 0.62, this equation reduces to $v = 0.82\sqrt{2gh}$, or the coefficient of velocity of the issuing jet is 0.82. Since the cross-section of the stream at the outer end of the tube is the same as that of the tube, the coefficient of contraction for that end is unity, and hence (Art. 46) the mean value of the coefficient of discharge is also 0.82.

While this theoretic discussion does not take account of losses due to the small frictional resistances along the sides of the tube after the stream has expanded, the mean results of the experiments of Venturi and Bossut give closely the same coefficient. Hence both theory and practice agree in establishing as an average value for the short tube,

$$\text{Coefficient of discharge } c = 0.82$$

This coefficient, however, ranges from 0.83 for low heads to 0.79 for high heads. It is greater for large tubes than for small ones, its law of variation being probably the same as for orifices (Art. 47), but sufficient experiments have not been made to state definite values in the form of a table.

A standard orifice gives on the average about 61 percent of the theoretic discharge, but by the addition of a tube this may be increased to 82 percent. The velocity-head of the jet from the tube is, however, much less than that from the orifice. For, let v be the velocity and h the head, then (Art. 45) for the standard orifice

$$v = 0.98\sqrt{2gh} \quad \text{or} \quad v^2/2g = 0.96\,h$$

and similarly for the standard tube

$$v = 0.82\sqrt{2gh} \quad \text{or} \quad v^2/2g = 0.67\,h$$

Accordingly the velocity-head of the stream from the standard orifice is 96 percent of the theoretic velocity-head, and that of the stream from the standard tube is only 67 percent. Or if jets are directed vertically upward from a standard orifice and tube, as in Fig. 78*c*, that from the former rises to the height 0.96 h, while that from the latter rises to the height 0.67 h, where h is the head measured downward from the surface of water in the reservoir to the point of exit from the orifice.

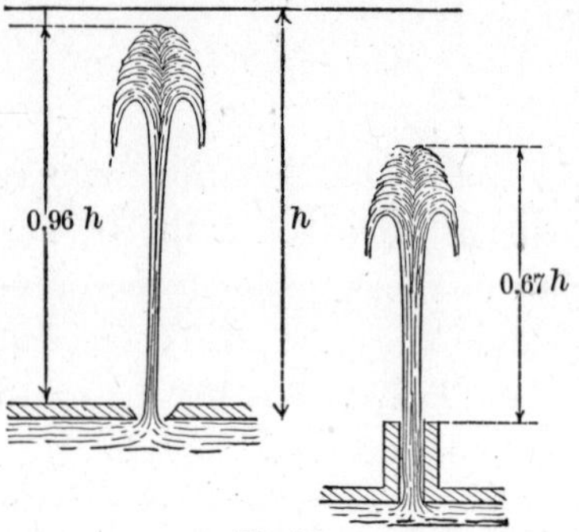

Fig. 78*c*.

The energy lost in the stream from the standard orifice is hence 4 percent of the theoretic energy, but 33 percent is lost in the stream from the standard tube. In reality energy is never lost, but is merely transformed into other forms of energy. In the tube the one-third of the total energy which has been called lost is only lost because it cannot be utilized as work; it is, in fact, transformed into heat, which raises the temperature of the water. The above explanation shows that most of this loss is due to impact resulting from sudden expansion of the stream.

The loss of head in the flow from the short tube is large, but not so large as might be expected from theoretical considerations based on the known coefficients for orifices. When the tube has a length of only two diameters, the water does not touch its inner surface, and the flow occurs as from a standard orifice. The velocity in the plane of the inner end is then 61 percent of the theoretic velocity, since the mean coefficient of discharge is 0.61. Now when the tube is sufficiently increased in length, its outer end will be filled, and if the contraction still exists, it might be inferred that the coefficient for that end would be also 0.61; this would give a velocity-head of $(0.61)^2 h$ or $0.37\,h$, so that the loss of head would be $0.63\,h$. Actually, however, the coefficient is found to be 0.82 and the loss of head only $0.33\,h$. It hence appears that further explanation is needed to account for the increased discharge and energy.

In the first place, a loss of about $0.04\,h$ occurs at the inner end of the tube in the same manner as in the standard orifice, and only the head $0.96\,h$ is then available for the subsequent phenomena. If the coefficient c_c for the contracted section has the value 0.62, the velocity in that section is

$$v' = \frac{0.82}{0.62}\sqrt{2gh} = 1.32\sqrt{2gh}$$

and the velocity-head for that section is

$$v'^2/2g = 1.75\,h$$

and consequently the pressure-head in that section is

$$0.96\,h - 1.75\,h = -0.79\,h$$

There exists therefore a negative pressure or partial vacuum near the inner end of the tube which is sufficient to lift a column of water to a height of about three-fourths the head. This conclusion has been confirmed by experiment for low heads, and was in fact first discovered experimentally by Venturi. For high heads it is not valid, since in no event can atmospheric pressure raise a column of water higher than about 34 feet (Art. 4); probably under high heads the coefficient of contraction of the stream in the tube becomes much greater than 0.62.

The cause of the increased discharge of the tube over the orifice is hence a partial vacuum, which causes a portion of the atmospheric head of 34 feet to be added to the head h, so that the flow at the contracted section occurs as if under the head $h + h_1$. The occurrence of this partial vacuum is attributed to the friction of the water on the air. When the flow begins, the stream is surrounded by air of the normal atmospheric pressure which is imprisoned as the stream fills the tube. The friction of the moving water carries some of this air out with it, thus rarefying the remaining air. This rarefaction, or negative pressure, is followed by an increased velocity of flow, and the process continues until the air around the contracted section is so rarefied that no more is removed, and the flow then remains permanent, giving the results ascertained by experiment. The partial vacuum causes neither a gain nor loss of head, for although it increases the velocity-head at the contracted section to 1.75 h, there must be expended 0.79 h in order to overcome the atmospheric pressure at the outer end of the tube. The experiments of Buff have proved that in an almost complete vacuum the discharge of the tube is but little greater than that of the orifice.*

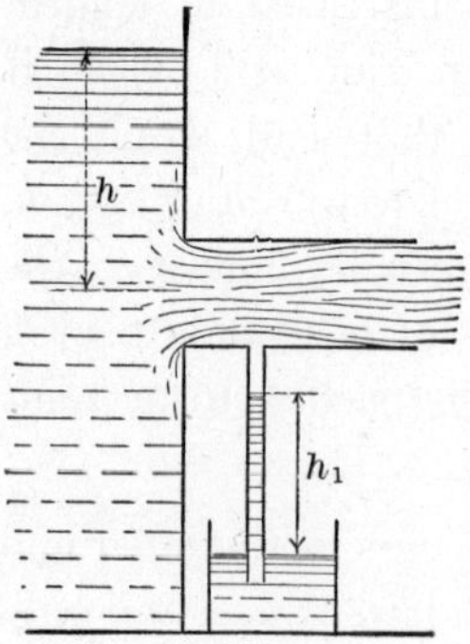

Fig. 78*d*.

Prob. 78. When the coefficient of contraction for the contracted section is 0.70, find the probable coefficient of discharge and also the negative pressure-head.

Art. 79. Conical Converging Tubes

Conical converging tubes are used when it is desired to obtain a high efficiency in the energy of the stream of water. At *A*, Fig. 79, is shown a simple converging tube, consisting of a frustum of a cone, and at *B* is a similar frustum provided with a cylindrical tip. The proportions of these converging tubes, or mouthpieces, vary somewhat in practice, but the cylindrical tip when employed is of a length equal to about 2½ times its inner diameter, while the conical part is eight or ten times the length of that

* Annalen der Physik und Chemik, 1839, vol. 46, p. 242.

diameter, the angle at the vertex of the cone being between 10 and 20 degrees.

The stream from a conical converging tube like *A* suffers a contraction at some distance beyond the end. The coefficient of discharge is higher than that of the standard tube, being generally between 0.85 and 0.95, while the coefficient of velocity is higher still. Experiments made by d'Aubuisson and Castel on conical converging tubes 0.04 meters long and 0.0155 meters in diameter at the small end, under a head of 3 meters, furnish the coefficients of discharge and velocity given in Table 79.

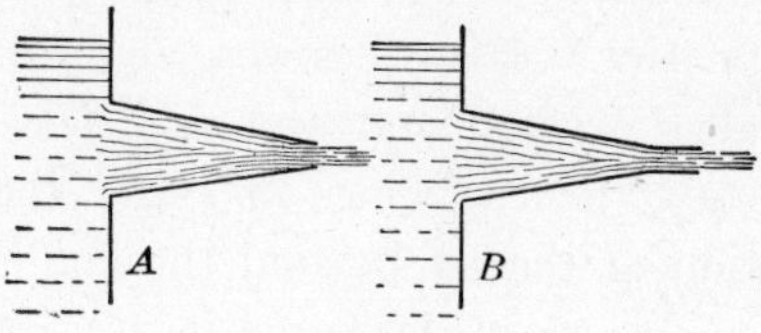

Fig. 79.

TABLE 79. COEFFICIENTS FOR CONICAL TUBES

Angle of Cone	Discharge c	Velocity c_v	Contraction c_c
0° 00′	0.829	0.829	1.00
1 36	.866	.867	
4 10	.912	.910	
7 52	.930	.932	0.998
10 20	.938	.951	.986
13 24	.946	.963	.983
16 36	.938	.971	.966
21 00	.919	.972	.945
29 58	.895	.975	.918
48 50	.847	.984	.861

The former of these was determined by measuring the actual discharge (Art. 46), and the latter by the range of the jet (Art. 45). The coefficient of contraction as computed from these is given in the last column, and this applies to the jet at the smallest section, some distance beyond the end of the tube. While these values show that the greatest discharge occurred for an angle of about 13½°, they also indicate that the coefficient of velocity increases with the convergence of the cone, becoming about equal to that of a standard orifice for the last value. Hence the table seems to teach that a conical frustum does not usually give as high a velocity as a standard orifice.

Under very high heads, over 300 feet, Hamilton Smith found the actual discharge to agree closely with the theoretical, or the coefficient of discharge was nearly 1.0, and in some cases slightly greater.* His tubes were about 0.9 feet long, 0.1 feet in diameter at the small end and 0.35 feet at the large end, the angle of convergence being 17°. As these figures indicate a contraction of the jet beyond the end, it cannot be supposed that the coefficient of discharge in any case was really as high as his experiments indicate. Under these high heads the cylindrical tip applied to the end of a tube produced no effect on the discharge, the jet passing through without touching its surface.

Prob. 79. When the coefficient of discharge of a tube is 0.98 and the coefficient of velocity of the jet is 0.995, compute the coefficient of contraction of the jet.

Art. 80. Inward Projecting Tubes

Inward projecting tubes, as a rule, give a less discharge than those whose ends are flush with the side of the reservoir, due to the greater convergence of the lines of direction of the filaments of water. At A and B, Fig. 80, are shown inward projecting tubes so short that the water merely touches their inner edges, and hence they may more properly be called orifices. Experiment shows that the case at A, where the sides of the tube are

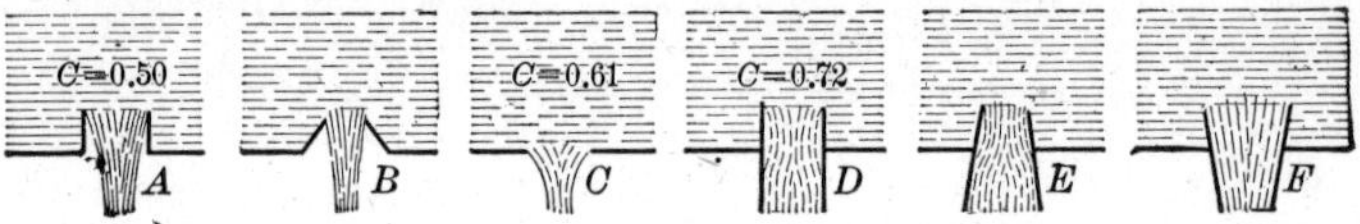

Fig. 80.

normal to the side of the reservoir, gives the minimum coefficient of discharge $c = 0.5$, while for B the value lies between 0.5 and that for the standard orifice at C. The inward projecting cylindrical tube at D has been found to give a discharge of about 72 percent of the theoretic discharge, while the standard tube

* Hydraulics (London and New York, 1886), p. 286.

(Art. 78) gives 82 percent. For the tubes E and F the coefficients depend upon the amount of inward projection, and they are much larger than 0.72 for both cases, when computed for the area of the smaller end.

It is usually more convenient to allow a water-main to project inward into the reservoir than to arrange it with its mouth flush to a vertical side. The case D, in Fig. 80, is therefore of practical importance in considering the entrance of water into the main. As the end of such a main has a flange, forming a partial bell-shaped mouth, the value of c is probably higher than 0.72. The usual value taken is 0.82, or the same as for the standard tube. Practically, as will be seen later, it makes little difference which of these is used, as the velocity in a water-main is slow and the resistance at the mouth is very small compared with the frictional resistances along its length.

Prob. 80. Find the coefficient of discharge for a tube whose diameter is one inch when the flow under a head of 9 feet is 22.1 cubic feet in 3 minutes and 30 seconds.

Art. 81. Diverging and Compound Tubes

In Fig. 81 is shown a diverging conical tube, BC, and two compound tubes. The compound tube ABC consists of two cones, the converging one, AB, being much shorter than the diverging one, BC, so that the shape roughly approximates to the form of the contracted jet which issues from an orifice in a thin plate. In the tube AE the curved converging part AB closely imitates the contracted jet, and BB is a short cylinder in which all the filaments of the stream are supposed to move in lines parallel to the axis of the tube, the remaining part being a frustum of a cone. The converging part of a compound tube is often called a mouthpiece and the diverging part an adjutage.

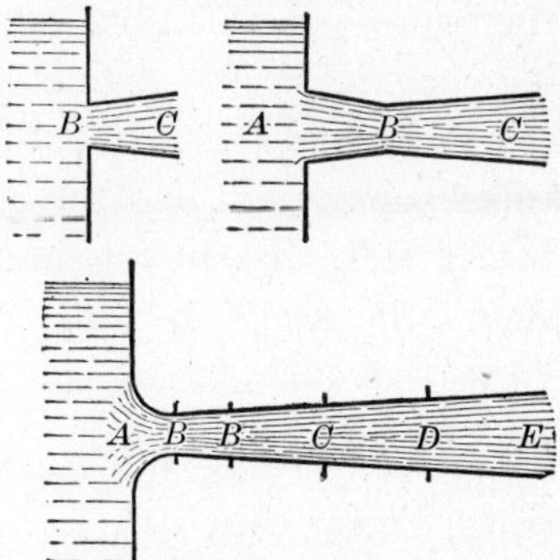

Fig. 81.

Many experiments with these tubes have shown the interesting fact that the discharge and the velocity through the smallest section, *B*, are greater than those due to the head; or, in other words, that the coefficients of discharge and velocity for this section are greater than unity. One of the first to notice this was Bernouilli in 1738, who found $c = 1.08$ for a diverging tube. Venturi in 1791 experimented on such tubes, and showed that the angle of the diverging part, as also its length, greatly influenced the discharge. He concluded that c would have a maximum value of 1.46 when the length of the diverging part was nine times its least diameter, the angle at the vertex of the cone being $5^\circ\ 06'$. Eytelwein found $c = 1.18$ for a diverging tube like *BC* in Fig. 81, but when this tube was used as an adjutage to a mouthpiece *AB*, thus forming a compound tube *ABC*, he found $c = 1.55$.

The experiments of Francis in 1854 on a compound tube like *ABCDE* are very interesting.* The curve of the converging part *AB* was a cycloid, *BB* was a cylinder, and the diameters at *A*, *B*, *C*, *D*, and *E* were 1.4, 0.102, 0.145, 0.234, and 0.321 feet. The piece *BB* was 0.1 feet long, and the others each 1 foot; these were made to screw together, so that experiments could be made on different lengths. A sixth piece, *EF*, not shown in the figure, was also used, which was a prolongation of the diverging cone, its largest diameter being 0.4085 feet. The tubes were cast iron, and quite smooth. The flow was measured with the tubes submerged, and the effective head varied from about 0.01 to 1.5 feet. Excluding heads less than 0.1 feet, the following shows the range in value of the coefficients of discharge:

	c for Section *BB*	c for Outer End
for tube *AB*,	0.80 to 0.94	0.80 to 0.94
for tube *AC*,	1.43 to 1.59	0.70 to 0.78
for tube *AD*,	1.98 to 2.16	0.37 to 0.41
for tube *AE*,	2.08 to 2.43	0.21 to 0.24
for tube *AF*,	2.05 to 2.42	0.13 to 0.15

* Lowell Hydraulic Experiments, 4th Edition, pp. 209–232.

The maximum discharge was thus found to occur with the tube *AE*, and to be 2.43 times the theoretic discharge that would be expected for the small section *BB*. In general the coefficients increased with the heads, the value 2.08 being for a head of 0.13 feet and 2.43 for a head of 1.36 feet; for 1.39 feet, however, c was found to be 2.26.

These coefficients of discharge are the same as the coefficients of velocity, since the tube was entirely filled. Thus, when the coefficient for the section *BB* was 2.43, the velocity was

$$v = 2.43\sqrt{2gh},$$

and the velocity-head was

$$v^2/2g = (2.43)^2h = 5.90h$$

Therefore the flow through the section *BB* was that due to a head 5.9 times greater than the actual head of 1.36 feet; or, in other words, the energy of the water flowing in *BB* was 5.9 times the theoretic energy. Here, apparently, is a striking contradiction of the fundamental law of the conservation of energy. The explanation of this apparent contradiction is the same as that given in Art. 78 for the short-tube adjutage. The increased velocity and discharge is due to the occurrence of a partial vacuum near the inner end of the adjutage *BC*. The pressure of the atmosphere on the water in the reservoir thus increases the hydrostatic pressure due to the head, and the increased flow results. The energy at the smallest section is accordingly higher than the theoretic energy, but the excess of this above that due to the head must be expended in overcoming the atmospheric pressure on the outer end of the tube, so that in no case does the available exceed the theoretic energy. No contradiction of the law of conservation therefore exists.

To render this explanation more definite, let the extreme case be considered where a complete vacuum exists near the inner end of the adjutage, if that were possible, as it perhaps might be with a tube of a certain form. Let h be the head of water in feet on the center of the smallest section. The mean atmospheric pressure on the water in the reservoir is equivalent to a head of 34 feet (Art. 4). Hence the total head which causes the discharge into the vacuum is $h + 34$

and the velocity of flow is nearly $\sqrt{2g(h+34)}$. Neglecting the resistances, which are very slight if the entrance is curved, the coefficients of velocity and discharge can now be found; thus:

$$\text{for } h = 100, \qquad v = \sqrt{2g \times 134} = 1.16\sqrt{2gh}$$
$$\text{for } h = 10, \qquad v = \sqrt{2g \times 44} = 2.10\sqrt{2gh}$$
$$\text{for } h = 1, \qquad v = \sqrt{2g \times 35} = 5.92\sqrt{2gh}$$

The coefficient hence increases as the head decreases. That this is not the case in the above experiments is undoubtedly due to the fact that the vacuum was only partial, and that the degree of rarefaction varied with the velocity. The cause of the vacuum, in fact, is to be attributed to the velocity of the stream, which by friction removes a part of the air from the inner end of the adjutage.

It follows from this explanation that the phenomena of increased discharge from a compound tube could not be produced in the absence of air. The experiment has been tried on a small scale under the receiver of an air-pump, and it was found that the actual flow through the narrow section diminished the more complete the rarefaction. It also follows that it is useless to state any value as representing, even approximately, the coefficient of discharge for such tubes.

Prob. 81. Compute the pressure per square inch in the section BB of Francis' tube when $h = 1.36$ feet and $c = 2.43$. What is the height of the column of water that can be lifted by a small pipe inserted at BB?

Art. 82. Submerged Tubes

As shown in Art. 51 the effective head h which causes the flow through a submerged orifice or tube is the difference in the level of the water above and below the orifice or tube. This difference h, as in Fig. 82, also represents the loss of head occasioned by the flow through the tube. The discharge through a submerged tube is probably somewhat less than that from the same tube when discharging freely into the air. Stewart,* at the laboratory of the

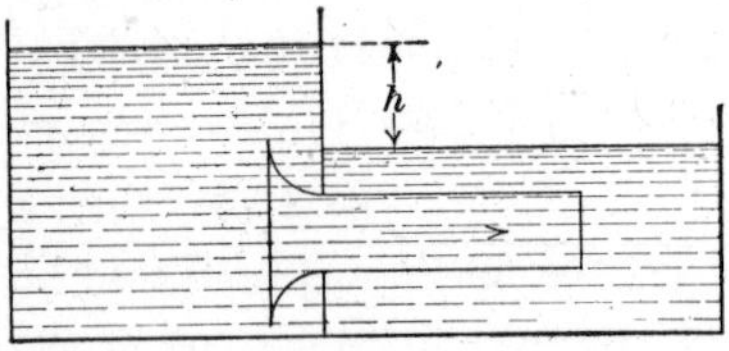

Fig. 82.

* Engineering Record, Sept. 28, 1907.

University of Wisconsin, experimented on large submerged tubes from 4 feet by 4 feet square. These tubes varied in length from 0.3 to 14.0 feet, while the heads *h* ranged from 0.05 to 0.30 feet. Experiments were made under various conditions of entrance by placing at the mouth of the tubes an elliptical mouthpiece as shown in Fig. 82. This mouthpiece was made in four parts, and after experiments with the straight square-edged tube had been run, others with the bottom of the mouthpiece in place, with the bottom and one side, with the bottom and two sides, and with all four of its parts in position were made.

In the following table are shown the results of these experiments; the coefficients in the first line opposite each head being those for the square-edged tube, while those in the second line are for the same tube with the full elliptical mouthpiece in position as shown.

TABLE 82. COEFFICIENTS FOR SUBMERGED TUBES

Head in Feet	Length of Tube in Feet						
	0.31	0.62	1.25	2.50	5.00	10.00	14.00
0.05	0.631	0.650	0.672	0.769	0.807	0.824	0.838
	.948			.943	.940	.927	.931
0.10	0.611	0.631	0.647	0.718	0.763	0.780	0.795
	.932			.911	.899	.892	.893
0.15	0.609	0.628	0.644	0.708	0.758	0.779	0.794
	.936			.910	.899	.893	.894
0.20	0.609	0.630	0.647	0.711	0.768	0.794	0.809
	.948			.923	.911	.906	.905
0.25	0.610	0.634	0.652	0.720	0.782	0.812	0.828
	.965			.938	.928		
0.30	0.614	0.639	0.660	0.731	0.769	0.832	0.850

From an inspection of these results it appears that the coefficients for the square-edged tubes increase both with the head and with the length of the tube, while for the tubes fitted with the mouthpiece they increase with the head but decrease with the length of the tube. This behavior is readily explained if it be remembered that the larger quantities carried with the mouthpiece in position must cause more friction and so cause a reduction in the effective head. The length of the square-edged tubes experimented on was evidently not sufficient to cause the friction in them to overcome the tendency to greater discharge due to contraction at entrance and subsequent expansion in the tube.

Prob. 82. What will be the discharge through a submerged square-edged tube 5 feet by 4 feet in section and 10 feet long, when the difference between the water levels above and below it is 0.5 feet?

Art. 83. Nozzles and Jets

For fire service two forms of nozzles are in use. The smooth nozzle is essentially a conical tube like *A* in Fig. 79, the larger end being attached to a hose, but it is often provided with a cylindrical tip and sometimes the larger end is curved, as shown in Fig. 83*a*. The ring nozzle is a similar tube, but its end is con-

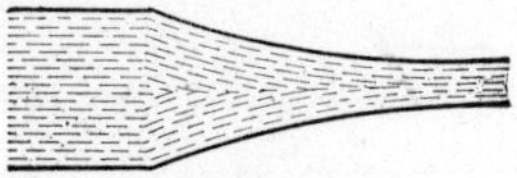

Fig. 83*a*.

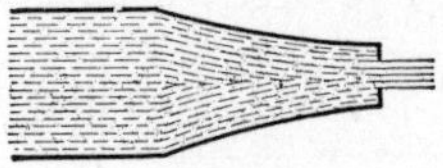

Fig. 83*b*.

tracted so that the water issues through an orifice smaller than the end of the tube. The experiments of Freeman show that the mean coefficient of discharge is about 0.97 for the smooth nozzle and about 0.74 for the ring nozzle.* The smooth nozzle is used much more than the ring nozzle.

Let d be the diameter of the pipe or hose and D the diameter of the outlet at the end of the nozzle, and let v and V be the corresponding velocities. Let h_1 be the pressure-head at the entrance to the nozzle; then the effective head at the entrance to the nozzle is

$$H = h_1 + \frac{v^2}{2g}$$

and the velocity at the end of the nozzle is $V = c_v \sqrt{2gH}$, where c_v is the coefficient of velocity. The reasoning of Art. 50 applies here, if the ratio D^2/d^2 is used in place of a/A, and h_1 in place of h, and hence

$$V = c_v \sqrt{\frac{2gh_1}{1 - c^2(D/d)^4}} \qquad (83)_1$$

* Transactions American Society of Civil Engineers, 1889, vol. 21, pp. 303–482.

is the velocity of flow from the nozzle, c being the coefficient of discharge. The discharge per second is, from formula $(50)_2$,

$$q = 0.7854 D^2 \sqrt{\frac{2gh_1}{(1/c)^2 - (D/d)^4}} \qquad (83)_2$$

The effective head at the nozzle entrance is

$$H = \frac{1}{c_v^2} \cdot \frac{V^2}{2g} = \frac{h_1}{1 - c^2(D/d)^4}$$

and the velocity-head of the issuing jet is

$$\frac{V^2}{2g} = \frac{c_v^2 h_1}{1 - c^2(D/d)^4}$$

which gives the height to which the jet would rise if there were no atmospheric resistances. In these formulas D/d is an abstract number, and to find its value D and d may be taken in any unit of measure.

When h_1 and D are in feet, g is to be taken as 32.16 feet per second per second. Then $(83)_1$ gives V in feet per second and $(83)_2$ gives q in cubic feet per second. When the gage at the nozzle entrance gives the pressure p_1 in pounds per square inch, h_1 in feet is found from $2.304 p_1$. It is a common practice in figuring on fire-streams to compute the discharge in gallons per minute. For this case, if D is taken in inches,

$$q = 29.83 D^2 \sqrt{\frac{p_1}{(1/c)^2 - (D/d)^4}}$$

gives the discharge in gallons per minute.

For smooth nozzles the value of the coefficient of velocity c_v is the same as that of the coefficient of discharge c, since the jet issues without contraction. The experiments of Freeman furnish the following mean values of the coefficient of discharge for smooth cone nozzles of different diameters under pressure-heads ranging from 45 to 180 feet:

Diameter in inches =	$\frac{3}{4}$	$\frac{7}{8}$	1	$1\frac{1}{8}$	$1\frac{1}{4}$	$1\frac{3}{8}$
Coefficient c =	0.983	0.982	0.972	0.976	0.971	0.959

These values were determined by measuring the pressure p_1 and the discharge q, from which c can be computed by the last formula. For example, a nozzle having a diameter of 1.001 inches at the end and 2.50 inches at the base discharged 208.5 gallons per minute under a pressure of 50 pounds per square inch at the entrance. Here $D = 1.001$, $d = 2.5$, $p_1 = 50$, and $q = 208.5$, and inserting these in the formula and solving for c, there is found $c = 0.971$.

In ring nozzles the ring which contracts the entrance is usually only $\frac{1}{16}$ or $\frac{1}{8}$ inch in width. The effect of this is to diminish the discharge, but the stream is sometimes thrown to a slightly greater height. On the whole, ring nozzles seem to have no advantage over smooth ones for fire purposes. As the stream contracts after leaving the nozzle, the coefficient of velocity c_v is greater than the coefficient of discharge c. The value of c being about 0.74, that of c_v is probably a little larger than 0.97. In using $(83)_1$ for ring nozzles these values of c_v and c should be inserted, but in using $(83)_2$ only the value of c is needed.

According to Freeman's experiments, the discharge of a $\frac{7}{8}$-inch ring nozzle is the same as that of a $\frac{3}{4}$-inch smooth nozzle, while the discharge of a $1\frac{1}{4}$-inch ring nozzle is about 20 percent greater than that of a 1-inch smooth nozzle. The heights of vertical jets from a $1\frac{1}{4}$-inch ring nozzle are about the same as those from a 1-inch smooth nozzle, while the jets from a $1\frac{3}{8}$-inch ring nozzle are slightly less in height than those from a $1\frac{1}{4}$-inch smooth nozzle.

The vertical height of a jet from a nozzle is very much less, on account of the resistance of the air, than the value deduced above for $V^2/2g$. For instance, let a smooth nozzle 1 inch in diameter attached to a 2.5-inch hose have $c = 0.97$ and the pressure-head $h_1 = 230$ feet; then the computation gives the velocity-head $V^2/2g$ as 221 feet, whereas the average of the highest drops in still air will be about 152 feet high and the main body of water will be several feet lower. Table 83, compiled from the results of Freeman's experiments, shows for three different smooth nozzles the height of vertical jets, column A giving the heights reached by the average of the highest drops in still air, and column B the maximum limits of height as a good effective fire-stream

TABLE 83. VERTICAL JETS FROM SMOOTH NOZZLES

Indicated Pressure at Entrance to Nozzle Pounds per Square Inch	From $\frac{3}{4}$-inch Nozzle			From 1-inch Nozzle			From $1\frac{1}{4}$-inch Nozzle		
	Height in Feet		Discharge Gallons per Minute	Height in Feet		Discharge Gallons per Minute	Height in Feet		Discharge Gallons per Minute
	A	B		A	B		A	B	
10	20	17	52	21	18	93	22	19	148
20	40	33	73	43	35	132	44	37	209
30	59	48	90	63	51	161	66	53	256
40	78	60	104	83	64	186	86	67	296
50	93	67	116	101	73	208	107	77	331
60	104	72	127	117	79	228	126	85	363
70	114	76	137	130	85	246	140	91	392
80	123	79	147	140	89	263	150	95	419
90	129	81	156	147	92	279	157	99	444
100	134	83	164	152	96	295	161	101	468

with moderate wind. The discharges given depend only on the pressure, and are the same for horizontal as for vertical jets.

The maximum horizontal distance to which a jet can be thrown is also a measure of the efficiency of a nozzle. The following, taken from Freeman's tables, gives the horizontal distances at the level of the nozzle reached by the average of the extreme drops in still air. The practical horizontal distance for an effective fire-stream is, however, only about one-half of these figures.

Pressure at nozzle entrance,	20	40	60	80	100 pounds.
From $\frac{3}{4}$-inch smooth nozzle,	72	112	136	153	167 feet.
From 1-inch smooth nozzle,	77	133	167	189	205 feet.
From $1\frac{1}{4}$-inch smooth nozzle,	83	148	186	213	236 feet.
From $1\frac{1}{8}$-inch ring nozzle,	76	131	164	186	202 feet.
From $1\frac{1}{4}$-inch ring nozzle,	78	138	172	196	215 feet.
From $1\frac{3}{8}$-inch ring nozzle,	79	144	180	206	227 feet.

The ball nozzle, often used for sprinkling, has a cup at the end of the nozzle and within the cup a ball, so that the jet issuing from the tip of the nozzle is deflected sidewise in all directions. This apparatus exhibits a striking illustration of the principle of negative pressure, for the ball is not driven away from the tip, but is held close to it by the atmospheric pressure, the negative pressure-head being caused by the high velocity of the sheet of water around the ball. The cup is usually so arranged that the ball cannot be driven out of it, for this might occur under the first impact of the jet, but when the flow has become steady, there is no tendency of this kind, and the ball is seen slowly revolving upon the cushion of water without touching any part of the cup.

Prob. 83. A nozzle $1\frac{3}{8}$ inches in diameter attached to a play-pipe $2\frac{1}{2}$ inches in diameter discharges 310.6 gallons per minute under an indicated pressure of 30 pounds per square inch. Find the velocity of the jet and the coefficient c_1.

Art. 84. Lost Head in Long Tubes

When water issues from an orifice, tube, pipe, or nozzle with the velocity v, its velocity-head is $v^2/2g$, and it is only this part of the total effective head h that can be utilized for the production of work. The lost head then is

$$h' = h - \frac{v^2}{2g}$$

Now if c_1 is the coefficient of velocity for the section where the discharge occurs, the velocity v is given by $c_1\sqrt{2gh}$, and hence

$$h' = \left(\frac{1}{c_v^2} - 1\right)\frac{v^2}{2g} \qquad (84)_1$$

is a general expression for the lost head in terms of the velocity-head. For the standard orifice (Art. 45), the mean value of c_v is 0.98 and for an orifice perfectly smooth c_v is 1.00; hence from $(84)_1$

$$h' = 0.04\frac{v^2}{2g} \quad \text{and} \quad h' = 0$$

are the losses of head for these two cases.

For the standard short cylindrical tube (Art. 78) the value of c_v is about 0.82, and the loss of head is

$$h' = \left(\frac{1}{0.82^2} - 1\right)\frac{v^2}{2g} = 0.49\frac{v^2}{2g}$$

For the inward projecting cylindrical tube (Art. 80) the value of c_v is about 0.72, and hence the loss of head is

$$h' = \left(\frac{1}{0.72^2} - 1\right)\frac{v^2}{2g} = 0.93\frac{v^2}{2g}$$

Accordingly the loss of head for the inward projecting tube is nearly equal to the velocity-head of the issuing stream, while that from the standard tube is about one-half the velocity-head.

When a tube is longer than three diameters, it becomes a long tube or a pipe. Here the loss of head is much greater because the water meets with frictional resistances along the interior surface, and the longer the pipe, the greater is this resistance and the slower is the velocity. The formula $(84)_1$ gives the total loss of head for this case also. For example, the experiments of Eytelwein and others have given values of c_v for the cases below, and from these the corresponding values of the total lost head have been computed. Let l denote the length of the pipe and d its diameter, the end connected with the reservoir being arranged like the standard tube; then

$$\text{for } l = 12d \qquad c_v = 0.77 \qquad h' = 0.69\, v^2/2g$$
$$\text{for } l = 36d \qquad c_v = 0.67 \qquad h' = 1.23\, v^2/2g$$
$$\text{for } l = 60d \qquad c_v = 0.60 \qquad h' = 1.77\, v^2/2g$$

Now in each of these cases the amount $0.49\, v^2/2g$ is lost in entering the tube and in impact, as in the standard short tube. Hence the loss of head in friction in the remaining length of the pipe is $h'' = h' - 0.49v^2/2g$, or

$$\text{for } l = 12d \qquad h'' = 0.20\, v^2/2g$$
$$\text{for } l = 36d \qquad h'' = 0.74\, v^2/2g$$
$$\text{for } l = 60d \qquad h'' = 1.28\, v^2/2g$$

which shows that the frictional losses increase with the length of the pipe. The length of the pipe in which the entrance losses occur is about $3d$; hence if $3d$ be subtracted from each of the above lengths, the lengths in which the friction loss occurs are $9d$, $33d$, and $57d$, and it is seen that the above losses of head in friction are closely proportional to these lengths. By these and many other experiments it has been shown that the loss of head in friction varies directly with the length of the pipe.

The lost head has here been expressed in terms of the velocity-head, but it can also be expressed in terms of the total head h

that causes the flow. For, substituting in $(84)_1$ the value of v given by $c_v\sqrt{2gh}$, it reduces to

$$h' = (1 - c_v^2)h \qquad (84)_2$$

Thus, for the standard short tube $h' = 0.33\,h$; for the inward projecting tube $h' = 0.48\,h$, and for the above tube or pipe whose length is 60 diameters $h' = 0.64\,h$.

Prob 84. Find the ratio of the kinetic energy in the jet from a standard orifice to that in the jet from a standard tube, the diameters of orifice and tube being the same.

Art. 85. Inclined Tubes and Pipes

The tubes discussed in this chapter have generally been regarded as horizontal, but, if this is not the case, the formulas for velocity and discharge may be applied to them by measuring the head from the water level in the reservoir down to the center of the head of the pipe. Thus, for the nozzles of Art. 83, it is understood that the tip is at the same level as the gage which registers the pressure p_1 or the pressure-head h_1; if the tip be lower than the gage by the vertical distance d_1, the true pressure-head to be used in the formula is $h_1 + d_1$; if it be higher, the true pressure-head is $h_1 - d_1$. Then the velocity-head $v^2/2g$ is to be measured upward from the tip of the nozzle.

The theorem of Bernouilli, given in Art. 31, is true for inclined as well as for horizontal pipes under uniform flow, but it will be convenient to express it in a slightly different form. Let a_1 and a_2 be two sections of a pipe where the velocities are v_1 and v_2, and the pressure-heads are h_1 and h_2, and let the flow be steady so that the same weight of water, W, passes each section in one second. Let MN be any horizontal plane lower than the lowest section, as for instance the sea level, and let e_1 and e_2 be the elevations of a_1

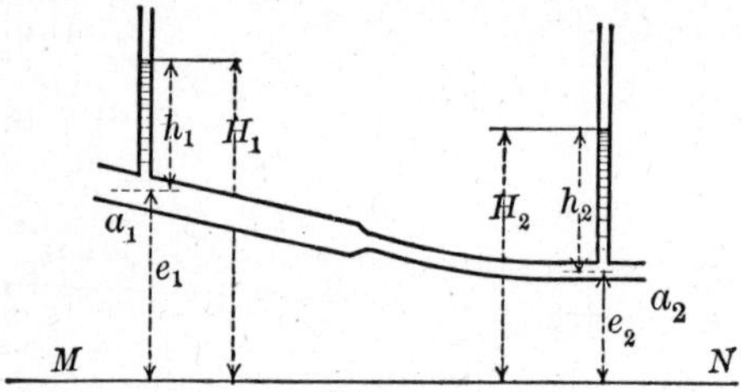

Fig. 85.

and a_2 above it. With respect to this plane the weight W at a_1 has the potential energy We_1, the pressure-energy Wh_1, and the kinetic energy $W \cdot v_1^2/2g$, or the total energy is

$$W\left(e_1 + h_1 + \frac{v_1^2}{2g}\right)$$

Similarly with respect to this plane the energy of W in a_2 is

$$W\left(e_2 + h_2 + \frac{v_2^2}{2g}\right)$$

If no losses of energy occur between the two sections, these expressions are equal, and hence

$$e_1 + h_1 + \frac{v_1^2}{2g} = e_2 + h_2 + \frac{v_2^2}{2g} \qquad (85)_1$$

and hence the theorem of Bernouilli may be stated as follows:

In any pipe, under steady flow without impact or friction, the gravity-head plus the pressure-head plus the velocity-head is a constant quantity for every section.

Now let H_1 and H_2 be the heights of the water levels in the piezometer tubes above the datum plane; then $e_1 + h_1 = H_1$ and $e_2 + h_2 = H_2$, and accordingly $(85)_1$ becomes

$$H_1 + \frac{v_1^2}{2g} = H_2 + \frac{v_2^2}{2g} \qquad (85)_2$$

or, the piezometer elevation for a_1 plus the velocity-head is equal to the sum of the corresponding quantities for any other section.

This theorem belongs to theoretical hydraulics, in which frictional resistances are not considered. Under actual conditions there is always a loss of energy or head, so that when water flows from a_1 to a_2, the first member of the above equation is larger than the second. Let Wh' be the loss in energy, then this is equal to the difference of the energies in a_1 and a_2 with respect to the datum plane, and

$$h' = (e_1 + h_1) - (e_2 + h_2) + \frac{v_1^2}{2g} - \frac{v_2^2}{2g}$$

or

$$h' = H_1 - H_2 + \frac{v_1^2}{2g} - \frac{v_2^2}{2g} \qquad (85)_3$$

that is, the lost head is equal to the difference in level of the water surfaces in the piezometer tubes plus the differences of the velocity-heads. When the pipe is of the same size at the two sections, the velocities v_1 and v_2 are equal when the flow is uniform, and the lost head is simply

$$h' = H_1 - H_2 \qquad (85)_4$$

Piezometers or pressure gages hence furnish a very convenient method of determining the head lost in friction in a pipe of uniform size. For a pipe of varying section the velocities v_1 and v_2 must also be known, in order to use $(85)_3$ for finding the lost head.

Prob. 85. A large Venturi water meter placed in a pipe of 57.823 square feet cross-section had an area of 7.047 square feet at the throat. When the discharge was 54.02 cubic feet per second, the elevations of the water levels in the piezometers at a_1 and a_2 in Fig. 38*a* were 99.858 and 98.951 feet. Compute the loss of head between the two sections.

Art. 86. Velocities in a Cross-section

Thus far the velocity has been regarded as uniform over the cross-section of the tube or pipe. On account of the roughness of the surface, however, the velocity along the surface is always smaller than that near the middle of the cross-section. There appears to be no theoretical method of finding the law which connects the velocity of a filament with its distance from the center of the pipe, and yet it is probable that such a law exists. The mean velocity is evidently greater than the velocity at the surface and less than the velocity at the middle, and if the position of a filament were known whose velocity is the same as the mean velocity, a Pitot tube (Art. 41) with its tip at that position would directly measure the mean velocity.

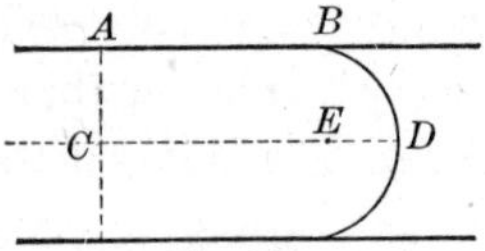

Fig. 86*a*.

Let Fig. 86*a* be a longitudinal section of a pipe, and let *AB* be laid off to represent the surface velocity v_s and *CD* to represent the central velocity v_c. Then the velocity v at any distance y from the axis will be an abscissa parallel to the axis and limited by the line *AC* and the curve *BD*. Suppose this curve to be a parabola whose equation is $y^2 = mx$, the origin being at D and x measured toward the left. When y is equal to the radius of the pipe r, the value of x is $v_c - v_s$ and hence $m = r^2/(v_c - v_s)$. The velocity v_y at the distance y above the axis is $v_c - x$, and accordingly

$$v_y = v_c - (v_c - v_s)\, y^2/r^2 \qquad (86)_1$$

It thus is seen that the velocity at any distance from the axis cannot be found unless the surface and central velocities are known. The position of the filament having the same velocity as the mean velocity v can, however, be determined, since the mean velocity is the mean length of the solid of revolution whose section is shown by the broken lines. This solid consists of a cylinder having the volume $\pi r^2 v_s$ and a paraboloid having the volume $\frac{1}{2}\pi r^2(v_c - v_s)$, and the sum of these is $\frac{1}{2}\pi r^2(v_c + v_s)$. Dividing this by the area of the cross-section gives $\frac{1}{2}(v_c + v_s)$ as the value of the mean velocity, and inserting this for v_y in the above equation there is found $y = 0.71r$ for the ordinate of a filament whose velocity is the same as mean velocity v. If the parabolic curve gives the true law of variation of velocity, a Pitot tube with its tip placed $0.29r$ below the top of the pipe would measure the mean velocity directly.

The first measurements of velocities of filaments were made by Freeman in 1888 with the Pitot tube.* They were on jets issuing from fire nozzles and also from a $1\frac{1}{8}$-inch tube under high velocities. For smooth nozzles the velocities were practically constant for a distance of $0.6r$ from the center, and then rapidly decreased, and the ratio of the surface velocity to the central velocity was about 0.77. For the pipe the velocities decreased quickly near the center, but more rapidly toward the surface. The velocity curve for the nozzle lies outside and that for the pipe lies within the parabolic curve represented by the equation $(86)_1$.

Bazin made experiments in 1893 on jets from standard orifices, using also the Pitot tube.† He found the velocities near the center to be smaller than others within $0.2r$ of the surface. Thus

* Transactions American Society of Civil Engineers, 1889, vol. 21, p. 412.

† Experiments on the Contraction of the Liquid Vein. Trautwine's translation, New York, 1896.

if $v_y = c_v\sqrt{2gh}$, the following are some of his values of c_v for a vertical circular and a vertical square orifice, h being always the head on the center.

$r =$	+0.8	+0.6	+0.2	0.0	−0.2	−0.6	−0.8
$c_v =$	0.68	0.64	0.62	0.63	0.64	0.72	0.86
$c_v =$	0.71	0.67	0.64	0.64	0.65	0.71	0.82

These are for velocities in the plane of the orifice, and he found similar variations for a section of the jet at a distance from the orifice of about one-half its diameter.

Judd and King,* in their experiments on orifices (Art. 45), traversed the jets with a Pitot tube and found that at the contracted section the velocity in all parts of the jet was uniform.

Cole, in 1897, made measurements of velocities in pipes,† using the Pitot tube with a differential gage (Art. 37). For pipes 4, 6, and 12 inches in diameter he found the ratio of the mean velocity to the center velocity to range from 0.91 to 1.01, while for a 16-inch pipe he found it to range from 0.83 to 0.86. His velocity curves show that the surface velocity was 60 percent or more of the center velocity.

Williams, Hubbell, and Fenkell, in 1899, made numerous measurements of velocities in water mains with the Pitot tube, and arrived at the conclusions that the ratio of the mean velocity to the central velocity was about 0.84, and that the surface velocity was about one-half the central velocity.‡ These ratios agree with an ellipse better than with a parabola. Let the curve BD in Fig. 86a be an ellipse having the semi-axes ED and BE, the ellipse being tangent to the pipe surface at B. As before, let AB represent the surface velocity v_s and CD the central velocity v_c; then ED is $v_c - v_s$ and BE is the radius r. The equation of the ellipse with respect to E as an origin is

$$(v_c - v_s)^2 y^2 + r^2 x^2 = (v_c - v_s)^2 r^2$$

* Engineering News, Sept. 27, 1906.

† Transactions American Society of Civil Engineers, 1902, vol. 47, p. 276.

‡ Transactions American Society of Civil Engineers, 1902, vol. 47, p. 63.

in which x is measured toward the right and y-upward. The velocity v_y at any distance y from the axis CD is $v_s + x$, and accordingly

$$v_y = v_s + (v_c - v_s)\sqrt{1 - y^2/r^2} \qquad (86)_2$$

Now the mean velocity is the mean length of the solid of revolution formed by the cylinder whose volume is $\pi r^2 v_s$ and the semi-ellipsoid whose volume is $\frac{2}{3}\pi r^2(v_c - v_s)$. The volume of the solid is hence $\pi r^2(\frac{2}{3}v_c + \frac{1}{3}v_s)$ and the mean velocity is $\frac{2}{3}v_c + \frac{1}{3}v_s$. Inserting this for v_y in $(86)_2$, there is found $y = 0.75r$ for the position of the filament having the same velocity as the mean velocity, while the parabola gave $y = 0.71r$. If v_s is one-half of v_c, the mean velocity under the elliptic law is $\frac{2}{3}v_c + \frac{1}{3}v_s = 0.83v_c$, while under the parabolic law it is $\frac{1}{2}v_c + \frac{1}{2}v_s = 0.75v_c$.

Much irregularity is observed in velocity curves plotted from actual measurements, this being due to pulsations in the water and to errors of observations. The above experiments were on pipes having diameters of 12, 16, 30, and 42 inches and under velocities ranging from 0.5 to 7.5 feet per second; and they are a very valuable addition to the knowledge of this subject. The conclusion that v_s is one-half of v_c is, however, one that appears to be liable to some doubt. The conclusion that the mean velocity v is about $0.84v_c$ appears well established, and a Pitot tube with its tip at the center of the pipe will hence determine a fair value of the mean velocity, several readings being taken in order to eliminate errors of observation.

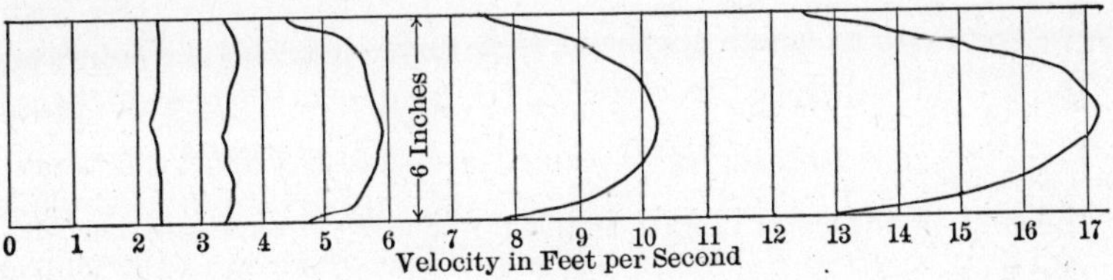

Fig. 86*b*.

In the case of fountain flow (Art. 87), Lawrence and Braunworth * found that the velocities in the cross-section depend on whether or not the flow out of the top of the pipe occurs as in a

* Transactions American Society of Civil Engineers, vol. 57.

jet or as over a weir. Thus, in Fig. 86*b* the velocity curves for a vertical 6-inch cast-iron pipe are shown for velocities ranging from 2 to 17 feet per second. These velocities were obtained from the expression $v = \sqrt{2gh}$, where h was measured by a Pitot tube.

Prob. 86. Let $v_s = 3$ and $v_c = 6$ feet per second. Plot the parabola from formula $(86)_1$ and the ellipse from formula $(86)_2$.

Art. 87. Fountain Flow

When a stream of water rises and flows out of the top of a vertical pipe of diameter D, the flow, if the head H to which it rises above the top of the pipe is small, is practically the same as that over a thin-edged circular weir. As H increases there comes a transition period during which the character of the flow resembles neither that over a circular weir nor that of a jet. Lawrence and Braunworth * experimented on the fountain flow of water from pipes 2, 4, 6, 9, and 12 inches in diameter. They measured the heads H both by means of a Pitot tube and by sighting on two rods and across the top of the pipe. The water discharged during the experiments was measured volumetrically. From the discussion of these experiments the following formulas were deduced:

$$q = 8.80\, D^{1.25} H^{1.35} \quad \text{and} \quad q = 5.57\, D^{1.99} H^{0.53}$$

the first being for weir and the second for jet flow. Here D and H are in feet and q in cubic feet per second, H being measured by means of sighting across the top of the flow as above described.

For cases in which the head H is measured with a Pitot tube the formulas deduced were

$$q = 8.80\, D^{1.29} H^{1.29} \quad \text{and} \quad q = 5.84\, D^{2.025} H^{0.53}$$

the first of these, as before, being applicable to weir and the second to jet flow.

In general the average results given by these formulas are correct within 3 percent for the jet condition, while for the condition of the weir flow using the Pitot tube for the measurement of the head the average accuracy is within 4 percent. Single

* Transactions American Society of Civil Engineers, vol. 57, p. 209.

measurements cannot be depended upon closer than to within about twice the above limits of accuracy.

In the following table are shown the computed discharges in cubic feet per second for various sizes of pipes under various heads, the heads being observed by means of a Pitot tube.

TABLE 87. DISCHARGES IN CUBIC FEET PER SECOND FOR FOUNTAIN FLOW FROM VERTICAL PIPES

Head in Feet	Diameter of Pipe in Inches							
	1	2	4	6	8	12	18	24
0.02			0.014	0.023	0.033	0.055	0.092	0.134
0.04		0.014	0.035	0.055	0.080	0.133	0.223	0.324
0.06		0.023	0.059	0.093	0.136	0.227	0.380	0.549
0.08	0.010	0.032	0.085	0.136	0.197	0.330	0.550	0.802
0.10	0.011	0.039	0.114	0.180	0.262	0.439	0.731	1.08
0.15	0.014	0.054	0.184	0.307	0.442	0.742	1.28	1.84
0.20	0.016	0.065	0.243	0.438	0.645	1.08	1.87	2.66
0.30	0.020	0.082	0.325	0.662	1.03	1.81	3.12	4.45
0.40	0.023	0.096	0.385	0.832	1.36	2.66	4.50	6.50
0.50	0.026	0.108	0.435	0.975	1.65	3.35	5.98	8.62
0.75	0.033	0.133	0.539	1.23	2.18	4.73	9.50	14.80
1.00	0.038	0.155	0.627	1.43	2.57	5.73	12.27	20.20
1.50	0.047	0.192	0.778	1.77	3.18	7.22	16.25	28.08
2.00	0.055	0.224	0.906	2.06	3.71	8.41	19.15	33.75
3.00	0.068	0.278	1.16	2.56	4.60	10.42	23.80	42.55
4.00	0.079	0.324	1.32	2.98	5.36	12.15	27.70	49.60
5.00	0.089	0.365	1.47	3.36	6.03	13.67	31.20	55.80
6.00	0.098	0.401	1.62	3.70	6.64	15.05	34.40	61.40
7.00	0.107	0.435	1.76	4.02	7.20	16.34	37.30	66.70
8.00	0.115	0.467	1.89	4.31	7.73	17.55	40.05	71.60
9.00	0.122	0.498	2.01	4.59	8.23	18.66	42.65	76.20
10.00	0.129	0.527	2.13	4.86	8.70	19.79	45.10	80.55

In the above table the condition of weir flow obtains for all figures above the upper horizontal lines, the condition intermediate between weir and jet flow holds for all figures between the two sets of horizontal lines, while that of jet flow obtains for all figures below the second set of horizontal lines.

At the point where the condition of weir flow changes to that of jet flow both of the above equations should theoretically hold true.

By equating the second members of these equations the critical head at which the nature of the flow changes is found to be about 0.6 D for all values of H between 0.1 and 3.0 feet. Practically, however, the exact point at which the change occurs cannot be exactly determined.

Prob. 87. Compute the flow from a vertical pipe 14 inches in diameter when the head above the top of the pipe, as measured by a Pitot tube, is 0.04 feet. Also compute the discharge when the head is 7.6 feet.

Art. 88. Computations in Metric Measures

Nearly all the formulas of this chapter are rational and may be used in all systems of measures. In the metric system lengths are to be taken in meters, areas in square meters, velocities in meters per second, discharges in cubic meters per second, and using for the acceleration constants the values given in Table 9*c*.

(Art. 83) The coefficients of discharge and velocity for smooth fire nozzles 2.0, 2.5, 3.0, and 3.5 centimeters in diameter are 0.983, 0.972, 0.973, and 0.959, respectively. In using the formula $(83)_2$ the values of d and h_1 should be taken in meters, but in finding the ratio D/d the values of D and d may be in centimeters or any other convenient unit. The constant g being 9.80 meters per second, the discharge q will be in cubic meters per second. When it is desired to use the gage reading p_1 in kilograms per square centimeter and to take D in centimeters, the formula

$$q = 65.96 c_v D^2 \sqrt{\frac{p_1}{1 - c^2(D/d)^4}}$$

may be used for finding the discharge in liters per minute.

Prob. 88*a*. Compute the loss of head which occurs when a pipe, discharging 18.5 cubic meters per second, suddenly enlarges in diameter from 1.25 to 1.50 meters.

Prob. 88*b*. Find the coefficient of discharge for a tube 8 centimeters in diameter when the flow under a head of 4 meters is 18.37 cubic meters in 5 minutes and 15 seconds.

Prob. 88*c*. Compute the discharge from a smooth nozzle 2.5 centimeters in diameter, attached to a hose 7.5 centimeters in diameter, when the pressure at the entrance is 5.2 kilograms per square centimeter.

CHAPTER 8

FLOW OF WATER THROUGH PIPES

Art. 89. Fundamental Ideas

Pipes made of clay were used in very early times for conveying water. Pliny says that they were two digits (0.73 inches) in thickness, that the joints were filled with lime macerated in oil, and that a slope of at least one-fourth of an inch in a hundred feet was necessary in order to insure the free flow of water.* The Romans also used lead pipes for conveying water from their aqueducts to small reservoirs and from the latter to their houses. Frontinus gives a list of twenty-five standard sizes of pipes,† varying in diameter from 0.9 to 9 inches, which were made by curving a sheet of lead about ten feet long and soldering the longitudinal joint. The Romans had confused ideas of the laws of flow in pipes, their method of water measurement being by the area of cross-section, with little attention to the head or pressure. They knew that the areas of circles varied as the squares of the diameters, and their unit of water measurement was the quinaria, this being a pipe $1\frac{1}{4}$ digits in diameter; then the denaria pipe, which had a diameter of $2\frac{1}{2}$ digits, was supposed to deliver 4 quinarias of water.

In modern times lead pipes have also been used for house service, but these are now largely superseded by either iron pipes or iron pipes lined with lead or tin. For the mains of city water supplies cast-iron pipes are most common, and since 1890 steel-riveted pipes have come into use for large sizes. Lap-welded wrought-iron or steel pipes are used in some cases where the pressure is very high, and large wooden stave pipes are in use in the western part of the United States.

* Natural History, book 31, chapter 31, line 5.

† Herschel, Water Supply of the City of Rome (Boston, 1899), p. 36.

The simplest case of the flow of water through a pipe is that where the diameter of the pipe is constant and the discharge occurs entirely at the open end. This case will be discussed in Arts. 90–99, and afterwards will be considered the cases of pipes of varying diameter, a pipe with a nozzle at the end, and pipes with branches. Most of the principles governing the simple case apply with slight modification to the more complex ones. Pipes used in engineering practice range in diameter from $\frac{1}{2}$ inch up to 10 feet or more.

The phenomena of flow for this common case are apparently simple. The water from the reservoir, as it enters the pipe, meets with more or less resistance, depending upon the manner of connecting, as in tubes (Art. 80). Resistances of friction and cohe-

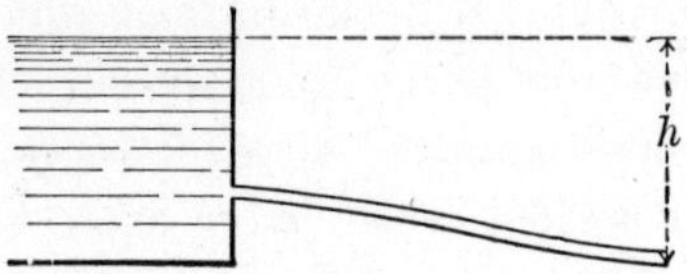

Fig. 89a.

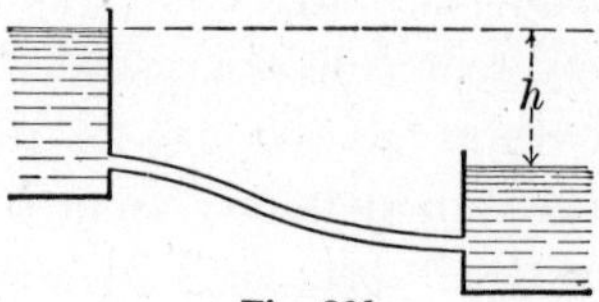

Fig. 89b.

sion must then be overcome along the interior surface, so that the discharge at the end is much smaller than in the tube (Art. 84). When the flow becomes steady, the pipe is entirely filled throughout its length; and hence the mean velocity at any section is the same as that at the end, since the size is uniform. This velocity is found to decrease as the length of the pipe increases, other things being equal, and becomes very small for great lengths, which shows that nearly all the head has been lost in overcoming the resistances. The length of the pipe is measured along its axis, following all the curves, if there be any. The velocity considered is the mean velocity, which is equal to the discharge divided by the area of the cross-section of the pipe. The actual velocities in the cross-section are greater than this mean near the center and less than it near the interior surface of the pipe, the law of distribution being that explained in Art. 86.

The object of the discussion of flow in pipes is to enable the discharge which will occur under given conditions to be determined, or to ascertain the proper size which a pipe should have in order to deliver a given discharge. The subject cannot, however, be developed with the definiteness which characterizes the flow from orifices and weirs, partly because the condition of the interior surface of the pipe greatly modifies the discharge, partly because of the lack of experimental data, and partly on account of defective theoretical knowledge regarding the laws of flow. In orifices and weirs errors of two or three percent may be regarded as large with careful work; in pipes such errors are common, and are generally exceeded in most practical investigations. It fortunately happens, however, that in most cases of the design of systems of pipes errors of five and ten percent are not important, although they are of course to be avoided if possible, or, if not avoided, they should occur on the side of safety.

The head which causes the flow is the difference in level from the surface of the water in the reservoir to the center of the end, when the discharge occurs freely into the air as in Fig. 89*a*. If h be this head, and W the weight of water discharged per second, the theoretic potential energy per second is Wh; and if v be the actual mean velocity of discharge, the kinetic energy of the discharge is $W \cdot v^2/2g$. The difference between these is the energy which has been transformed into heat in overcoming the resistances. Thus the total head is h, the velocity-head of the outflowing stream is $v^2/2g$, and the lost head is $h - v^2/2g$. If the lower end of the pipe is submerged, as in Fig. 89*b*, the head h is the difference in elevation between the two water levels.

The total loss of head in a straight pipe of uniform size consists of two parts, as in a long tube (Art. 84). First, there is a loss of head h' due to entrance, which is the same as in a short cylindrical tube, and secondly there is a loss of head h'' due to the frictional resistance of the interior surface. The loss of head at entrance is always less than the velocity-head and in this chapter it will be expressed by the formula

$$h' = m\frac{v^2}{2g} \qquad (89)_1$$

in which m is 0.93 for the inward projecting pipe, 0.49 for the standard end, and 0 for a perfect mouthpiece, as shown in Art. 84. When the condition of the end is not specified, the value used for m will be 0.5, which supposes that the arrangement is like the standard tube, or nearly so. For short pipes, however, it may be necessary to consider the particular condition of the end, and then m is to be computed from

$$m = (1/c_v)^2 - 1 \qquad (89)_2$$

in which the coefficient c_v is to be selected from the evidence presented in the last chapter.

It should be noted that the loss of head at entrance is very small for long pipes. For example, it is proved by actual gagings that a clean cast-iron pipe 10 000 feet long and 1 foot in diameter discharges about $4\frac{1}{4}$ cubic feet per second under a head of 100 feet. The mean velocity then is, if q be the discharge and a the area of the cross-section,

$$v = \frac{q}{a} = \frac{4.25}{0.7854} = 5.41 \text{ feet per second,}$$

and the probable loss of head at entrance hence is

$$h' = 0.5 \times 0.01555 \times 5.41^2 = 0.23 \text{ feet,}$$

or only one-fourth of one per cent of the total head. In this case the effective velocity-head of the issuing stream is only 0.45 feet, which shows that the total loss of head is 99.55 feet, of which 99.32 feet are lost in friction.

Prob. 89. Under a head of 20 feet a pipe 1 inch in diameter and 100 feet long discharges 15 gallons per minute. Compute the loss of head at entrance.

Art. 90. Loss of Head in Friction

The loss of head due to the resisting friction of the interior surface of a pipe is usually large, and in long pipes it becomes very great, so that the discharge is only a small percentage of that due to the head. Let h be the total head on the end of the pipe where the discharge occurs, $v^2/2g$ the velocity-head of the issuing stream, h' the head lost at entrance, and h'' the head lost in friction. Then if the pipe is straight, so that no other losses of head occur,

$$h = h' + h'' + \frac{v^2}{2g}$$

Inserting for the entrance-head h' its value from Art. 89, this equation becomes

$$h = m\frac{v^2}{2g} + h'' + \frac{v^2}{2g}$$

which is a fundamental formula for the discussion of flow in straight pipes of uniform size.

The head lost in friction may be determined for a particular case by measuring the head h, the area a of the cross-section of the pipe, and the discharge per second q. Then q divided by a gives the mean velocity v, and from the above equation, inserting for m its value from $(89)_2$, there is found

$$h'' = h - \frac{1}{c_v^2} \cdot \frac{v^2}{2g}$$

which serves to compute h'', the value of c_v being first selected according to the condition of the end. This method is not a good one for short pipes because of the uncertainty regarding the coefficient c_v (Art. 84), but for long pipes it gives precise results.

Another method, and the one most generally employed, is by the use of piezometers (Art. 85). A portion of the pipe being selected which is free from sharp curves, two piezometer tubes are inserted into which the water rises, or the pressure-heads are measured by gages (Art. 36). The difference of level of the water surfaces in the piezometer tubes is then the head lost in the pipe between them (Art. 85), and this loss is caused by friction alone if the pipe be straight and of uniform size.

By these methods many observations have been made upon pipes of different sizes and lengths under different velocities of flow, and the discussion of these has enabled the approximate laws to be deduced which govern the loss of head in friction, and tables to be prepared for practical use. These laws are:

1. The loss of head in friction is directly proportional to the length of the pipe.
2. It is inversely proportional to the diameter of the pipe.
3. It increases nearly as the square of the velocity.
4. It is independent of the pressure of the water.
5. It increases with the roughness of the interior surface.

These five laws may be expressed by the formula

$$h'' = f\frac{l}{d}\frac{v^2}{2g} \qquad (90)$$

in which l is the length of the pipe, d its diameter, f is an abstract number which depends upon the degree of roughness of the surface, and $v^2/2g$ is the velocity-head due to the mean velocity.

This formula may be justified by reasonings based on the assumption that what has been called the loss in friction is really caused by impact of the particles of water against each other. Fig. 90 represents a pipe with the roughness of its surface enormously exaggerated and imperfectly shows the disturbances thereby caused. As any particle of water strikes a protuberance on the surface, it is deflected and its velocity diminished, and then other particles of water in striking against it also undergo a diminution of velocity.

Fig. 90.

Now in this case of impact the resisting force F acting over each square unit of the surface is to be regarded as varying with the square of the velocity (Arts. 27 and 76). The total resisting friction for a pipe of length l and diameter d is then πdlF, and the work lost in one second is $dl\pi Fv$. Let W be the weight of water discharged in one second, then Wh'' is also the energy lost in one second. But $W = wq$, if w be the weight of a cubic unit of water and q the discharge per second, and the value of q is $\frac{1}{4}\pi d^2 v$. Then, equating the two expressions for the lost energy, and replacing F by Cv^2 where C is a constant, there results

$$h'' = \frac{4}{w}\frac{l}{d}F = \frac{4C}{w}\frac{l}{d}v^2.$$

Now C must increase with the roughness of the surface and hence this expression is the same in form as (90), and it agrees with the five laws of experience.

Values of h'' having been found by experiments, in the manner described above, values of the quantity f can be computed. In this way it has been found that f varies not only with the roughness of the interior surface of the pipe, but also with its diameter, and with the velocity of flow. From the discussions of Fanning, Smith, and others, the mean values of f given in Table 90*a* have been compiled, which are applicable to clean cast-iron and wrought-iron pipes, either smooth or coated with coal-tar, and laid with close joints.

Table 90*a*. Friction Factors for Clean Iron Pipes

Diameter in Feet	Velocity in Feet per Second						
	1	2	3	4	6	10	15
0.05	0.047	0.041	0.037	0.034	0.031	0.029	0.028
0.1	.038	.032	.030	.028	.026	.024	.023
0.25	.032	.028	.026	.025	.024	.022	.021
0.5	.028	.026	.025	.023	.022	.020	.019
0.75	.026	.025	.024	.022	.021	.019	.018
1.	.025	.024	.023	.022	.020	.018	.017
1.25	.024	.023	.022	.021	.019	.017	.016
1.5	.023	.022	.021	.020	.018	.016	.015
1.75	.022	.021	.020	.018	.017	.015	.014
2.	.021	.020	.019	.017	.016	.014	.013
2.5	.020	.019	.018	.016	.015	.013	.012
3.	.019	.018	.016	.015	.014	.013	.012
3.5	.018	.017	.016	.014	.013	.012	
4.	.017	.016	.015	.013	.012	.011	
5.	.016	.015	.014	.013	.012		
6.	.015	.014	.013	.012	.011		

The quantity f may be called the friction factor, and the table shows that its value ranges from 0.05 to 0.01 for new clean iron pipes. A rough mean value, often used, is

$$\text{Friction factor } f = 0.02$$

It is seen that the tabular values of f decrease both when the diameter and when the velocity increases, and that they vary most rapidly for small pipes and low velocities. The probable error of a tabular value of f is about one unit in the third decimal place, which is equivalent to an uncertainty of 10 percent when $f = 0.011$, and to 5 percent when $f = 0.021$. The effect of this is to render computed values of h'' liable to the same uncertainties; but the effect upon computed velocities and discharges is much less, as will be seen in Art. 93.

To determine, therefore, the probable loss of head in friction, the velocity v must be known, and f is taken from Table 90a for the given diameter of pipes. The formula (90) then gives the probable loss of head in friction. For example, let l = 10 000 feet, d = 1 foot, v = 5.41 feet per second. Then from Table 90a the factor f is 0.021, and

$$h'' = 0.021 \times \frac{10\,000}{1} \times 0.455 = 95.5 \text{ feet},$$

which is to be regarded as an approximate value, liable to an uncertainty of 5 percent.

TABLE 90b. FRICTION HEAD FOR 100 FEET OF CLEAN IRON PIPE

Diameter in Feet	Velocity in Feet per Second						
	1	2	3	4	6	10	15
	Feet	Feet	Feet	Feet	Feet	Feet	Feet
0.05	1.46	5.10	10.3	16.9	34.7		
0.1	0.59	1.99	4.20	6.97	14.5	37.3	
0.25	.20	0.70	1.46	2.40	5.37	13.7	29.4
0.5	.09	.32	0.70	1.14	2.46	6.22	13.3
0.75	.05	.21	.45	0.73	1.57	3.94	8.40
1.	.04	.15	.32	.55	1.12	2.80	5.95
1.25	.03	.11	.25	.42	0.85	2.11	4.48
1.5	.02	.09	.20	.33	.67	1.66	3.50
1.75	.02	.07	.16	.26	.54	1.33	2.80
2.	.02	.06	.13	.21	.45	1.09	2.27
2.5	.01	.05	.10	.16	.34	0.81	1.68
3.	.01	.04	.07	.12	.26	.67	1.40
3.5	.01	.03	.06	.10	.21	.53	
4.		.02	.05	.08	.17	.42	
5.		.02	.04	.06	.13		
6.		.01	.03	.05	.10		

From Table 90a and formula (90) the losses of head in friction for 100 feet of clean cast-iron pipe have been computed for different values of d and f and are given in Table 90b, from which approximate computations may be rapidly made. Thus, for the above data, by interpolation in Table 90b, there is found 0.952 feet for the loss in 100 feet of pipe, and then for 10 000 feet the loss of head is 95.2 feet.

Prob. 90. Determine the actual loss of head in friction from the following experiment: l = 60 feet, h = 8.33 feet, d = 0.0878 feet, q = 0.03224 cubic feet per second, and c = 0.8. Compute the probable loss for the same data from formula (90) and also from Table 90*b*.

Art. 91. Loss of Head in Curvature

Thus far the pipe has been regarded as straight, so that no losses of head occur except at entrance and in friction. But when the pipe is laid on a curve, the water suffers a change in direction whereby an increase of pressure is produced in the direction of the radius of the curve and away from its center (Art. 156). This increase in pressure causes eddying motions of the water, from which impact results and energy is transformed into heat. The total loss of head h''' due to any curve evidently increases with its length, and should be greater for a small pipe than for a large one. Hence the loss of head due to the curvature of a pipe may be written

$$h''' = f_1 \frac{l}{d} \frac{v^2}{2g} \qquad (91)_1$$

in which l is the length of the curve, d the diameter of the pipe, v the mean velocity of flow, and f_1 is an abstract number called the curve factor, that depends upon the ratio of the radius of the curve to the diameter of the pipe. Let R be the radius of the circle in which the center line of the pipe is laid. Then, if R is infinity, the pipe is straight and f_1 = 0; but as the ratio R/d decreases, the value of f_1 increases.

There are few experiments from which to determine the values of f_1. Weisbach, about 1850, from a discussion of his own experiments and those of Castel, deduced a formula for the value of $f_1 l/d$ for curves of one-fourth of a circle,* and from this the following values of the curve factor f_1 have been computed:

for R/d =	20	10	5	3	2	1.5	1.0
f_1 =	0.004	0.008	0.016	0.030	0.047	0.072	0.184

These values of f_1 are applicable only to small smooth iron pipes where the entire curve is without joints, since most of the pipes

* Die Experimentale Hydraulik (Freiberg, 1855), p. 159. Mechanics of Engineering (New York, 1870), vol. 1, p. 898.

on which the above experiments were made were probably of this kind.

Freeman, in 1889, made measurements of the loss of head in fire hose 2.49 and 2.64 inches in diameter, and the curves were complete circles of 2, 3, and 4 feet radius.* From the results given for the smaller hose the following values of the curve factor f_1 have been found:

for $R/d =$	19.2	14.4	9.6
$f_1 =$	0.0033	0.0034	0.0048

while for the larger hose the values are

for $R/d =$	18.2	13.6	9.1
$f_1 =$	0.0032	0.0041	0.0040

These values are in fair agreement with those given above for the small iron pipes.

Williams, Hubbell, and Fenkell, in 1898 and 1899, made measurements in Detroit on cast-iron water mains having curves of 90°. From their results for a 30-inch pipe the values of the curve factor f_1 have been computed and are found to be as follows:

for $R/d =$	24	16	10	6	4	2.4
$f_1 =$	0.036	0.037	0.047	0.060	0.062	0.072

while from their work on a 12-inch pipe the values are

for $R/d =$	4	3	2	1
$f_1 =$	0.05	0.06	0.06	0.20

Of these values, those derived from the larger pipe are the most reliable, and it is seen that they are much greater than the values deduced from Weisbach's investigations on small pipes. Probably some of this increase is due to the circumstance that the curves had rougher surfaces and that the joints were nearer together than on the straight portions. These experiments † were made with the Pitot tube in the manner explained in Arts. 41 and 86. They show that the law of distribution of the velocities in the cross-section is quite different from that for a straight pipe,

* Transactions American Society of Civil Engineers, 1889, vol. 21, p. 363.
† Transactions American Society of Civil Engineers, 1902, vol. 47.

the maximum velocity being not at the center, but between the center and the outside of the curve.

From the experiments of Schoder,* on 6-inch pipe and bends of 90°, the following values of f have been computed for velocities of 5 and 16 feet per second:

	for $R/d =$	20	15	10	6	5	2
$v = 5$,	$f_1 =$	0.008	0.004	0.010	0.020	0.018	0.049
$v = 16$,	$f_1 =$	0.008	0.009	0.011	0.021	0.022	0.059

The data given by Davis,* from his experiments on pipe about $2\frac{1}{16}$ inches in diameter for bends of 90°, enable the following values of f_1 to be computed for velocities of 5 and 15 feet per second:

	for $R/d =$	10	6	5	4	2	1
$v = 5$,	$f_1 =$	0.023	0.024	0.027	0.032	0.081	0.323
$v = 15$,	$f_1 =$	0.027	0.051	0.052	0.058	0.144	0.394

From the experiments of Brightmore,† on pipes 4 inches in diameter and for bends of 90°, the values of f_1 given below have been computed for velocities of 5 and 10 feet per second:

	for $R/d =$	10	6	5	4	2	1
$v = 5$,	$f_1 =$	0.013	0.033	0.034	0.036	0.105	0.406
$v = 10$,	$f_1 =$	0.013	0.034	0.040	0.046	0.127	0.365

While the above values of f_1 are few in number, and not wholly in accord, yet they may serve as a basis for roughly estimating the loss of head due to curvature. For example, let there be two curves of 24 and 16 feet radius in a pipe 2 feet in diameter, each curve being a quadrant of a circle. The ratios R/d are 12 and 8, and the values of f_1, taken from those deduced above from the large Detroit pipe, are 0.044 and 0.053. The lengths of the curves are 37.7 and 25.1 feet, and then from $(91)_1$

$$h''' = 0.044 \frac{37.7}{2} \frac{v^2}{2g} = 0.83 \frac{v^2}{2g}$$

$$h''' = 0.053 \frac{25.1}{2} \frac{v^2}{2g} = 0.66 \frac{v^2}{2g}$$

* Transactions American Society of Civil Engineers, vol. 52.

† Proceedings Institution of Civil Engineers, vol. 169.

are the losses of head for the two cases. Here it is seen that the easier curve gives the greater loss of head. By the use of the values of f_1 deduced from Weisbach's investigation, the loss of head is much smaller and the sharper curve gives the greater loss of head, since the coefficients of the velocity-head are found to be 0.13 and 0.14 instead of 0.83 and 0.66. The subject of losses in curves is, indeed, in an uncertain state, since sufficient experiments have not been made either to definitely establish the validity of $(91)_1$ or to determine authoritative values of the curve factor f_1. Probably it will be found that f_1 varies with the diameter d as well as with the ratio R/d.

When there are several curves in a pipe line, the value of $f_1(l/d)$ for each curve is to be found and then these are to be added in order to find the total loss of head. Thus, in general,

$$h''' = m_1 \frac{v^2}{2g} \qquad (91)_2$$

is the total loss of head, in which m_1 represents the sum of the values of $f_1(l/d)$ for all the curves. It must be remembered, however, that this loss of head is occasioned by the fact that the pipe is curved and that it is to be added to the loss caused by friction along the entire length of the pipe. In other words the curve factor f_1 does not include the friction factor f.

The lost head due to curvature in a pipe line is usually low compared with that lost in friction, since the number of curves is usually made as small as possible. For example, take a pipe 1000 feet long and 3 inches in diameter, which has ten curves, five being of 90° and 6 inches radius and five being of 57°.3 and 5 feet radius. From (90), using 0.02 for the mean friction factor, the loss of head in friction is 80 $v^2/2g$. From $(91)_1$, using the curve factors deduced from Weisbach, the loss of head for the five sharp curves is 0.74 $v^2/2g$, and that for the five easy curves is 0.4 $v^2/2g$.

Prob. 91. If the central angle of a curve of 18 inches radius is 57°.3, what is the length of the curve? If a hose, $2\frac{1}{2}$ inches in diameter, is laid on this curve, compute the loss in head due to curvature when the velocity in the hose is 30 feet per second and also when it is 15 feet per second.

Art. 92. Other Losses of Head

Thus far the cross-section of the pipe has been supposed to be constant, so that no losses of head occur except at entrance (Art. 89), in friction (Art. 90), and in curvature (Art. 91). But if the pipe contains valves, or has obstructions in its cross-section, or is of different diameters, other losses occur which are now to be considered.

The figures show three kinds of valves for regulating the flow in pipes: *A* being a valve consisting of a vertical sliding-gate, *B* a cock-valve formed by two rotating segments, and *C* a throttle-valve or circular disk which moves like a damper in a stovepipe.

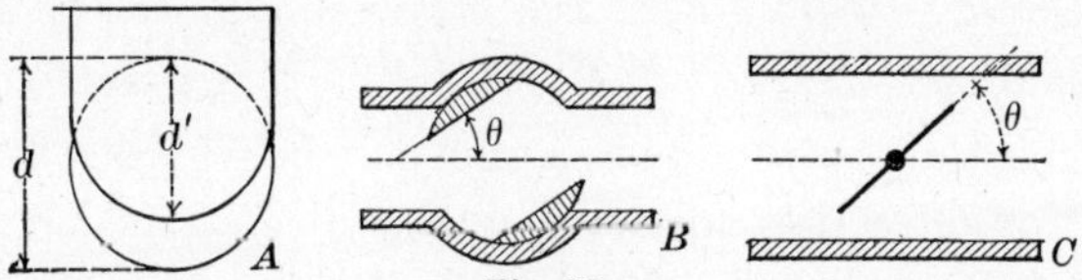

Fig. 92.

The loss of head due to these may be very large when they are sufficiently closed so as to cause a sudden change in velocity. It may be expressed by

$$h'''' = m\frac{v^2}{2g}$$

in which *m* has the following values, as determined by Weisbach from his experiments on pipes of small diameter.* For the gate-valve let *d'* be the vertical distance that the gate is lowered below the top of the pipe; then

for $d'/d = 0$	$\frac{1}{8}$	$\frac{1}{4}$	$\frac{3}{8}$	$\frac{1}{2}$	$\frac{5}{8}$	$\frac{3}{4}$	$\frac{7}{8}$
$m = 0.0$	0.07	0.26	0.81	2.1	5.5	17	98

For the cock-valve let θ be the angle through which it is turned, as shown at *B* in Fig. 92; then

for $\theta = 0°$	10°	20°	30°	40°	50°	55°	60°	65°
$m = 0°$	0.29	1.6	5.5	17	53	106	206	486

In like manner, for the throttle-valve the coefficients are:

for $\theta = 5°$	10°	20°	30°	40°	50°	60°	65°	70°
$m = 0.24$	0.52	1.5	3.9	11	33	118	256	750

* Mechanics of Engineering, vol. 1, Coxe's translation, p. 902.

The number m hence rapidly increases and becomes very great when the valve is fully closed, but as the velocity is then zero there is no loss of head. The velocity v here, as in other cases, refers to that in the main part of the pipe, and not to that in the contracted section formed by the valve.

Kuichling's experiments * on a gate-valve for a 24-inch pipe give values of m which are somewhat greater than those deduced by Weisbach from pipes less than 2 inches in diameter. Considering the great variation in size, the agreement is, however, a remarkable one. He found

for $d'/d =$	$\frac{1}{3}$	$\frac{5}{12}$	$\frac{1}{2}$	$\frac{5}{8}$	$\frac{3}{4}$	$\frac{59}{72}$
$m =$	0.8	1.6	3.3	8.6	22.7	41.2

and his computed value of m when d'/d equals $\frac{7}{8}$ is 75.6.

An accidental obstruction in a pipe may be regarded as causing a contraction of section, followed by a sudden expansion, and the loss of head due to it is, by Art. 77,

$$h'''' = \left(\frac{a}{a'} - 1\right)^2 \frac{v^2}{2g} = m\frac{v^2}{2g}$$

where a is the area of the section of the pipe, and a' that of the diminished section. This formula shows that when a' is one-half of a, the loss of head is equal to the velocity-head, and that m rapidly increases as a' diminishes. The same formula gives the loss of head due to the sudden enlargement of a pipe from the area a' to a.

Air-valves are placed at high points on a pipe line in order to allow the escape of air that collects there. Mud-valves or blow-offs are placed at low points in order to clean out deposits that may be formed as well as to empty the pipe when necessary. These are arranged so as not to contract the section, and the losses of head caused by them are generally very small. When a blow-off pipe is opened and the water flows through it with the velocity v, the loss of head at its entrance, even when the edges are rounded, is as high as or higher than $0.56\ v^2/2g$, according to the experiments of Fletcher.

* Transactions American Society of Civil Engineers, 1892, vol. 26, p. 449.

In the following pages the symbol h'''' will be used to denote the sum of all the losses of head due to valves and contractions of section. Then

$$h'''' = m_2 \frac{v^2}{2g} \tag{92}$$

in which m_2 will denote the sum of all the values of m due to these causes. In case no mention is made regarding these sources of loss they are supposed not to exist, so that both m_2 and h'''' are simply zero.

Prob. 92. Which causes the greater loss of head in a 24-inch pipe, a gate-valve one-half closed, or five 90° curves of 16 feet radius?

Art. 93. Formula for Mean Velocity

The mean velocity in a pipe can now be deduced for the condition of steady flow. The total head being h, and the effective velocity-head of the issuing stream being $v^2/2g$, the lost head is $h - v^2/2g$, and this must be equal to the sum of its parts, or

$$h - \frac{v^2}{2g} = h' + h'' + h''' + h''''$$

Substituting in this the values of the four lost heads, as determined in the four preceding articles, it becomes

$$h - \frac{v^2}{2g} = m\frac{v^2}{2g} + f\frac{l}{d}\frac{v^2}{2g} + m_1\frac{v^2}{2g} + m_2\frac{v^2}{2g}$$

and by solving for v there is found

$$v = \sqrt{\frac{2gh}{1 + m + f(l/d) + m_1 + m_2}} \qquad (93)_1$$

which is the general formula for the mean velocity in a pipe of constant cross-section.

The most common case is that of a pipe which has no curves, or curves of such large radius that their influence is very small, and which has no partially closed valves or other obstructions. For this case both m_1 and m_2 are zero, and, taking m as 0.5, the formula becomes

$$v = \sqrt{\frac{2gh}{1.5 + f(l/d)}} \qquad (93)_2$$

which applies to the great majority of cases in engineering practice.

In this formula the friction factor f is a function of v to be taken from Table 90a, and hence v cannot be directly computed, but must be obtained by successive approximations. For example, let it be required to compute the velocity of discharge from a pipe 3000 feet long and 6 inches in diameter under a head of 9 feet. Here l = 3000, d = 0.5, and h = 9 feet, and taking for f the rough mean value 0.02, formula $(93)_2$ gives

$$v = \sqrt{\frac{2 \times 32.16 \times 9}{1.5 + 0.02 \times 3000 \times 2}} = 2.2 \text{ feet per second.}$$

The approximate velocity is hence 2.2 feet per second and entering the table with this, the value of f is found to be 0.026. Then the formula gives

$$v = \sqrt{\frac{2 \times 32.16 \times 9}{1.5 + 0.026 \times 3000 \times 2}} = 1.92 \text{ feet per second.}$$

This is to be regarded as the probable value of the velocity, since the table gives f = 0.026 for v = 1.92. In this manner by one or two trials the value of v can be computed so as to agree with the corresponding value of f.

To illustrate the use of the general formula $(93)_1$ let the pipe in the above example be supposed to have forty 90° curves of 6 inches radius, and to contain two gate-valves which are half closed. Then from Arts. 91 and 92 there are found m_1 = 11.6 for the curves and m_2 = 4.2 for the gates. The mean velocity then is

$$v = \sqrt{\frac{2 \times 32.16 \times 9}{17.3 + 0.026 \times 6000}} = 1.83 \text{ feet per second,}$$

which is but a trifle less than that found before. With a shorter pipe, however, the influence of the curves and gates in retarding the flow would be more marked.

The head required to produce a given velocity v can be obtained from $(93)_1$ or $(93)_2$. Thus from the general formula the required head is

$$h = (1 + m + f(l/d) + m_1 + m_2)\frac{v^2}{2g}$$

in which for common computations m = 0.5, while m_1 and m_2 are neglected.

The error in the computed velocity due to an error of one unit in the last decimal of the friction factor f is always relatively less than the error in f itself. For instance, where v is computed for the above example with $f = 0.025$, which is 4 percent less than 0.026, its value is found to be 1.96 feet per second, or 2 percent greater than 1.92. In general the percentage of error in v is less than one-half of that in f. It hence appears that computed velocities are liable to probable errors ranging from 1 to 5 percent, owing to imperfections in the tabular values of f for new clean pipes. This uncertainty is as a rule still further increased by various causes, so that 5 percent is to be regarded as a common probable error in computations of velocity and discharge from pipes.

Velocities greater than 15 feet per second are very unusual in pipes, and but little is known as to the values of f for such cases. For velocities less than 0.5 feet per second, the values of f are also not known (Art. 110), so that only a rough reliance can be placed upon computations. The usual velocity in water mains is less than five feet per second, it being found inadvisable to allow swifter flow on account of the great loss of head in friction.

Prob. 93. Using for f the mean value 0.02 compute the head required to cause a velocity of 10 feet per second in a pipe 15 000 feet long and 18 inches in diameter.

Art. 94. Computation of Discharge

The discharge per second from a pipe of given diameter is found by multiplying the velocity of discharge by the area of the cross-section of the pipe, or

$$q = \tfrac{1}{4}\pi d^2 v = 0.7854\, d^2 v \qquad (94)$$

in which v is to be found by the method of the last article.

For example, let it be required to find the discharge in gallons per minute from a clean pipe 3 inches in diameter and 1500 feet long under a head of 64 feet. Here $d = 0.25$, $l = 1500$, and $h = 64$ feet. Then for $f = 0.02$ the velocity is found from $(93)_2$ to be 5.82 feet per second; then from Table 90a is found $f = 0.024$ and the velocity is 5.30 feet per second. The discharge in cubic feet per second is

$$q = 0.7854 \times 0.25^2 \times 5.30 = 0.260$$

which is equal to 116.7 gallons per minute. This is the probable result, which is liable to the same uncertainty as the velocity, say about 3 percent; so that strictly the discharge should be written 116.7 ± 3.6 gallons per minute.

By inserting the value of v from $(93)_2$ in the above expression for q it becomes

$$q = \tfrac{1}{4}\pi d^2 \sqrt{\frac{2gh}{1.5 + f(l/d)}}$$

and from this the head required to produce a given discharge is

$$h = \frac{8}{\pi^2 g}(1.5 + fl/d)\frac{q^2}{d^4}$$

These formulas are not more convenient for precise computations than the separate expressions for v, q, and h previously established, since v must be computed in order to select f from the table. For approximate computations, however, when f may be taken as 0.02, they may advantageously be used. In the English system of measures h and d are to be taken in feet and q in cubic feet per second, and the constants in these two formulas have the values

$$\tfrac{1}{4}\pi\sqrt{2g} = 6.299 \qquad 8/\pi^2 g = 0.0252$$

The last formula shows that the head required for a pipe of given diameter varies directly as the square of the proposed discharge. Thus, if a head of 50 feet delivers 8 cubic feet per second through a certain pipe, a head of about 200 feet will be necessary in order to obtain 16 cubic feet per second.

Prob. 94. What head is required to discharge 6 gallons per minute through a pipe 1 inch in diameter and 1000 feet long?

Art. 95. Computation of Diameter

It is an important practical problem to determine the diameter of a pipe to discharge a given quantity of water under a given head and length. The last equation above serves to solve this case, if the curve and valve resistances be omitted, as all the quantities in it except d are known. This equation reduces to

$$d^5 = \frac{8}{\pi^2 g}(1.5d + fl)\frac{q^2}{h}$$

and for the English system of measures this becomes

$$d = 0.4789\left[(1.5d + fl)\frac{q^2}{h}\right]^{\frac{1}{5}} \tag{95}$$

which is the formula for computing d when h, l, and d are in feet and q is in cubic feet per second. The value of the friction factor f may be taken as 0.02 in the first instance, and the d in the right-hand member being neglected, an approximate value of the diameter is computed. The velocity is next found by the formula

$$v = q/a = q/0.7854d^2$$

and from the Table 90*a* the value of f thereto corresponding is selected. The computation for d is then repeated, placing in the right-hand member the approximate value of d. Thus by one or two trials the diameter is computed which will very closely satisfy the given conditions.

For example, let it be required to determine the diameter of a new pipe which will deliver 500 gallons per second, its length being 4500 feet and the head 24 feet. Here the discharge is

$$q = 500/7.481 = 66.84 \text{ cubic feet per second.}$$

The approximate value of d then is

$$d = 0.479\left(\frac{0.02 \times 4500 \times 66.84^2}{24}\right)^{\frac{1}{5}} = 3.35 \text{ feet.}$$

From this the mean velocity of flow is

$$v = \frac{66.84}{0.7854 \times 3.35^2} = 7.6 \text{ feet per second,}$$

and from the table the value of f for this diameter and velocity is found to be 0.013. Then

$$d = 0.479\left[(1.5 \times 3.35 + 0.013 \times 4500)\frac{66.84^2}{24}\right]^{\frac{1}{5}}$$

from which d = 3.125 feet. With this value of d the velocity is now found to be 8.71 feet, so that no change results in the value of f. The required diameter of the pipe is therefore 3.1 feet, or about 37 inches; but as the regular market sizes of pipes furnish only 36 inches and 40 inches, one of these must be used, and it will be on the side of safety to select the larger.

It is very important, in determining the size of a pipe, to also consider that the interior surface may become rough by corrosion and incrustation, thus increasing the value of the friction factor and diminishing the discharge. It has been found that some waters deposit incrustations which in a few years render the values of f more than double those given in Table 90*a*. In Art. 106 will be found values of the friction factor as determined by experiment on various pipes of different ages. The increase in f from these causes is not likely to be so great in a large pipe as in a small one, but it is not improbable that for the above example they might be sufficient to make f as large as 0.03. Applying this value to the computation of the diameter from the given data there is found $d = 3.6$ feet = about 43 inches.

The sizes of iron pipes generally found in the market are $\frac{1}{2}$, $\frac{3}{4}$, 1, $1\frac{1}{2}$, $1\frac{3}{4}$, 2, 3, 4, 6, 8, 10, 12, 16, 18, 20, 24, 27, 30, 36, 40, 44, and 48 inches, while intermediate and larger sizes must be made to order. The computation of the diameter is merely a guide to enable one of these sizes to be selected, and therefore it is entirely unnecessary that the numerical work should be carried to a high degree of precision. In fact, three-figure logarithms are usually sufficient to determine reliable values of d from formula (95).

Prob. 95. Compute the diameter of a pipe to deliver 50 gallons per minute under a head of 4 feet when its length is 500 feet. Also when its length is 5000 feet.

Art. 96. Short Pipes

A pipe is said to be short when its length is less than about 500 times its diameter, and very short when the length is less than about 50 diameters. In both cases the coefficient c_1 should be estimated according to the condition of the upper end as precisely as possible, and the length l should not include the first three diameters of the pipe, as that portion properly belongs to the tube which is regarded as discharging into the pipe. In attempting to compute the discharge for such pipes, it is often found that the velocity is greater than given in Table 90*a*, and hence that the friction factor f cannot be ascertained. For this reason no accurate estimate can be made of the discharge from short pipes under high heads, and fortunately it is not often necessary to use them in engineering constructions.

For example, let it be required to compute the velocity of flow from a pipe 1 foot in diameter and 100 feet long under a head of 100 feet, the upper end being so arranged that $c_1 = 0.80$, and hence $m = 0.56$ (Art. 89). Neglecting m_1 and m_2, since the pipe has no curves or valves, formula $(93)_1$ for the velocity becomes

$$v = \sqrt{\frac{2gh}{1.56 + f(l/d)}}$$

and, using for f the rough mean value 0.02 and taking l as 97 feet, there is found 42.9 feet per second for the mean velocity. Now there is no experimental knowledge regarding the value of the friction factor f for such high velocities in iron pipes, but judging from the table it is probable that f may be about 0.015. Using this instead of 0.02 gives for v the value 46 feet per second.

The general equation for the velocity of discharge deduced in Art. 93 may be applied to very short pipes by writing $l - 3d$ in place of l, and placing for m its value in terms of the coefficient c_v. It then becomes

$$v = \sqrt{\frac{2gh}{\frac{1}{c_v^2} + f\frac{l - 3d}{d}}} \qquad (96)$$

If in this l equals $3d$, the velocity is $c_v\sqrt{2gh}$, which is the same as for the short cylindrical tube. If $l = 12d$, $f = 0.02$, and $c_v = 0.82$, it gives $v = 0.774\sqrt{2gh}$, which agrees well with the value given by Art. 84 for this case. If $l = 60d$, it gives $v = 0.613\sqrt{2gh}$, which is 2 percent greater than the value given by Art. 84.

Prob. 96. Compute the discharge per second for a pipe 1 inch in diameter and 40 inches long under a head of 4 feet.

Art. 97. Long Pipes

For long pipes the loss of head at entrance becomes very small compared with that lost in friction, and the velocity-head is also small. Formula $(93)_2$ for the mean velocity is

$$v = \sqrt{\frac{2gh}{1.5 + f(l/d)}}$$

in which the first term in the denominator represents the effect of the velocity-head and the entrance-head, the mean value of the latter being 0.5. Now it may safely be assumed that 1.5 may be neglected in comparison with the other term, when the error thus produced in v is less than 1 percent. Taking for f its mean value, this will be the case when

$$\frac{\sqrt{1.5+0.02\,l/d}}{\sqrt{0.02\,l/d}}=1.01, \quad \text{whence} \quad \frac{l}{d}=3750$$

Therefore, when l is greater than about $4000d$ the pipe will be called long.

For long pipes under uniform flow the velocity is found from the above equation by dropping 1.5, and the discharge is found by multiplying this mean velocity by the area of the cross-section. Hence the formulas for velocity and discharge are

$$v=\sqrt{\frac{2ghd}{fl}} \qquad q=\tfrac{1}{4}\pi\sqrt{\frac{2ghd^5}{fl}} \tag{97$_1$}$$

which for the English system of measures becomes

$$v=8.02\sqrt{\frac{hd}{fl}} \qquad q=6.30\sqrt{\frac{hd^5}{fl}} \tag{97$_2$}$$

From these expressions for q the general and special formulas for computing the diameter of the pipe for a given discharge, length, and head are found to be

$$d^5=\frac{8}{\pi^2 g}\,\frac{flq^2}{h} \qquad d=0.479\left(\frac{flq^2}{h}\right)^{\frac{1}{5}} \tag{97$_3$}$$

These equations show that for very long pipes the discharge varies directly as the $2\frac{1}{2}$ power of the diameter, and inversely as the square root of the length.

In the above formulas, d, h, and l are to be taken in feet, q in cubic feet per second, and f is to be found from Table 90a, an approximate value of v being first obtained by taking f as 0.02. It should not be forgotten that computations of discharge or diameter from these formulas are liable to uncertainty on account of imperfect knowledge regarding the friction factors. Especially when the velocities are lower than one or higher than fifteen feet per second the results obtained can be regarded as rough estimates only. The value of h in these formulas is really the friction-head h'', since in their deduction the other heads, h', h''', and h'''', have been neglected as insensible. Hence when the diameter d, the length l, the total head h, and the discharge q have been measured for a long pipe the friction factor f may be computed. In this manner much of the data was obtained from which Table 90*a* has been compiled.

For circular orifices and for short tubes of equal length under the same head, the discharge varies as the square of the diameter. For pipes of equal length under a given head the discharges vary more rapidly owing to the influence of friction, for formula $(97)_2$ shows that if f be constant, q varies as $d^{\frac{5}{2}}$. The relative discharging capacities of pipes hence vary approximately as the $2\frac{1}{2}$ powers of their diameters. Thus, if two pipes of diameters d_1 and d_2 have same length and head, and if q_1 and q_2 be their discharges,

$$q_1/q_2 = d_1^{\frac{5}{2}}/d_2^{\frac{5}{2}} \quad \text{or} \quad q_2 = (d_2/d_1)^{\frac{5}{2}} q_1$$

For example, if there be two pipes of 6 and 12 inches diameter, d_2/d_1 equals 2 and hence $q_2 = 5.7q_1$, or the second pipe discharges nearly six times as much as the first. In a similar manner it can be shown that 32 pipes of 6 inches diameter have the same discharging capacity as 1 pipe 24 inches in diameter.

When the variation in the friction factor is taken into account, the formula gives

$$q_2 = q_1(d_2/d_1)^{\frac{5}{2}}(f_1/f_2)^{\frac{1}{2}}$$

Now as the values of f vary not only with the diameter but with the velocity, a solution cannot be made except in particular cases. For the above example let the velocity be about 3 feet per second; then from the table $f_1 = 0.023$ and $f_2 = 0.019$, and accordingly

$$q_2 = q_1(2)^{\frac{5}{2}}(1.2)^{\frac{1}{2}} = 6.2q_1$$

or the 12-inch pipe discharges more than six times as much as the 6-inch pipe.

Prob. 97. Compute the diameter required to deliver 15 000 cubic feet per hour through a pipe 26 500 feet long under a head of 324.7 feet. If this quantity is carried in two pipes of equal diameter, what should be their size?

Art. 98. Piezometer Measurements

Let a piezometer tube be inserted into a pipe at any point D_1 at the distance l_1 from the reservoir measured along the pipe line. Let A_1D_1 be the vertical depth of this point below the water level of the reservoir; then if the flow be stopped at the end C, the water rises in the tube to the point A_1. But when the flow occurs, the water level in the piezometer stands at some point C_1, and the pressure-head at D_1 is h_1, or C_1D_1 in the figure. The distance A_1C_1 then represents the velocity-head plus all the losses of head between D_1 and the reservoir. If no losses of head occur except at entrance and in friction, the value of A_1C_1 then is

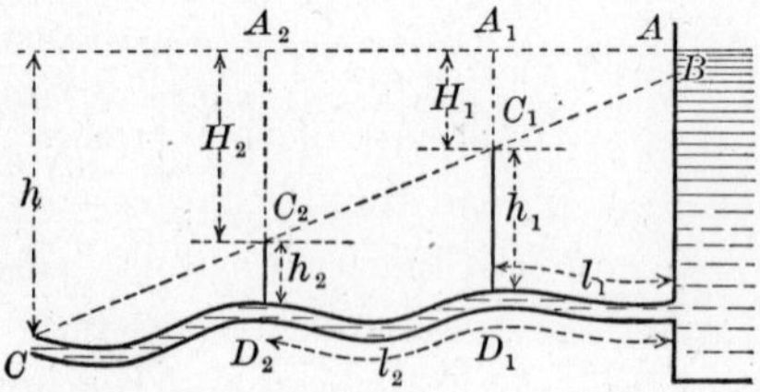

Fig. 98*a*.

$$H_1 = \frac{v^2}{2g} + m\frac{v^2}{2g} + f\frac{l_1}{d}\frac{v^2}{2g}$$

from which the piezometric height can be found when v has been determined by direct measurement or by gaging.

For example, let the total length l = 3000 feet, d = 6 inches, h = 9 feet, and m = 0.5. Then, as in Art. 93, there is found f = 0.026 and v = 1.917 feet per second. The position of the top of the piezometric column is then given by

$$H_1 = (1.5 + 0.052\, l_1) \times 0.05714$$

and the height of that column above the pipe is

$$h_1 = \overline{A_1D_1} - H_1$$

Thus if l_1 = 1000 feet, H_1 = 3.06 feet; and if l_1 = 2000 feet, H_1 = 6.03 feet. If the pipe is so laid that A_1D_1 is 9 feet, the corresponding pressure-heads are then 5.94 and 2.97 feet.

For a second piezometer inserted at D_2 at the distance l_2 from the entrance, the value H_2 is

$$H_2 = \frac{v^2}{2g} + m\frac{v^2}{2g} + f\frac{l_2}{d}\frac{v^2}{2g}$$

Subtracting from this the expression for H_1, there is found

$$H_2 - H_1 = f\frac{l_2 - l_1}{d}\frac{v^2}{2g} \qquad (98)_1$$

The second member of this formula is the head lost in friction in the length $l_2 - l_1$ (Art. 90), and the first member is the difference of the piezometer elevations. Thus is again proved the principle of Art. 85, that the difference of two piezometer elevations shows the head lost in the pipe between them; in Art. 85 the elevations H_1 and H_2 were measured upward from the datum plane, while here they have been measured downward from the water level in the reservoir.

By the help of this principle the velocity of flow in a pipe may be approximately determined. A line of levels is run between the points D_1 and D_2, which are selected so that no sharp curves occur between them, and thus the difference $H_2 - H_1$ is found, while the length $l_2 - l_1$ is ascertained by careful chaining. Then, from the above formula,

$$v = \sqrt{\frac{2g(H_2 - H_1)d}{f(l_2 - l_1)}} \qquad (98)_2$$

from which v can be computed by the help of the friction factors in Table 90*a*. For example, Stearns, in 1880, made experiments on a conduit pipe 4 feet in diameter under different velocities of flow.* In experiment No. 2 the length $l_2 - l_1$ was 1747.2 feet, and the difference of the piezometer levels was 1.243 feet. Assuming for f the mean value 0.02, and using 32.16 feet per second per second for g, the velocity was

$$v = \sqrt{\frac{64.32 \times 1.243 \times 4}{0.02 \times 1747}} = 3.0 \text{ feet per second.}$$

This velocity in the table of friction factors gives $f = 0.015$ for a 4-foot pipe. Hence, repeating the computation, there is found $v = 3.50$ feet per second; it is accordingly uncertain whether the value of f is 0.015 or 0.014. If the latter value be used, there is found $v = 3.62$ feet per second. The actual velocity, as determined by measurement of the water over a weir, was 3.738 feet

* Transactions American Society of Civil Engineers, 1885, vol. 14, p. 4.

per second, which shows that the computation is in error about 4 percent.

In order that accurate results may be obtained with piezometers it is necessary, particularly under low pressure-heads, that the tubes be inserted into the pipe at right angles. If they be inclined with or against the current, the pressure-head h_1 will be greater or less than that due to the pressure at the mouth. Let θ be the angle between the direction of the flow and the inserted piezometer tube. Since the impulse in the direction of the current is proportional to the velocity-head (Art. 27), the component of this in the direction of the inserted tube tends to increase the normal pressure-height h_1 when θ is less than 90° and to decrease it when θ is greater than 90°. Thus

$$h_0 = h_1 + n\frac{v^2}{2g}\cos\theta$$

may be written as approximately applicable to the two cases in which n is a coefficient the value of which has not been ascertained. In this, if the tube be inserted normal to the pipe, $\theta = 90°$ and h_0 becomes h_1, the height due to the static pressure in the pipe; if $v = 0$, the angle θ has no effect upon the piezometer readings. But if θ differs from 90° by a small angle, the error in the reading may be large when the velocity in the pipe is high. Fig. 98*b* illustrates the three cases.

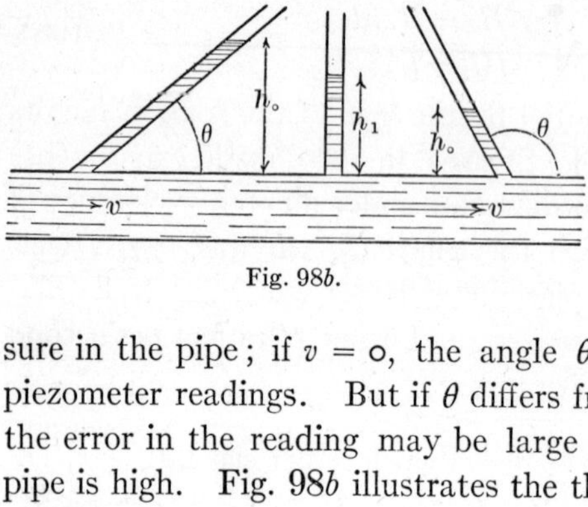

Fig. 98*b*.

The question as to the point from which the pressure-head should be measured deserves consideration. In the figures of preceding articles h_1 and h_2 have been estimated upward from the center of the pipe, and it is now to be shown that this is probably correct. Let Fig. 98*c* represent a cross-section of a pipe to which are attached three piezometers as shown. If there be no velocity in the tube or pipe, the

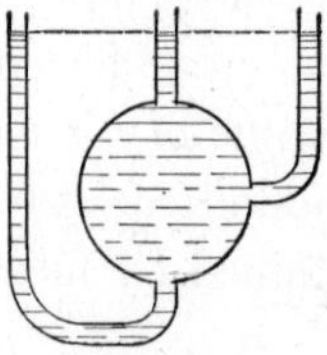
Fig. 98*c*.

water surface stands at the same level in each piezometer, and the mean pressure-head is certainly the distance of that level above the center of the cross-section. If the water in the pipe be in motion, probably the same would hold true. Referring to formula $(75)_1$ and to Fig. 75*a*, it is also seen that if there be no velocity $h' = h_1 - h_2$, which cannot be true unless $h_1 - h_2 = 0$, since there can be no loss of head in the transmission of static pressures; hence h_1 and h_2 cannot be measured from the top of the section. In any event, since the piezometer heights represent the mean pressures, it appears that they should be reckoned upward from the center of the section. The piezometer couplings for hose devised by Freeman are arranged with connections on the top, bottom, and sides, as are also those used for the Venturi meter (Art. 38), and thus the results obtained correspond to mean pressures or pressure-heads. Even in cases where the two points of connection are so near together that the difference $H_2 - H_1$, can be measured by a differential manometer (Art. 37), the method of connecting the tubes to the pipes should receive careful attention.

Prob. 98. At a point 500 feet from the reservoir, and 28 feet below its surface, a pressure gage reads 10.5 pounds per square inch; at a point 8500 feet from the reservoir and 280.5 feet below its surface, it reads 61 pounds per square inch. If the pipe is 12 inches in diameter, compute the discharge.

Art. 99. The Hydraulic Gradient

The hydraulic gradient is a line which connects the water levels in piezometers placed at intervals along the pipe; or rather, it is the line to which the water levels would rise if piezometer tubes were inserted. In Fig. 98*a* the line *BC* is the hydraulic gradient, and it is now to be shown that for a pipe of uniform size this is approximately a straight line. For a pipe discharging freely into the air, as in Fig. 98*a*, this line joins the outlet end with a point *B* near the top of the reservoir. For a pipe with submerged discharge, as in Fig. 99*a*, it joins the lower water level with the point *B*.

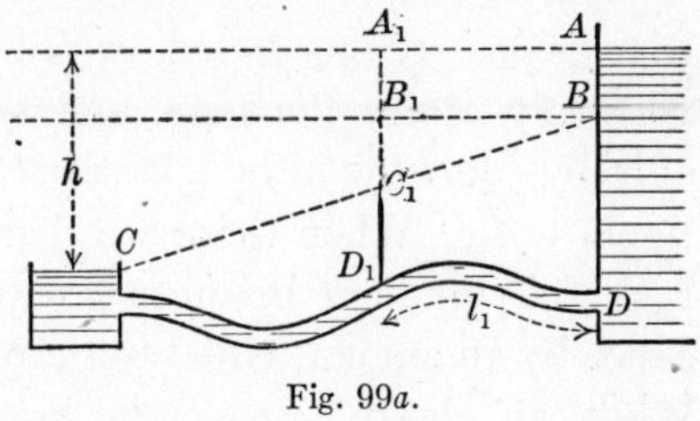

Fig. 99*a*.

Let D_1 be any point on the pipe distant l_1 from the reservoir, measured along the pipe line. The piezometer there placed rises to C_1, which is a point in the hydraulic gradient. The equation of this line with reference to the origin A is given by the first equation of Art. 98, or

$$H_1 = (1 + m)\frac{v^2}{2g} + f\frac{l_1}{d}\frac{v^2}{2g}$$

in which H_1 is the ordinate A_1C_1, and l_1 is the abscissa AA_1, provided that the length of the pipe is sensibly equivalent to its horizontal projection. In this equation the first term of the second member is constant for a given velocity, and is represented in the figure by AB or A_1B_1; the second term varies with l_1, and is represented by B_1C_1. The gradient is therefore a straight line, subject to the provision that the pipe is laid approximately horizontal; which is usually the case in practice, since quite material vertical variations may exist in long pipes without sensibly affecting the horizontal distances.

When the variable point D_1 is taken at the outlet end of the pipe, H_1 becomes the head h, and l_1 becomes the total length l, agreeing with the formula of Art. 93, if the losses of head due to curvature and valves be omitted. When D_1 is taken very near the inlet end, l_1 becomes zero and the ordinate H_1 becomes AB, which represents the velocity-head plus the loss of head at entrance to the pipe.

When there are easy horizontal curves in a pipe line, the above conclusions are unaffected, except that the gradient BC is always vertically above the pipe, and therefore can be called straight only by courtesy, although as before the ordinate B_1C_1 is proportional to l_1. When there are sharp curves, the inclination of the hydraulic gradient becomes greater and it is depressed at each curve by an amount equal to the loss of head which there occurs. When an obstruction occurs in a pipe, or a valve is partially closed, there is a sudden depression of the gradient at the obstruction or at the valve.

If the pipe is so laid that a portion of it rises above the hydraulic gradient as at D_1 in Fig. 99*b*, an entire change of condition generally results. If the pipe is closed at C, all the piezometers stand in the line AA, at the same level as the surface of the reservoir. When the valve at C is opened, the flow at first occurs under normal conditions, h being the head and BC the hydraulic gradient. The pressure-head at D_1 is then negative, and represented by D_1C_1. As a consequence the air which is carried along in the pipe with the water collects at the summit D_1 and acts like an obstruction there, so that the pipe from D_1 to C is only partly filled with water. The hydraulic gradient is then shifted to BD_1, the discharge occurs at D_1 under the head A_1D_1, while the remainder of the pipe acts merely as a channel to deliver the flow. It usually happens that this change results in a great diminution of the discharge, so that it has been necessary to dig up and relay portions of a pipe line which have been inadvertently run above the hydraulic gradient. This trouble can always be avoided by preparing a profile of the proposed route, drawing the hydraulic gradient upon it, and excavating the pipe trench well below the gradient. In cases where the cost of this excavation is so great that it is resolved to lay the pipe above the gradient, all the joints of the pipe above the gradient should be made absolutely tight so that no air can enter the pipe and interrupt the flow.

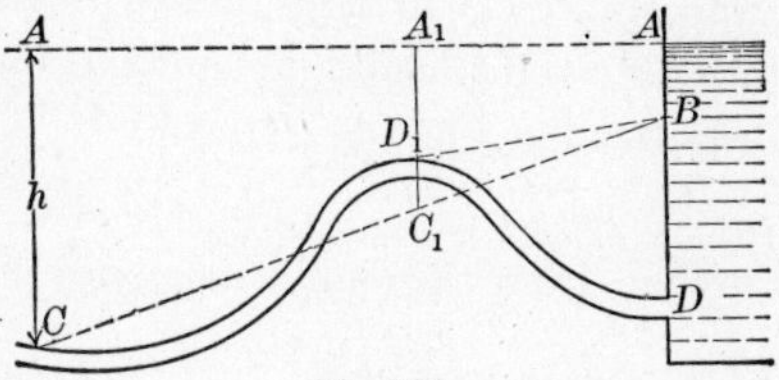

Fig. 99*b*.

When a large part of the pipe lies above the hydraulic gradient it is called a siphon. Conditions sometimes exist which require a pipe line to be laid as a siphon for a short distance. In such a case an air chamber is sometimes built at the highest elevation so that air may collect in it instead of in the pipe, and provision is made for recharging the siphon when the flow ceases by admitting water at the highest elevation, or by operating a suction-pump placed there, or by forcing water into the pipe by a pump located at a lower elevation. Probably the largest siphon ever constructed is that laid about 1885 at Kansas City, Mo., it being 42 inches in diameter, and 730 feet long, with the summit 10 feet above the general level of the pipe line. The air that collected at the summit was removed by operating a steam ejector for a few minutes each day.*

The pressure head h_1 at any point on the pipe line distant l_1 from the reservoir may be expressed in terms of static head, combined velocity-head and entrance-head h', and friction-head h'' by inspection of Fig. 99a; thus,

$$h_1 = A_1D_1 - h' - h''$$

Further, from the similar triangles in the figure,

$$h'' = (h - h')(l_1/l)$$

that is, the loss in friction in the distance l_1 is proportional to l_1. For long pipes, in which h' is small, this may be written $h'' = h(l_1 l)$, or the friction loss at any point on the pipe line is proportional to the total head and to the distance of the point from the reservoir.

The above discussion shows that it is immaterial where the pipe enters the reservoir, provided that it enters below the hydraulic gradient point B. It is also not to be forgotten that the whole investigation rests on the assumption that the lengths l_1 and l are sensibly equal to their horizontal projections.

Prob. 99. A pipe 3 inches in diameter discharges 538 cubic feet per hour under a head of 12 feet. At a distance of 300 feet from the reservoir the depth of the pipe below the water surface in the reservoir is 4.5 feet. Compute the probable pressure-head at this point.

Art. 100. A Compound Pipe

A compound pipe is one having different sizes in different portions of its length. The change from one length to another should be made by a "reducer," which is a conical frustum several feet long, so that losses of head due to sudden enlargement or contraction are avoided (Arts. 76, 77). Let d_1, d_2, d_3, etc., be the diameters; l_1, l_2, l_3, etc., the corresponding lengths, the total length being $l_1 + l_2 +$ etc. Let v_1, v_2, etc., be the velocities in the different sections. Neglecting the loss of head at entrance and also that lost in curvature, the total head h may be placed equal to the loss of head in friction, or

$$h = f_1 \frac{l_1}{d_1} \frac{v_1^2}{2g} + f_2 \frac{l_2}{d_2} \frac{v_2^2}{2g} + \text{etc.}$$

* Engineering News, 1891, vol. 26, p. 519; 1893, vol. 29, pp. 423, 588.

Now if the discharge per second be q, and the flow be steady

$$v_1 = q/\tfrac{1}{4}\pi d_1^2 \qquad v_2 = q/\tfrac{1}{4}\pi d_2^2, \quad \text{etc.}$$

Substituting these velocities and solving for q, gives

$$q = \tfrac{1}{4}\pi \sqrt{\frac{2gh}{f_1\dfrac{l_1}{d_1^5} + f_2\dfrac{l_2}{d_2^5} + \text{etc.}}} \tag{100}$$

in which the friction factors f_1, f_2, etc., corresponding to the given diameters and computed velocities are found from Table 90*a*.

For example, consider the case of a pipe having only two sizes; let $d_1 = 2$ and $l_1 = 2800$ feet, $d_2 = 1.5$ and $l_2 = 2145$ feet, and $h = 127.5$ feet. Using for f_1 and f_2 the mean value, 0.02, and making the substitutions in the formula, there is found

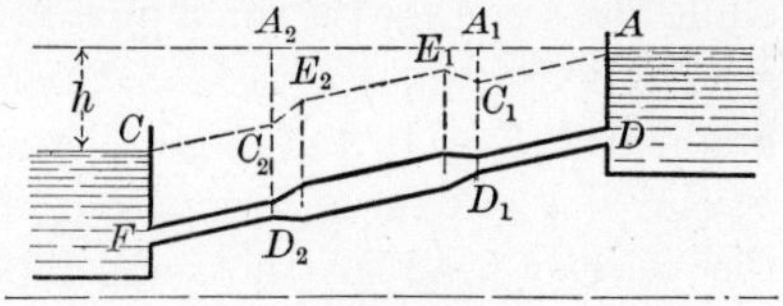

Fig. 100.

$$q = 26.2 \text{ cubic feet per second}$$

from which $v_1 = 8.3$ and $v_2 = 14.8$ feet per second
Now from Table 90*a* it is seen that $f_1 = 0.015$ and $f_2 = 0.015$; and repeating the computation,

$$q = 30.2 \text{ cubic feet per second}$$

whence $v_1 = 9.6$ and $v_2 = 17.1$ feet per second.

These results are probably as definite as the table of friction factors will allow, but are to be regarded as liable to an uncertainty of several percent.

To determine the diameter of a pipe which will give the same discharge as the compound one, it is only necessary to replace the denominator in the above value of q by fl/d^5, where $l = l_1 + l_2$ + etc., and d is the diameter required. Taking the values of f as equal, this gives

$$\frac{l}{d^5} = \frac{l_1}{d_1^5} + \frac{l_2}{d_2^5} + \text{etc}$$

Applying this to the above example, it becomes

$$\frac{4945}{d^5} = \frac{2800}{2^5} + \frac{2145}{1.5^5}$$

from which $d = 1.68$ feet, or about 20 inches.

A compound pipe is sometimes used to prevent the hydraulic gradient from falling below the pipe line. Thus, it is seen in Fig. 100 that the hydraulic gradient rises at D_1 and falls at D_2, and that its slope over the larger pipe is less than over the smaller one. These slopes and the amount of rise at D_1 can be computed for a given case. Using the above numerical data, the loss of head in friction for 100 feet of the large pipe is

$$h'' = 0.015 \frac{100}{2} \frac{v_1^2}{2g} = 1.07 \text{ feet,}$$

while the same for the small pipe is 4.55 feet. Hence the slope of the gradients AC_1 and C_2C is more than four times as rapid as that of the gradient E_1E_2. In the large pipe at D_1 the velocity-head is $0.01555 \times 9.6^2 = 1.43$ feet, and, supposing that no loss occurs in the reducer, the velocity-head for the small pipe is 4.55 feet. The vertical rise C_1E_1 of the hydraulic gradient at D_1 is hence the rise in pressure-head $4.55 - 1.43 = 3.12$ feet, and a fall of equal amount occurs at D_2.

When a portion of a small pipe is to be replaced by a large one, it is immaterial in what part of the length it is introduced, for it is seen that formula (100) takes no note of where the length l_1 is placed in the total distance l. The Romans knew that an increase in the diameter of a pipe after leaving the reservoir would increase the discharge, and the law passed by the Roman senate about the year 10 B.C. forbade a consumer to attach a larger pipe to the standard pipe within 50 feet of the reservoir to which the latter was connected.*

Prob. 100. At Rochester, N.Y., there is a pipe 102 277 feet long, of which 50 828 feet is 36 inches in diameter and 51 449 feet is 24 inches in diameter. Under a head of 143.8 feet this pipe is said to have discharged in 1876 about 14 cubic feet per second and in 1890 about 10½ cubic feet per second. Compute the discharge by (100), and draw the hydraulic gradient.

Art. 101. A Pipe with a Nozzle

Water is often delivered through a nozzle in order to perform work upon a motor or for the purposes of hydraulic mining, the nozzle being attached to the end of a pipe which brings the flow from a reservoir. In such a case it is desirable that the pressure at the entrance to the nozzle should be as great as possible, and

* Herschel, Water Supply of the City of Rome (Boston, 1889), p. 77.

this will be effected when the loss of head in the pipe is as small as possible. The pressure column in a piezometer, supposed to be inserted at the end of the pipe, as shown at C_1D_1 in Fig. 101, measures the pressure-head there acting, and the height A_1C_1 measures the lost head plus the velocity-head, the latter being very small.

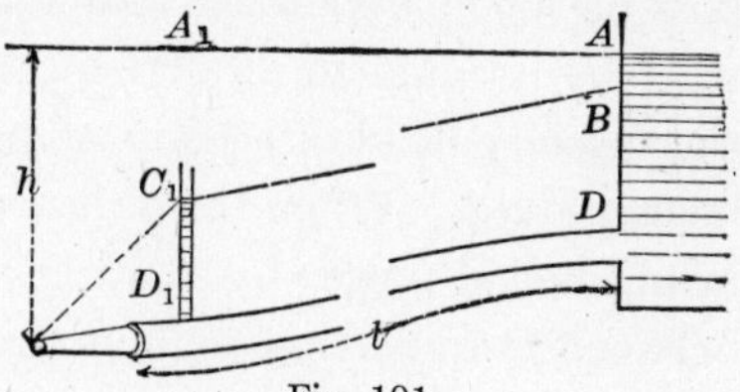

Fig. 101.

Let h be the total head on the end of the nozzle, D its diameter, and V the velocity of the issuing stream. Let d and v be the corresponding quantities for the pipe, and l its length. Then the effective velocity-head of the issuing stream is $V^2/2g$, and the lost head is $h - V^2/2g$. This lost head consists of several parts: that lost at the entrance D; that lost in friction in the pipe; that lost in curves and valves, if any; and lastly, that lost in the nozzle. Then the principle of energy gives the equation

$$h - \frac{V^2}{2g} = m\frac{v^2}{2g} + f\frac{l}{d}\frac{v^2}{2g} + m_1\frac{v^2}{2g} + m_2\frac{v^2}{2g} + m'\frac{V^2}{2g}$$

Here m is determined by Art. 89, f by Art. 90, m_1 by Art. 91, m_2 by Art. 92, while m' for the nozzle is found in the same manner as m is found for the pipe, or $m' = (1/c_v)^2 - 1$, where c_v is the coefficient of velocity for the nozzle (Art. 83). This value of m' takes account of all losses of head in the nozzle, so that it is unnecessary to consider its length; for a perfect nozzle c_v is unity and m' is zero.

The velocities v and V are inversely as the areas of the corresponding cross-sections (Art. 31), since the flow is steady, whence $V = v(d/D)^2$. Inserting this in the above equation and solving for v gives, if m_1 and m_2 be neglected,

$$v = \sqrt{\frac{2gh}{m + f(l/d) + (1/c_v)^2(d/D)^4}} \qquad (101)$$

for the velocity in the pipe. The velocity and discharge from the nozzle are then given by

$$V = (d/D)^2 v \qquad q = \tfrac{1}{4}\pi D^2 V$$

and the velocity head of the jet is $V^2/2g$. These equations show that the greatest value of V obtains when D is as small as possible compared to d, and that the greatest discharge occurs when D is equal to d. When the object of a nozzle is to utilize the velocity-head of a jet, a large pipe and a small nozzle should be employed. When the object is to utilize the energy of the jet in producing power by a water wheel, there is a certain relation between D and d that renders this a maximum (Art. 161).

As a numerical example, the effect of attaching a nozzle to the pipe whose discharge was computed in Art. 94 will be considered. There $l=1500$, $d=0.25$, and $h=64$ feet; $m=0.5$, $v=5.3$ feet, and $q=0.26$ cubic feet per second. Now let the nozzle be one inch in diameter at the small end, or $D=0.0833$ feet, and let its coefficient c_v be 0.98. Here $d/D=3$, and for $f=0.025$ the velocity in the pipe is

$$v = \sqrt{\frac{2 \times 32.16 \times 64}{0.5 + 0.025 \times 1500 \times 4 + 1.041 \times 81}}$$

or $v=4.2$ feet per second. The effect of the nozzle, therefore, is to reduce the velocity in the pipe. The velocity of the jet at the end of the nozzle is, however,

$$V = v(d/D)^2 = 37.8 \text{ feet per second,}$$

and the discharge per second from the nozzle is

$$q = \tfrac{1}{4}\pi D^2 V = 0.206 \text{ cubic feet}$$

which is about 20 percent less than that of the pipe before the nozzle was attached. The nozzle, however, produces a marvelous effect in increasing the energy of the discharge; for the velocity-head corresponding to 5.3 feet per second is only 0.44 feet, while that corresponding to 37.8 feet per second is 22.2 feet, or about 50 times as great. As the total head is 64 feet, the efficiency of the pipe and nozzle is about 35 percent.

If the pressure-head h_1 at the entrance of the nozzle be observed, either by a piezometer tube or by a pressure gage, the velocity of discharge from the nozzle can be computed by the formula

$$V = \sqrt{\frac{2\,gh_1}{(1/c_v)^2 - (D/d)^4}}$$

the demonstration of which is given in Art. 83. This can be used when a hose and nozzle is attached at any point of a pipe or at a hydrant. It can also be used to compute h_1 when V has been found. Thus, for the above example,

$$h_1 = \left(\frac{1}{c_v^2} - \frac{D^4}{d^4}\right)\frac{V^2}{2g} = 22.8 \text{ feet}$$

which shows that the loss of head in the nozzle is about 0.6 feet. The loss of head at entrance, for this case, is about 0.2 feet, and the loss of head in friction in the pipe is 41.0 feet.

Prob. 101. A pipe 12 inches in diameter and 4320 feet long leads from a reservoir to a gravel bank against which water is delivered from a nozzle 2 inches in diameter. The head on the end of the nozzle is 320 feet and the coefficient of velocity of the nozzle is 0.97. Compute the velocity in the pipe, the velocity-head of the jet, and the discharge.

Art. 102. House-service Pipes

A service pipe which runs from a street main to a house is connected to the former at right angles, and usually by a corporation cock or by a "ferrule." The loss of head at entrance in such cases is hence larger than in those before discussed, and m should probably be taken as at least equal to unity. The pipe, if of lead, is frequently carried around sharp corners by curves of small radius; if of iron, these curves are formed by pieces forming a quadrant of a circle into which the straight parts are screwed, the radius of the center line of the curve being but little larger than the radius of the pipe, so that each curve causes a loss of head equal nearly to double the velocity-head (Art. 91). For new iron pipes the loss of head due to friction may be estimated by the rules of Art. 90 or by Table 90*b*.

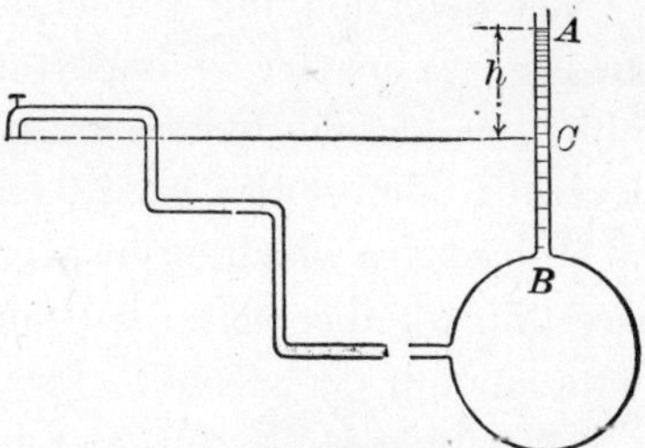

Fig. 102*a*.

A water main should be so designed that a certain minimum pressure-head h_1 exists in it at times of heaviest draft. This pressure-head may be represented by the height of the piezometer column AB, which would rise in a tube supposed to be inserted in the main, as in Fig. 102a. The head h which causes the flow in the pipe is then the difference in level between the top of this column and the end of the pipe, or AC. Inserting for h this value, the formulas of Arts. 94 and 95 may be applied to the investigation of service pipes in the manner there illustrated. As the sizes of common house-service pipes are regulated by the practice of the plumbers and by the market sizes obtainable, it is not often necessary to make computations regarding the flow of water through them.

The velocity of flow in the main has no direct influence upon that in the pipe, since the connection is made at right angles. But as that velocity varies, owing to the varying draft upon the main, the effective head h is subject to continual fluctuations. When there is no flow in the main, the piezometer column rises until its top is on the same level as the surface of the reservoir; in times of great draft it may sink below C, so that no water can be drawn from the service pipe.

The detection and prevention of the waste of water by consumers is a matter of importance in cities where the supply is limited and where meters are not in use. Of the many methods devised to detect this waste, one by the use of piezometers may be noticed, by which an inspector without entering a house may ascertain whether water is being drawn within, and the approximate amount per second. Let M be the street main from which a service pipe MOH runs to a house H. At the edge of the sidewalk a tube OP is connected to the service pipe, which has a three-way cock at O, which can be turned from above. The inspector, passing on his rounds in the night-time, attaches a pressure gage at P and turns the cock O so as to shut off the water from the house and allow the full pressure of the main p_1 to be registered.

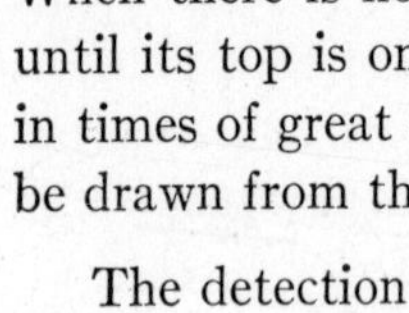

Fig. 102b.

Then he turns the cock so that the water may flow into the house, while it also rises in OP and registers the pressure p_2. Then if p_2 is less than p_1, it is certain that waste is occurring within the house, and the amount of this may be approximately computed and the consumer be notified accordingly.

The pitometer, which consists of a rated Pitot tube (Art. 41), facing the current in the pipe, with a differential gage (Art. 37) to determine the pressure-head due to the current, is also used for the measurement of the flow in water mains and for the detection of water waste. A photographic record of the difference in height of the columns of liquid in the gage tube is kept, and this shows the discharge through the water main at any instant, as also all fluctuations in the flow.* (See Art. 38.)

When the pressure in the street main is very high, a pressure regulator may be placed between the main and the house in order to reduce the pressure and thus allow lighter pipes to be used in the house. Fig. 102*c* shows the principle of its action, where *A* represents the pipe from the main and *B* the pipe leading to the house. A weight *W* is placed upon a piston which covers the opening into the chamber *C*. This weight and that of the piston are sufficient to overcome a certain unit-pressure in *C*, and therefore the unit-pressure in *B* is less than that in *A* by that amount. For example, suppose the pressure in *A* to be 100 pounds per square inch, and let it be required that the pressure in *B* shall not rise above 60 pounds per square inch; then the piston must be so weighted that it may exert on the water in *C* a pressure of 40 pounds per square inch. When water is drawn out anywhere along the pipe *B*, the pressure in the chamber above the piston falls below 60 pounds per square inch, and hence the piston rises and water flows from *A* into *B* until the pressure is restored. Instead of a weight, a spring is generally used, or sometimes a weighted lever.

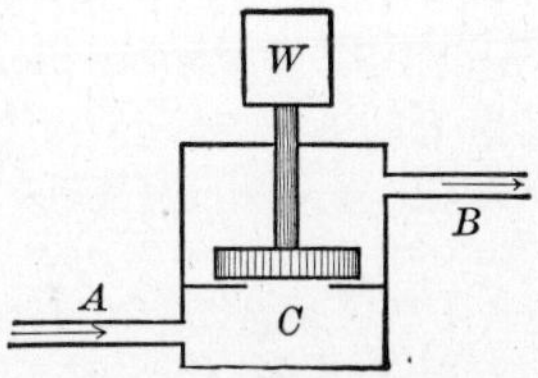

Fig. 102*c*.

Large-sized pressure regulators are also used to control and maintain a constant pressure in distributing mains in cases where

* Engineering Record, 1903, vol. 47, p. 122.

a low service level is fed from one of higher pressure, or in situations where it is desired to maintain a pressure which shall not exceed a fixed maximum.

Prob. 102. In Fig. 102*b* let the house pipe be one inch in diameter and the pressure at the gage be 34 pounds per square inch when there is no flow. The distance from the main to the gage is 16 feet and from the gage to the end of the pipe is 29 feet. At the end of the pipe, which is 5 feet higher than the gage, 2.1 gallons of water are drawn per minute. Compute the pressure at the gage.

Art. 103. Operating and Regulating Devices

In the operation of nearly every water works system certain special apparatus is employed in order to maintain nearly constant conditions within the system and under the variable draft to which it is subjected. These forms of apparatus are designed to operate automatically and so to do away with hand regulation. Many of these are designed, as described under meters in Art. 38, to trace on a chart a continuous autographic record of the pressure, of the water level, or of the discharge. Among these are pressure gages (Art. 36), water stage registers (Art. 34), and rate of flow gages (Art. 38).

Air valves are attached to water mains in situations where air is likely to accumulate within the pipe and by its presence interfere with the flow of the water or be carried along within the pipe and produce dangerous water hammer. Valves of this type permit the air within the pipe to escape, but automatically close and prevent the passage of water. They are also placed on all of the principal summits of riveted steel and other pipes so as to admit air into the pipe in case of a sudden break and thus prevent its collapse under external atmospheric pressure. In the case of cast-iron pipes, on account of the strength of their shells, this precaution is not usually necessary. The principle of the operation of the air valve is simply that of a float placed in a chamber above and connected with the pipe from which the air is to be removed. When air accumulates in the pipe, it passes up into the chamber; the float falls, and in falling, by means of a lever, operates and opens a valve. The air then escapes under the pressure of the water until the float again rises and causes the valve to close.

Pressure regulators operating on the principle described in Art. 102 are employed for the purpose of controlling and maintaining a constant pressure in distributing systems in situations where a low service level is fed from one of higher pressure. They may also be used to regulate the flow between reservoirs situated at different elevations. In the larger sized regulators the valve which controls the flow is operated by a pair of differential pistons connecting with a chamber, the pressure in which is caused to vary with fluctuations in pressure on the two sides of the regulator. The variations in pressure within this chamber are intensified by two small-sized regulators which connect directly to the high and low pressure sides of the large regulator. That on the upstream side of the main regulator is designed to close under an increase in pressure, while that on the downstream side will tend to open as the pressure rises. The effect of any difference in pressure on the two sides of the main regulator is therefore promptly reflected in the pressure within the chamber, and the differential pistons at once move to open or close the regulating valve in the effort to maintain within the pipe the predetermined constant pressure at which the apparatus has been set. A sixteen-inch regulator of this type will control the pressure within narrow limits and pass through it, as may be necessary to accomplish this purpose, quantities up to 10 or 15 millions of gallons per day.

Relief valves for the purpose of preventing the pressure within a pipe from rising above some predetermined limit, either on account of a sudden falling off of the draft or by water hammer, are also made to operate on the principle described in Art. 102, but in the reverse direction. The regulating valve described in the preceding paragraph may also be adapted for this use by simply making the necessary adjustments of the small regulators.

In certain situations and principally in connection with the operation of filtration plants it is desirable that the flow within a pipe shall be maintained at a constant rate. This may be accomplished by permitting the water to pass into an open chamber, from which it flows over and through a circular weir supported on floats. As the water rises in the chamber the weir also rises, and a constant relation is thus obtained between the height of the water and that of the weir crest. In order to limit the necessary height of the chamber the float may be made to operate a butterfly valve on the inlet pipe, so that when the float rises the valve will partly close and thus diminish the quantity of water entering the chamber. Conversely as the float falls the valve is opened and more water permitted to enter. In neither of these two cases can the flow in the outlet pipe exceed the predetermined capacity of the circular weir. Another form of the rate of flow controller is that in which a balanced valve is operated by the differences in pressure at the throat and downstream end of a Venturi tube inserted in the line. This valve will open or close as the quantity of water decreases or increases below or above some fixed quantity. In this manner a smaller or greater loss of head is automatically introduced into the system, and since the discharge is proportional to the square root of the effective head, the mechanism operates in such a manner as to maintain a constant flow.

For determining the discharge or rate of flow within a pipe at any instant either a Venturi meter or a Pitot tube with the necessary connections may be used, as described in Arts. 38 and 41.

Loss of head gages are used in cases where it is desired to indicate at one place the loss of head which occurs between two points on a system. The most usual application is in the case of a filter bed where the loss of head is constantly varying on account of the clogging of the filter surface. In this situation a loss of head gage indicates at once whether or not a filter should be put out of service and cleaned. A gage for this service consists of a float in each of two chambers, the chambers being connected with the pipe or filter system at the points between which it is desired to measure the difference or loss of head. One of the floats is connected by means of a wire to a horizontal axis which carries a pointer, while the other is connected to another horizontal axis which carries the dial on which the pointer indicates. The two horizontal axes are concident, and the reading of the pointer indicates the loss of head. If the water in both of the chambers rises or falls an equal amount, the pointer will still indicate the same loss of head, as the directions of rotation of the pointer and dial are the same. In order to avoid a movable dial other forms of this apparatus are arranged by the introduction of a differential mechanism, so that the loss of head is directly indicated by the pointer on a stationary dial.

Valves for maintaining a constant level in a tank or reservoir are usually constructed, for small sizes, of a ball float operating a cock as it rises and falls by means of a system of levers. On larger work an ordinary gate valve operated by a hydraulic cylinder and piston may be used. A float either on the water surface itself or on the surface of mercury in a vessel connecting with the water operates a small three-way valve which admits the water either above or below the piston of the hydraulic valve and so either closes or opens it as the water level rises above or falls below a fixed elevation. In order to prevent such valves from closing too rapidly and thus inducing water hammer, the ports of the three-way valve may be made quite small so as to cause the water to pass very slowly into the operating cylinder or else another piston may be introduced into the system and so arranged that the water behind it is permitted to escape through an orifice the size of which can be regulated. By this means the time of closing can be very nicely adjusted.

All automatic devices are more or less likely to get out of order. This is simply due to the inherent difficulty in attaining perfection in any device. In order that they may at all times retain their adjustment and properly perform the functions for which they have been designed they must be frequently inspected and always kept in good condition and repair. The selection of any particular form of regulating, control, or recording device will depend upon the conditions under which it is to operate and upon the past performance of the mechanism as attested by the experience of those who have used it.

Prob. 103. Make a sketch showing the arrangement above described for maintaining a constant level in a tank by means of a gate valve operated by a hydraulic cylinder. Show also the arrangement of the dampening piston for preventing too rapid closing of the valve.

Art. 104. Water Mains in Towns

The simplest case of the distribution of water is that where a single main is tapped by a number of service pipes near its end, as shown in Fig. 104. In designing such a main the principal consideration is that it should be large enough so that the pressure-head h_1, when all the pipes are in draft, shall be amply sufficient to deliver the water into the highest houses along the line.

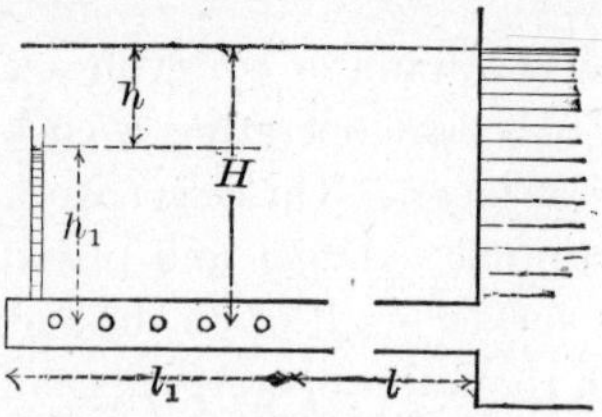

Fig. 104.

It is generally recommended that this pressure-head in commercial and manufacturing districts should not be less than 150 feet, and in suburban districts not less than 100 feet. The height H to the surface of the water in the reservoir will always be greater than h_1, and the pipe is to be so designed that the losses of head may not reduce h_1 below the limit assigned. The head h to be used in the formulas is the difference $H - h_1$. The discharge per second q being known or assumed, the problem is to determine the proper diameter d of the water main.

A strict theoretical solution of even this simple case leads to very complicated calculations, and in fact cannot be made without knowing all the circumstances regarding each of the service pipes. Considering that the result of the computation is merely to enable one of the market sizes to be selected, it is plain that great precision cannot be expected, and that approximate methods may be used to give a solution entirely satisfactory. It will then be assumed that the service pipes are connected with the main at equal intervals, and that the discharge through each is the same under maximum draft. The velocity v in the main then decreases and becomes 0 at the dead end. The loss of head per linear foot in the length l_1 (Fig. 104) is hence less than in l. To determine the total loss of head in the length l_1, let v_1 be the velocity at a distance x from the dead end; then $v_1 = v \cdot x/l_1$ and the loss of head in friction in the length δx is

$$\delta h'' = f\frac{\delta x}{d}\frac{{v_1}^2}{2g} = f\frac{x^2}{d{l_1}^2}\frac{v^2}{2g}\delta x$$

and hence between the limits 0 and l_1 that loss of head is

$$h'' = f\frac{l_1}{3d}\frac{v^2}{2g} \qquad (104)$$

provided that f remains constant. This is really not the case, but no material error is thus introduced, since f must be taken larger than the tabular values in order to allow for the deterioration of the inner surface of the main. The loss of head in friction for a pipe which discharges uniformly along its length may therefore be taken at one-third of that which occurs when the discharge is entirely at the end.

Now neglecting the loss of head at entrance and the effective velocity-head of the discharge, the total head h is entirely consumed in friction, or

$$h = f\frac{l}{d}\frac{v^2}{2g} + f\frac{l_1}{3d}\frac{v^2}{2g}$$

Placing in this for v its value in terms of the total discharge q and the diameter of the pipe, and solving for d, gives

$$d^5 = (l + \tfrac{1}{3}l_1)\frac{16fq^2}{2g\pi^2 h}$$

This is the same as the formula of Art. 97, except that l has been replace by $l + \frac{1}{3}l_1$. The diameter in feet then is

$$d = 0.479(l + \tfrac{1}{3}l_1)^{\frac{1}{5}}\left(\frac{fq^2}{h}\right)^{\frac{1}{5}}$$

when h and l are in feet and q in cubic feet per second.

For example, consider a village consisting of a single street with length $l_1 = 3000$ feet, and upon which there are 100 houses, each furnished with a service pipe. The probable population is then 500, and taking 100 gallons per day as the consumption per capita, this gives for the average discharge per second along the length l_1

$$q = \frac{500 \times 100}{7.48 \times 3600 \times 24} = 0.0774 \text{ cubic feet,}$$

and since the maximum draft is often double of the average, q will be taken as 0.15 cubic feet per second. The length l to the reservoir is 4290 feet, whose surface is 90.5 feet above the dead end of the main, and it is required that under full draft the pressure-head in the main shall be 75 feet. Then $h = 90.5 - 75 =$

15.5 feet, and taking f = 0.03 in order to be on the safe side, the formula gives

$$d = 0.36 \text{ feet} = 4.3 \text{ inches.}$$

Accordingly a four-inch pipe is nearly large enough to satisfy the imposed conditions.

To consider the effect of fire service upon the diameter of the main, let there be four hydrants placed at equal intervals along the line l_1, each of which is required to deliver 20 cubic feet per minute under the same pressure-head of 75 feet. This gives a discharge 1.33 cubic feet per second, or, in total, q = 1.33 + 0.15 = 1.5 cubic feet. Inserting this in the formula, and using for f the same value as before,

$$d = 0.897 \text{ feet} = 10.8 \text{ inches.}$$

Hence a ten-inch pipe is at least required to maintain the required pressure when the four hydrants are in full draft at the same time with the service pipes.

Prob. 104. Compute the velocity v and the pressure-head h_1 for the above example, if the main is 8 inches in diameter and the discharge be 1.5 cubic feet per second. Also when the main is 12 inches in diameter.

Art. 105. Branches and Diversions

In Fig. 105*a* is shown a main of length l and diameter d, connected with a storage reservoir, which has two branches with lengths l_1 and l_2, and diameters d_1 and d_2 leading to two smaller distributing reservoirs. These data being given, as also the heads H_1 and H_2 under which the flow occurs, it is required to find the discharges q_1 and q_2.

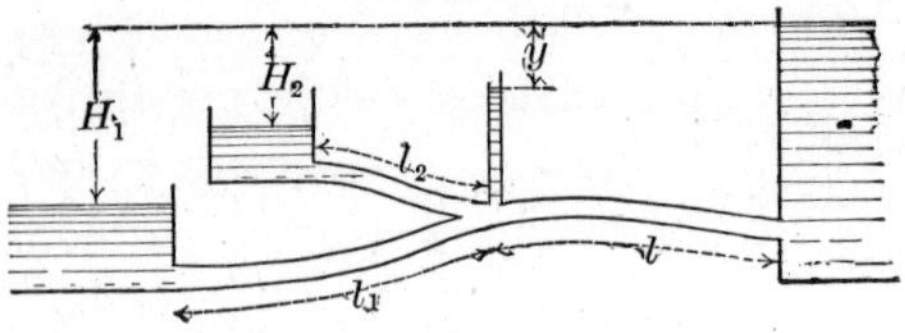

Fig. 105*a*.

Let v, v_1, and v_2 be the corresponding velocities; then for long pipes, in which all losses except those due to friction may be neglected, the friction-heads for the two branches are

$$H_1 - y = f_1 \frac{l_1}{d_1} \frac{v_1^2}{2g} \qquad H_2 - y = f_2 \frac{l_2}{d_2} \frac{v_2^2}{2g}$$

where y is the difference in level between the reservoir surface and the surface of the water in a piezometer tube supposed to be inserted at the junction. This y is the friction-head consumed in the flow in the large main, and hence from formula (90) its value is

$$y = f\frac{l}{d}\frac{v^2}{2g}$$

Inserting this in the two equations, and placing for the velocities their values in terms of the discharges, they become

$$\frac{2g\pi^2}{16}H_1 = f\frac{l}{d^5}(q_1+q_2)^2 + f_1\frac{l_1}{d_1^5}q_1^2$$

$$\frac{2g\pi^2}{16}H_2 = f\frac{l}{d^5}(q_1+q_2)^2 + f_2\frac{l_2}{d_2^5}q_2^2$$

from which the values of q_1 and q_2 are best obtained by trial.

When it is required to determine the diameters from the given lengths, heads, and discharges, there are three unknown quantities, d, d_1, d_2, to be found from only two equations, and the problem is indeterminate. If, however, d be assumed, values of d_1 and d_2 may be found; and as d may be taken at pleasure, it appears that an infinite number of solutions is possible. Another way is to assume a value of y, corresponding to a proper pressure-head at the junction; then the diameters are directly found from formula $(97)_3$ for long pipes, in which h is replaced by y for the large main, and by $H_1 - y$ and $H_2 - y$ for the two branches.

When two reservoirs, A_1 and A_2, are at a higher elevation than a third one into which they are to deliver water by pipes of length l_1 and l_2, both of which connect with a third pipe of length l which leads to the third reservoir, the above formulas also apply. In this case H_1 and H_2 are the heights of the water levels in the reservoirs A_1 and A_2 above that in the third reservoir.

When the principal main of a water-supply system enters a town, it divides into branches which deliver the water to different districts, and when such branches connect again with the principal main, they form what may be called "diversions." Figure 105*b* shows a simple case, A being the reservoir and AB the principal main, while the pipe lines BCE and BDE form two routes or diversions through which water can flow to F. Let the main AB have the length l and the diameter d, the line BCE the length l_1 and the diameter d_1, the line BDE the length l_2 and the diameter d_2, while the line EF has the length l_3 and the diameter d_3. Suppose that no water is drawn from the pipes except at F and beyond, that the pressure-head Ff at F is h_3, and that the static head Ff_1 on F is h, and let it be required to find the velocity and discharge for each of the pipes. The total head H lost in friction is $h - h_3$, and if W, W_1, W_2, and W_3 represent the weights of water

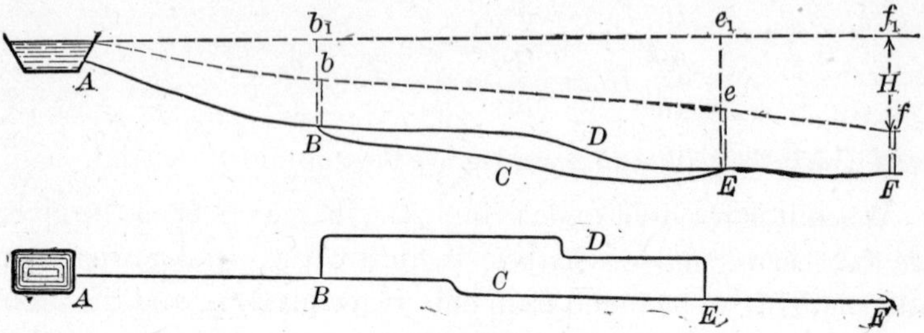

Fig. 105b.

that pass any sections of the four pipes per second, the theorem of energy, neglecting the entrance head at A and the velocity-head at F, gives

$$WH = Wf\frac{l}{d}\frac{v^2}{2g} + W_1 f_1 \frac{l_1}{d_1}\frac{v_1^2}{2g} + W_2 f_2 \frac{l_2}{d_2}\frac{v_2^2}{2g} + W_3 f_3 \frac{l_3}{d_3}\frac{v_3^2}{2g}$$

Now referring to the figure where piezometers are shown on the profile at B and E it is seen that the loss of head in friction is the same for the diversions BCE and BDE; accordingly there must exist the condition

$$f_1 \frac{l_1}{d_1}\frac{v_1^2}{2g} = f_2 \frac{l_2}{d_2}\frac{v_2^2}{2g}$$

and since W equals $W_1 + W_2$ and also equals W_3, the above energy equation reduces to the simple form

$$H = f\frac{l}{d}\frac{v^2}{2g} + f_1 \frac{l_1}{d_1}\frac{v_1^2}{2g} + f_3 \frac{l_3}{d_3}\frac{v_3^2}{2g}$$

The values of v_1 and v_3 in terms of v are now to be inserted in this equation in order to determine v. From the conditions of continuity of flow and that of equality of friction-head in the diversions, are found three equations,

$$d_3^2 v_3 = d^2 v \qquad d_1^2 v_1 + d_2^2 v_2 = d^2 v \qquad v_1 \sqrt{f_1 l_1 / d_1} = v_2 \sqrt{f_2 l_2 / d_2}$$

and accordingly, if the square roots of the quantities $f_1 l_1 / d_1$ and $f_2 l_2 / d_2$ be called e_1 and e_2 for the sake of abbreviation,

$$v_3 = \frac{d^2}{d_3^2} v \qquad v_2 = \frac{e_1 d^2}{e_2 d_1^2 + e_1 d_2^2} v \qquad v_1 = \frac{e_2 d^2}{e_2 d_1^2 + e_1 d_2^2} v$$

The above formula for H then reduces to

$$2gH = \left[f \frac{l}{d} + f_1 \frac{l_1}{d_1} \cdot f_2 \frac{l_2}{d_2} \left(\frac{e_1 d^2}{e_2 d_1^2 + e_1 d_2^2} \right)^2 + f_3 \frac{l_3}{d_3} \left(\frac{d}{d_3} \right)^4 \right] v^2$$

from which v can be computed. Then v_1, v_2, and v_3 may be found, as also the discharges q, q_1, q_2, and q_3.

As a numerical example, let l = 10 000, l_1 = 2200, l_2 = 2800, l_3 = 1200 feet, and d = 12, d_1 = 8, d_2 = 10, d_3 = 10 inches; let F be 184 feet below the water level in the reservoir and let the required pressure-head at F be 155 feet, so that H = 29 feet. Taking for the friction factors the mean value 0.02 (Art. 90), the value of fl/d is 200, that of $f_1 l_1/d_1$ is 66, that of $f_2 l_2 / d_2$ is 67.2, and that of $f_3 l_3 / d_3$ is 28.8. The value of e_1 is then 8.12 and that of e_2 is 8.20, while d/d_3 is 1.2. Inserting these in the last formula, there is found v = 2.45 feet per second; then v_1 = 2.16, v_2 = 2.14, and v_3 = 3.53 feet per second. As a check on these results the friction-heads for the four pipes may be computed, and these are found to be 18.6 feet for l, 4.8 feet for l_1 and l_2, and 5.5 feet for l_3; the sum of these is 28.9 feet, which is a sufficiently close agreement with the given 29.0 feet for a preliminary computation. The discharges are $q = q_3$ = 1.93, q_1 = 0.75, q_2 = 1.18 cubic feet per second, and the sum of q_1 and q_2 equals q, as should be the case. The computation may now be repeated, if thought necessary, the above velocities being used to take better values of the friction factors from Table 90*a*.

There are marked analogies between the flow of water in pipes and the flow of electricity in metallic conductors. Thus in Fig. 105*b*, let *BCE* and *BDE* be two wires that carry the electric current passing from A to F. If C_1 and C_2 be the currents in these circuits and R_1 and R_2 the resistances of the wires, it is an electric law that $R_1C_1 = R_2C_2$, or the currents are inversely as the resistances. For water the discharges q_1 and q_2 are analogous to the electric currents, and, from the above equation, which expresses the equality of the friction-heads, it is seen that

$$(f_1l_1/d_1^5)^{\frac{1}{2}} q_1 = (f_2l_2/d_2^5)^{\frac{1}{2}} q_2$$

and accordingly the same law holds if the coefficients of q_1 and q_2 be called resistances. If there be a third diversion BGE of length l_4 and diameter d_4 connecting B and E, the current or the discharge through AB divides between the three diversions according to the same law, and

$$f_4 \frac{l_4}{d_4} \frac{v_4^2}{2g} = f_1 \frac{l_1}{d_1} \frac{v_1^2}{2g} = f_2 \frac{l_2}{d_2} \frac{v_2^2}{2g}$$

from which it is seen that $(f_4l_4/d_4^5)^{\frac{1}{2}}q_4$ is equal to each of the corresponding expressions for the other diversions. This subject was more fully discussed in Art. 202 of the ninth edition of this book.

Prob. 105. From a reservoir A a pipe 10 000 feet long and 16 inches in diameter runs to a point B from which two diversions lead to E. The diversion BCE is 1600 feet long and 10 inches in diameter, while BDE consists of 2000 feet of 10-inch pipe and 1500 feet of 8-inch pipe. From the junction E, a pipe EF, 1000 feet long and 12 inches in diameter, leads to the business section of the town, where it is desired to have four fire streams deliver a total discharge of 900 gallons per minute through four hose lines of $2\frac{1}{2}$-inch smooth rubber-lined hose and $1\frac{1}{8}$-inch smooth nozzles. The point F is 180 feet below the water level in the reservoir. Compute the velocity and discharge for each pipe and hose line, the friction-head lost in each and the pressure-head at the end F.

Art. 106. Cast-iron Pipes

Cast-iron pipes generally range in size from 4 inches to 60 inches in diameter the larger sizes being usually made to order. They are cast in 12-foot lengths and dipped into a hot bath of coal-tar. The joints are of the bell and spigot type, the space about the spigot being filled with lead or other material so as to form a tight joint.

Some waters act rapidly on cast-iron causing the formation of tubercules of iron rust to such an extent that in the course of years the diameter of the pipe may be reduced by fully 50 percent. Various machines have been devised for removing such incrustations and deposits by scraping and thus in part restoring the original capacity of the pipe. No definite rule can be laid down for the selection of a proper friction factor for use in the design of a pipe. Each particular case must be carefully studied and the proper factor determined upon. Many experiments have been made in order to determine the friction factor in clean cast-iron pipes, and the results are tabulated in Table 90*a*. Other experiments have been made on pipes of various ages and a few of the results are here given in Table 106 in order to illustrate the range which is to be expected in the values of the friction factor.

TABLE 106. ACTUAL FRICTION FACTORS FOR CAST-IRON PIPES

Diameter in Inches	Age in Years	Velocity in Feet per Second			Reference
		2.0	3.0	4.0	
12	0	0.021	0.019	0.018	Trans. Am. Soc. C. E., vol. 47
12	15	0.076		—	Hering's Kutter *
12	22	0.121	0.127	—	Hering's Kutter *
20	5	0.019	0.022	—	Trans. Am. Soc. C. E., vol. 35
20	22	0.069	0.071	0.074	Hering's Kutter *
36	1¼			0.015	Trans. Am. Soc. C. E., vol. 44
36	3⅓			0.059	Trans. Am. Soc. C. E., vol. 44
48	0			0.013	Trans. Am. Soc. C. E., vol. 35
48	7	0.028		—	Trans. Am. Soc. C. E., vol. 28
48	16	0.023	0.023	0.023	Trans. Am. Soc. C. E., vol. 35

An inspection of the foregoing table indicates the great range in the values of the friction factor which are caused by progressive deterioration of the interior surface of a cast-iron pipe. Due allowance for this increase of the friction factor with age must be made in designing pipe lines and water mains.

Prob. 106. Compare the discharge of a new cast-iron pipe 20 inches in diameter and 10 000 feet long under a head of 100 feet with that of the same pipe when 25 years old.

* Hering and Trautwine's translation of Gauguillet and Kutter's Flow of Water in Rivers and Other Channels, New York, 1889, p. 155.

Art. 107. Riveted Pipes

Pipes 36 inches and larger in diameter have been made of wrought-iron or steel plates riveted together. Wrought-iron, however, is now but little used, on account of its higher cost, except in the form of thin sheets for temporary pipes. Each section usually consists of a single plate, which is bent into the circular form and the edges united by a longitudinal riveted lap joint. The different sections are then riveted together in transverse joints so as to form a continuous pipe. At AB (Fig. 107a) is shown the so-called taper joint, where the end of each section

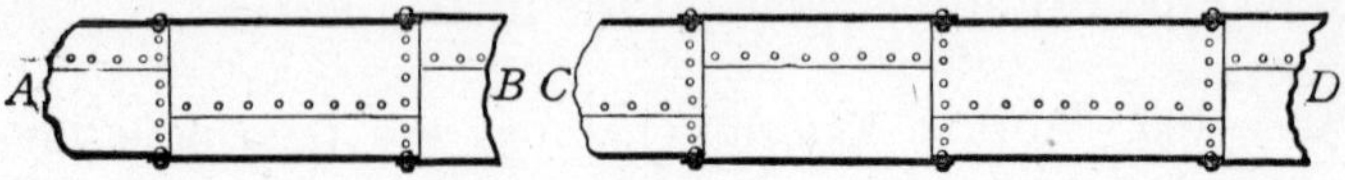

Fig. 107a.

goes into the end of the following one, as in a stovepipe, the flow occurring in the direction from A to B. At CD is seen the method of cylinder joints where the sections are alternately larger and smaller. For the large sizes double rows of rivets are used both in the longitudinal and transverse joints, the style of riveted joint depending on the pressure of water to be carried by the pipe. Riveted pipes have also been built with butt joints on both longitudinal and transverse seams, lap plates being on the outside.

Pipes of this kind have long been in use in California in temporary mining operations, the diameters being from 0.5 to 1.5 feet. In 1876 one was laid at Rochester, N.Y., partly 2 and partly 3 feet in diameter. Since 1892 several lines of large diameter have been constructed, notably the East Jersey pipe of 3, 3.5 and 4 feet diameter, the Allegheny pipe of 5 feet diameter, and the Ogden and Jersey City pipes of 6 feet diameter. The steel pipe siphons now under construction on the Catskill Aqueduct for the city of New York vary in diameter from 9.5 to 11.2 feet. These pipes will be covered with concrete as a protection against exterior corrosion and will be lined inside with 2 inches of Portland cement mortar both as a protective coating, as well as for the purpose of increasing their capacity. This, it may be noted, is a re-adoption of the old cement-lined pipe and it may be stated that the capacity of a pipe so lined is about 25 percent greater than that of the same pipe without such lining.

Owing to the friction caused by the rivets and joints the discharge from riveted pipes is less than that from cast-iron pipes in which the obstruction caused by the joints is very slight. The following values of the friction factor f, which have been derived from the data given by Herschel,* are applicable to new clean riveted pipes coated with asphaltum in the usual manner.

Velocity in feet per second,	$v =$	1	2	3	4	5	6
Cylinder joints	3 ft. diam., $f =$	0.035	0.029	0.024	0.021	0.019	0.017
	4 ft. diam., $f =$	0.025	0.022	0.020	0.020	0.021	0.021
Taper joints	$3\frac{1}{2}$ ft. diam., $f =$	0.025	0.024	0.023	0.022	0.022	0.022
	4 ft. diam., $f =$	0.027	0.026	0.025	0.024	0.023	0.023

These friction factors are approximately double those given for new cast-iron pipes in Art. 90, this increase being largely due to the friction of the rivet heads and lapped joints though some of it is probably chargeable to the roughness of the asphaltum coating. It must be noted that these factors increase with age, thus when four years old the upper end of the above 4-foot cylinder joint pipe gave the following values:

Velocity in feet per second, $v =$	1	2	3	4	5	6
Cylinder joint 4 ft. diam., $f =$	0.042	0.032	0.030	0.029	0.029	0.029

while the lower portion of this same pipe gave the following values:

Velocity in feet per second, $v =$	1	2	3	4	5	6
Cylinder joint 4 ft. diam., $f =$	0.027	0.024	0.023	0.024	0.024	0.024

The diminution in capacity here shown during a period of 4 years is greater for the upper than for the lower part of the line and this is to be ascribed in part at least to the greater number of vegetable growths which occur in most lines near, and for some distance below their intakes.

When this same pipe was 15 years old (Art. 121) the values of the friction factor for its upper end were as follows:

Velocity in feet per second, $v =$	1	2	3	4	5	6
Cylinder joint 4 ft. diam., $f =$			0.036	0.036		

* 115 Experiments on the Carrying Capacity of Large, Riveted, Metal Conduits, New York, 1897.

and at this same age the values for its lower end were:

Velocity in feet per second, $v =$	1	2	3	4	5	6
Cylinder joint 4 ft. diam., $f =$	0.046	0.034	0.032	0.031		

Similarly the $3\frac{1}{2}$-foot-diameter taper joint pipe above referred to, when 11 years old, gave the following values for the friction factor:

Velocity in feet per second, $v =$	1	2	3	4	5	6
Taper joint $3\frac{1}{2}$ ft. diam., $f =$	0.050	0.036	0.034	0.032		

Experiments on the 6-foot Jersey City Water Supply Company* taper joint pipe gave the following values for the friction factor at ages of 2 months to $5\frac{1}{2}$ years:

Velocity in feet per second, $v =$	1	2	3	4
at $\frac{1}{6}$ year, $f =$	0.021	0.022	0.022	0.022
at $1\frac{1}{3}$ years, $f =$	0.029	0.026	0.026	0.025
at $2\frac{2}{3}$ years, $f =$	0.034	0.029	0.027	0.027
at $5\frac{1}{2}$ years, $f =$	0.036	0.034	0.035	

Gagings by Marx, Wing, and Hoskins† of the flow through a steel riveted pipe 6 feet in diameter with butt joints when new, and again after two years' use furnish the following values of the friction factor f:

Velocity in feet per second, $v =$	1	2	3	4	5	6
1897, $f =$	0.021	0.021	0.022	0.021		
1899, $f =$	0.038	0.027	0.025	0.024	0.023	0.023

These results indicate a marked diminution with age in carrying capacity. This reduction is in part due to the formation of blisters in the asphaltum coating, which is generally used, in part, to the formation of tubercules or rust spots and in part to vegetable growths and incrustations formed by deposits from the water.

The so-called lock-bar pipe (Fig. 107*b*) was first used on the Coolgardie line in Australia and since 1900 has been introduced to a considerable extent in the United States. In this style of pipe the transverse joints are made up with rivets, as in the ordinary riveted pipe, but the

* Here published by courtesy of Jersey City Water Supply Company.

† Transactions American Society of Civil Engineers, 1898, vol. 40, p. 471; and 1900, vol. 44, p. 34.

longitudinal joints are made by clamping the edges of the plates under heavy pressure into a grooved bar which thus holds them together and makes a joint of exceptional strength. No longitudinal rivets therefore interfere with the flow, and as the plates of which the pipe is made can be used with their longer edges parallel to the axis of the pipe, the number of transverse joints can be reduced from 50 to 60 per cent. The carrying capacity of this style of pipe is probably materially in excess of that of riveted pipe, but no recorded experiments are available from which values of the friction factor can be stated.

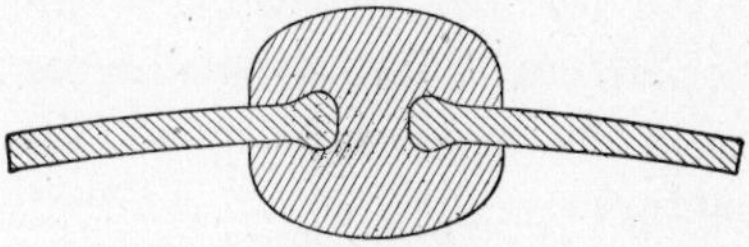
Fig. 107*b*.

Prob. 107. Construct curves showing the progressive increase with age in the value of the friction factor *f* for riveted steel pipes of 42, 48, and 60 inches in diameter.

Art. 108. Wood Pipes

Wood pipes were used in several American cities during the years 1750–1850, these being made of logs laid end to end, a 3 or 4 inch hole having been first bored through each log. Pipes formed of redwood staves were first used in California about 1880, these staves being held in place by bands of wrought-iron arranged so that they could be tightened by a nut and screw. Several long lines of these large conduit pipes have been built in the Rocky mountains and Pacific states. They have also been used there for city mains to a limited extent and recently have been introduced in the East on main distributing lines.

Gagings of a wood pipe 6 feet in diameter were made by Marx, Wing, and Hoskins, in connection with those of the steel pipe cited in Art. 107. The values of the friction factor *f* deduced from their results for velocities ranging from 1 to 5 feet per second are

Velocity in feet per second,	$v =$ 1	2	3	4	5
1897,	$f =$ 0.026	0.019	0.017	0.016	
1899,	$f =$ 0.019	0.018	0.017	0.017	0.017

These show that this wood pipe became smoother after two years' use, while the steel pipe became rougher.

T. A. Noble's gagings of wood pipes 3.67 and 4.51 feet in diameter furnish similar values of f.* For the smaller pipe f ranges from 0.021 to 0.019, with velocities ranging from 3.5 to 4.8 feet per second. For the larger pipe f ranges from 0.019 to 0.016, with velocities ranging from 2.3 to 4.7 feet per second. From Adams' measurements on a pipe 1.17 feet in diameter the values of f range from 0.027 to 0.020, with velocities ranging from 0.7 to 1.5 feet per second. Noble's discussion of all the recorded gagings on wood pipes show certain unexplained discrepancies, and he proposes special empirical formulas to be used for precise computations. Wooden stave pipes after being in service some time may undergo considerable alterations in form, as the circle is apt to be deformed into an ellipse.

By the help of the formulas of the preceding pages, computations for the velocity and discharge of steel and wood pipes under given heads may be readily made. As such pipes are generally long, the formulas of Art. 97 will usually apply. In designing a pipe line a liberal factor of safety should be introduced by taking a value of f sufficiently large so that the discharge may not be found deficient after a few years' use has deteriorated its surface.

Prob. 108. What is the discharge, in gallons per day, of a wood stave pipe 5 feet in diameter when the slope of the hydraulic gradient is 47.5 feet per mile?

Art. 109. Fire Hose

Fire hose is generally $2\frac{1}{2}$ inches in diameter, and lined with rubber to reduce the frictional losses. The following values of the friction factor f have been deduced from the experiments of Freeman.†

Velocity in feet per second,	$v =$ 4	6	10	15	20
Unlined linen hose,	$f =$ 0.038	0.038	0.037	0.035	0.034
Rough rubber-lined cotton,	$f =$ 0.030	0.031	0.031	0.030	0.029
Smooth rubber-lined cotton,	$f =$ 0.024	0.023	0.022	0.019	0.018
Discharge, gallons per minute	= 61	92	153	230	306

By the help of this table computations may be made on flow of water through fire hose in the same manner as for pipes. It is

* Transactions American Society of Civil Engineers, 1902, vol. 49, pp. 112, 143.

† Transactions American Society of Civil Engineers, 1889, vol. 21, p. 303; 346.

seen that the friction factors for the best hose are slightly less than those given for $2\frac{1}{2}$-inch pipes in Table 90*a*.

When the hose line runs from a steamer to the nozzle, instead of from a reservoir, the head h is that due to the pressure p at the steamer pump (Art. 11). If this hose line is of uniform diameter the velocity in the hose and nozzle may be computed by Art. 101 and the discharge is then readily found. For example, let the hose be $2\frac{1}{2}$ inches in diameter and 400 feet long, the pressure at the steamer be 100 pounds per square inch, which corresponds to a head of 230.4 feet, and the nozzle be $1\frac{1}{8}$ inches in diameter with a coefficient of velocity of 0.98. Then, neglecting the loss of head at entrance, and using for f the value 0.03, the velocity from the nozzle is found to be 66.0 feet per second, which gives a velocity-head of 67.7 feet and a discharge of 180 gallons per minute. The head lost in friction is $230.4-67.7=162.7$ feet, of which 2.8 feet are lost in the nozzle and the remainder in the hose.

Sometimes the hose near the steamer is larger in diameter than the remaining length. Let l_1 be the length and d_1 the diameter of the larger hose, and l_2 and d_2 the same quantities for the smaller hose. Let c_v be the coefficient of velocity for a smooth nozzle, D its diameter, and V the velocity of the stream issuing from the nozzle. By reasoning as in Arts. 93 and 101, and neglecting losses of head at entrance and in curvature, there is found for the velocity at the end of the nozzle

$$V = \sqrt{\frac{2gh}{f_1 \frac{l_1}{d_1}\left(\frac{D}{d_1}\right)^4 + f_2 \frac{l_2}{d_2}\left(\frac{D}{d_2}\right)^4 + \frac{1}{c_v^2}}} \qquad (109)$$

and the discharge is given by $q=\frac{1}{4}\pi D^2 V$. For example, let $h=230.4$, $l_1=100$, $l_2=300$ feet; $d_1=3$, $d_2=2.5$, $D=1.125$ inches; $c_v=0.98$, and $f_1=f_2=0.03$. Then, by the formula $V=69.7$ feet per second, which gives a velocity-head of 75.5 feet and a discharge of 190 gallons per minute. This example is the same as that of the preceding paragraph, except that a larger hose is used for one-fourth of the length, and it is seen that its effect is to increase the velocity-head nearly 12 per cent and the discharge nearly 6 per cent. For this case the head lost in friction is 154.9 feet, of which 3.1 feet are lost in the nozzle and the remainder in the 400 feet of hose.

In using the above formula the tip of the nozzle is supposed to be on the same level with the pressure gage at the steamer pump and the head h is given in feet by 2.304 p, where p is the gage reading in pounds per square inch. When the tip of the nozzle is a vertical distance z above this gage, h is to be replaced by $h - z$ in the formula; when it is the same vertical distance below the gage, h is to be replaced by $h + z$. In the former case gravity decreases and in the latter case it increases the velocity and discharge. The above formula applies also to the case of a hose connected to a hydrant, if h is the effective-head at the entrance, that is, the pressure-head plus the velocity-head in the hydrant. In Art. 201 will be found further discussions regarding pumping through fire hose.

At a hydrant of diameter d_1 the pressure-head is h_1. To this is attached a hose of length l and diameter d and to the end of the hose a nozzle of diameter D and velocity coefficient c_v. Neglecting losses at entrance and in curvature the formula for computing the velocity of the jet issuing from the nozzle, when its tip is held at the same level as the gage that indicates the pressure-head, is

$$V = \sqrt{\frac{2gh_1}{f\dfrac{l}{d}\left(\dfrac{D}{d}\right)^4 + \dfrac{1}{c_v^2}}}$$

Prob. 109. When the pressure-gage at the steamer indicates 83 pounds per square inch, a gage on the leather hose 800 feet distant reads 25 pounds. Compute the value of the friction factor f, the discharge per minute being 121 gallons. If the second gage be at the entrance to a $1\frac{1}{4}$-inch nozzle, compute its coefficient of velocity.

Art. 110. Other Formulas for Flow in Pipes

The formulas thus far presented in this chapter are based upon the assumption that all losses of head vary with the square of the velocity. This is closely the case for the velocities common in engineering practice, but for velocities smaller than 0.5 feet per second the losses of head due to friction have been found to vary at a less rapid rate, and in fact nearly as the first power of the velocity. Probably at usual velocities the loss of head in friction is composed of two parts, a small part varying directly with the velocity which is due to cohesive resistance along the surface, and a large part varying as the square of the velocity which is due to impact as illustrated in Fig. 90. This was recognized by the early hydraulicians who, after defining the friction head and friction factor as in (90), by the formula

$$h'' = f\frac{l}{d}\frac{v^2}{2g}$$

endeavored to express f in terms of the velocity v. Thus, D'Aubisson deduced

$$f = 0.0269 + \frac{0.00484}{v}$$

and Weisbach advocated the form

$$f = 0.0144 + \frac{0.0172}{\sqrt{v}}$$

Darcy, on the other hand, expressed f in terms of d, namely,

$$f = 0.0199 + \frac{0.00167}{d}$$

All these expressions are for English measures, v being in feet per second and d in feet. Later investigations show, however, that f varies with both v and d, and the best that can now be done is to tabulate its values as in Table 90*a*. In fact it may be said that the theory of the flow of water in pipes at common velocities is not yet well understood.

Many attempts have been made to express the velocity of flow in a long pipe by an equation of the form

$$v = \alpha \cdot d^{\beta}(h/l)^{\gamma}$$

in which α, β, and γ are to be determined from experiments in which v, d, h, and l have been measured. The exponential formula deduced by Lampe for clean cast-iron pipes varying in diameter from one to two feet is

$$v = 77.7\, d^{0.694}(h/l)^{0.555} \tag{110}$$

in which d, h, and l are to be taken in feet, and v will be found in feet per second. From this are derived

$$q = 61.0\, d^{2.694}(h/l)^{0.555} \qquad d = 0.217\, q^{0.371}(l/h)^{0.206}$$

by which discharge and diameter may be computed. Other investigators find different values of β and γ, the values $\beta = \frac{2}{3}$ and $\gamma = \frac{1}{2}$ being frequently advocated.

The formula of Chezy (Art. 113), that of Kutter (Art. 118), that of Bazin (Art. 122), and that of Williams and Hazen (Art. 124), are often used for long pipes, care being taken to select the proper value of c for the first, of n for the second, of m for the third, and of c for the fourth. The formulas of Kutter and Bazin are sometimes more advantageous than the others since in using them the roughness of the surface of the pipe can better be taken into account.

The formulas of this chapter do not apply to very small pipes and very low velocities, and it is well known that for such conditions the loss of head in friction varies as the first power of the velocity. This was shown in 1843 by Poiseuille, who made experiments in order to study the phenomena of the flow of blood in veins and arteries. For pipes of less than 0.03 inches diameter he found the head h to be given by $h = C_1 lv/d_2$ where C_1 is a constant factor for a given temperature, v is the velocity, d the diameter, and l the length of the pipe. Later researches indicate that the laws expressed by this equation also hold for large pipes provided the velocity be very small, and that there is a certain critical velocity at which the law changes and beyond which $h = C_2 lv^2/d$, as for the common cases in engineering practice. This critical point appears to be that where the filaments cease to move in parallel lines and where the impact disturbances illustrated in Fig. 90 begin. For a very small pipe the velocity may be high before this critical point is reached; for a large pipe it happens at very low velocities. Experiments devised by Reynolds enable the impact disturbance to be actually seen as the critical velocity is passed, so that its existence is beyond question. It may also be noted that the velocity of flow through a submerged sand filter bed varies directly as the first power of the effective head.

Prob. 110. Solve Problems 94 and 95 by the use of the above formulas of Lampe.

Art. 111. Computations in Metric Measures

Nearly all the formulas of this chapter are rational in form, the coefficient of velocity c_1, the factors f and f_1, and the factors m, m_1, m_2, and m' are abstract numbers which have the same values in all systems of measures.

(Art. 90) The mean value of the friction factor f is 0.02, and Table 111*a* gives closer values corresponding to metric arguments. For

Table 111*a*. Friction Factors for Clean Iron Pipes

Arguments in Metric Measures

Diameter in Centimeters	Velocity in Meters per Second					
	0.3	0.6	1.0	1.5	2.5	4.5
1.5	0.047	0.041	0.036	0.033	0.030	0.028
3.	.038	.032	.030	.027	.025	.023
8.	.031	.028	.026	.024	.023	.021
16.	.027	.026	.025	.023	.021	.019
30.	.025	.024	.023	.021	.019	.017
40.	.024	.023	.022	.019	.018	.016
60.	.022	.020	.019	.017	.015	.013
90.	.019	.018	.016	.015	.013	.012
120.	.017	.016	.015	.013	.012	
180.	.015	.014	.013	.012		

example, let l = 3000 meters, d = 30 centimeters = 0.3 meters, and v = 1.75 meters per second. Then from the table f is 0.022, and

$$h'' = 0.022 \times \frac{3000}{0.3} \times \frac{1.75^2}{19.6} = 34.3 \text{ meters,}$$

which is the probable loss of head in friction. By the use of Table 111*b* approximate computations may be made more rapidly, thus for this case the loss of head for 100 meters of pipe is found to be 1.10 meters, hence for 3000 meters the loss of head is 33 meters.

(Art. 94) The metric value of $\frac{1}{4}\pi\sqrt{2g}$ is 3.477 and that of $8/\pi^2 g$ is 0.2653.

(Art. 95) When (95) is used in the metric system, the constant 0.4789 is to be replaced by 0.6075; here q is to be in cubic meters per second, and l and d in meters.

TABLE 111*b*. FRICTION HEAD FOR 100 METERS OF CLEAN IRON PIPE

Metric Measures

Diameter in Centimeters	Velocity in Meters per Second					
	0.3	0.6	1.0	1.5	2.5	4.5
	Meters	Meters	Meters	Meters	Meters	Meters
1.5	1.44	5.02	12.2			
3.	0.58	1.96	5.10	10.3	26.6	
8.	.18	0.64	1.66	3.45	9.23	27.1
16.	.08	.30	.80	1.65	4.09	12.3
30.	.04	.15	.39	0.80	2.02	5.85
40.	.03	.10	.28	.54	1.43	4.13
60.	.02	.06	.16	.33	0.80	2.24
90.	.01	.04	.09	.19	.46	1.38
120.		.02	.06	.12	.32	
180.		.01	.04	.08		

(Art. 97) In $(97)_2$ the two constants are 4.43 and 3.48 instead of 8.02 and 6.30. In $(97)_3$ the constant is 0.607 instead of 0.479.

(Arts. 106, 107, and 108) The friction factors f for cast iron, steel and wood pipes may be taken for metric arguments by using the velocities in meters per second, namely, by writing 0.3, 0.6, 0.9, 1.2, 1.5, 1.8 meters per second, instead of 1, 2, 3, 4, 5, 6 feet per second.

(Art. 109) For fire hose the values of the friction factor f for metric data are as follows, for hose 6.35 centimeters in diameter:

Velocity, meters per second,	$v = 1.22$	1.83	3.05	4.57	6.10
Unlined linen hose,	$f = 0.038$	0.038	0.037	0.035	0.034
Rough rubber-lined cotton,	$f = 0.030$	0.031	0.031	0.030	0.029
Smooth rubber-lined cotton,	$f = 0.024$	0.023	0.022	0.019	0.018
Discharge, liters per minute,	= 231	348	579	871	1158

(Art. 110) In the metric system the formulas for the friction factor f are the same as those in the text, except that the numerator of the last term is to be divided by 3.28 in the formulas of D'Aubisson and Darcy and by 1.81 in that of Weisbach. Lampe's formula is

$$v = 54.1\, d^{0.694}(h/l)^{0.555}$$

and his formulas for discharge and diameter are

$$q = 42.5\, d^{2.694}(h/l)^{0.555} \qquad d = 0.249\, q^{0.371}(h/l)^{0.206}$$

in which d, h, and l are in meters, v in meters per second, and q in cubic meters per second.

Prob. 110*a*. Compute the diameter, in centimeters, for a pipe to deliver 500 liters per minute under a head of 2 meters, when its length is 100 meters. Also when the length is 1000 meters.

Prob. 110*b*. Compute the velocity-head and discharge for a pipe 1 meter in diameter and 856 meters long under a head of 64 meters. Compute the same quantities when a smooth nozzle 5 centimeters in diameter is attached to the end of the pipe.

Prob. 110*c*. A compound pipe has the three diameters 15, 20, and 30 centimeters, the lengths of which are 150, 600, and 430 meters. Compute the discharge under a head of 16 meters.

Prob. 110*d*. A steel-riveted pipe 1.5 meters in diameter is 7500 meters long. Compute the velocity and discharge under a head of 30.5 meters.

Prob. 110*e*. The value of C_1 in Poiseuille's formula for small pipes is 0.0000177 for English measures at 10° centigrade. Show that its value is 0.0000690 for metric measures.

Prob. 110*f*. In Fig. 105*b* let the pipe AB be 3000 meters long and 30 centimeters in diameter, BCD be 800 meters long and 20 centimeters in diameter, BCE be 1000 feet long and 20 centimeters in diameter, and EF be 300 meters long and 30 centimeters in diameter. Compute the velocity and discharge for each pipe when the total lost head H is 12.5 meters.

CHAPTER 9

FLOW IN CONDUITS AND CANALS

Art. 112. Definitions

From the earliest times water has been conveyed from place to place in artificial channels, such as troughs, aqueducts, ditches, and canals, there being no head to cause the flow except that due to the slope. The Roman aqueducts were usually rectangular channels about $2\frac{1}{2}$ feet wide and 5 feet deep, lined with cement, sometimes running underground and sometimes supported on arches. The word "conduit" will be used as a general term for a channel of any shape lined with timber, mortar, or masonry, and will also include large metal pipes, troughs, and sewers. Conduits may be either open, as in the case of troughs, or closed, as in sewers and most aqueducts. Ditches and canals are conduits in earth without artificial lining. Most of the principles relating to conduits and canals apply also to streams, and the word "channel" will be used as applicable to all cases.

The wetted perimeter of the cross-section of a channel is that part of its boundary which is in contact with the water. Thus, if a circular sewer of diameter d be half full of water, the wetted perimeter is $\frac{1}{2}\pi d$. In this chapter the letter p will designate the wetted perimeter.

The hydraulic radius of a water cross-section is its area divided by its wetted perimeter, and the letter r will be used to designate it. If a is the area of the cross-section, the hydraulic radius of that section is found by

$$r = a/p$$

The letter r is of frequent occurrence in formulas for the flow in channels; it is a linear quantity which is always expressed in the same unit as p, and hence its numerical value is different in different systems of measures. It is frequently called the hydraulic depth or hydraulic mean depth, because for a shallow section its value is but little less than the mean depth of the water. Thus, in Fig. 112, if b be the breadth on the water surface, the mean depth is a/b, and the hydraulic radius is a/p; and these are nearly equal, since the length of p is but slightly larger than that of b.

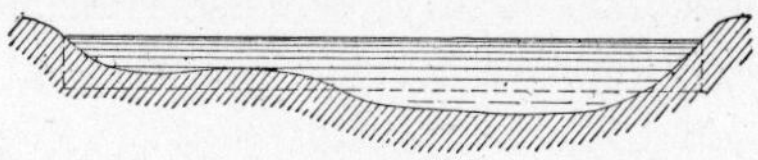

Fig. 112.

The hydraulic radius of a circular cross-section filled with water is one-fourth of the diameter; thus

$$r = a/p = \tfrac{1}{4}\,\pi d^2/\pi d = \tfrac{1}{4}d$$

The same value is also applicable to a circular section half filled with water, since then both area and wetted perimeter are one-half their former values.

The slope of the water surface in the longitudinal section, designated by the letter s, is the ratio of the fall h to the length l in which that fall occurs, or

$$s = h/l$$

The slope is hence expressed as an abstract number, which is independent of the system of measures employed. To determine its value with precision h must be obtained by referring the water level at each end of the line to a bench-mark by the help of a hook gage or other accurate means, the benches being connected by level lines run with care. The distance l is not measured horizontally but along the inclined channel, and it should be of considerable length in order that the relative error in h may not be large. If $s = o$ there is no slope and no flow; but when there is even the smallest slope the force of gravity furnishes a component acting down the inclined surface, and motion ensues. The velocity of flow evidently increases with the slope.

The flow in a channel is said to be steady when the same quantity of water per second passes through each cross-section. If an empty channel be filled by admitting water at its upper end, the flow is at first non-steady or variable, for more water passes through one of the upper sections per second than is delivered at the lower end. But after sufficient time has elapsed the flow becomes steady; when this occurs the mean velocities in different sections are inversely as their areas (Art. 31).

Uniform flow is that particular case of steady flow where all the water cross-sections are equal, and the slope of the water surface is parallel to that of the bed of the channel. If the sections vary, the flow is said to be non-uniform, although the condition of steady flow is still fulfilled. In this chapter only the case of uniform flow will be discussed.

The velocities of different filaments in a channel are not equal, as those near the wetted perimeter move slower than the central ones, owing to the retarding influence of friction. The mean of all the velocities of all the filaments in a cross-section is called the mean velocity v. Thus if v', v'', etc., be velocities of different filaments,

$$v = \frac{v' + v'' + \text{etc.}}{n}$$

in which n is the number of filaments. Let a be the area of the cross-section and let each filament have the small cross-section of area a'; then $n = a/a'$, and hence,

$$av = a'(v' + v'' + \text{etc.})$$

But the second member is the discharge q; that is, the quantity of water passing the given cross-section in one second. Therefore the mean velocity may be also determined by the relation

$$v = q/a$$

The filaments which are here considered are in part imaginary, for experiments show that there is a constant sinuous motion of particles from one side of the channel to the other. The best definition for mean velocity hence is, that it is a velocity which multiplied by the area of the cross-section gives the discharge, or $v = q/a$.

Prob. 112. Compute the hydraulic radius of a rectangular trough whose width is 5.6 feet and depth 2.8 feet.

Art. 113. Formula for Mean Velocity

When all the wetted cross-sections of a channel are equal, and the water is neither rising nor falling, having attained the condition of steady flow, the flow is said to be uniform. This is the case in a conduit or canal of constant size and slope whose supply does not vary. The same quantity of water per second then passes each cross-section, and consequently the mean velocity in each section is the same. This uniformity of flow is due to the resistances along the interior surface of the channel, for were it perfectly smooth the force of gravity would cause the velocity to be accelerated. The entire energy of the water due to the fall h is hence expended in overcoming resistances caused by surface roughness. A part overcomes friction along the surface, but most of it is expended in eddies of the water, whereby impact results and heat is generated. A complete theoretic analysis of this complex case has not been perfected, but if the velocity be not small, the discussion given for pipes in Art. 90 applies equally well to channels.

Let W be the weight of water passing any cross-section in one second, F the force of friction per square unit along the surface, p the wetted perimeter, and h the fall in the length l. The potential energy of the fall is Wh. The total resisting friction is Fpl, and the energy consumed per second is $Fplv$, if v be the velocity. Accordingly $Fplv$ equals Wh. But the value of W is wav, if w is the weight of a cubic foot of water and a the area of the cross-section in square feet. Therefore $Fpl = wah$, and since a/p is the hydraulic radius r, and h/l is the slope s, this reduces to $F = wrs$, which is an approximate expression for the resisting force of friction on one square unit of the surface of the channel. In order to establish a formula for the mean velocity the value of F must be expressed in terms of v, and this can only be done by studying the results of experiments. These indicate that F is approximately proportional to the square of the mean velocity. Therefore if c is a constant, the mean velocity is

$$v = c\sqrt{rs} \qquad (113)$$

which is the formula first advocated by Chezy in 1775. This is really an empirical expression, since the relation between F and v is derived from experiments. The coefficient c varies with the roughness of the bed and with other circumstances.

Another method of establishing Chezy's formula for channels is to consider that when a pipe on a uniform slope is not under pressure, the hydraulic gradient coincides with the water surface. Then formula (90) may be used by replacing h'' by h and d by its value $4r$. Accordingly

$$h = \tfrac{1}{4} f \frac{l}{r} \frac{v^2}{2g} \quad \text{or} \quad v = \sqrt{8g/f}\,\sqrt{rs}$$

in which the quantity $\sqrt{8g/f}$ is the Chezy coefficient.

This coefficient c is different in different systems of measures since it depends upon g. For the English system it is found that c usually lies between 30 and 160, and that its value varies with the hydraulic radius and the slope, as well as with the roughness of the surface. To determine the value of c for a particular case the quantities v, r, and s are measured, and then c is computed. To find r and s linear measurements and leveling are required. To determine v the flow must be gaged either in a measuring vessel or by an orifice or weir, or, if the channel be large, by floats or other indirect methods described in the next chapter, and then the mean velocity v is computed from $v = q/a$. It being a matter of great importance to establish a satisfactory formula for mean velocity, thousands of such gagings have been made, and from the records of these the values of the coefficients given in the tables in the following articles have been deduced.

Prob. 113. Compute the value of c for a circular masonry conduit 6 feet in diameter which delivers 65 cubic feet per second when running half full, its slope or grade being 1.5 feet in 1000 feet.

Art. 114. Circular Conduits, Full or Half Full

When a circular conduit of diameter d runs either full or half full of water, the hydraulic radius is $\tfrac{1}{4}d$, and the Chezy formula for mean velocity is

$$v = \text{c}\sqrt{rs} = \text{c}\cdot\tfrac{1}{2}\sqrt{ds}$$

The velocity can then be computed when c is known, and for this purpose Table 114 gives Hamilton Smith's values of c for pipes and conduits having quite smooth interior surfaces and no sharp bends.* The discharge per second then is

$$q = av = \mathrm{c} \cdot \tfrac{1}{2}a\sqrt{ds}$$

in which a is either the area of the circular cross-section or one-half that section, as the case may be.

TABLE 114. COEFFICIENTS C FOR CIRCULAR CONDUITS

Diameter in Feet	Velocity in Feet per Second						
	1	2	3	4	6	10	15
1.	96	104	109	112	116	121	124
1.5	103	111	116	119	123	129	132
2.	109	116	121	124	129	134	138
2.5	113	120	125	128	133	139	143
3.	117	124	128	132	136	143	147
3.5	120	127	131	135	139	146	151
4.	123	130	134	137	142	150	155
5.	128	134	139	142	147	155	
6.	132	138	142	145	150		
7.	135	141	145	149	153		
8.	137	143	148	151			

To use Table 114 a tentative method must be employed since c depends upon the velocity of flow. For this purpose there may be taken roughly

$$\text{mean Chezy coefficient } \mathrm{c} = 125$$

and then v may be computed for the given diameter and slope; a new value of c is then taken from the table and a new v computed; and thus, after two or three trials, the probable mean velocity of flow is obtained. The value of the diameter d must be expressed in feet.

For example, let it be required to find the velocity and discharge of a semicircular conduit of 6 feet diameter when laid on a grade of 0.1 feet in 100 feet. First,

$$v = 125 \times \tfrac{1}{2}\sqrt{6 \times 0.001} = 4.8 \text{ feet per second.}$$

* Hydraulics (London and New York, 1886), p. 271.

For this velocity the table gives 147 for c; hence

$$v = 147 \times \tfrac{1}{2} \sqrt{0.006} = 5.7 \text{ feet per second.}$$

Again, from the table c = 150, and

$$v = 150 \times \tfrac{1}{2} \sqrt{0.006} = 5.8 \text{ feet per second.}$$

This shows that 150 is a little too large; for c = 149.5, v is found to be 5.79 feet per second, which is the final result. The discharge per second now is

$$q = 0.7854 \times \tfrac{1}{2} \times 36 \times 5.79 = 81.9 \text{ cubic feet,}$$

which is the probable flow under the given conditions.

To find the diameter of a circular conduit to discharge a given quantity under a given slope, the area a is to be expressed in terms of d in the above equation, which is then to be solved for d; thus,

$$d = \left(\frac{8q}{\pi c \sqrt{s}}\right)^{\frac{2}{5}} \qquad d = \left(\frac{16q}{\pi c \sqrt{s}}\right)^{\frac{2}{5}}$$

the first being for a conduit running full and the second for one running half full. Here c may at first be taken as 125; then d is computed, the approximate velocity found from $v = q/\frac{1}{4}\pi d^2$, and with this value of v a value of c is selected from the table, and the computation for d is repeated. This process may be continued until the corresponding values of c and v are found to be in close agreement.

As an example of the determination of diameter let it be required to find d when $q = 81.9$ cubic feet per second, $s = 0.001$, and the conduit runs full. For c = 125 the formula gives $d = 4.9$ feet, whence $v = 4.37$ feet per second. From the table c may be now taken as 142, and repeating the computation $d = 4.64$ feet, whence $v = 4.84$ feet per second, which requires no further change in the value of c. As the tabular coefficients are based upon quite smooth interior surfaces, such as occur only in new, clean, iron pipes, or with fine cement finish, it might be well to build the conduit 5 feet or 60 inches in diameter. It is seen from the previous example that a semicircular conduit of 6 feet diameter carries the same amount of water as is here carried by one of 4.64 feet diameter which runs entirely full.

Circular conduits running full of water are long pipes and all the formulas and methods of Arts. 94 and 95 can be applied also to their discussion. From Art. 113 it is seen that

$$c = \sqrt{8g/f} \quad \text{or} \quad c = 16.04/\sqrt{f}$$

in which f is to be taken from Table 90*a*. Values of c computed in this manner will not generally agree closely with the coefficients of Smith, partly because the values of f are given only to three decimal places, and partly because Table 90*a* for pipes was constructed from experiments on smoother surfaces than those of conduits. An agreement within 5 per cent in mean velocities deduced by different methods is all that can generally be expected in conduit computations, and if the actual discharge agrees as closely as this with the computed discharge, the designer can be considered a fortunate man.

All of the laws deduced in the last chapter regarding the relation between diameter and discharge, relative discharging capacity, etc., hence apply equally well to circular conduits which run either full or half full. If the conduit be full, it matters not whether it be laid truly to grade or whether it be under pressure, since in either case the slope s is the total fall h divided by the total length. Usually, however, the word "conduit" implies a uniform slope for considerable distances, and in this case the hydraulic gradient coincides with the surface of the flowing water.

Prob. 114. Find the diameter of a circular conduit to deliver when running full 16 500 000 gallons per day, its slope being 0.00016.

Art. 115. Circular Conduits, Partly Full

Let a circular conduit with the slope s be partly full of water, its cross-section being a and hydraulic radius r. Then the mean velocity and the discharge are given by

$$v = c\sqrt{rs} \qquad q = ca\sqrt{rs}$$

The mean velocity is hence proportional to $\sqrt{r}$ and the discharge to $a\sqrt{r}$, provided that c be a constant. Since, however, c varies slightly with r, this law of proportionality is only approximate.

When a circular conduit of diameter d runs either full or half full, its hydraulic radius is $\frac{1}{4}d$ (Art. 112). If it is filled to the depth d' (Fig. 115), the wetted perimeter is

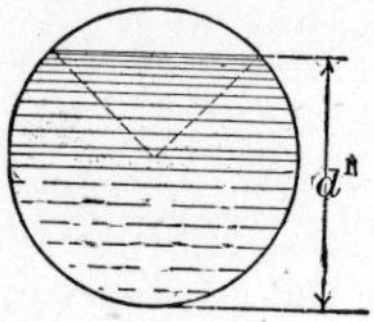

Fig. 115.

$$p = \tfrac{1}{2}\pi d + d \operatorname{arc\,sin} \frac{2d' - d}{d}$$

and the sectional area of the water surface is

$$a = \tfrac{1}{4}dp + (d' - \tfrac{1}{2}d)\sqrt{d'(d - d')}$$

From these p and a can be computed, and then r is found by dividing a by p. Table 115 gives values of p, a, and r for a circle of diameter unity for different depths of water. To find from it the hydraulic radius for any other circle it is only necessary to multiply the tabular values of r by the given diameter d. The table shows that the greatest value of the hydraulic radius occurs when $d' = 0.81d$, and that it is but little less when $d' = 0.8d$. In the fifth and sixth columns of the table are given values of $\sqrt{r}$ and $a\sqrt{r}$ for different depths in the circle of diameter unity; these are approximately proportional to the velocity and discharge which occur in a circle of any size. The table shows that the greatest velocity occurs when the depth of the water is about eight-

TABLE 115. CROSS-SECTIONS OF CIRCULAR CONDUITS

Depth a		Wetted Perimeter p	Sectional Area a	Hydraulic Radius r	Velocity $\sqrt{r}$	Discharge $a\sqrt{r}$
Full	1.0	3.142	0.7854	0.25	0.5	0.393
	0.95	2.691	0.7708	0.286	0.535	0.413
	0.9	2.498	0.7445	0.298	0.546	0.406
	0.81	2.240	0.6815	0.3043	0.552	0.376
	0.8	2.214	0.6735	0.3042	0.552	0.372
	0.7	1.983	0.5874	0.296	0.544	0.320
	0.6	1.772	0.4920	0.278	0.527	0.259
Half Full	0.5	1.571	0.3927	0.25	0.5	0.196
	0.4	1.369	0.2934	0.214	0.463	0.136
	0.3	1.159	0.1981	0.171	0.414	0.0820
	0.2	0.927	0.1118	0.121	0.348	0.0389
	0.1	0.643	0.0408	0.0635	0.252	0.0103
Empty	0.0	0.0	0.0	0.0	0.0	0.0

tenths of the diameter, and that the greatest discharge occurs when the depth is about $0.95d$, or $\frac{19}{20}$ of the diameter.

By the help of Table 115 the velocity and discharge may be computed when c is known, but it is not possible on account of the lack of experimental knowledge to state precise values of c for different values of r in circles of different sizes. However, it is known that an increase in r increases c, and that a decrease in r decreases c. The following experiments of Darcy and Bazin show the extent of this variation for a semicircular conduit of 4.1 feet diameter, and they also teach that the nature of the interior surface greatly influences the values of c. Two conduits were built, each with a slope $s = 0.0015$ and $d = 4.1$ feet. One was lined with neat cement, and the other with a mortar made of cement with one-third fine sand. The flow was allowed to occur with different depths, and the discharges per second were gaged by means of orifices; this enabled the velocities to be computed, and from these the values of the coefficient c were found. The following are a portion of the results obtained, d' denoting the depth of water in the conduit, r the hydraulic radius, v the mean velocity, and all linear demensions being in English feet:

For cement lining				For mortar lining			
d'	r	v	c	d'	r	v	c
2.05	1.029	6.06	154	2.04	1.022	5.55	142
1.61	0.867	5.29	147	1.69	0.900	4.94	135
1.03	0.605	4.16	138	1.09	0.635	3.87	125
0.59	0.366	3.02	129	0.61	0.379	2.87	120

It is here seen that c decreases quite uniformly with r, and that the velocities for the mortar lining are 8 or 10 per cent less than those for the neat cement lining.

The value of the coefficient c for these experiments may be roughly expressed for English measures by

$$c = c_1 - 16\left(\tfrac{1}{2}d - d'\right)$$

in which c_1 is the coefficient for the conduit when running half full. How this will apply to different diameters and velocities is not known; when d' is greater than $0.8d$, it will probably prove incorrect. In practice, however, computations on the flow in partly filled conduits are of rare occurrence.

Prob. 115. Compute the hydraulic radius for a circular conduit of 4.1 feet diameter, when it is three-fourths filled with water, and also the mean velocity when it is lined with neat cement and laid on a grade of 0.15 feet per 100 feet.

Art. 116. Rectangular Conduits

In designing an open rectangular trough or conduit to carry water there is a certain ratio of breadth to depth which is most advantageous, because thereby either the discharge is the greatest or the least amount of material is required for its construction. Let b be the breadth and d the depth of the water section, then the area a is bd and the wetted perimeter p is $b + 2d$. If the area a is given, it may be required to find the relation between b and d so that the discharge may be a maximum. If the wetted perimeter p is given, the relation between b and d to produce the same result may be demanded. It is now to be shown that in both cases the breadth is double the depth, or $b = 2d$. This is called the most advantageous proportion for an open rectangular conduit, since there is the least head lost in friction when the velocity and discharge are the greatest possible.

Let r be the hydraulic radius of the cross-section, or

$$r = \frac{a}{p} = \frac{bd}{b + 2d}$$

then, from the Chezy formula (113), the expressions for the velocity and discharge are

$$v = c\sqrt{s}\sqrt{\frac{bd}{b + 2d}} \qquad q = c\sqrt{s}\sqrt{\frac{b^3d^3}{b + 2d}}$$

In these expressions it is required to find the relation between b and d, which renders both v and q a maximum.

Let the wetted perimeter p be given, as might be the case when a definite amount of lumber is assigned for the construction of a trough; then $b + 2d = p$, or $d = \frac{1}{2}(p - b)$, and

$$v = c\sqrt{s}\sqrt{\frac{b(p - b)}{2p}} \qquad q = c\sqrt{s}\sqrt{\frac{b^3(p - b)^3}{8p}}$$

in which p is a constant. Differentiating either of these expressions with respect to b and equating the derivative to zero, there is found $b = \frac{1}{2}p$, and hence $d = \frac{1}{4}p$. Accordingly $b = 2d$, or the breadth is double the depth.

Again, let the area a be given, as might be the case when a definite amount of rock excavation is to be made; then $bd = a$, or $d = a/b$, and

$$v = \text{c}\sqrt{s}\sqrt{\frac{ab}{b^2 + 2a}} \qquad q = \text{c}\sqrt{s}\sqrt{\frac{a^3b}{b^2 + 2a}}$$

in which a is constant. By equating the first derivative to zero, there is found $b^2 = 2a$, and hence $d^2 = \frac{1}{2}a$. Accordingly $b = 2d$, or the breadth is double the depth, as before.

It is seen in the above cases that the maximum of both v and q occur when r is a maximum, or when $r = \frac{1}{2}d$. It is indeed a general rule that r should be a maximum in order to secure the least loss of head in friction. The circle has a greater hydraulic radius than any other figure of equal area.

In these investigations c has been regarded as constant, although strictly it varies somewhat for different ratios of b to d. The rule deduced is, however, sufficiently close for all practical purposes. It frequently happens that it is not desirable to adopt the relation $b = 2d$, either because the water pressure on the sides of the conduit becomes too great or because it is advisable to limit the velocity so as to avoid scouring the bed of the channel. Whenever these considerations are more important than that of securing the greatest discharge, the depth is made less than one-half the breadth.

The velocity and discharge through a rectangular conduit are expressed by the general equations

$$v = \text{c}\sqrt{rs} \qquad q = av = \text{c}a\sqrt{rs}$$

and are computed without difficulty for any given case when the coefficient c is known. To determine this, however, is not easy, for it is only from recorded experiments that its value can be ascertained. When the depth of the water in the conduit is one-half of its width, thus giving the most advantageous section, the values of c for smooth interior surfaces may be estimated by the use of Table 114 for circular conduits, although c is probably smaller for rectangles than for circles of equal area. When the depth of the water is less or greater than $\frac{1}{2}d$, it must be remembered that c increases with r. The value of c also is subject to slight variations with the slope s, and to great variations with the degree of roughness of the surface.

Table 116, derived from Smith's discussion of the experiments of Darcy and Bazin, gives values of c for a number of wooden and masonry conduits of rectangular sections, all of which were laid on the grade of 0.49 per cent or $s = 0.0049$. The great influence

TABLE 116. COEFFICIENTS C FOR RECTANGULAR CONDUITS

Unplaned Plank $b = 3.93$ Feet		Unplaned Plank $b = 6.53$ Feet		Neat Cement $b = 5.94$ Feet		Brick $b = 6.27$ Feet	
d	c	d	c	d	c	d	c
0.27	99	0.20	89	0.18	116	0.20	89
.41	108	.30	101	.28	125	.31	98
.67	112	.46	109	.43	132	.49	104
.89	114	.60	113	.56	135	.57	105
1.00	114	.72	116	.63	136	.65	105
1.19	116	.78	116	.69	136	.71	106
1.29	117	.89	118	.80	137	.85	107
1.46	118	.94	120	.91	138	.97	110

of roughness of surface in diminishing the coefficient is here plainly seen. For masonry conduits with hammer-dressed surfaces c may be as low as 60 or 50, particularly when covered with moss and slime.

Prob. 116. Find the size of a trough, whose width is double its depth, which will deliver 125 cubic feet per minute when its slope is 0.002, taking the coefficient c as 100.

ART. 117. TRAPEZOIDAL SECTIONS

Ditches and conduits are often built with a bottom nearly flat and with side slopes, thus forming a trapezoidal section. The side slope is fixed by the nature of the soil or by other circumstances, the grade is given, and it may be then required to ascertain the relation between the bottom width and the depth of water, in order that the section shall be the most advantageous. This can be done by the same reasoning as used for the rectangle in the last article, but it may be well to employ a different method, and thus be able to consider the subject in a new light.

Let the trapezoidal channel have the bottom width b, the depth d, and let θ be the angle made by the side slopes with the horizontal. Let it be required to discharge q cubic units of water per second. Now $q = \text{c}a\sqrt{rs}$, and the most advantageous proportions may be said to be those that will render the cross-section a a minimum for a given discharge, for thus the least excavation, will be required. From Fig. 117,

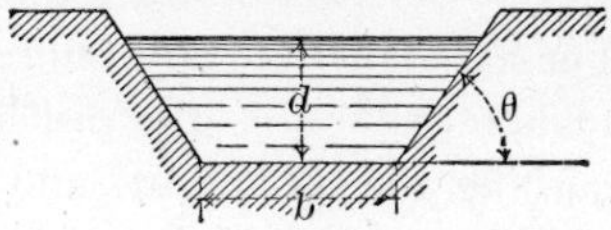

Fig. 117.

$$a = d(b + d\cot\theta) \qquad p = b + 2d/\sin\theta$$

and from these the value of r may be expressed in terms of a, d, and θ; inserting this in the formula for q, it reduces to

$$\frac{\text{c}^2sa^3}{d} - \frac{q^2a}{d^2} = q^2\left(\frac{2}{\sin\theta} - \cot\theta\right)$$

in which the second member is a constant. Obtaining the first derivative of a with respect to d, and then replacing q^2 by its value c^2a^2rs, there results

$$d = 2q^2/\text{c}^2a^2s \qquad d = 2r$$

which is the relation that renders the area a a minimum; that is, the advantageous depth is double the hydraulic radius. Now since $a/p = r$, it is easy to show that

$$b + 2d\cot\theta = 2d/\sin\theta$$

or, the top width of the water surface should equal the sum of the two side slopes in order to give the most advantageous section. Since c has been regarded constant, the conclusion is not a rigorous one, although it may safely be followed in practice. As in all cases of an algebraic minimum, a considerable variation in the value of the ratio d/b may occur without materially effecting the value of the area a. In many cases it is not possible to have so great a depth of water as the rule $d = 2r$ requires because of the greater cost of excavation at such depth, or because width rather than depth may be needed for other reasons.

When a trapezoidal channel is to be built, the general formulas $v = c\sqrt{rs}$ and $q = av$ may be used to obtain a rough approximation to the discharge, c being assumed from the best knowledge at hand. The formula of Kutter (Art. 118) or that of Bazin (Art. 122) may be used to determine c when the nature of the bed of the channel is known. For a channel already built, computations cannot be trusted to give reliable values of the discharge on account of the uncertainty regarding the coefficient, and in an important case an actual gaging of the flow should be made. This is best effected by a weir, but if that should prove too expensive, the methods explained in the next chapter may be employed to give more precise results than can usually be determined by computation from any formula.

The problem of determining the size of a trapezoidal channel to carry a given quantity of water does not require c to be determined with great precision, since an allowance should be made on the side of safety. For this purpose the following values may be used, the lower ones being for small cross-sections with rough and foul surfaces, and the higher ones for large cross-sections with quite smooth and clean earth surfaces:

For unplaned plank,	c = 100 to 120
For smooth masonry,	c = 90 to 110
For clean earth,	c = 60 to 80
For stony earth,	c = 40 to 60
For rough stone,	c = 35 to 50
For earth foul with weeds,	c = 30 to 50

To solve this problem, let a and p be replaced by their values in terms of b and d. The discharge then is

$$q = cd(b + d\cot\theta)\sqrt{\frac{d(b + d\cot\theta)s\sin\theta}{b\sin\theta + 2d}}$$

Now when q, c, θ, and s are known, the equation contains two unknown quantities, b and d. If the section is to be the most advantageous, b can be replaced by its value in terms of d as above found, and the equation then has but one unknown.

Or in general, if $b = md$, where m is any assumed number, a solution for the depth gives the formula

$$d^5 = \frac{q^2(m\sin\theta + 2)}{c^2 s(m + \cot\theta)^3 \sin\theta}.$$

For the particular case where the side slopes are 1 on 1 or $\theta = 45°$, and the bottom width is to be equal to the water depth, or $m = 1$, this becomes

$$d = 0.863\,(q^2/c^2 s)^{\frac{1}{5}}$$

These formulas are analogous to those for finding the diameter of pipes and circular conduits, and the numerical operations are in all respects similar. It is plain that by assigning different values to m numerous sections may be determined which will satisfy the imposed conditions, and usually the one is to be selected that will give both a safe velocity and a minimum cost. In Art. 120 will be found an example of the determination of the size of a trapezoidal canal.

Prob. 117. If the value of c is 71, compute the depth of a trapezoidal section to carry 200 cubic feet of water per second, θ being 45°, the slope s being 0.001, and the bottom width being equal to the depth. Compute also the area of the cross-section and the mean velocity.

Art. 118. Kutter's Formula

An elaborate discussion of all recorded gagings of channels was made by Ganguillet and Kutter in 1869, from which an important empirical formula was deduced for the coefficient c in the Chezy formula $v = c\sqrt{rs}$. The value of c is expressed in terms of the hydraulic radius r, the slope s, and the degree of roughness of the surface, and may be computed when these three quantities are given. When r is in feet and v in feet per second, Kutter's formula for the Chezy coefficient c is

$$c = \frac{\dfrac{1.811}{n} + 41.65 + \dfrac{0.00281}{s}}{1 + \dfrac{n}{\sqrt{r}}\left(41.65 + \dfrac{0.00281}{s}\right)} \qquad (118)$$

in which n is an abstract number whose value depends only upon the roughness of the surface. By inserting this value of c in the Chezy formula for v, the mean velocity depends upon r, s, and the roughness of the surface. Ganguillet and Kutter gave the following values of n for different surfaces:*

n = 0.010 for well-planed timber or smooth cement,
n = 0.012 for common boards,
n = 0.013 for ashlar or neatly-jointed brickwork,
n = 0.017 for rubble masonry,
n = 0.025 for channels in earth, brooks and rivers,
n = 0.030 for streams with detritus or aquatic plants.

The formula of Kutter has received a wide acceptance on account of its application to all kinds of surfaces. Notwithstanding that it is purely empirical, and hence not perfect, it is to be regarded as a formula of great value, so that no design for a conduit or channel should be completed without employing it in the investigation, even if the final construction be not based upon it. The formula shows that the coefficient c always increases with r, that it decreases with s when r is greater than 3.28 feet, and that it increases with s when r is less than 3.28 feet. When r equals 3.28 feet, the value of c is simply $1.811/n$. It is not likely that future investigations will confirm these laws of variation in all respects.

Numerous observations on natural and artificial channels have furnished data for determining values of the factor of roughness n; values of the slope s, the hydraulic radius r, and the mean velocity v are determined by field measurements for a certain channel, and then the corresponding n is computed from (118). Ganguillet and Kutter used hundreds of such measurements in their discussion; hundreds of others have since been made from which the six classes above mentioned have been greatly extended. The most recent discussions are those of Horton, which have utilized a large number of observations made on canals and rivers in the United States. The final results of Horton † are as follows, in which

* Flow of Water in Rivers and Other Channels. Translated, with additions, by Hering and Trautwine, New York, 1889.

† Engineering News, February 24, 1916, p. 373.

Table 118. Values of *n* for Kutter's Formula

Surface.	Perfect.	Good.	Fair.	Bad.
Uncoated cast-iron pipe	0.012	0.013	0.014	0.015
Coated cast-iron pipe	0.011	0.012†	0.013†	
Commercial wrought-iron pipe, black	0.012	0.013	0.014	0.015
Commercial wrought-iron pipe, galv	0.013	0.014	0.015	0.017
Smooth brass and glass pipe	0.009	0.010	0.011	0.013
Smooth lockbar and welded "OD" pipe	0.010	0.011†	0.013†	
Riveted and spiral steel pipe	0.013	0.015†	0.017†	
Vitrified sewer pipe	{ 0.010 / 0.011 }	0.013†	0.015	0.017
Glazed brickwork	0.011	0.012	0.013†	0.015
Brick in cement mortar; brick sewers	0.012	0.013	0.015†	0.017
Neat cement surfaces	0.010	0.011	0.012	0.013
Cement mortar surfaces	0.011	0.012	0.013†	0.015
Concrete pipe	0.012	0.013	0.015	0.016
Wood-stave pipe	0.010	0.011	0.012	0.013
Plank Flumes:				
Planed	0.010	0.012†	0.013	0.014
Unplaned	0.011	0.013†	0.014	0.015
With battens	0.012	0.015†	0.016	
Concrete-lined channels	0.012	0.014†	0.016†	0.018
Cement-rubble surface	0.017	0.020	0.025	0.030
Dry-rubble surface	0.025	0.030	0.033	0.035
Dressed-ashlar surface	0.013	0.014	0.015	0.017
Semicircular metal flumes, smooth	0.011	0.012	0.013	0.015
corrugated	0.0225	0.025	0.0275	0.030
Canals and Ditches:				
Earth, straight and uniform	0.017	0.020	0.0225†	0.025
Rock cuts, smooth and uniform	0.025	0.030	0.033†	0.035
Rock cuts, jagged and irregular	0.035	0.040	0.045	
Winding sluggish canals	0.0225	0.025†	0.0275	0.030
Dredged earth channels	0.025	0.0275†	0.030	0.033
Canals with rough stony beds, weeds on earth banks	0.025	0.030	0.035†	0.040
Earth bottom, rubber sides	0.028	0.030†	0.033†	0.035
Natural Stream Channels:				
(1) Clean, straight bank, full stage, no rifts or deep pools	0.025	0.0275	0.030	0.033
(2) Same as (1), but some weeds and stones	0.030	0.033	0.035	0.040
(3) Winding, some pools and shoals, clean	0.033	0.033	0.040	0.045
(4) Same as (3), lower stages, more ineffective slope and sections	0.040	0.045	0.050	0.055
(5) Same as (3), some weeds and stones	0.035	0.040	0.045	0.050
(6) Same as (4), stony sections	0.045	0.050	0.055	0.060
(7) Sluggish river reaches, rather weedy or with very deep pools	0.050	0.060	0.070	0.080
(8) Very weedy reaches	0.075	0.100	0.125	0.150

those marked † are to be commonly used in designing artificial channels.

Kutter's formula implies that for a given channel the factor n is independent of v, r, and s. Thus, for a certain stage of water let n be found, then for a somewhat higher stage, the values of v, r, and s will be larger than before. Since no change in the character of the channel surface has occurred, it might be supposed that n, as derived by computation for the two cases, would remain unchanged, but as a matter of fact this is rarely true. Sometimes n is smaller for the higher than for the lower stage and sometimes it is greater; part of this discrepancy is probably due to errors of observation, but yet there remain differences that can be explained only by supposing that the formula is imperfect.

The greatest uncertainty in the use of Kutter's formula occurs in applying it to streams of very slight slope. The introduction of the slope s into the formula was made by Ganguillet and Kutter on account of observations on the Mississippi river where the slopes were very small. These observations have since been shown to be imperfect, not only on account of the very great difficulty of measuring small slopes with precision, but also on account of the use of double floats in determining the mean velocities. A new discussion of all trustworthy observations is greatly needed and will probably be made before the end of the twentieth century, but in the meantime Kutter's formula will continue to be used. Its successful use in any given case will depend upon the care with which the computer consults the records of actual gagings in order to obtain the proper value of the factor n.

In the following articles are given tables of c for a few cases, and these might be greatly extended, as has been done by Kutter and others. But this is scarcely necessary except for special lines of investigation, since for single cases there is no difficulty in directly computing it for given data. For instance, take a rectangular trough of unplaned plank 3.93 feet wide on a slope of 4.9 feet in 1000 feet, the water being 1.29 feet deep. Here

$s=0.0049$, and $r=0.779$ feet. Then n being 0.012, the value of c to be used in the Chezy formula is found to be

$$c=\frac{\frac{1.811}{0.012}+41.65+\frac{0.00281}{0.0049}}{1+\frac{0.012}{\sqrt{0.779}}\left(41.65+\frac{0.00281}{0.0049}\right)}=123$$

The data here used are taken from Table 116, where the actual value of c is given as 117; hence in this case Kutter's formula is about 5 per cent in excess. As a second example, the following data from the same table will be taken: a rectangular conduit in neat cement, $b=5.94$ feet, $d=0.91$ feet, $s=0.0049$. Here $n=0.010$, and $r=0.697$ feet. Inserting all values in the formula, there is found $c=148$, which is 8 percent greater than the true value 138. Thus is shown the fact that errors of 5 and 10 percent are to be regarded as common in calculations on the flow of water in conduits and canals.

Prob. 118. The Sudbury conduit is of horse-shoe form and lined with brick laid with cement joints one-quarter of an inch thick, and laid on a slope of 0.0001895. Compute the discharge in 24 hours when the area is 33.31 square feet and the wetted perimeter 15.21 feet.

Art. 119. Sewers

Why do you use egg-shape sewer — small flow have high vel.

Sewers smaller in diameter than 18 inches are always circular in section. When larger than this, they are built with the section either circular, egg-shaped, or of the horse-shoe form. The last shape is very disadvantageous when a small quantity of sewage is flowing, for the wetted perimeter is then large compared with the area, the hydraulic radius is small, and the velocity becomes low, so that a deposit of the foul materials results. As the slope of sewer lines is often very slight, it is important that such a form of cross-section should be adopted to render the velocity of flow sufficient to prevent this deposit. A velocity of 2 feet per second is found to be about the minimum allowable limit, and 4 feet per second need not be usually exceeded.

The egg-shaped section is designed so that the hydraulic radius may not become small even when a small amount of sewage is flowing. One of the most common forms is that shown in Fig. 119, where the greatest width DD is two-thirds of the depth HM. The arch DHD is a semicircle described from A as a center. The invert LML is a portion of a circle described from B as a center, the distance BA being three-fourths of DD and the radius BM being one-half of AD. Each side DL is described from a center C so as to be tangent to the arch and invert. These relations may be expressed more concisely by

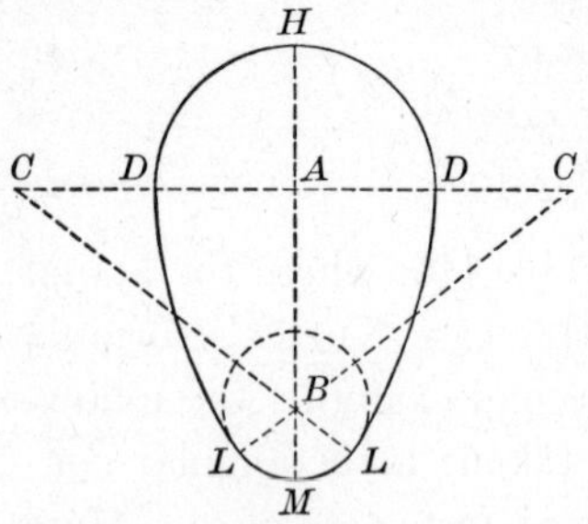

Fig. 119.

$$HM = 1\tfrac{1}{2}D \qquad AB = \tfrac{3}{4}D \qquad BM = \tfrac{1}{4}D \qquad CL = 1\tfrac{1}{2}D$$

in which D is the horizontal diameter DD.

Computations on egg-shaped sewers are usually confined to three cases, namely, when flowing full, two-thirds full, and one-third full. The values of the sectional areas, wetted perimeters, and hydraulic radii for these cases, as given by Flynn,* are

	a	p	r
Full	$1.1485\ D^2$	$3.965\ D$	$0.2897\ D$
Two-thirds full	$0.7558\ D^2$	$2.394\ D$	$0.3157\ D$
One-third full	$0.2840\ D^2$	$1.375\ D$	$0.2066\ D$

This shows that the hydraulic radius, and hence the velocity, is but little less when flowing one-third full than when flowing with full section.

Egg-shaped sewers and small circular ones are formed by laying consecutive lengths of clay or cement pipe whose interior surfaces are quite smooth when new, but may become foul after use. Large sewers of circular section are made of brick, and are more apt to become foul than smaller ones. In the separate system, where systematic flushing is employed and the pipes are small, foulness of surface is not so common as in the combined system, where the storm water is alone used for this purpose.

* Van Nostrand's Magazine, 1883, vol. 28, p. 138.

In the latter case the sizes are computed for the volume of storm water to be discharged, the amount of sewage being very small in comparison.

The discharge of a sewer pipe enters it at intervals along its length, and hence the flow is not uniform. The depth of the flow increases along the length, and at junctions the size of the pipe is enlarged. The strict investigation of the problem of flow is accordingly one of great complexity. But considering the fact that the sewer is rarely filled, and that it should be made large enough to provide for contingencies and future extensions, it appears that great precision is unnecessary. The practice, therefore, is to discuss a sewer for the condition of maximum discharge, regarding it as a channel with uniform flow. The main problem is that of the determination of size; if the form is circular, the diameter is found, as in Art. 114, by

$$d = (8\, q/\pi c \sqrt{s})^{\frac{2}{5}} = 1.45\, (q/c \sqrt{s})^{\frac{2}{5}}$$

If the form is egg-shaped and of the proportions above explained, the discharge when running full is

$$q = ac\sqrt{rs} = 1.1485\, D^2 c \sqrt{0.2897\, Ds}$$

from which the value of D is found to be

$$D = 1.21 (q / c\sqrt{s})^{\frac{2}{5}}$$

Thus, when q has been determined and c is known, the required sizes for given slopes can be computed. The velocity should also be found in order to ascertain if it is low enough to prevent scouring (Art. 135).

Experiments from which to directly determine the coefficient c for the flow in sewers are few in number, but since the sewage is mostly water, it may be approximately ascertained from the values for similar surfaces. Kutter's formula has been extensively employed for this purpose, using 0.015 for the coefficient of roughness. Table 119 gives values of c for three different slopes and for two classes of surfaces. The values for the degree of roughness represented by $n =$ 0.017 are applicable to sewers with quite rough surfaces of masonry; those for $n =$ 0.015 are applicable to sewers with ordinary smooth surfaces, somewhat fouled or tuberculated by deposits, and are the

TABLE 119. KUTTER'S COEFFICIENTS C FOR SEWERS

Hydraulic Radius r in Feet	$s = 0.00005$		$s = 0.0001$		$s = 0.01$	
	$n = 0.015$	$n = 0.017$	$n = 0.015$	$n = 0.017$	$n = 0.015$	$n = 0.017$
0.2	52	43	58	48	68	57
0.3	60	51	66	56	76	64
0.4	65	56	73	61	83	70
0.6	76	65	82	70	90	76
0.8	82	72	87	76	95	82
1.	88	77	92	80	99	87
1.5	100	86	103	89	108	93
2.	106	94	108	96	111	99
3.	116	103	118	104	118	105

ones to be generally used in computations. By the help of this table and the general equations for mean velocity and discharge, all problems relating to flow in sewers can be readily solved.

Prob. 119. The grade of a sewer is 1 foot in 1004, and its discharge is to be 130 cubic feet per second. What should be the diameter of the sewer if it is circular?

ART. 120. DITCHES AND CANALS

Ditches for irrigating purposes are of a trapezoidal section, and the slope is determined by the fall between the point from which the water is taken and the place of delivery. If the fall is large, it may not be possible to construct the ditch in a straight line between the two points, even if the topography of the country should permit, on account of the high velocity which would result. A velocity exceeding 2 feet per second may often injure the bed of the channel by scouring, unless it be protected by riprap or other lining. For this reason, as well as for others, the alignment of ditches and canals is often circuitous.

The principles of the preceding articles are sufficient to solve all usual problems of uniform flow in such channels when the values of the Chezy coefficient C are known. These are perhaps best determined by Kutter's formula, and for greater convenience Table 120 has been prepared which gives their values for three

TABLE 120. KUTTER'S COEFFICIENTS C FOR CHANNELS

Hydraulic Radius r in Feet	$s = 0.00005$		$s = 0.0001$		$s = 0.01$	
	$n = 0.025$	$n = 0.030$	$n = 0.025$	$n = 0.030$	$n = 0.025$	$n = 0.030$
0.5	38	31	41	33	47	37
1.	49	40	52	42	56	45
1.5	57	47	59	48	62	51
2.	64	52	65	53	67	54
3.	72	59	72	59	72	60
4.	77	64	77	64	76	63
5.	81	68	80	68	79	66
6.	86	72	84	71	80	68
8.	91	76	87	74	82	70
10.	96	80	91	80	85	73
15.	105	89	97	84	90	77
25.	114	100	101	92	95	82

slopes and two degrees of roughness. By interpolation in this table values for intermediate data may also be found; for instance, if the hydraulic radius be 3.5 feet, the slope be 1 on 1000, and n be 0.025, the value of c is found to be 74.5.

As an example of the use of the table let it be required to find the width and depth of a ditch of most advantageous cross-section, whose channel is to be in tolerably good order, so that $n=0.025$. The amount of water to be delivered is 200 cubic feet per second and the grade is 1 in 1000, the side slopes of the channel being 1 on 1. From Art. 117 the relation between the bottom width and the depth of the water is, since θ is 45°,

$$b = d\left(\frac{2}{\sin\theta} - 2\cot\theta\right) = 0.828d$$

The area of the cross-section then is

$$a = d(b + d\cot\theta) = 1.828d^2$$

and the wetted perimeter of the cross-section is

$$p = b + \frac{2d}{\sin\theta} = 3.656d$$

whence the hydraulic radius is $0.5d$, as must be the case for all trapezoidal channels of most advantageous section. Now, since d is unknown, c cannot be taken from the table, and as a first approximation let it be supposed to be 60. Then in the general formula for q the above values are substituted, giving

$$200 = 60 \times 1.828d^2 \sqrt{0.5d \times 0.001}$$

from which d is found to be 5.8 feet. Accordingly $r = 2.9$ feet, and from the table c is about 71. Repeating the computation with this value of c, there is found $d = 5.44$ feet, which, considering the uncertainty of c, is sufficiently close. The depth may then be made 5.5 feet, the bottom width is

$$b = 0.828 \times 5.5 = 4.55 \text{ feet,}$$

and the area of the cross-section is

$$a = 1.828 \times 5.5^2 = 55.3 \text{ square feet,}$$

which gives for the mean velocity

$$v = \frac{200}{55.3} = 3.62 \text{ feet per second.}$$

This completes the investigation if the velocity is regarded as satisfactory. But for most earths this would be too high, and accordingly the cross-section of the ditch must be made wider and of less depth in order to make the hydraulic radius smaller and thus diminish the velocity.

The following statements show approximately the velocities which are required to move different materials:

0.25 feet per second moves fine clay,
0.5 feet per second moves loam and earth,
1.0 feet per second moves sand,
2.0 feet per second moves gravel,
3.0 feet per second moves pebbles 1 inch in size,
4.0 feet per second moves spalls and stones,
6.0 feet per second moves large stones.

The mean velocity in a channel may be somewhat larger than these values before the materials will move, because the velocities along the wetted perimeter are smaller than the mean velocity. More will be found on this subject in Art. 135.

Prob. 120. A ditch is to discharge 200 cubic feet per second with a mean velocity of 3.4 feet per second. If its bottom width is 16 feet and the side slopes are 1 on 1, compute the depth of water and the slope of the ditch.

Art. 121. Large Steel, Wood, and Cast-iron Pipes

Long pipes of large size are usually regarded as conduits even when running under pressure, for in formula $(97)_1$ the ratio h/l may be replaced by the slope s and the diameter d is four times the hydraulic radius r; then it becomes

$$v = \sqrt{8g/f}\sqrt{rs} = c\sqrt{rs}$$

which is the same as the Chezy formula. Values of c may be directly computed from observed values of v, r, and s, and this has been done by many experimenters. When values of c are known, all computations for long pipes may be made exactly like those for circular conduits.

In the following Table 121*a* * are shown the results of experiments on a number of steel pipes ranging from 33 to 108 inches in diameter and from new to 15 years of age. The experiments were made at velocities ranging from 1.0 to 6.0 feet per second, and the values given in the table are those read from mean curves of the plottings of the results of the experiments. In the column headed "Material and Joint" the letters *S* and *W* refer to steel and wrought iron respectively, while the letters *B*, *C*, and *T* refer to the style of the joint used in the construction of the pipe, *B* indicating butt, *C* cylinder, and *T* taper joint, respectively. The experiments bracketed together in the first

* Following are the sources from which the results tabulated in this table have been obtained:

Nos. 1, 2, and 10. Transactions American Society of Civil Engineers, Vol. 26, p. 203.

Nos. 3, 4, 5, 6, 7, 8, 11, 12, 13, 15, 16, 24. Herschel's 115 Experiments, New York, 1897.

Nos. 9, 14, and 17 are here shown through courtesy of Morris R. Sherrerd, Chief Engineer, Department of Public Works, Newark, N.J.

Nos. 18, 19. Transactions American Society of Civil Engineers, Vol. 40, p. 471, and Vol. 44, p. 34.

Nos. 20–25. From The Jersey City Water Supply Co., Paterson, N. J.

No. 26. From C. A. Van Keuren, Chief Engineer, Jersey City, N. J.

Table 121*a*. Actual Coefficients C for Riveted Steel Pipes

Reference Number	Diameter in Inches	Location	Material and Joint	Age in Years	Velocity in Feet per Second: 1.0	1.5	2.0	2.5	3.0	4.0	5.0	6.0
1	33	Oregon	SC	0						123		
2	35	Oregon	SC	0					127	127		
3	36	New Jersey	SC	0	86	91	95	99	103	111	117	124
4	36	New Jersey	SC	4							106	
5	36	New York	WC	14		82						
6	38	New York	SC	0					115	109		
7	42	New Jersey	ST	0	96	103	108	111	113	113	111	110
8	42	New Jersey	ST	0	101	103	104	105	106	108	108	108
9	42	New Jersey	ST	11	72	79	84	86	87	88		
10	42	Oregon	SC	0				116				
11	48	New Jersey	ST	0	97	99	100	102	102	104	105	105
12	48	New Jersey	SC	0	101	105	109	111	113	113	112	112
13	48	New Jersey	SC	4	78	85	90	92	93	94	94	95
14	48	New Jersey	SC	15					84	84		
15	48	New Jersey	SC	0	101	105	109	111	113	113	112	112
16	48	New Jersey	SC	4	97	101	103	105	105	104	104	104
17	48	New Jersey	SC	15	76	83	87	89	90	91		
18	72	Utah	SB	0	110	111	110	108	108	111		
19	72	Utah	SB	2	82	92	98	101	102	104	105	105
20	72	New Jersey	ST	$\frac{1}{6}$	111	110	109	109	109	109		
21	72	New Jersey	ST	$1\frac{1}{3}$	95	99	100	100	100	101		
22	72	New Jersey	ST	$2\frac{1}{3}$	87	93	95	96	97	98		
23	72	New Jersey	ST	$4\frac{1}{2}$	85	86	87	86	85			
24	72	New Jersey	ST	$5\frac{1}{2}$	90	92	92	92	91			
25	72	New Jersey	ST	$7\frac{1}{6}$	85	87	88	89	89			
26	72	New Jersey	ST	$12\frac{1}{6}$			87	87	87			
27	108	Massachusetts	WC	5	116	113	110	109	108	106		

column were made at different ages as shown on the same pipe and indicate the deterioration which is to be expected with age. (See Art. 107.) Experiments numbered 12 and 15 are one and the same and are shown twice in order that comparison may more readily be made with experiments 13 and 14 and 16 and 17. Experiments 12 and 15 were made on the entire length of the pipe referred to, while 13 and 14 were made on its upper end and 16 and 17 on its lower end. It is to be noted that the coefficients shown in experiment 23, when the pipe was four and a half years old, are lower than those shown by experiments 24, 25 and 26, notwithstanding that the pipe was nearly eight years older when the observations of experiment 26 were made. This apparent improvement in the condition of the pipe has been due to the fact that shortly after experiment 23 was made a plant for sterilizing the water carried by the pipe was put into operation. Almost as soon as the sterilization was begun large masses of vegetable matter which had been growing in the pipe were discharged from its lower end, thus indicating that most vegetable growths cannot continue to live in water which has been so treated. In spite of this cleaning out of the vegetable growths, with which, by the way, many water mains are well supplied, the deterioration of the carrying capacity of the pipe has continued to increase, but at a much slower rate. In fact the coefficients have decreased for the last seven years at the rate of only $\frac{5}{7}$ point per year while for the first year alone the loss was nearly 9 points.

This result is interesting, as it permits of drawing some comparison of the relative effect of vegetable fouling with that of tuberculation due to the rusting of the pipe itself. The former apparently is controlling during the early years, while the latter, though relatively slow in action, is nevertheless a continuing factor. But it must not be forgotten that all of the fouling of the pipe during the early years of its life cannot be ascribed to vegetable growths. This pipe was protected against corrosion by a dipped asphalt coating and all coatings of this nature tend to become rough by the formation of blisters which are about as large as a pigeon's egg and of which ofttimes as many as forty are to be found on a square foot. These blisters sometimes become brittle with age and break off, thus leaving the metal of the pipe exposed but at the same time reducing the frictional losses.

For wooden stave pipes the gagings of Noble and those of Marx, Wing, and Hoskins, already referred to in Art. 108, furnish the following values of the coefficient c, those given for the 6-foot diameter in the first line being for new pipe and those in the second line after two years' use.

Velocity in feet per second, $v =$	1	2	3	4	5
3.7 feet diameter c =			(109)	113	116
4.5 feet diameter c =	(112)	122	126	128	
6.0 feet diameter c =	100	115	122	125	
6.0 feet diameter c =	116	120	121	122	122

Here the two values in parentheses have been found by a graphic discussion of the results of the observations. For the first of these pipes the valve of Kutter's n ranges from 0.013 to 0.012, while for the second and third it is practically constant at 0.013.

Many gagings have been made on cast-iron pipes, and the results show great variations which can be ascribed to many causes; among these may be mentioned the progressive deterioration due to age as well as that due to the particular kind of water carried by the pipe, the care with which the pipe has been laid, and with which the joints have been made. In Table 121*b* are shown the values of the coefficient c for certain pipes of different diameters and ages and for varying velocities. The friction factors for these same gagings are given in Art. 106.

As illustrating the values of n in Kutter's formula for some of the experiments shown in Table 121*a* the following, for experiments 18, 19 and 26 are here given:

Velocity in feet per second =	1.0	2.0	3.0	4.0	5.0
Experiment 18, $n=$	0.013	0.014	0.015	0.014	
Experiment 19, $n=$	0.018	0.016	0.015	0.015	0.015
Experiment 26, $n=$		0.018	0.018		

The deep concrete-lined tunnels which are coming into use on water supply systems as well as in sewer work are strictly

TABLE 121*b*. ACTUAL COEFFICIENTS c FOR CAST-IRON PIPES

Diameter in Inches	Age in Years	Velocity in Feet per Second				Reference
		1.0	2.0	3.0	4.0	
12	0	101	110	115	118	Trans. Am. Soc. C.E., vol. 47
12	15	65	58			Hering's Kutter *
12	22	49	46	45		Hering's Kutter *
20	5		115	109		Trans. Am. Soc. C.E., vol. 35
20	25		61	60	59	Hering's Kutter *
36	1¼				130	Trans. Am. Soc. C.E., vol. 44
36	3⅓				66	Trans. Am. Soc. C.E., vol. 44
48	0				141	Trans. Am. Soc. C.E., vol. 35
48	7		96			Trans. Am. Soc. C.E., vol. 28
48	16		107	105	105	Trans. Am. Soc. C.E., vol. 35

to be considered as masonry pipes, since they flow entirely full of water under high pressure. Perhaps the most notable example of these tunnels is to be found on the Catskill aqueduct (Art. 123). During the summer of 1915 experiments were made on two of these tunnels and the results are given below.†

Length of Tunnel	Coefficient			Diameter of Tunnel
	$v=2$	$v=3$	$v=4$	
24,880 feet	150	149	147	14.5 feet
24,249 feet	149	149	149	14.5 feet

It is to be noted that these coefficients are higher than those of riveted steel pipes and are also larger than those of cast-iron pipes, though the increase shown is most likely due to the larger hydraulic radius, which in the case of the 14.5 foot tunnel is 3.62, while for a 48-inch pipe it is but 1.0.

When the above experiments were made these tunnels were new and clean. It may be expected that with age these coefficients will drop to from 125 to 130. The value of the friction factor corresponding to the values of *c* as determined by the experiments on these deep tunnels is 0.012.

* Hering and Trautwine's translation of Ganguillet and Kutter's Flow of Water in Rivers and other Channels, New York, 1889, p. 155.

† By courtesy of J. Waldo Smith, Chief Engineer, Board of Water Supply, City of New York.

In the case of those portions of the Catskill aqueduct which lie on the hydraulic gradient the coefficients are nearly the same as for the pressure tunnels, as indicated in the following tabulation:

Mean Velocity	Coefficient	Hydraulic Radius	Mean Depth
3.85	145	2.90	4.30
4.35	148	3.55	5.70
4.70	151	4.10	7.50
5.10	154	4.50	9.10

The cross-section of this aqueduct is similar to that shown in Fig. 126*b*. It is 17.5 feet wide, 17 feet high and is laid on a slope of 0.00021. The above results were obtained when it was new and clean, and are to be considered as maximums. Results of gagings on other similar aqueducts are to be found in Art. **123.**

Prob. 121. Compare the diameter of a cylinder joint riveted steel pipe 25 000 feet long to carry 30 000 000 gallons daily at a loss of head of 5 feet per mile with the diameter of a cast-iron pipe for the same service.

Art. 122. Bazin's Formula

In 1897 Bazin proposed a formula for open channels as the result of an extended discussion of the most reliable gagings.* In it the coefficient c is expressed in terms of the hydraulic radius and the roughness of the surface, but the slope does not enter:

$$v = \mathrm{c}\sqrt{rs} \qquad \mathrm{c} = \frac{87}{0.552 + m/\sqrt{r}} \tag{122}$$

This is for English measures, r being in feet and v in feet per second, and the quantity m has the following values:

m = 0.06 for smooth cement or matched boards,
m = 0.16 for planks and bricks,
m = 0.46 for masonry,
m = 0.85 for regular earth beds,
m = 1.30 for canals in good order,
m = 1.75 for canals in very bad order,

* Annales des ponts et chaussées, 1897, 4e trimestre, pp. 20–70.

Table 122 gives values of c computed from (122) for these values of m and for several values of r, from which coefficients may be selected for particular surfaces. It may be noted that for a per-

TABLE 122. BAZIN'S COEFFICIENTS C FOR CHANNELS

Hydraulic Radius r in Feet	$m = 0.06$	$m = 0.16$	$m = 0.46$	$m = 0.85$	$m = 1.30$	$m = 1.75$
0.5	136	111	72			
1.	142	122	86	62		
1.5	145	127	94	70	54	
2.	146	131	100	76	60	49
3.	148	135	107	84	67	56
4.	149	137	111	89	72	61
5.	150	140	115	94	78	67
6.	151	141	117	96	80	69
8.	152	143	122	101	85	73
10.	152	144	125	106	91	79
15.			131	113	98	87
25.				121	107	97

fectly smooth surface where $m = 0$, the formula gives $v = 158\sqrt{rs}$, which cannot be correct since uniform velocity could not obtain on such a surface. For this extreme case Kutter's formula appears to be more satisfactory, for if $n = 0$ the value of c is infinite. However, no empirical formula can be tested by applying it to an extreme case.

A comparison of the values of c obtained from the formulas of Kutter and Bazin only serves to emphasize the uncertainty regarding the selection of the proper coefficient in particular cases. Kutter's $n = 0.010$ corresponds to Bazin's $m = 0.06$, and for several different hydraulic radii the coefficients for this degree of roughness are as follows:

Hydraulic radius r in feet,	1	3	5	7
From Bazin's formula,	c = 142	148	150	151
From Kutter, $s = 0.01$,	c = 156	179	187	191
From Kutter, $s = 0.001$,	c = 155	178	187	192
From Kutter, $s = 0.00005$,	c = 140	178	193	203

While the agreement is fair for a hydraulic radius of one foot, it fails to be satisfactory for larger radii. This is perhaps a severe comparison because it is probable that no channel in neat cement has ever been constructed having a hydraulic radius as great as 7 feet, but it serves to show that these empirical formulas differ widely when applied to unusual cases. For the present, at least, the formula of Kutter appears to receive the most general acceptance, but undoubtedly the time will come when it will be replaced by a more satisfactory one. An actual gaging of the discharge by the method of Art. 131 will always give more reliable information than can be obtained from any formula.

For a hydraulic radius of 3.28 feet Kutter's formula for c reduces to the convenient expression

$$c = 1.811/n \quad \text{whence} \quad v = \frac{1.811}{n}\sqrt{rs}$$

and this may be used for approximate computations when r lies between 2 and 6 feet. Here n is the roughness factor, the values of which are given in Art. 118. When $r = 3.28$ feet, Bazin's formula gives $c = 136$ for brickwork, while Kutter's gives $c = 140$; for canals in good order Bazin's formula gives $c = 69$, while Kutter's gives $c = 72$. The comparison is very satisfactory, and so close an agreement is not generally to be expected when computations are made from different formulas. The formula of Bazin is largely used in France and England, and that of Kutter in other countries.

Prob. 122. Solve Problem 118 by the use of Bazin's coefficients.

Art. 123. Masonry Conduits

Masonry conduits or aqueducts for conveying water have been used since the days of ancient Rome. In cases where large quantities of water are to be carried on small slopes and where the topography of the country is at a suitable elevation they offer the most economical means for its conveyance. The Sudbury and Wachusett aqueducts for the supply of Boston, the Jersey City aqueduct for the supply of that city, the Los Angeles aqueduct for the supply of the city of Los Angeles in California, the old Croton and the New Croton, and the Catskill aqueducts for the supply of New York City are among the largest and longest which have yet been constructed. Large portions of these aqueducts are in tunnels on the hydraulic gradient, and in the case of the Catskill aqueduct of a total of 110 miles of main conduit nearly 30 percent is in rock tunnel from 300 to 1100 feet below the surface. The Catskill tunnels, completed in 1916, are lined with concrete, are circular in cross-section, and their diameters range from 11 to 15 feet.

Relatively few experiments for determining the coefficients of flow have been made on these aqueducts. From their gagings of the Sudbury aqueduct, Fteley and Stearns * determined a formula for mean velocity. The cross-section of this aqueduct, which is laid on a slope of 0.0002, consists of a part of a circle 9.0 feet in diameter, having an invert of 13.22 feet radius, whose span is 8.3 feet and depression 0.7 feet, the axial depth of the conduit being 7.7 feet. It is lined with brick, having cement joints $\frac{1}{4}$ of an inch thick. The flow was allowed to occur with different depths, for each of which the discharge was determined by weir measurement. A discussion of the results led to the conclusion that in the portion with the brick lining the coefficient c had the value $127r^{0.12}$ when r is in feet, and hence results the exponential formula

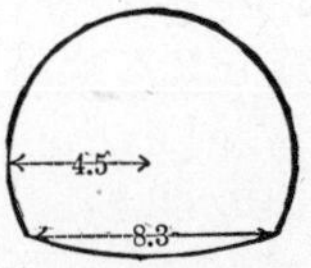

Fig. 123*a*.

$$v = 127\, r^{0.12} \sqrt{rs} = 127\, r^{0.62} s^{0.50}$$

In a portion of this conduit where the brick lining was coated with pure cement, the coefficient was found to be from 7 to 8 percent greater than $127r^{0.12}$. In another portion where the brick lining was covered with a cement wash laid on with a brush, the coefficient was from 1 to 3 percent greater. For a long tunnel in which the rock sides were ragged, but with a smooth cement invert it was found to be about 40 percent less.

Gagings on the New Croton Aqueduct † showed that the mean velocity when the aqueduct was new could be represented by the

* Transactions American Society of Civil Engineers, 1883, vol. 13, p. 114.
† Engineering Record, 1895, vol. 32, p. 223.

expression $v = 124r^{0.56}\sqrt{s}$. This aqueduct is constructed of brick laid in close mortar joints. Its cross-section is shown in Fig. 126*b*. It is 13.53 feet in height by 13.6 feet in maximum width. The radius of its invert is 18.5 feet, the span of the invert chord is 12.0 feet, and the depression of the invert below the chord is 1.0 foot. Its slope is 0.0003.

Gagings on various portions of the aqueduct of the Jersey City Water Supply Company,* a cross-section of which is shown in Fig. 123*b*, gave, when the aqueduct was new, values of the coefficient c in the Chezy formula of from 122 to 145, while the average value of n in Kutter's formula was 0.0127. The value of the mean velocity in this conduit is closely given by the expression $v = 131r^{0.50}s^{0.50}$, where s is the observed slope of the water surface. This slope during the experiments varied from 0.00011 to 0.00036, the aqueduct being laid on a slope of 0.000095. This conduit is of concrete which was cast against smooth wooden forms, the invert being made of screeded and troweled concrete.

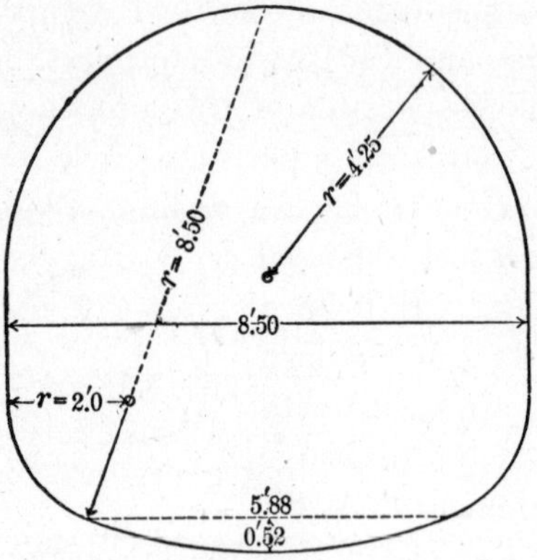

Fig. 123*b*.

Owing to the fouling of such conduits as the result of vegetable growths and the deposition of materials from the water, a diminution in capacity of from 10 to 20 percent with age may be expected, and accordingly corresponding allowances should be made in the design.

It is to be noted that Kutter's formula (Art. 118) indicates that c steadily increases with the hydraulic radius if n and the slope be constant. The results of the experiments above quoted, however, indicate that c becomes constant and has a maximum value

* By courtesy of Jersey City Water Supply Company, Paterson, N. J.

of not far from 140 for new and smooth concrete channels with hydraulic radii larger than 3.0 feet. (See Art. 121.)

For computations on concrete-lined irrigation ditches and canals Kutter's formula is generally used. Measurements by the U. S. Department of Agriculture * show that n ranges from 0.10 to 0.019, about 0.014 being an average value for new and smooth work, and that c ranges from 150 to 60. For such ditches there is much variation in slopes, and the hydraulic radius is usually less than 2 feet. Table 119 may be used to find approximate values of c for such channels. Growths of moss or deposits of sand increase n.

For wooden flumes about the same range in values of n and c is found, the amount of slime or moss on the sides exercising much influence. Metal flumes without projecting bands usually give values of n less than 0.013.

Prob. 123. Compute the mean velocity in the New Croton Aqueduct when it is flowing one-half full.

Art. 124. Other Formulas for Channels

Many attempts have been made to express the mean velocity and discharge in a channel by the formulas

$$v = Cr^x s^y \qquad q = aCr^x s^y$$

where x and y are derived from the data of observations by processes similar to those explained in Art. 42. As a rule these attempts have not proved successful except for special classes of conduits, as the exponents of r and s vary with different values of r and with different degrees of roughness. For conduits having the same kind of surface a formula of this kind may be established which will give good results. The values $x = \frac{2}{3}$ and $x = \frac{3}{4}$ are frequently advocated, y being not far from $\frac{1}{2}$; with such values C is found to vary less for certain classes of surfaces than the c of the Chezy formula, and this seems to be the only strong argument in favor of exponential formulas.

Among the many exponential formulas which have been advocated, those derived by Foss may be cited. For surfaces corresponding to Kutter's values of n less than 0.017 he finds †

$$r^{\frac{11}{6}} = Cr^{\frac{4}{3}}s \qquad \text{or} \qquad v = C^{\frac{6}{11}}r^{\frac{8}{11}}s^{\frac{6}{11}}$$

* Scobey, in Bulletin 194 (Washington, 1915), pp. 19–20.

† Journal of Association of Engineering Societies, 1894, vol. 13, p. 295.

in which C has the following values:

for n	$= 0.009$	0.010	0.011	0.012	0.013	0.015	0.017
C	$= 23\,000$	19 000	15 000	12 000	10 000	8 000	6 000

For surfaces corresponding to Kutter's values of n greater than 0.018, his formula is

$$v^2 = Cr^{\frac{4}{3}}s \qquad \text{or} \qquad v = C^{\frac{1}{2}}r^{\frac{2}{3}}s^{\frac{1}{2}}$$

and the values of C for this case are

for n	$= 0.020$	0.025	0.030	0.035
C	$= 5000$	3000	2000	1000

For circular sections running full he also proposes the formula $s = 0.0065q^{\frac{11}{6}}/d^5$. These formulas are open to objection on account of the great range in the values of C.

Tutton*, as the result of a study of many experiments, proposed the formula $v = Cr^{(1.17-m)}s^m$, where s and r represent the slope and hydraulic radius as in the Chezy formula. The values of m ranged from 0.48 for tarred iron pipes to 0.58 for pipes of lead, tin, and zinc, the average for all cases being $m = 0.54$. Using this value, the formula became

$$v = Cr^{0.63}s^{0.54}$$

for which the value of C was given as from 127 to 153 for new cast-iron pipes, from 83 to 98 for lap-riveted iron pipes, from 127 to 153 for wooden pipes, and about 188 for lead, tin, and zinc pipes.

Williams and Hazen † have discussed experiments on both pipes and open channels, and have proposed an exponential formula that is equivalent to

$$v = 1.318\,cr^{0.63}s^{0.54}$$

in which c has different values for different surfaces and sections, but its range of values is less than that of the C of the Chezy formula. The values of c and C are the same when r is 1 foot and s is 0.001. The greater the roughness of the surface, the smaller is c; in general, c is supposed to vary but little for different values of r. The following shows the range of the mean values of c found from the records of experiments with different surfaces:

* Transactions Engineers' Society of Western New York, April, 1896.

† Hydraulic Tables, New York, 1910.

For coated new cast-iron pipes,	from 111 to 146
For tuberculated cast-iron pipes,	from 16 to 112
For riveted pipes,	from 97 to 142
For wooden stave pipes,	from 113 to 129
For new wrought-iron pipes,	from 113 to 124
For fire hose, rubber lined,	from 116 to 140
For masonry aqueducts,	from 118 to 145
For brick sewers,	from 102 to 141
For plank aqueducts, unplaned,	from 113 to 120
For masonry sluiceways,	from 34 to 75
For canals in earth,	from 33 to 71

The authors of this formula suggest that in computations for pipe capacity *c* be taken as 100 for cast-iron, 95 for riveted steel, 120 for wooden, 110 for vitrified pipes, 100 for brick sewers, and 120 for first-class masonry conduits.

The circumstance that values of *C* in some of the exponential formulas of this article have a smaller range of values than the c of the Chezy formula is sometimes cited as an argument in their favor. While this is a good argument, the fact must not be overlooked that probably the true theoretic formula for mean velocity in a pipe or channel is of the form noted in the first paragraph of Art. 110.

In conclusion, it may be noted that when the velocity is very low, the Chezy formula is not valid. In such a case the velocity does not vary with the square root of the slope, but with its first power, the same conditions obtaining as in pipes (Art. 110). A glacier moving in its bed at the rate of a few feet per year has a velocity directly proportional to its slope. Water flowing in a channel with a velocity less than one-quarter of a foot per second follows the same law, and the formulas of this chapter cannot be applied. The formula for this case is $v = Cr^2s$, but values of *C* are not known. It is greatly to be desired that series of experiments should be made for determining values of *C*.

Prob. 124. Compute the fall of the water surface in a length of 1000 feet for a ditch where $v = 3.62$ feet per second, $r = 2.75$ feet, and $n = 0.025$; first by Williams and Hazen's formula, and second, by formula (122) and Bazin's coefficients.

Art. 124½. Biel's Formula

In 1907 Biel proposed * a new formula for flow in pipes and channels; in English measures it is

$$v^2 = \frac{1811rs}{0.0663 + \dfrac{f}{\sqrt{r}} + \dfrac{8\ 2k}{(100f+2)v\sqrt{r}}} \qquad (124\tfrac{1}{2})$$

in which v is the mean velocity, r the hydraulic radius, f a factor of roughness of the channel, and k a quantity which expresses the viscosity of the fluid. The following are values of k for water:

At 32° F., $k = 0.0179$; at 50° F., $k = 0.0135$; at 68° F., $k = 0.0100$, and the values of the factor of roughness are:

$f = 0.018$ for planed matched boards and wrought-iron pipes;
$f = 0.036$ for new cast-iron pipes and smooth cement pipes;
$f = 0.054$ for rough boards and smooth brickwork;
$f = 0.072$ for smooth masonry or brick channels;
$f = 0.29$ for rough masonry and earth canals with bank walls;
$f = 0.50$ for canals in earth and regular streams;
$f = 0.75$ for canals and rivers with stones and weeds;
$f = 1.06$ for canals and rivers in bad condition.

In 1914 Camerer published † an extended table from which values of the denominator in (124½) can be taken for given values of f and r, a rough value of v being first assumed. This triple-entry table is not a satisfactory one and hence no attempt will be made here to put it into English measures. It will be observed that (124½) is a quadratic equation with v as the unknown quantity, and hence it appears to the authors that the most feasible plan is to solve the equation for each case as it arises. For this purpose let

$$M = \frac{4.1k}{(100f+2)\,(0.0663\sqrt{r}+f)} \qquad N = \frac{1811r^{\frac{3}{2}}s}{0.0663\sqrt{r}+f}$$

and then the solution of the quadratic equation gives

$$v = -M + \sqrt{N + M^2} \quad \text{or closely} \quad v = -M + \sqrt{N}$$

* Zeitschrift Verein deutscher Ingenieure, Mittheilungen über Forscharbeiten, Heft 44.

† Wasserkraftmaschinen (Berlin, 1914), pp. 104–110.

For example take a rectangular trough of unplaned timber 3.93 feet wide on a slope of 4.9 feet per 10.0 feet, the water being 1.29 feet deep. Here $r = 0.779$ feet and $s = 0.0049$. Then, f being 0.054, the value of M for 50° F. is 0.067, that of N is 54.32, and the mean velocity v is 7.30 feet per second. For the same data Kutter's formula, with $n = 0.012$, gives 7.60 feet per second and Bazin's formula, with $m = 0.16$, gives 7.09 feet per second. Since the observed velocity was 7.23 feet per second Biel's formula yields the best result for this case.

Biel gives the following as showing the relation between his f and Kutter's n:

Kutter's n	0.010	0.012	0.013	0.020	0.025	0.030	0.035
Biel's f	0.018	0.054	0.072	0.29	0.50	0.75	1.06

That this is not quite satisfactory for rivers is shown by the six following comparisons in which Kutter's n is known.*

	r in feet	s	obs. v	n	v by Biel, $F=50°$
Rhine Delta	11.08	0.0001044	3.16	0.025	3.05
Missouri River	17.70	0.0002337	6.20	0.025	6.25
Rhine at Basle	6.89	0.001218	6.38	0.030	6.14
Isar River	1.86	0.002500	4.02	0.030	3.59
Mississippi River	24.10	0.0000825	3.59	0.035	3.57
Salzach River	3.87	0.001796	4.45	0.035	4.56

Biel claims that his formula applies to the flow of oil and fluids in pipes as well as to water, and also to air and gases, for such cases, however, the factor k in the formula is quite different from the values stated above for water, it being the ratio of the viscosity factor of the liquid or gas to its specific gravity. Biel's formula shows that a rise of temperature increases the mean velocity of any liquid or gas.

Prob. 124½. In U. S. Geological Survey Paper No. 18 is given a record of the gaging of the Bear River in Idaho, where the bed was of clay and gravel; the hydraulic radius was 2.31 feet, the slope was 0.00062, and the observed mean velocity was 2.36 feet per second. Compute the mean velocity by the formulas of Kutter, Bazin and Biel.

* Ganguillet and Kutter's Flow of Water, translated by Hering and Trautwine, New York, 1901.

Art. 125. Losses of Head

The only loss of head thus far considered is that due to friction, but other sources of loss may often exist. As in the flow in pipes, these may be classified as losses at entrance, losses due to curvature, and losses caused by obstructions in the channel or by changes in the area of cross-section.

When water is admitted to a channel from a reservoir or pond through a rectangular sluice, there occurs a contraction similar to that at the entrance into a pipe, and which may be often observed in a slight depression of the surface, as at D in Fig. 125*a*. At this point, therefore, the velocity is greater than the mean velocity v, and a loss of energy or head results from the subsequent expansion, which is approximately measured by the difference of the depths d_1 and d_2, the former being taken at the entrance of the channel, and the latter below the depression where the uniform flow is fully established. According to the experiments of Dubuat, made late in the eighteenth century, the loss of head for this case is

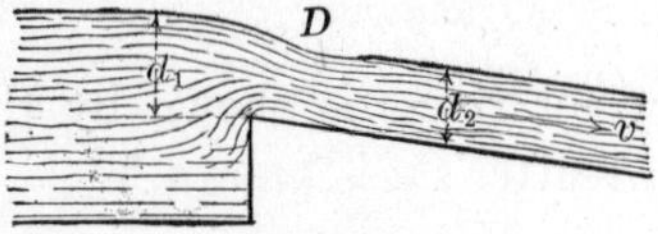

Fig. 125*a*.

$$d_1 - d_2 = m\frac{v^2}{2g}$$

in which m ranges between 0 and 2 according to the condition of the entrance. If the channel be small compared with the reservoir, and both the bottom and side edges of the entrance be square, m may be nearly 2; but if these edges be rounded, m may be very small, particularly if the bottom contraction is suppressed. The remarks in Chap. 5 regarding suppression of the contraction apply also here, and it is often important to prevent losses due to contraction by rounding the approaches to the entrance. Screens are sometimes placed at the entrance to a channel in order to keep out floating matter; if the cross-section of the channel is n times that of the meshes of the screen, the loss of head, according to $(76)_2$, is $(n - 1)^2v^2/2g$.

The loss of head due to bends or curves in the channel is small if the curvature be slight. Undoubtedly every curve offers a resistance to the change in direction of the velocity, and thus requires an additional head to cause the flow beyond that needed to overcome the frictional resistances. Several formulas have been proposed to express this loss, but they all seem unsatisfactory, and hence will not be presented here, particularly as the data for determining their constants are very scant. It will be plain that the loss of head due to a curve increases with its length, as in pipes (Art. 91). When a channel turns with a right angle, as in Fig. 125*b*, the loss of head may be taken as equal to the velocity-head, since the experiments of Weisbach on such bends in pipes indicate that value. In this case there is a contraction of the stream after passing the corner, and the subsequent expansion of section and the resulting impact causes the loss of head.

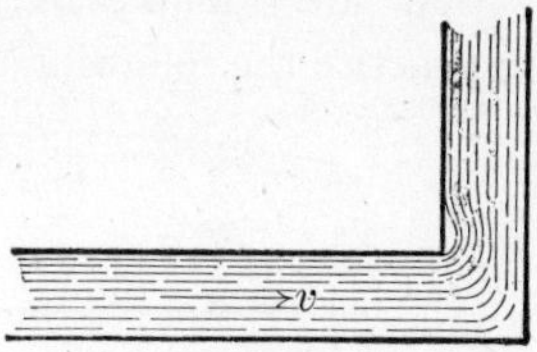

Fig. 125*b*.

The losses of head caused by sudden enlargement or by sudden contraction of the cross-section of a channel may be estimated by the rules deduced in Arts. 76 and 77. In order to avoid these losses changes of section should be made gradually, so that energy may not be lost in impact. Obstructions or submerged dams may be regarded as causing sudden changes of section, and the accompanying losses of head are governed by similar laws. The numerical estimation of these losses will generally be difficult, but the principles which control them will often prove useful in arranging the design of a channel so that the maximum work of the water can be rendered available. But as all losses of head are directly proportional to the velocity-head $v^2/2g$, it is plain that they can be rendered inappreciable by giving to the channel such dimensions as will render the mean velocity very small. This may sometimes be important in a short conduit or flume which conveys water from a pond or reservoir to a hydraulic motor, particularly in cases where the supply is scant, and where all the available head is required to be utilized.

If no losses of head exist except that due to friction, this can be computed from (113) if the velocity v and the coefficient c be known. For since the value of s is v^2/c^2r and also h/l, where h is the fall expended in overcoming friction, h may be found from

$$h = ls = lv^2/c^2r \qquad (125)$$

but this computation will usually be liable to much error.

As an example of the computations which sometimes occur in practice the following actual case will be discussed. From a canal

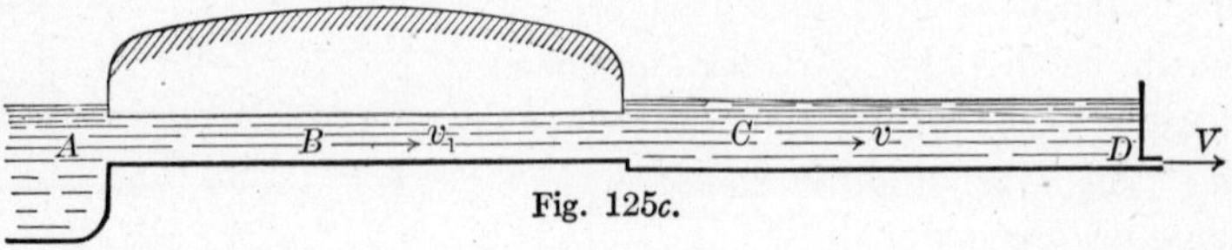

Fig. 125c.

A water is carried through a cast-iron pipe B to an open wooden forebay C, where it passes through the orifice D and falls upon an overshot wheel. At the mouth of the pipe is a screen, the area between the meshes being one-half that of the cross-section of the pipe. The pipe is 3 feet in diameter and 32 feet long. The forebay is of unplaned timber, 5 feet wide and 38 feet long, and it has three right-angled bends. The orifice is 5 inches deep and 40 inches wide, with standard sharp edges on top and sides and contraction suppressed on lower side so that its coefficient of contraction is about 0.68 and its coefficient of velocity about 0.98. The water level in the canal being 3.75 feet above the bottom of the orifice, it is required to find the loss of head between the points A and D.

The total head on the center of the orifice is $3.75-0.208 = 3.542$ feet. Let v_1 be the mean velocity in the pipe, v that in the forebay, and V that in the contracted section beyond the orifice. The area of the cross-section of the pipe is 7.07 square feet; that of the forebay, taking the depth of water as 3.7 feet, is 18.5 square feet, and that of the contracted section of the jet issuing from the orifice is 0.945 square feet. It will be convenient to express all losses of head in terms of the velocity-head $v^2/2g$, and hence the first operation is to express v_1 and V in terms of v, or $v_1 = 2.62v$ and $V = 19.6v$. Starting with the screen, the loss of head due to expansion of section after the water passes through it is, by Art. 76,

$$h' = \frac{(2v_1 - v_1)^2}{2g} = 6.9\frac{v^2}{2g}$$

The loss of head in friction in the pipe, using 0.02 for the friction factor, is, by Art. 90,

$$h' = f\frac{l}{d}\frac{v_1^2}{2g} = 1.4\frac{v^2}{2g}$$

The loss of head in the expansion of section from the pipe to the forebay is, by Art. 76,

$$h' = \frac{(v_1 - v)^2}{2g} = 2.6\frac{v^2}{2g}$$

The loss of head in friction in the forebay, taking c from Table 122 for the hydraulic radius 1.5 feet and degree of roughness $m = 0.16$, is then found to be

$$h' = \frac{lv^2}{c^2 r} = 0.1\frac{v^2}{2g}$$

The loss of head in the three right-angled bends of the forebay is estimated, as above noted, by

$$h' = 3.0\frac{v^2}{2g}$$

The loss of head on the edges of the orifice is, by Art. 56,

$$h' = 0.041\frac{V^2}{2g} = 15.9\frac{v^2}{2g}$$

Now the total head is expended in these lost heads and in the velocity-head of the jet issuing from the orifice, or

$$3.542 = 29.9\frac{v^2}{2g} + \frac{V^2}{2g} = 417\frac{v^2}{2g}$$

from which the value of $v^2/2g$ is found to be 0.00851 feet. Finally the total loss of head or fall in the free surface of the water before reaching the orifice is

$$(29.9 - 15.9)\frac{v^2}{2g} = 14.0 \times 0.00851 = 0.119 \text{ feet},$$

and therefore the water surface at D is 0.119 feet lower than that at A, and the pressure-head on the center of the orifice is 3.433 feet. This is the result of the computations, but on making measurements with an engineer's level the water surface at D was found to be 0.125 feet lower than that at A; the error of the computed result is therefore 0.006 feet.

Prob. 125. Compute from the above data the velocities v, v_1, and V, and the discharge through the orifice. Show that the head lost in passing through the screen was 0.059 feet, which is about one-half of the total.

Art. 126. Velocities in a Cross-section

For a circular conduit running full and under pressure the velocities in different parts of the section vary similarly to those in pipes (Art. 86). When it is partly full, so that the water flows with a free surface, the air resistance along that surface is much smaller than that along the wetted perimeter, and hence the surface velocities are greater than those near the perimeter. Fig. 126*a* illustrates the variation of velocities in a cross-section of the

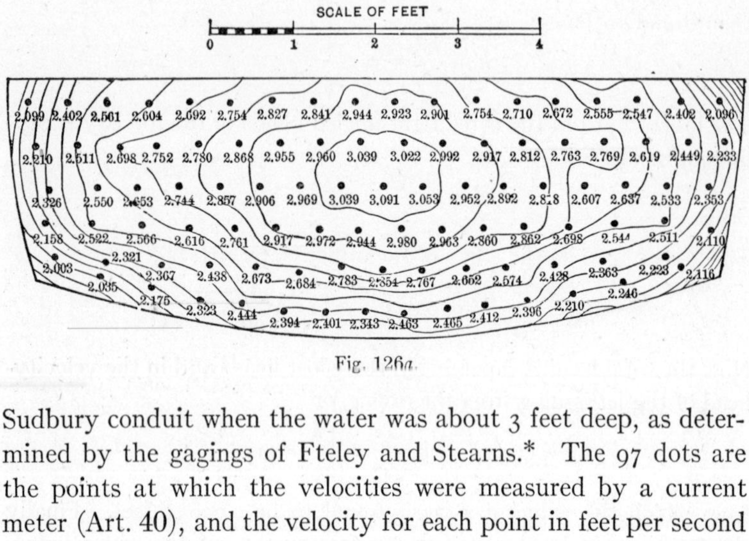

Fig. 126*a*.

Sudbury conduit when the water was about 3 feet deep, as determined by the gagings of Fteley and Stearns.* The 97 dots are the points at which the velocities were measured by a current meter (Art. 40), and the velocity for each point in feet per second is recorded below it. From these the contour curves were drawn which show clearly the manner of variation of velocity throughout this cross-section. Since the dots are distributed over the area quite uniformly, that area may be regarded as divided into 97 equal parts, in each of which the velocity is that observed, and hence the mean of the 97 observations is the mean velocity (Art. 39). Thus is found $v = 2.620$ feet per second, and this is 85 per cent of the maximum observed velocity.

Similarly Fig. 126*b* shows the results of an experiment on the New Croton Aqueduct.† In this case the average velocity de-

* Transactions American Society of Civil Engineers, 1883, vol. 12, p. 324.
† Report of The Aqueduct Commissioners, New York, 1895–1907.

termined from the 128 individual observations is 3.570, and this is 89 percent of the maximum observed velocity. A description of the methods followed in making the gagings on this aqueduct

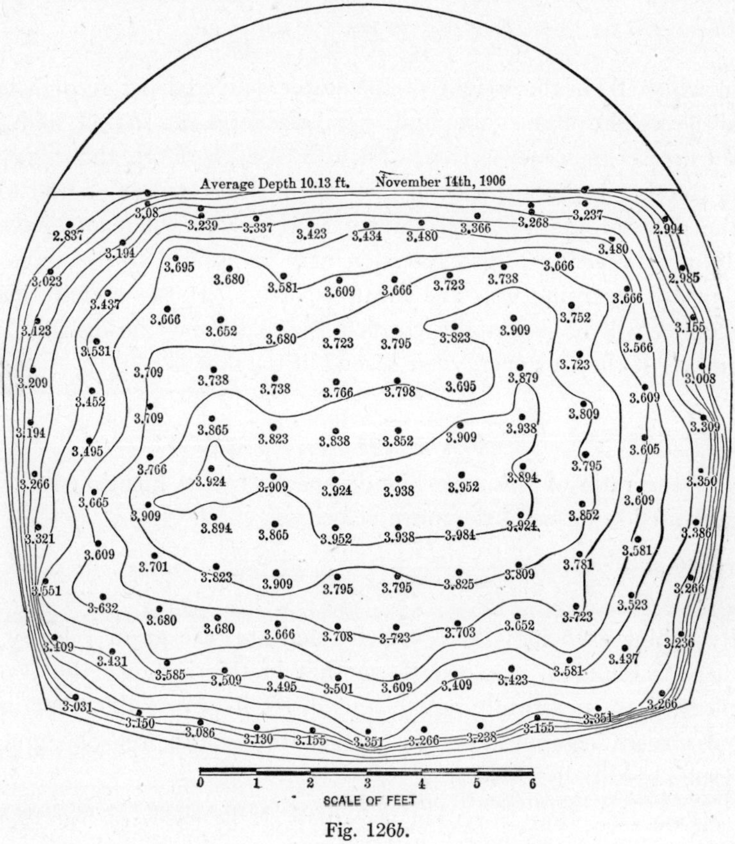

Fig. 126*b*.

is to be found at page 106 of vol. 66, Transactions American Society of Civil Engineers. See also Art. 123.

An examination of the distribution of velocities in Fig. 126*b* indicates that the maximum velocity does not occur at the center of the cross-section. This is due to the fact that the aqueduct at the point where the gaging was taken is located on a curve which tends to throw the maximum velocity away from the center and toward the outside of the curve.

If all the filaments of a stream of water in a channel have the same uniform velocity v, the kinetic energy per second of the flow is the weight of the discharge multiplied by the velocity-head; or

$$K = W\frac{v^2}{2g} = wq\frac{v^2}{2g} = wa\frac{v^3}{2g}$$

in which W is the weight of the water delivered per second, w is the weight of one cubic unit, q the discharge per second, and a the area of the cross-section. For this case, therefore, the energy of the flow is proportional to the area of the cross-section and to the cube of the velocity. Since, however, the filaments have different velocities, this expression may be applied to the actual flow by regarding v as the mean velocity. To show that this method will be essentially correct, Fig. 126*a* may be discussed, and for it the true energy per second of the flow is

$$K' = \frac{wa}{97}\left(\frac{v_1^3}{2g} + \frac{v_2^3}{2g} + \cdots + \frac{v_{97}^3}{2g}\right)$$

now the ratio of this true kinetic energy to the kinetic energy expressed in terms of the mean velocity is

$$\frac{K'}{K} = \frac{v_1^3 + v_2^3 + \cdots + v_{97}^3}{97v^3}$$

By cubing each individual velocity and also the mean velocity, there is found $K' = 0.9992K$, so that in this instance the two energies are practically equal, and hence it is probable that in most cases computations of energy from mean velocity give results essentially correct.

Prob. 126. Draw a vertical plane through the middle of Fig. 126*b* and construct a longitudinal vertical section showing the distribution of velocities. Also draw a horizontal plane through the region of maximum velocity and construct a longitudinal horizontal section. Ascertain whether the curves of velocity for these sections are best represented by parabolas or by ellipses.

Art. 127. Computations in Metric Measures

(Art. 113) The coefficient c in the Chezy formula depends upon the linear unit of measure. Let c_1 be the value when v and r are expressed in feet and c_2 the value when v and r are expressed in meters, and let g_1 and g_2 be the corresponding values of the acceleration of gravity. Then since $c = \sqrt{8g/f}$, it is seen that

$$c_2 = c_1\sqrt{g_2/g_1} = c_1\sqrt{9.80/32.16} = 0.552\, c_1$$

Hence any value of c in the English system may be transformed into the corresponding metric value by multiplying by 0.552. The metric value of c for conduits and canals usually lies between 16 and 100.

(Art. 114) Table 127*a* gives values of the Chezy coefficient c for circular conduits, full or half full. In using it a tentative method must be employed, and for this purpose there may be used at first,

$$\text{mean Chezy coefficient } c = 68$$

and then, after v has been computed, a new value of c is taken from the table and a new v is found. For example, let it be required to find the velocity and discharge of a circular conduit of 1.5 meters diameter when laid on a grade of 0.8 meters in 1000 meters. First,

$$v = 68 \times \tfrac{1}{2}\sqrt{1.5 \times 0.0008} = 1.18 \text{ meters per second,}$$

and for this velocity the table gives about 77 for c. A second computation then gives v = 1.33 meters per second and from the table c is 78.2. With this value is found v = 1.35 meters per second, which may be regarded as the final result. When running full, the discharge of this conduit is $0.7854 \times 1.5^2 \times 1.35 = 2.39$ cubic meters per second.

TABLE 127*a*. CHEZY COEFFICIENTS FOR CIRCULAR CONDUITS

Metric Measures

Diameter in Meters	Velocity in Meters per Second					
	0.3	0.6	0.9	1.5	3.0	4.5
0.3	53	57	60	63	67	68
0.5	57	61	64	67	71	73
0.7	61	65	68	71	76	78
0.9	64	68	70	74	79	81
1.1	66	70	72	76	81	83
1.3	68	72	74	78	83	
1.6	72	74	77	80		
2.0	74	77	79	83		
2.4	76	79	82			

(Art. 115) Table 115 is the same for all systems of measures. The results in Art. 115, for Bazin's semicircular conduits of 1.25 meters' diameter on a slope $s = 0.0015$, are as follows, when all dimensions are in meters:

For cement lining				For mortar lining			
d'	r	v	c	d'	r	v	c
0.625	0.314	1.85	85	0.625	0.312	1.69	78
0.491	0.264	1.61	81	0.515	0.275	1.51	75
0.314	0.185	1.27	76	0.332	0.194	1.18	69
0.180	0.112	0.92	71	0.186	0.116	0.88	66

Here the coefficient c for any depth d' may be roughly expressed by $c_1 - 30(\frac{1}{2}d - d')$, where c_1 is the coefficient for the conduit half full.

(Art. 116) Table 127*b* gives metric values of c for wooden and rectangular sections on a slope $s = 0.0049$, as determined by the work of Darcy and Bazin.

TABLE 127*b*. CHEZY COEFFICIENTS C FOR RECTANGULAR CONDUITS

Metric Measures

Unplaned Plank $b = 1.2$ Meters		Unplaned Plank $b = 2$ Meters		Neat Cement $b = 1.8$ Meters		Brick $b = 1.9$ Meters	
d	*c*	*d*	*c*	*d*	*c*	*d*	*c*
0.08	55	0.06	49	0.06	64	0.06	49
.15	60	.09	56	.08	69	.09	54
.18	61	.13	60	.13	73	.15	57
.27	63	.18	62	.17	74	.17	58
.30	63	.20	64	.19	75	.20	58
.36	64	.24	64	.21	75	.22	59
.39	65	.27	65	.24	76	.26	60
.44	65	.29	66	.27	76	.30	61

(Art. 117) In designing channels in earth the following values may be used for preliminary computations:

for unplaned plank,	c = 55 to 66
for smooth masonry,	c = 50 to 61
for clean earth,	c = 33 to 40
for stony earth,	c = 22 to 33
for rough stone,	c = 19 to 28
for earth foul with weeds	c = 17 to 28

(Art. 118) When r is in meters and v in meters per second, Kutter's formula takes the form

$$\mathrm{c} = \frac{\frac{1}{n} + 23 + \frac{0.00155}{s}}{1 + \frac{n}{\sqrt{r}}\left(23 + \frac{0.00155}{s}\right)} \qquad (127)_1$$

in which the number n depends upon the roughness of the surface, its values being those given in Art. 118. It may be noted that when the hydraulic radius r is one meter, the value of c is $1/n$.

(Art. 119) Metric coefficients for sewers will be found in Table 127*c*. As these are given to the nearest unit only, the error in using them is slightly greater than with the larger coefficients of the English system. In important cases the values of c may be directly computed from Kutter's formula.

TABLE 127*c*. KUTTER'S COEFFICIENTS C FOR SEWERS

Metric Measures

Hydraulic Radius r in Meters	$s = 0.00005$		$s = 0.0001$		$s = 0.01$	
	$n = 0.015$	$n = 0.017$	$n = 0.015$	$n = 0.017$	$n = 0.015$	$n = 0.017$
0.05	26	22	31	25	37	30
0.1	34	29	37	32	43	36
0.15	39	33	42	36	48	40
0.2	43	38	46	40	51	43
0.3	49	42	51	44	55	48
0.5	56	48	57	50	60	52
0.7	62	54	62	55	63	56
1.0	67	59	67	58	66	59

(Art. 120) Table 127*d* in metric measures corresponds to Table 120 in English measures and is used in the same manner.

(Art. 121) The metric coefficients c for steel, cast-iron, and wood pipes may be obtained from those in the text by multiplying by 0.552, while the velocities and diameters may easily be replaced by metric equivalents with the help of Table C at the end of this volume.

(Art. 122) The values of c in Table 127*e* have been taken from the more extended table published in 1897 by Bazin, while those in

Table 122 have been computed by (115). In metric measures Bazin's formula for channels is

$$v = c\sqrt{rs} \qquad c = \frac{87}{1 + m/\sqrt{r}} \qquad (127)_2$$

in which m has the same values as those given in Art. 122.

TABLE 127*d*. KUTTER'S COEFFICIENTS c FOR CHANNELS

Metric Measures

Hydraulic Radius r in Meters	$s = 0.00005$		$s = 0.0001$		$s = 0.01$	
	$n = 0.025$	$n = 0.030$	$n = 0.025$	$n = 0.030$	$n = 0.025$	$n = 0.030$
0.2	22	18	24	19	27	21
0.3	27	22	29	33	31	25
0.5	32	27	34	27	35	28
0.7	36	30	37	30	38	31
1.0	40	33	40	33	40	33
1.5	45	38	44	38	43	36
2.	48	41	47	40	45	38
3.	53	44	50	44	47	40
5.	59	50	53	47	51	43

TABLE 127*e*. BAZIN'S COEFFICIENTS c FOR CHANNELS

Metric Measures

Hydraulic Radius r in Meters	$m = 0.06$	$m = 0.16$	$m = 0.46$	$m = 0.85$	$m = 1.30$	$m = 1.75$
0.2	76.7	64.1	42.9			
0.4	79.4	69.4	50.4	37.1		
0.6	80.7	72.1	54.6	41.4	32.5	
0.8	81.5	73.8	57.4	44.6	35.5	29.4
1.0	82.0	75.0	59.6	47.0	37.8	31.6
1.5	82.9	76.9	63.2	51.3	42.2	35.8
2.0	83.4	78.1	65.6	54.3	45.3	38.9
2.5	83.8	79.0	67.4	56.6	47.7	41.1
3.	84.0	79.6	68.7	58.3	49.7	43.3
4.	84.4	80.9	71.5	61.0	52.7	46.4
5.	84.7	81.2	72.1	63.0	55.0	48.8
6.		81.6	73.2	64.6	56.8	50.7
8.			74.8	66.9	59.5	53.7
10.				68.5	61.6	56.0

(Art. 123) The metric formula for the Sudbury conduit is $v = 80.9r^{0.62}s^{0.5}$, and Foss' formula Art. 124 for circular conduits or large pipes when running full is $s = 0.0118q^{\frac{11}{8}}/d^5$.

(124½) The formula of Biel, in metric measures, is

$$v^2 = \frac{1000rs}{0.12 + \dfrac{f}{\sqrt{r}} + \dfrac{2.5k}{(100f + 2)v\sqrt{r}}}$$

in which the values of f and k are the same as in Art. 124½. This may be solved as a quadratic equation by putting

$$M = \frac{1.25k}{(100f + 2)(0.12\sqrt{r} + f)} \qquad N = \frac{1000r^{\frac{3}{2}}s}{0.12\sqrt{r} + f}$$

and then $v = -M + \sqrt{N + M^2}$ or closely $v = -M + \sqrt{N}$.

Prob. 127*a*. Compute the value of c for a circular conduit 1.4 meters in diameter which delivers 4.86 cubic meters per second when running full, its slope being 0.008.

Prob. 127*b*. Find the hydraulic radius for a circular conduit of 1.6 meters diameter when the water is 1.2 meters deep.

Prob. 127*c*. If the value of c is 30, compute the depth of a trapezoidal section to carry 10 cubic meters per second, the slope s being 0.0015, the bottom width double the depth, and the sides making an angle of 34° with the horizontal.

Prob 127*d*. A conduit lined with neat cement has a cross-section of 3.45 square meters and a wetted perimeter of 5.02 meters and its slope is 0.00025. Compute the discharge in liters per 24 hours, (*a*) by Kutter's formula, (*b*) by Bazin's formula, (*c*) by Williams and Hazen's fo mula, and (*d*) by Biel's formula.

CHAPTER 10

THE FLOW OF RIVERS

ART. 128. GENERAL CONSIDERATIONS

Steady flow in a river channel occurs when the same quantity of water passes each section in each unit of time; here the mean velocities in different sections vary inversely as the areas of those sections. Uniform flow is that particular case of steady flow where the sections considered are equal in area. Uniform flow and some other cases of steady flow will be mainly considered in this chapter. Non-steady flow occurs when the stage of a river is rising or falling, and Art. 134 treats of this case.

No branch of hydraulics has received more detailed investigation than that of the flow in river channels, and yet the subject is but imperfectly understood. The great object of all these investigations has been to devise a simple method of determining the mean velocity and discharge without the necessity of expensive field operations. In general it may be said that this end has not yet been attained, even for the case of uniform flow. Of the various formulas proposed to represent the relation of mean velocity to the hydraulic radius and the slope, none has proved to be of general practical value except the empirical one of Chezy given in the last chapter, and this is often inapplicable on account of the difficulty of measuring the slope s and determining the coefficient c. The fundamental equations for discussing the laws of variation in the mean velocity v and in the discharge q are

$$v = \mathrm{c}\sqrt{rs} \qquad\qquad q = a \cdot \mathrm{c}\sqrt{rs}$$

where a is the area of the cross-section and r its hydraulic radius, and all the general principles of the last chapter are to be taken as directly applicable to uniform flow in natural channels.

Kutter's formula for the value of c is probably the best in the present state of science, although it is now generally recognized that it gives too large values for small slopes. In using it the coefficients for rivers in good condition may be taken from Table 120, but for bad regimen n is to be taken at 0.03, and for wild torrents at 0.04 or 0.05. It is, however, too much to expect that a single formula should accurately express the mean velocity in small brooks and large rivers, and the general opinion now is that efforts to establish such an expression will not prove successful.

At the present time the formulas of Kutter (Art. 118), Bazin (Art. 122), and Biel (Art. $124\frac{1}{2}$) are the only ones that can properly be used for computing the mean velocity and discharge of a river. The results obtained are approximations only, and in any important case it is best to make actual gagings by the methods described in Arts. 130–132. When these formulas are used the width of the stream is to be divided into a number of parts and soundings taken at each point of division. The data are thus obtained from which the section-area a and its wetted perimeter p can be found, and then the hydraulic radius r is determined by $r = a/p$ (Art. 112).

The slope s is to be found by $s=h/l$. To determine the fall h a length l is to be measured, at each end of which bench-marks are established whose difference of elevation is found by precise levels. The elevations of the water surfaces below these benches are then to be simultaneously taken, whence the fall h in the distance l becomes known. As this fall is often small, it is very important that every precaution be taken to avoid error in the measurements, and that a number of them be taken in order to secure a precise mean. Care should be observed that the stage of water is not varying while these observations are being made, and for this and other purposes a permanent gage board must be established. It is also very important that the points upon the water surface which are selected for comparison should be situated so as to be free from local influences such as eddies, since these often cause marked deviations from the normal surface of the stream. If hook gages can be used for referring the water levels to the benches, probably the most accurate results can be obtained. It has been observed that the surface of a swiftly flowing stream is not a plane, but a cylinder, which is concave to the bed, its highest elevation being where the velocity is greatest, and hence the two points of reference should be located similarly with respect to the axis of the current. In spite of all precautions, however, the relative error in h will usually be large in the case of slight slopes, unless l be very long, which cannot often occur in streams under conditions of uniformity.

Owing to the uncertainty of determinations of discharge made in the manner just described, the common practice is to gage the stream by velocity observations, to which subject, therefore, a large part of this chapter will be devoted. The methods given are equally applicable to conduits and canals, and in Art. 133 will be found a summary which briefly compares the various processes.

Prob. 128. Which has the greater discharge, a stream 2 feet deep and 85 feet wide on a slope of 1 foot per mile, or a stream 3 feet deep and 40 feet wide on a slope of 2 feet per mile?

Art. 129. Velocities in a Cross-section

The mean velocity v is the average of all the velocities of all the small sections or filaments in a cross-section (Art. 112). Some of these individual velocities are much smaller, and others materially larger, than the mean velocity. Along the bottom of the stream, where the frictional resistances are the greatest, the velocities are the least; along the center of the stream they are the greatest. A brief statement of the general laws of variation of these velocities will now be made.

In Fig. 129 there is shown at A a cross-section of a stream with contour curves of equal velocity; here the greatest velocity is seen to be near the deepest part of the section a short distance below the surface. At B is shown a plan of the stream with arrows roughly representing the surface velocities; the greatest of these is seen to be near the deepest part of the channel, while the others diminish toward the banks, the curve showing the law of variation resembling an ellipse. At C is shown by arrows the variation of velocities in a vertical line, the smallest being at the bottom and the largest a short distance below the surface; concerning this curve there has been some contention, but it is now well established to be a parabola whose axis is horizontal. These are the general laws of the variation of velocity throughout the cross-section; the particular relations are of a complex character, and vary so greatly in channels of different kinds that it is difficult to formulate them, although many attempts to do so have been made. Some of these formulas which connect the mean velocity with particular velocities, such as the maximum surface velocity, mid-depth velocity in the axis of the stream, etc., will be given in Art. 132.

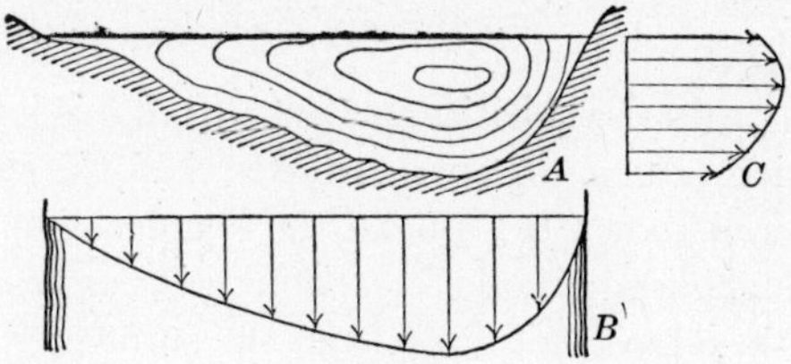

Fig. 129.

Considering the law of variation of surface velocities to be represented by an ellipse, its equation for a straight channel is

$$v_x = v_1 + (v_m - v_1)\sqrt{1 - (x/b)^2} \qquad (129)_1$$

in which b is the half-width of the river, v_1 the velocity at the banks, v_m the maximum velocity along the center line AC, and v_x the velocity at the distance x from the center line. Fig. 129a is a plan of a part of a straight river showing two surface ellipses, the full-line curve being for $v_1 = \frac{3}{4}v_m$ and the other for $v_1 = \frac{1}{4}v_m$. The mean surface velocity, found by dividing the area of the curve by its base DD is $0.215\,v_1 + 0.785\,v_m$ and it may be shown that this is equal to the surface velocity at a distance $0.62b$ from the center line AC.

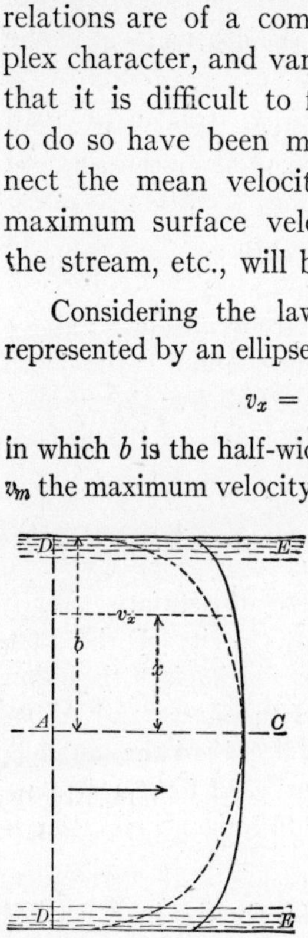

Fig. 129a.

Observations of surface velocities show much variation from these typical curves,* but on the whole they indicate an approximation to ellipses. The velocity v near the banks may vary considerably, depending upon the depth of water there; it is sometimes greater

* Roorkee Hydraulic Experiments (1881), p. 187.

than one-half of the maximum velocity v_m. When v_1 is zero, the mean surface velocity is equal to $0.785\ v_m$; when v_1 is $0.75\ v_m$, the mean surface velocity is $0.946\ v_m$. These relations result from the assumption that the ellipse represents the law of variation.

As to velocities in a vertical, it has long been known that a floating raft or boat moves faster than the surface water. This fact was well known to Dubuat, the founder of modern hydraulics, but he was unable to explain it satisfactorily, as he considered that the velocities decreased uniformly from the surface to the bottom.* Later observations have conclusively proved that the maximum velocity is usually below the surface and this explains why the floating boat moves faster than the surface current.

Humphreys and Abbot deduced in 1861 from their observations on the Mississippi River † that the equation of the mean curve of velocities in a vertical line was

$$V_z = 3.261 - 0.7922(z/d)^2$$

in which V_z is the velocity in feet per second at any distance z above or below the horizontal axis of a parabolic curve and d is the depth of the water, the axis being at the depth $0.297d$ below the surface. It is more convenient to take the origin for the curve at the surface, and the equation then becomes

$$V_y = 3.191 + 0.471\ (y/d) - 0.792(y/d)^2$$

in which V_y is the velocity at the depth y below the surface. When $y = 0$, this equation gives the mean surface velocity of the Mississippi as 3.19 feet per second, and when $y = d$ it gives the mean bottom velocity as 2.87 feet per second. Humphreys and Abbot also found that the position of the horizontal axis of the parabola varied greatly with the wind, an up-stream wind of force 4 depressing it to mid-depth and a down-stream wind of force 5.3 elevating it to the surface.

The general equation of the parabola of velocities in a vertical line, with origin at the surface, is

$$V_y = V_o + My - Ny^2$$

* Dubuat, Principes de hydraulique, vol. 1.

† Physics and Hydraulics of Mississippi River, ed. 1876, p. 243.

in which y is now taken in terms of the depth unity (Fig. **129***b*), V_y is the velocity at the depth y, V_o the velocity at the surface, and M and N are constants. When $y = o$, then $V_y = V_o$; the value of y which renders $(129)_2$ a maximum is $M/2N$, and designating this by m, the equation becomes

$$V_y = V_o + 2mNy - Ny^2 \qquad (129)_2$$

The area included between the curve and the axis of ordinates AB, Fig. 129*b*, is now found and this, divided by the total depth unity, gives the mean velocity in the vertical as

$$V = V_o + mN - \tfrac{1}{3}N \qquad (129)_3$$

Equating the right-hand members of $(129)^2$ and $(129)^3$, there results

$$y^2 - 2my = \tfrac{1}{3} - m$$

as an equation from which the depth y can be computed at which

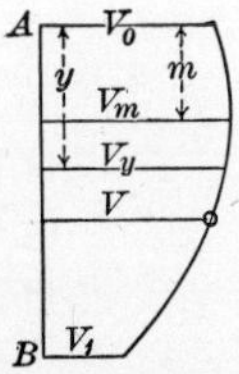

Fig. 129*b*.

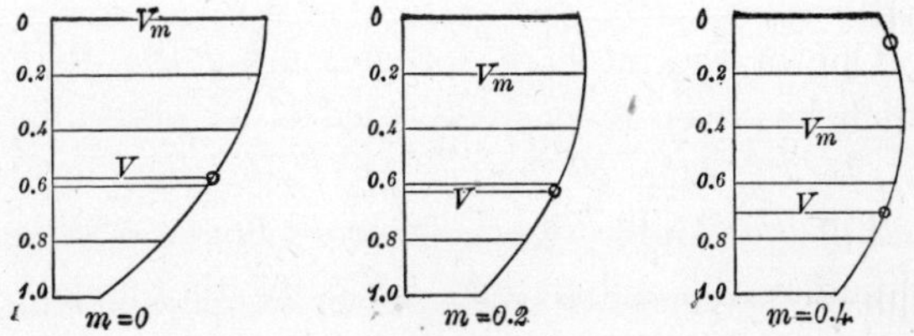

Fig. 129*c*.

the velocity V_y is equal to the mean velocity in the vertical. From this the following results are found for different positions of the axis, m being the depth of that axis below the surface:

For m o=	o	0.1	0.2	0.3	$\frac{1}{3}$	0.4
Depth for mean=	0.577	0.593	0.616	0.651	0.667	0.706

One of the methods of gaging given in Art. 130 depends upon these results. When m is $\frac{1}{3}$ the surface velocity is also equal to the mean; when $m = 0.4$ there is also a point at the depth 0.094 where the velocity is equal to the mean V. Fig. 129*c* shows the three curves of velocities in a vertical for the cases $m = o$, $m = 0.2$, $m = 0.4$.

Two points on the parabola can be found so that the average of the velocities at those depths is equal to the mean velocity V in the vertical. Let y_1 and y_2 be the depths of these points. Then from $(129)_2$ the average of the two velocities is

$$V_o + 2mN\frac{y_1 + y_2}{2} - N\frac{y_1^2 + y_2^2}{2}$$

and equating this to the second member of $(129)_3$, the quantities V_o and N cancel out, and there is found

$$m(y_1 + y_2) - \tfrac{1}{2}(y_1^2 + y_2^2) = m - \tfrac{1}{3}$$

This is satisfied when $y_1 + y_2 = 1$ and $y_1^2 + y_2^2 = \frac{2}{3}$ and from these equations are found the values $y_1 = 0.211$ and $y_2 = 0.789$. One of the methods of gaging given in Art. 130 depends upon these values.

Prob. 129. Prove that the average of three velocities taken at the depths 0.15, 0.50, 0.85 on a vertical line will give the mean velocity in that vertical.

Art. 130. Velocity Measurements

One of the methods for measuring the discharge of streams which has been extensively used is by observing the velocity of flow by the help of floats. Of these there are three kinds, surface floats, double floats, and rod floats. Surface floats should be sufficiently submerged so as to thoroughly partake of the motion of the upper filaments, and should be made of such a form as not to readily be affected by the wind. The time of their passage over a given distance is determined by two observers at the ends of a base on shore by stop-watches; or only one watch may be used, the instant of passing each section being signaled to the time-keeper. If l be the length of the base, and t the time of passage in seconds, the velocity of the float is $v = l/t$. When there are many observations, the numerical work of division is best done by taking the reciprocals of t from a table and multiplying them by l, which for convenience may be an even number, such as 100 or 200 feet.

A sub-surface float consists of a small surface float connected by a fine cord or wire with the large real float, which is weighted so as to remain submerged and keep the cord reasonably taut. The surface float should be made of such a form as to offer but slight resistance to the motion, while the lower float is large, it being the object of the combination to determine the velocity of the lower one alone. This arrangement has been extensively used, but it is probable that in all cases the velocity of the large float is somewhat affected by that of the upper one, as well as by the friction of the cord. In general the use of these floats is not to be encouraged, if any other method of measurement can be devised.

The rod float is a hollow cylinder of tin, which can be weighted by dropping in pebbles or shot so as to stand vertically at any depth. When used for velocity determinations, they are weighted so as to reach nearly to the bottom of the channel, and the time of passage over a known distance determined as above explained. It is often stated that the velocity of a rod float is the mean velocity of all the filaments in contact with it. Theoretically this is not the case, but the rod moves a little slower. However, in practice a rod cannot reach quite to the bed of the stream, and Francis has deduced the following empirical formula for finding the mean velocity V_m of all the filaments between the surface and the bed from the observed velocity V_r of the rod:

$$V_m = V_r(1.012 - 0.116\sqrt{d'/d})$$

in which d is the total depth of the stream and d' the depth of water below the bottom of the rod.* This expression is probably not a valid one, unless d' is less than about one-quarter of d; usually it will be best to have d' as small as the character of the bed of the channel will allow.

The log formerly used by seamen for ascertaining the speed of vessels may be often conveniently used as a surface float when rough determinations only are required, it being thrown from a boat or bridge. The cord of course must be previously stretched when wet, so that its length may not be altered by the immersion; if graduated by tags or knots in divisions of six feet, the log may be allowed to float for one minute, and then the number of divi-

* Lowell Hydraulic Experiments, 4th Edition, p. 195.

un out in this time will be ten times the velocity in feet second.

The determination of particular velocities in streams by means of floats appears to be simple, but in practice many uncertainties are found to arise, owing to wind, eddies, local currents, etc., so that a number of observations are required to obtain a precise mean result.

For conduits, canals, and for many rivers the use of a current meter will often be found to be more satisfactory and less expensive if many observations are required. Comparisons between the results of float and rod gagings have been made by Murphy.* These comparisons include those made at the Cornell University laboratory between the weir and the current meter in 1900.

Other current indicators less satisfactory for work in streams are the Pitot tube and the hydrometric pendulum, shown in Fig. 130*a*. The former has not been found valuable for river measurements, although it has proved to be an instrument of great precision for other classes of work (Art. 41), and the latter, although used by some of the early hydraulicians, has long been discarded as giving only rough indications. The same may be said of the hydrometric balance, in which weights measure the intensity of the pressure of the current, and of the torsion balance, in which the pressure of the current on a submerged plate causes the tightening of a spring. These instruments were used only for measurements of velocities in small channels, and they are now mere curiosities.

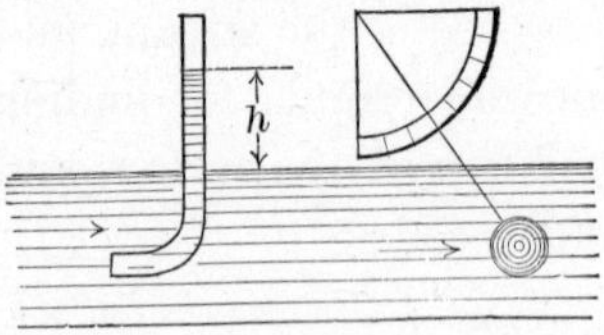

Fig. 130*a*.

The current meter, described in Art. 40, is generally operated from a bridge or cable in the case of a small stream, but it must be often operated from an anchored boat in large rivers. In the latter case precise measurements of surface velocities may be difficult on account of the eddies around the boat. Even when operated from a bridge, it is not easy to obtain successful results when the velocity exceeds 4 or 5 feet per second, and special

* Water Supply and Irrigation Paper No. 95, Washington, 1904.

expedients are necessary to keep the meter in position. However, the current meter, accurately rated, will in general do better work than can be done by floats.

In using the current meter for the determination of velocity four principal methods are used on the work of the U. S. Geological Survey; these have been reviewed by Hoyt.* In the first a vertical velocity curve is determined by placing the meter at regular vertical intervals from the surface of the water to the bottom of the stream and observing the velocity at each such interval. The points so selected are usually from 10 to 20 per cent of the water depth apart. On plotting the velocities obtained, a curve results which graphically indicates the variations in the velocity as they are dependent on the depth. The average velocity in the vertical can be determined by averaging all of the observations, or more accurately by ascertaining the area fixed by the curve and the axis of ordinates and then dividing this area by the depth of the water in the vertical. Thus in Fig. 130*b* the mean velocity is the area *ABC* divided by the depth 9.5 feet.

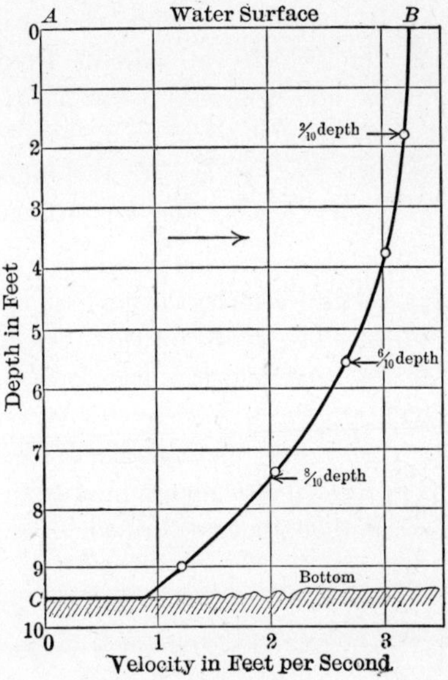

Fig. 130*b*.

In the second of these four methods the velocities at distances below the surface of 0.2 and 0.8 of the depth are determined and the mean taken as the average velocity in the vertical. Many observations have proven that this method is correct, and theoretically it is based on the mathematical fact that if the velocity curve be a parabola, then the mean velocity in the vertical will be the average of those at 0.2113 and 0.7887 of the water depth (Art. 129).

The third of these methods consists in observing the velocity

* Transactions American Society of Civil Engineers, 1910, vol. 66.

at a distance below the surface equal to 0.6 of the water depth. This procedure is also based on the assumption that the velocity curve is a parabola whose axis is parallel to the water surface and lies below it from 0 to 0.3 of the water depth; here it can be shown mathematically that the abscissa which represents the mean velocity lies between 0.58 and 0.65 of the water depth (Art. 120).

In the fourth method the mean velocity is determined by observing the velocity at a point from 0.5 to 1.0 feet below the water surface and applying a coefficient determined by observation. This coefficient ranges from 0.78 to 0.98, and Hoyt* recommends the following. For average streams in moderate freshets 0.90; during floods from 0.90 to 0.95, and for ordinary stages of flow from 0.85 to 0.90.

In the following tabulation are shown the results obtained in 476 vertical velocity curves* on 34 rivers in various parts of the United States. The depths of these streams ranged from 1.6 to 27.5 feet and the observed velocities from 0.25 to 9.59 feet per second. The figures given are the coefficients by which the average velocities determined by the various methods should be multiplied in order to obtain the mean velocity as determined from the vertical velocity curve in the first method above described.

Method	Coefficient		
	Maximum	Minimum	Mean
2	1.026	0.970	1.001
3	1.03	0.95	0.99
4	0.98	0.79	0.98

In the 476 velocity curves above referred to it was found that the point of mean velocity occurred at from 58 to 71 percent of the water depth below the surface, and that the average of all the curves showed it to be at 0.62 of the depth.

In cases where the stream to be measured is frozen over it has been found that the best work is done by the vertical velocity curve method, though the 2 and 8 tenths depth method also gives good results. A résumé of studies of the flow under ice by Murphy † indicates that

* Transactions American Society of Civil Engineers, 1910, vol. 66.
† U. S. Water Supply and Irrigation Paper No. 95, 1904.

the maximum velocity is to be found at from 35 to 40 percent of the water depth below the under surface of the ice and that the mean velocity occurs at two points, the first from 0.08 to 0.13 and the second from 0.68 to 0.74 of the water depth below the under surface of the ice.

The so-called integration method of determining the average velocity in a vertical consists in moving the meter at a uniform rate from the surface to the bottom and back again. Each point is thus passed over twice, and the average velocity indicated should be the mean velocity in the vertical. Probably a better method is to take the average of three velocities observed at 0.15, 0.50, and 0.85 of the depth (see Prob. 129).

Prob. 130. A rod float runs a distance of 100 feet in 42 seconds, the depth of the stream being 6 feet, while the foot of the rod is 6 inches above the bottom. Compute the mean velocity in the vertical.

Art. 131. Gaging the Discharge

For a very small stream the most precise method of finding the discharge is by means of a weir constructed for that purpose. Streams of considerable size often have dams built across them, and these may also be used like weirs with the help of the coefficients given in Art. 69, if there be no leakage through the dam. When there are no dams, the method now to be explained is generally employed. In all cases the first step should be to set up a vertical board gage, graduated to feet and tenths, and locate its zero with respect to the datum plane used in the vicinity, so that the stage of water may at any time be determined by reading the gage.

The place selected for the gaging should be one where the channel is free from obstructions and as nearly as possible free from bends and curves for some distance both up and down stream. One or more sections at right angles to the direction of the current are to be established, and soundings taken at intervals across the stream upon them, the water gage being read while this is done. The distances between the places of soundings are measured either upon a cord stretched across the stream or by other methods known to surveyors. The data are thus obtained for determining the areas a_1, a_2, a_3, etc., shown upon Fig.

131a, and the sum of these is the total area a. Levels should be run out upon the bank beyond the water's edge, so that in case of a rise of the stream the additional areas can be deduced. If a current meter is used, but one section is needed; if floats are used, at least two are required, and these must be located at a place where the channel is of as uniform size as possible.

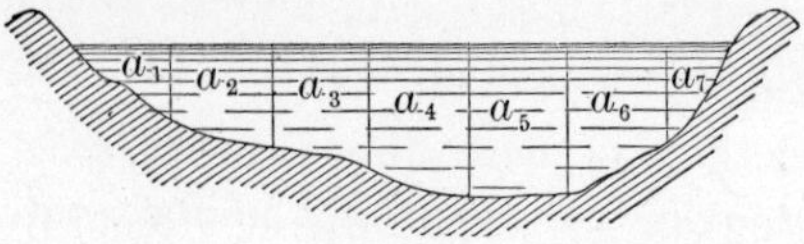

Fig. 131a.

The mean velocities v_1, v_2, v_3, etc., are next to be determined for each of the sub-areas. With a current meter this may be done by starting at one side of a subdivision, and lowering it at a uniform rate until the bottom is nearly reached, then moving it a few feet horizontally and raising it to the surface, then moving it a few feet horizontally and lowering it, and thus continuing until the sub-area has been covered. The velocity then deduced from the whole number of revolutions during the time of immersion is the mean velocity for the sub-area. Or, by using any one of the methods for determining the mean velocity in the vertical as described in Art. 130 the mean velocity may be determined. When rod floats are used, they are started above the upper section, and the times of passing to the lower one noted, as explained in Art. 130, the velocity deduced from a float at the middle of a sub-area being taken as the mean for that area. It will be found that the rod floats are more or less affected by wind, the direction and intensity of which should always be recorded in the field notes.

The discharge of the stream is the sum of the discharges through the several sub-areas, or

$$q = a_1v_1 + a_2v_2 + a_3v_3 + \text{ etc.}$$

and if this be divided by the total area a, the mean velocity for the entire section is determined.

If d_1, d_2, d_3, etc., are the depths in feet on the several verticals in Fig. 131a, and if v_1, v_2, v_3, etc., represent the mean velocities in feet per second in these verticals, while i is the constant interval in feet between them, then the discharge in cubic feet per second will be given by the formula

$$Q=\frac{i}{6}[d_1v_1+(d_1+d_2)(v_1+v_2)+d_2v_2]+\text{ etc.}$$

For most cases, however, sufficient accuracy will be given by the expression

$$Q=i\left[\left(\frac{d_1+d_2}{2}\right)\left(\frac{v_1+v_2}{2}\right)\right]+\text{ etc.}$$

and this is the method which has been adopted by the U. S. Geological Survey. It permits of ready computation, while at the same time it does not require absolute uniformity in the interval *i*. Stevens * has compared the various methods and formulas which have been used for the computation of the discharge in such cases.

The following notes give the details of a gaging of the Lehigh River, near Bethlehem, Pa., made at low water in 1885 by the use of rod floats. The two sections were 100 feet apart, and each was divided into 10 divisions of 30 feet width. In the second column are given the soundings in feet taken at the upper section, in the third the mean of the two areas in square feet, in the fourth the times of passage of the floats in seconds, in the fifth the velocities in feet per second, which were obtained by dividing 100 feet by the times, and in the last are the products a_1v_1, a_2v_2, which are the discharges for the subdivisions a_1, a_2, etc. The total discharge is found to be 826 cubic feet per second,

Subdivisions	Depths	Areas	Times	Velocities	Discharges
	0.0				
1		55.5	380	0.263	14.6
	3.0				
2		148.5	220	0.454	67.4
	6.0				
3		201.7	185	0.540	108.9
	7.1				
4		217.5	120	0.833	181.2
	7.0				
5		210.0	145	0.690	144.9
	7.0				
6		186.0	150	0.667	124.1
	5.3				
7		150.8	165	0.606	91.4
	4.3				
8		114.0	200	0.500	57.0
	3.0				
9		84.0	320	0.313	26.3
	2.2				
10		42.0	430	0.233	9.8
	0.0				
		$a=1410.0$			$q=825.6$

* Engineering News, June 25, 1908.

and the mean velocity is $v = 826/1410 = 0.59$ feet per second. A second gaging of the stream, made a week later, when the water level was 0.59 feet higher, gave for the discharge 1336 cubic feet per second, for the total area 1630 square feet, and for the mean velocity 0.82 feet per second.

In the following tabulation are illustrated both the field notes and the subsequent computations made to determine the discharge of a stream from a current meter gaging.

Distance from Initial Point	Depth of Water	Depth of Point of Observation	Time in Seconds	Meter Revolutions	Velocity			Mean Water Depth	Distance between Sections	Area of Section	Discharge Cubic Feet per Second
					At Point	Mean in Vertical	Mean in Section				
0	0	—	—	—	0	0					
		0.4	33	40	2.80		1.08	1.0	3.0	3.0	3.2
3	2	1.6	61	40	1.52	2.16					
		1.2	36	50	3.20		2.40	4.0	2.0	8.0	19.2
5	6	4.8	45	40	2.08	2.64					
		2.0	37	60	3.70		2.95	8.0	5.0	40.0	118.0
10	10	8.0	41	50	2.82	3.26					
		1.0	49	70	3.30		3.05	7.5	5.0	37.5	114.4
15	5	4.0	39	40	2.38	2.84					
		0.6	32	40	2.90		2.60	4.0	3.0	12.0	31.2
18	3	2.4	44	80	1.82	2.36					
							1.18	1.5	2.0	3.0	3.5
20	0	—			0	0					
								Totals	20.0	103.5	289.5

After a number of discharge measurements have been made at a particular gaging station and at a number of different gage heights or water stages it becomes possible to plot for the station a rating curve which will show the discharge of the stream at any given stage. It is also convenient, for purposes of record and comparison, to plot on the same sheet the curves of mean velocity and areas of the cross-sections for each of the gagings. As new measurements of discharge are made they, together with their corresponding velocities and areas, may then be plotted upon this sheet, and any errors or differences such as those due to a change in the stream bed become at once apparent. Such curves are shown in Fig. 131*b*.

After the discharge curve for a station has been established, it becomes possible, by keeping a record of the gage heights at the station, to determine the total quantity of water which passes the station in any given time. Observations on the gage height

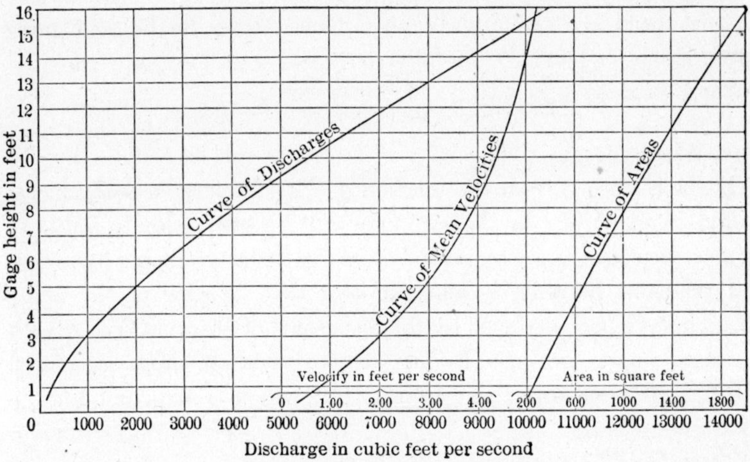

Fig. 131*b*.

may be made from two to three or more times a day, and in cases where the highest accuracy is desired a self-recording gage, such as described in Art. 34, should be installed for the purpose of getting a continuous record of the water height.

When changes in the bed of a stream occur as the result of scouring during freshets, or from the formation of bars or other causes, new rating curves must be constructed, and care should always be taken to see that all of the water flowing down the stream passes the section at which measurements are made. If diversions past the point of gaging occur, or in case two or more channels are found during times of high water, proper allowances or new gagings should be made.

As to the accuracy of the above described methods of gaging the discharge it may be said that with ordinary work, using rod floats, the discrepancies in results obtained under different conditions ought not to exceed 10 percent; and with careful work, using current meters, they may often be of a higher degree of precision. In any event the results derived from such gagings are more reliable than can be obtained by the use of any formula for the discharge of a stream.

Prob. 131. A stream 140 feet wide is divided into seven equal parts, the six soundings being 1.9, 4.0, 4.8, 4.6, 2.7, and 1.0 feet. The seven velocities as found by a current meter are 0.7, 1.6, 2.4, 3.5, 3.0, 1.4, and 0.6 feet per second. Compute the discharge.

Art. 132. Approximate Gagings

When the mean velocity v of a stream can be found, the discharge is known from the relation $q = av$, the area a being measured as explained in the last article. An approximate value of v may be ascertained by one or more float measurements by means of relations between it and the observed velocity of the floats which have been deduced by the discussion of observations. Such measurements are usually less expensive than those explained in Art. 131, and often give information which is sufficient for the inquiry in hand.

The ratio of the mean velocity v to the maximum surface velocity v_m has been found usually to lie between 0.7 and 0.85, and about 0.8 appears to be a rough mean value. Accordingly,

$$v = 0.8\, v_m$$

from which, if v_m be accurately determined, v can be computed with an uncertainty usually less than 20 percent. Many attempts have been made to deduce a more reliable relation between v and v_m. The following rule derived from the investigations of Bazin makes the relation dependent on the coefficient c, the value of which for the particular stream under consideration is to be obtained from the evidence presented in the last chapter:

$$v = v_m \Big/ \left(1 + \frac{25}{c}\right)$$

It is probable, however, that the relation depends more on the hydraulic radius and the shape of the section than upon the degree of roughness of the channel, which c mainly represents.

The influence of wind upon the surface velocities is so great that these methods of determining v may not give good results except in calm weather. A wind blowing up-stream decreases the surface velocities, and one blowing down-stream increases them, without materially affecting the mean velocity and discharge of the stream.

The ratio of the mean velocity V in any vertical to its surface velocity V_o is less variable, for it lies between 0.79 and 0.98, or

$$V = 0.86\ V_o$$

may be used with but an uncertainty of a few percent. If several velocities, V_1, V_2, etc., are determined by surface floats, the mean velocities v_1, v_2, etc., for the several sub-areas a_1, a_2, etc., are known, and the discharge is $q = a_1v_1 + v_2a_2 +$ etc., as before explained.

By means of a sub-surface float, or by a current meter, the velocity V' at mid-depth in any vertical may be measured. The mean velocity V in that vertical is approximately

$$V = 0.98\ V'$$

In this manner the mean velocities in several verticals across the stream may be determined by a single observation at each point, and these may be used, as in Art. 131, in connection with the corresponding areas to compute the discharge.

It was shown by the observation of Humphreys and Abbot on the Mississippi that the velocity V' is practically unaffected by wind, the vertical velocity curves for different intensities of wind intersecting each other at mid-depth. However, if the law of variation of velocities in a vertical is represented by the parabola (Art. 129), it would seem that the intersection should be at about 0.6 of the depth. Hence the above should be used with caution.

Since the maximum surface velocity is greater than the mean velocity v, and since the velocities at the shores are usually small, it follows that there are in the surface two points at which the velocity is equal to v. If by any means the location of either of these could be discovered, a single velocity observation would directly give the value of v. The position of these points is subject to so much variation in channels of different forms, that no satisfactory method of locating them has yet been devised.

In cases where it is desired to construct an approximate discharge curve and where only a few discharge measurements have been made, the method indicated by Stevens* may be followed. From a cross-section of the stream the values of $a\sqrt{r}$ in the Chezy formula $q = ac\sqrt{rs}$ may be determined for each gage height and a curve plotted. The discharge q then being known for several gage heights, it becomes possible to determine a value for $c\sqrt{s}$, which is nearly a constant, and the desired discharge curve can thus be approximated.

Other methods of making approximate gagings consist in adding a solution of some chemical or salt to the water of the stream to be measured at some point where thorough mixing will occur. If the strength of the chemical solution and the rate of its application are known, and if samples of the water of the stream are taken above the point where the solution is introduced and down-stream after thorough mixing has occurred, the discharge of the stream is then equal to the number of times the chemical solution has been diluted by the water of the stream multiplied by the rate of application of the chemical. For example, if 2 quarts of a solution of common salt containing 10 000 parts per million of chlorine be added each second to the stream and if a sample taken one-half a mile down-stream shows the chlorine to be 20 parts per million then the dilution has been 10 000/20 or 500 and the discharge then is 500 × 2 quarts = 1000 quarts per second. No account has here been taken of the chlorine naturally found in the water of the stream, and this must in all cases be allowed for. Stromeyer † has experimented in this manner with solutions of common salt and sulphuric acid. On small streams he found that the results agreed well with both the measurements of a weir and a Venturi meter, thus leading him to conclude that results correct within 1 percent can be obtained. This method has been used by Groat ‡ for measuring the discharge of turbines.

Benzenberg,§ in gaging the flow in a portion of the sewer system of Milwaukee where the sewer lay in a tunnel below the hydraulic gradient, injected a quantity of red eosine into the water at one end of the tunnel and observed its appearance at the other. He found that the color in the water was never distributed over a length

* Engineering News, July 18, 1907.

† Proceedings, Institution of Civil Engineers, vol. 160.

‡ Proceedings American Society of Civil Engineers, November, 1915.

§ Transactions American Society of Civil Engineers, December, 1893.

greater than 7 to 9 feet, and thus the mean velocity was determined with great accuracy. This experiment was of interest also in indicating the relatively small extent to which the particles of water in a given cross-section, such as that of a sewer, become separated from each other, even during a one-half mile journey.

Prob. 132. A stream 60 feet wide is divided into three sections, having the areas 32, 65, and 38 square feet, and the surface velocities near the middle of these are found to be 1.3, 2.6, and 1.4 feet per second. What is the approximate mean velocity of the stream and its discharge?

ART. 133. COMPARISON OF GAGING METHODS

This chapter, together with those preceding, furnishes many methods by which the quantity of water flowing through an orifice, pipe, or channel may be determined. A few remarks will now be made by way of summary and comparison.

The method of direct measurement in a tank is always the most accurate, but except for small quantities is expensive, and for large quantities is impracticable. Next in reliability and convenience come the methods of gaging by orifices and weirs. An orifice one foot square under a head of 25 feet will discharge about 24 cubic feet per second, which is as large a quantity as can usually be profitably passed through a single opening. A weir 20 feet long with a depth of 2.0 feet will discharge about 200 cubic feet per second, which may be taken as the maximum quantity that can be conveniently thus gaged. The number of weirs may be indeed multiplied for larger discharges, but this is usually forbidden by the expense of construction. Hence, for larger quantities of water indirect measurements must be adopted.

The formulas deduced for the flow in pipes and channels in Chaps. 8 and 9 enable an approximate estimation of their discharge to be determined when the coefficients and data which they contain can be closely determined. The remarks in Art. 128 indicate the difficulty of ascertaining these data for streams, and show that the value of the formulas lies in their use in cases of investigation and design rather than for precise gagings. For pipes an accurately rated water meter is a convenient method of measuring the discharge, while for conduits it will often be found difficult to devise an accurate and economical plan for precise determinations, unless the conditions are such that the discharge may be made to pass over a weir or to be retained in a large reservoir, the capacity of which is known for every tenth of a foot in depth. For large aqueducts, and for canals and streams, the usually available methods are those explained in this chapter. In the Catskill Aqueduct for the new water supply of New York City four Venturi meters of capacities up to about 800 cubic feet per second have been introduced (Art. 38).

Surface floats are not to be recommended except for rude determinations, because they are affected by wind and because the deduction of mean velocities from them is in many cases subject to much uncertainty. Nevertheless many cases arise in practice where the results found by the use of surface floats are sufficiently precise to give valuable information concerning the flow of streams. The double float for sub-surface velocity is used in deep and rapid rivers, where a current meter cannot be well operated on account of the difficulty of anchoring a boat. In addition to its disadvantages already mentioned may be noted that of expense, which becomes large when many observations are to be taken.

The method of determining the mean velocities in vertical planes by rod floats is very convenient in canals and channels which are not too deep or too shallow. The precision of a velocity determination by a rod float is always much greater than that of one taken by the double float, so that the former is to be preferred when circumstances will allow. In cases where the velocity is rapid, or where there are no bridges over the stream, rod floats may often give results more reliable than can be obtained by any other method.

Current-meter observations are those which now generally take the highest rank for precision in streams where the conditions are not abnormal. The first cost of the outfit is greater than that required for rod floats, but if much work is to be done, it will prove the cheaper. The main objection is the difficulty of use in cases of high velocities and to the errors which may be introduced from the lack of proper rating; this is required to be done at intervals, since it is found that the relation between the velocity and the rccorded number of revolutions may change during use.

In the execution of hydraulic operations which involve the measurement of water a method is to be selected which will give the highest degree of precision with given expenditure, or which will secure a given degree of precision at a minimum expense. Any one can build a road, or a water-supply system; but the art of engineering teaches how to build it well, and at the least cost of construction and maintenance. Similarly the science of hydraulics teaches the laws of flow and records the results of experiments, so that when the discharge of a conduit is to be measured or a stream is to be gaged, the engineer may select that method which will furnish the required information in the most satisfactory manner and at the least expense.

Prob. 133. Consult Humphreys and Abbot's Physics and Hydraulics of the Mississippi River (Washington, 1862 and 1876), and find two methods of measuring the velocity of a current different from those described in the preceding pages.

Art. 134. Variations in Discharge

When the stage of water rises and falls, a corresponding increase or decrease occurs in the velocity and discharge. The relation of these variations to the change in depth may be approximately ascertained in the following manner, the slope of the water surface being regarded as remaining uniform: Let the stream be wide, so that its hydraulic radius is nearly equal to the mean depth d; then

$$v = c\sqrt{ds} = cs^{\frac{1}{2}}d^{\frac{1}{2}}$$

Differentiating this with respect to v and d gives

$$\delta v / v = \tfrac{1}{2}\, \delta d / d$$

Here the first member is the relative change in velocity when the depth varies from d to $d \pm \delta d$, and the equation hence shows that the relative change in velocity is one-half the relative change in depth. For example, a stream 3 feet deep, and with a mean velocity of 4 feet per second, rises so that the depth is 3.3 feet;

then $dv = 4 \times \frac{1}{2} \times 0.3/3 = 0.2$, and the velocity of the stream becomes $4 + 0.2 = 4.2$ feet per second.

In the same manner the variation in discharge may be found. Let b be the breadth of the stream, then

$$q = cbd\sqrt{ds} = cbs^{\frac{1}{2}}d^{\frac{3}{2}}$$

and by differentiating with respect to q and d,

$$\delta q/q = \tfrac{3}{2}\,\delta d/d$$

Hence the relative change in discharge is $1\frac{1}{2}$ times that of the relative change in depth. This rule, like the preceding, supposes that δd is very small, and will not apply to large variations in the depth of the water.

The above conclusions may be expressed as follows: If the mean depth changes 1 percent, the velocity changes 0.5 percent, and the discharge changes 1.5 percent. They are only true for streams with such cross-sections that the hydraulic radius may be regarded as proportional to the depth, and even for such sections are only exact for small variations in d and v. They also assume that the slope s remains the same after the rise or fall as before; this will be the case if a condition of permanency is established, but, as a rule, while the stage of water is rising the slope is increasing, and while falling the slope is decreasing.

Gages for reading the stages of water are now set up on many rivers, and daily observations are taken. Such a gage is usually a vertical board graduated to feet and tenths and set if possible with its zero below the lowest known water level. Another form is the box-and-chain gage, which consists of a box fastened on a bridge with a graduated scale within it and a chain that can be let down to the water level; the length of the chain being known, the gage height can then be read from the scale if its zero is set so that the reading will be zero when the end of the chain just touches the water surface when it is at zero height. Such observations of the daily stage of a river are of great value in planning engineering constructions, and they are now made at many stations by the United States government through the Department of Agriculture and the Geological Survey Bureau.

When several measurements of the discharge of a stream have been made for different stages of water, a curve may be drawn to show the law of variation of discharge (Art. 131), and from this curve the discharge corresponding to any given stage of water may be approximately ascertained. Fig. 131*b* shows a typical discharge curve. Fig. 134 shows the actual discharge curve for the Lehigh River at Bethlehem, Pa., the ordinates being the

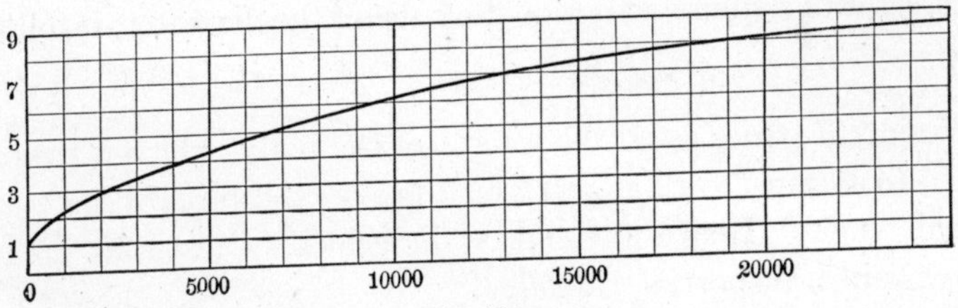

Fig. 134.

heights of the water level as read on the gage, and the abscissas being the discharges of the river in cubic feet per second; this is only a part of the discharge curve for that river, as the water has been known to rise to 22.5 feet and the corresponding discharge was over 100 000 cubic feet per second. Each station on a river has its own distinctive discharge curve, for the local topography determines the heights to which the water level will rise.

Prob. 134. A stream of 4 feet mean depth delivers 800 cubic feet per second. What will be the discharge when the depth is decreased to 3.87 feet? If the stream is 100 feet wide, what will be the velocity when the depth is 4.12 feet?

Art. 135. Transporting Capacity of Currents

The fact that the water of rapid streams transports large quantities of earthy matter, either in suspension or by rolling it along the bed of the channel, is well known, and has already been mentioned in Art. 120. It is now to be shown that the diameters of bodies which can be moved by the pressure of a current vary as the square of its velocity, and that their weights vary as the sixth power of the velocity.

When water causes sand or pebbles to roll along the bed of a channel, it must exert a force approximately proportional to the square of the velocity and to the area exposed (Art. 27), or if d is the diameter of the body and C a constant, the force which is required to move it horizontally is

$$F = Cd^2v^2$$

But if motion just occurs, this force is also proportional to the weight of the body, because the frictional resistance of one body upon another varies as the normal pressure or weight. And as the weight of a sphere varies as the cube of the diameter, it follows that

$$d^3 = Cd^2v^2 \qquad \text{or} \qquad d = Cv^2$$

Now since d varies as v^2, the weight of the body, which is proportional to d^3, must vary as v^6; which proves the proposition enunciated above. Hence an increase in velocity causes far greater increase in transporting capacity.

Since the weight of sand and stones when immersed in water is only about one-half their weight in air, the frictional resistances to their motion are slight, and this helps to explain the circumstance that they are so easily transported by currents of moderate velocity. It is found by observation that a pebble about one inch in diameter is rolled along the bed of a channel when the velocity is about $3\frac{1}{2}$ feet per second; hence, according to the above theoretical deduction, a velocity five times as great, or $17\frac{1}{2}$ feet per second, will carry along stones of 25 inches diameter. This law of the transporting capacity of flowing water is only an approximate one, for the recorded experiments seem to indicate that the diameters of moving pebbles on the bed of a channel do not vary quite as rapidly as the square of the velocity. The law, moreover, is applicable only to bodies of similar shape, and cannot be used for comparing round pebbles with flat spalls. The following table gives the velocities on the bed or bottom of the channel which are required to move the materials stated. The corresponding mean velocities in the last column are derived from the empirical formula deduced by Darcy,

$$v = v' + 11\sqrt{rs}$$

in which v' is the bottom and v the mean velocity. The bottom or transporting velocities were deduced by Dubuat from experiments in small troughs, and hence are probably slightly less than the velocities which would move the same materials in channels of natural earth.

	Bottom velocity	Mean velocity
Clay, fit for pottery,	0.3	0.4
Sand, size of anise-seed,	0.4	0.5
Gravel, size of peas,	0.6	0.8
Gravel, size of beans,	1.2	1.6
Shingle, about 1 inch in diameter,	2.5	3.5
Angular stones, about 1½ inches,	3.5	4.5

The general conclusion to be derived from these figures is that ordinary small, loose earthy materials will be transported or rolled along the bed of a channel by velocities of 2 or 3 feet per second. It is not necessarily to be inferred that this movement of the materials is of an injurious nature in streams with a fixed regimen, but in artificial canals the subject is one that demands close attention. The velocity of the moving objects after starting has been found to be usually less than half that of the current.*

In a silt-bearing stream there is a certain critical velocity V_0 at which all silt already in suspension is carried on without being deposited and at which no further silt is scoured from the sides and bottom. This velocity, according to the investigation of Kennedy,† is given by $V_0 = md^{0.64}$ where d is the depth of the stream and m is 0.82 for light sandy silt, 0.99 for sandy loam, and 1.07 for coarse silt. Kennedy also found that the amounts of silt carried in the same stream varied with the square root of the fifth power of the velocities, so that if x and x_0 are amounts carried at velocities V and V_0 then $x = x_0 \, (V/V_0)^{\frac{5}{2}}$. When V is greater than V_0, then $x - x_0$ is the amount of scour due to the change of velocity; when V is less than V_0, then $x_0 - x$ is the amount of deposit due to the change of velocity.

Prob. 135. In the early history of the earth the moon was half its present distance from the earth's center, and the tides were about eight times

* Herschel, on the erosive and abrading power of water, in Journal Franklin Institute, 1878, vol. 75, p. 330.

† Proceedings, Institution of Civil Engineers, vol. 119, 1894–95, p. 281.

as high as at present. It is supposed that these tides rolled over the low lands and moved great rocks from place to place. The greatest velocity of such a wave is $\sqrt{gd}$, where d is the depth of the water. What is the probable weight and size of the largest rock that such a current would move?

Art. 136. Influence of Dams

When a dam is built across a stream, it is often desired to compute its height so that the water level may stand at a given elevation. Thus in the figures, CC represents the surface of the stream before the construction of the dam, the depth of the water being D, and it is required to find the height G of the dam so that

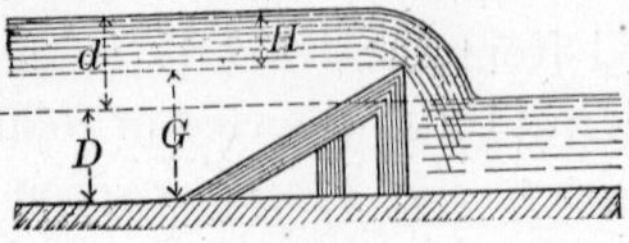

Fig. 136a.

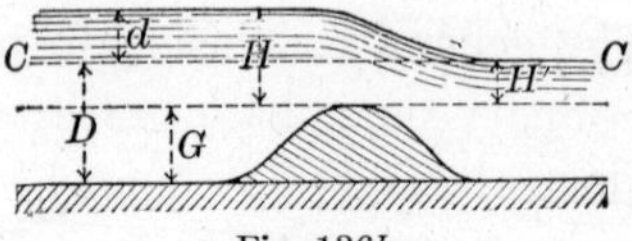

Fig. 136b.

the water surface may be raised the vertical distance d. There are two cases, the first where the crest is above the original water level CC, and the second where it is below that level; in both cases the discharge q must be known in order to compute the height of the dam.

When the crest is not submerged, as in Fig. 136a, it is seen that the value of G is $D + d - H$, where H is the head on the crest. Now from Art. 64 the value of q is $\text{M}b(H + 1\frac{1}{3}h)^{\frac{3}{2}}$, where b is the length of the crest and h is the head due to velocity of approach. Hence there results

$$G = D + d + 1\tfrac{1}{3}h - (q/\text{M}b)^{\frac{2}{3}} \qquad (136)_1$$

in which M is to be taken from Art. 69. For example, let the discharge be 18 000 cubic feet per second, let the width of the stream above the dam be 600 feet, and the width on the crest be 525 feet; also let D and d be 8.5 and 6.0 feet, and let M be 3.33. The mean velocity of approach is

$$v = \frac{18\,000}{600 \times 14.5} = 2.1 \text{ feet per second}$$

whence the velocity-head is $h = 0.0155 \times 2.1^2 = 0.07$ feet. Then from the formula there results $G = 9.9$ feet.

When the dam is a low one its crest will be submerged. Here Fig. 136*b* gives $H = D + d - G$ and $H' = D - G$. Inserting these heads in formula $(67)_2$, there is found

$$G = D + \tfrac{2}{3}d - \tfrac{2}{3}q/\text{M}b\sqrt{d} \qquad (136)_2$$

where the coefficient M lies between 3.09 and 3.37, depending on the value of H'/H, and as a mean 3.1 may be used. For example, let $D = 4.0$, $d = 1.0$, $b = 50$ feet, and $q = 400$ cubic feet per second; then G is found to be 2.95 feet. Now H' and H are 1.05 and 2.05 feet, whence $H'/H = 0.51$, and from Art. 67 the value of M is 3.11, which shows that the assumed value 3.1 is close enough.

Another problem is to find the height d to which the water will rise when the dam is to be built to the height G. For the dam of Fig. 136*a* this is

$$d = D + (q/Mb)^{\frac{2}{3}} - G - 1\tfrac{1}{2}h \qquad (136)_3$$

and for the submerged dam (Fig. 136*b*) it is found from

$$d^{\frac{3}{2}} + \tfrac{3}{2}(D - G)d^{\frac{1}{2}} = q/Mb \qquad (136)_4$$

In these M may be taken as about 3.3 for $(136)_3$ or about 3.1 for $(136)_4$, or closer values may be found from Arts. 69 and 67. Example: for a submerged crest let $D = 5.2$, $G = 3.2$, $b = 75$ feet, and $q = 500$ cubic feet per second; then, taking M as 3.1, the solution of the cubic equation $(136)_4$ gives $d = 0.40$ feet. Here $H = 2.40$ and $H' = 2.0$ feet, whence $H'/H = 0.54$ and from Art. 67 a better value of M is 3.14. A second computation now gives $d = 0.39$ feet.

Prob. 136. For a submerged dam let $D = 3.2$, $G = 2.2$, $b = 60$ feet, $q = 400$ cubic feet per second. Compute the height d to which the water will rise.

Art. 136½. Backwater due to Bridge Piers

When bridge piers are built in a stream, its cross-section is diminished and the water surface up-stream from the bridge stands at a greater height than before. The most common problem is to find how high the water will rise when the original width B is to be contracted to the width b, the width of the pier being $B - b$. Let q be the discharge of the stream, D the depth of the water before the construction of the piers, and d the rise in the water level due to the piers (Fig. 136½). Regarding the section as rectangular, the original area is BD, the area where the water rises between the piers is bD, and that upstream from the bridge is $B(D + d)$. The area bD may be regarded as an orifice from which the water issues under the head d aided by the velocity of approach. Applying formula $(50)_3$ to this case, A is to be replaced by $B(D + d)$ and a by bD, also h is to be replaced by d and q by BVv, where v is the mean

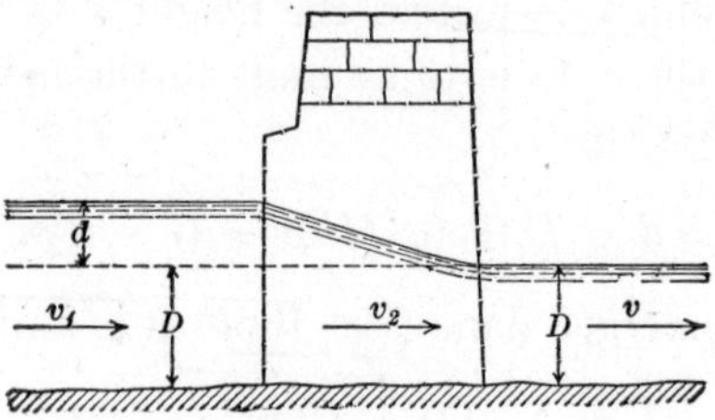

Fig. 136½a.

velocity of the stream before the construction of the piers; then $(50)_3$ reduces to

$$d = \frac{v^2}{2g}\left(\left(\frac{B}{cb}\right)^2 - \left(\frac{D}{D+d}\right)^2\right) \qquad (136\tfrac{1}{2})_1$$

which is a formula for the backwater rise d due to the obstruction caused by the piers.

In this formula c is a coefficient which takes account of contraction and frictional losses as the water flows by the piers. There is a lack of definite knowledge regarding its proper values. It is, however, clear that the rise d must be zero when b equals B, and hence c is 1.00 for this extreme condition. Also when b is very small compared with B, the case is roughly that of a small orifice, hence from the tables in Art. 47 it is concluded that the value of c is about 0.75 when b/B is 0. Now, about

1805, Funk made observations in the river Weser * from which it appears that c was 0.97 when b/B was 0.82. From these three conditions there is found the formula

$$c = 0.75 + 0.35(b/B) - 0.10(b/B)^2 \qquad (136\tfrac{1}{2})_2$$

Unfortunately Funk's observations were not very precise and hence this expression for c can be regarded as approximate only. Experiments for determining c are much needed and such might readily be made in the hydraulic laboratories of engineering colleges.

To use the formula $(136\frac{1}{2})^1$ it is best at first to take d as zero in the second member and then compute. The value found for d is then to be inserted in the second member and a recomputation be made. For example, let $B = 167.4$, $b = 149.2$, and $D = 10.0$ feet; also let the mean velocity in the uncontracted section be 3.20 feet per second, whence $v^2/2g = 0.159$ feet. Here $b/B = 0.891$ and from $(136\frac{1}{2})_2$ there is found $c = 0.982$. Then, taking d as zero in the second member of $(136\frac{1}{2})_1$, the first computation gives $d = 0.049$ feet. Inserting this in the second member and recomputing there is found $d = 0.050$ feet, while a third computation gives essentially the same value. Hence the probable backwater rise in this case may be put at 0.05 feet.

Numerous formulas have been deduced for the backwater rise due to bridge piers, but they are all more or less defective, so that computed values should be regarded as approximations liable to some uncertainty, unless based on coefficients which have been determined by observations applicable to the case in hand. The above formula $(136\frac{1}{2})_1$ was deduced by W. R. Hutton in 1882,† although it had been previously used in a slightly different form by Bresse and D'Aubission, it is well that it should be called Hutton's formula in honor of a distinguished American engineer.

The above formulas refer to a rectangular section. To extend them so as to cover actual sections of rivers, let A be the original uncontracted area, a the contracted area, and A_1 the

* Lehren der Hydrotechnik (Berlin, 1820), p. 131.

† Transactions American Society of Civil Engineers, 1882, p. 240.

enlarged area up-stream from the bridge. Then by similar reasoning as before, there is found for the probable backwater rise caused by the obstruction of the piers,

$$d = \frac{v^2}{2g}\left(\left(\frac{A}{ca}\right)^2 - \left(\frac{A}{A_1}\right)^2\right)$$

in which A_1 may usually be replaced by $A + Bd$, where B is the surface width. Also

$$c = 0.75 + 0.35(a/A) - 0.10(a/A)^2$$

seems the most probable expression now available for the coefficient in this general case.

The shape of the pier influences the degree of contraction and hence modifies the value of the coefficient c. In Fig. 136½*b* are shown

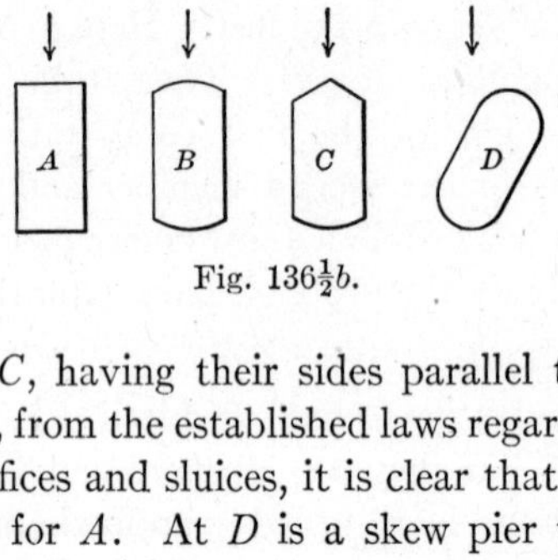

Fig. 136½*b*.

three piers A, B, C, having their sides parallel to the direction of the current. Here, from the established laws regarding the coefficient of discharge for orifices and sluices, it is clear that c should be larger for B and C than for A. At D is a skew pier where it might be thought that the area of obstruction is that projected on a plane normal to the current; this cannot be the case, since the dynamic pressure which causes the backwater rise is less for the actual inclined side of the pier than for such a projection (Art. 154). Experiments are much needed in order to ascertain values of c for piers of different shapes. According to Navier c is 0.85 for piers with square ends like A, 0.90 for piers like C when the angle at the front is obtuse, and 0.95 for piers with semi-circular ends like B, or piers like C when the front angle is acute. But these results should evidently be modified for the ratio of a to A.

Prob. 136½. A river 940 feet wide has a depth of 18.4 feet, and a mean velocity of 5.8 feet per second. Three piers, each 12 feet wide, are to be built across it. Compute the probable rise of backwater caused by the piers. Compute also the probable rise during a flood which increases the mean depth to 18.5 feet and the mean velocity to 5.8 feet per second.

Art. 137. Steady Non-uniform Flow

In Arts. 112–133 the slope of the channel, its cross-section, and its hydraulic radius have been regarded as constant. If these are variable in different reaches of the stream, the case is one of non-uniformity, and this will now be discussed. The flow is still regarded as steady, so that the same quantity of water passes each section per second, but its velocity and depth vary as the slope and cross-section change. Let there be several reaches $l_1, l_2, \cdots l_n$, which have the falls $h_1, h_2, \cdots h_n$, the water sections being $a_1, a_2, \cdots a_n$, the hydraulic radii $r_1, r_2, \cdots r_n$, and the velocities $v_1, v_2, \cdots v_n$. The total fall $h_1 + h_2 + \cdots + h_n$ is expressed by h. Now the head corresponding to the mean velocity in the first section is $v_1^2/2g$. The theoretic effective head for the last section is $h + v_1^2/2g$, while the actual velocity-head is $v_n^2/2g$. The difference of these is the head lost in friction; or by (125),

$$h + \frac{v_1^2}{2g} - \frac{v_n^2}{2g} = \frac{l_1 v_1^2}{c_1^2 r_1} + \frac{l_2 v_2^2}{c_2^2 r_2} + \cdots + \frac{l_n v_n^2}{c_n^2 r_n}$$

in which $c_1^2, c_2^2, \cdots c_n^2$ are the Chezy coefficients for the different lengths. Now let q be the discharge per second; then, since the flow is steady, the mean velocities are

$$v_1 = q/a_1 \qquad v_2 = q/a_2 \cdots v_n = q/a_n$$

and, inserting these in the equation, it reduces to

$$h = \frac{q^2}{2g}\left(\frac{1}{a_n^2} - \frac{1}{a_1^2}\right) + q^2\left(\frac{l_1}{c_1^2 a_1^2 r_1} + \frac{l_2}{c_2^2 a_2^2 r_2} + \cdots + \frac{l_n}{c_n^2 a_n^2 r_n}\right)$$

which is a fundamental formula for the discussion of steady flow through non-uniform channels. This formula shows that the discharge q is a consequence not only of the total fall h in the entire length of the channel, but also of the dimensions of the various cross-sections. The assumption has been made that a and r are constant in each of the parts considered; this can be realized by taking the lengths $l_1, l_2, \cdots l_n$ sufficiently short. If only one part be considered in which a and r are constant, a_n and a_1 are equal, all the terms but one in the second member disappear, and the last equation reduces to $q = ca\sqrt{rh/l}$, which is the Chezy formula for the discharge in a channel of uniform cross-section.

An important practical problem is that where the steady flow is non-uniform in a channel having a bed with constant slope, a condition which may be caused by an obstruction below the part considered or by a sudden fall below it. Let a_1 and a_2 be the areas of the two sections, l their distances apart, and v_1 and v_2 the mean velocities. Then, if a and r be average values of the areas and hydraulic radii of the cross-sections throughout the length l, the last formula becomes

$$h = \frac{q^2}{2g}\left(\frac{1}{a_2^2} - \frac{1}{a_1^2} + \frac{2gl}{c^2a^2r}\right)$$

Now the important problem is to discuss the change in depth between the two sections. For this purpose let A_1A_2 in Fig. 137 be the longitudinal profile of the water surface, let A_1D be horizontal, and A_1C be drawn parallel to the bed B_1B_2. The depths A_1B_1 and A_2B_2 are represented by d_1 and d_2, the latter being taken as the larger. Let i be the constant slope of the bed B_1B_2; then $DC = il$, and since $DA_2 = h$ and $A_2C = d_2 - d_1$, there is found for the fall in the length l,

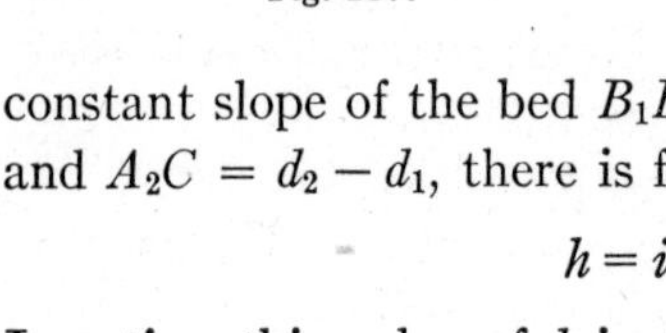

Fig. 137.

$$h = il - (d_2 - d_1)$$

Inserting this value of h in the preceding equation and solving for l, there is obtained the important formula

$$l = \frac{(d_2 - d_1) - \dfrac{q^2}{2g}\left(\dfrac{1}{a_1^2} - \dfrac{1}{a_2^2}\right)}{i - q^2/c^2a^2r} \qquad (137)_1$$

from which the length l corresponding to a change in depth $d_2 - d_1$ can be approximately computed. This formula is the more accurate the shorter the length l, since then the mean quantities

a and r can be obtained with greater precision, and c is subject to less variation.

The inverse problem, to find the change in depth when l is given, cannot be directly solved by this formula, because the areas are functions of the depths. When $d_2 - d_1$ is small compared with either d_1 or d_2, it is allowable to regard d_2 as equal to d_1 when they are to be added or multiplied together. Hence

$$\frac{1}{a_1^2} - \frac{1}{a_2^2} = \frac{a_2^2 - a_1^2}{a_1^2 a_2^2} = \frac{d_2^2 - d_1^2}{b^2 d_1^2 d_2^2} = \frac{(d_2 + d_1)(d_2 - d_1)}{b^2 d_1^4} = \frac{2(d_2 - d_1)}{b^2 d_1^3}$$

also making a equal to a_1 and r equal to d_1 in the last formula, and solving for $d_2 - d_1$, there is found

$$\frac{d_2 - d_1}{l} = \frac{i - q^2/c^2 b^2 d_1^3}{1 - q^2/g b^2 d_1^3} \qquad (137)_2$$

from which the change in depth can be computed when all the other quantities are given.

Fig. 137 is drawn for the case of depth increasing downstream, but the reasoning is general and the formulas apply equally well when the depth decreases with the fall of the stream. In the latter case the point A_2 is below C, and $d_2 - d_1$ will be negative. As an example, let it be required to determine the decrease in depth in a rectangular conduit 5 feet wide and 333 feet long, which is laid with its bottom level, the depth of water at the entrance being maintained at 2 feet, and the quantity supplied being 20 cubic feet per second. Here $l = 333$, $b = 5$, $d_1 = 2$, $q = 20$, and $i = 0$. Taking $c = 89$, and substituting all values in the formula, there is found $d_2 - d_1 = -0.09$ feet; whence $d_2 = 1.91$ feet, which is to be regarded as an approximate probable value. It is likely that values of $d_2 - d_1$ computed in this manner are liable to an uncertainty of 15 or 20 percent, the longer the distance l the greater being the error of the formula. In strictness also c varies with depth, but errors from this cause are small when compared to those arising in ascertaining its value from the tables.

Prob. 137. Explain why formula $(137)_2$ cannot be used for the above example when the slope i is 0.01.

ART. 138. THE SURFACE CURVE

In the case of steady uniform flow, in the channel where the bed has a constant grade, the slope of the water surface is parallel to that of the bed, and the longitudinal profile of the water surface is a straight line. In steady non-uniform flow, however, the slope of the water surface continually varies, and the longitudinal profile is a curve whose nature is now to be investigated. As in the last article, the width of the channel will be taken as constant, its cross-section will be regarded as rectangular, and it will be assumed that the stream is wide compared to its depth, so that the wetted perimeter may be taken as equal to the width and the hydraulic radius equal to the mean depth (Art. 112). These assumptions are closely fulfilled in many canals and rivers.

The last formula of the preceding article is rigidly exact if the sections a_1 and a_2 are consecutive, so that l becomes δl and $d_2 - d_1$ becomes δd. Making these changes,

$$\frac{\delta d}{\delta l} = \frac{i - q^2/c^2b^2d^3}{1 - q^2/gb^2d^3} \qquad (138)_1$$

in which d is the depth of the water at the place considered. This is the general differential equation of the surface curve, l being measured parallel to the bed BB, and d upward, while the angle whose tangent is the derivative $\delta d/\delta l$ is also measured from BB.

To discuss this curve, let CC be the water surface if the slope were uniform, and let D be the depth of the water in the wide

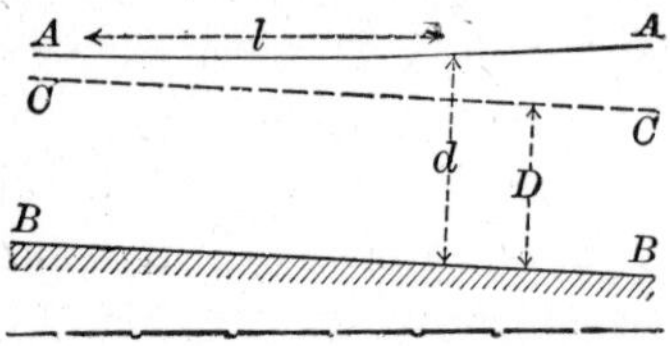

Fig. 138*a*.

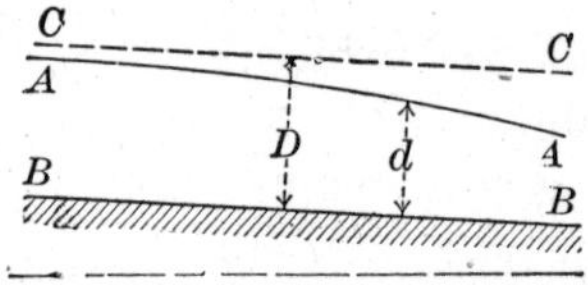

Fig. 138*b*.

rectangular channel. The slope s of the water surface is here equal to the slope i of the bed of the channel, and from the Chezy formula (113),

$$q = av = cbD\sqrt{ri} = cbD\sqrt{Di}$$

This value of q, inserted in the differential equation of the surface curve, reduces it to the form,

$$\frac{\delta d}{\delta l} = i \frac{1 - (D/d)^3}{1 - \frac{c^2 i}{g}(D/d)^3} \tag{138$_2$}$$

in which d and l are the only variables, the former being the ordinate and the latter the abscissa, measured parallel to the bed BB, of any point of the surface curve. The derivative $\delta d/\delta l$ is the tangent of the angle which the tangent at any point of the surface curve makes with the bed BB or the surface CC.

First, suppose that D is less than d, as in Fig. 138*a*, where AA is the surface curve under the non-uniform flow, and CC is the line which the surface would take in case of uniform flow. The numerator of $(138)_2$ is then positive, and the denominator is also positive, since i is very small. Hence δd is positive, and it increases with d in the direction of the flow; going up-stream it decreases with d, and the surface curve becomes tangent to CC when $d = D$. This form of curve is that usually produced above a dam; it is called the "backwater curve," and will be discussed in detail in Art. 140.

Second, let d be less than D, as in Fig. 138*b*. The numerator is then negative and the denominator positive; δd is accordingly negative and AA is concave to the bed BB, whereas in the former case it was convex. This form of surface curve is produced when a sudden fall occurs in the stream below the point considered; it is called the "drop-down curve" and is discussed in Art. 141.

Formula $(138)_1$ may also be put into another form by substituting for q its value bdv, where v is the mean velocity in the cross-section whose depth is d. It thus becomes

$$\frac{\delta d}{\delta l} = \frac{g}{c^2} \cdot \frac{v^2 - c^2 di}{v^2 - gd} \tag{138$_3$}$$

and by its discussion the same conclusions are derived as before. When v is equal to $c\sqrt{di}$, the inclination $\delta d/\delta l$ becomes zero, and the slope of the water surface is parallel to the bed of the stream. When v is less than $c\sqrt{di}$, the numerator is negative, and if the denominator is also negative, the case of Fig. 138*a* results. When v is greater than $c\sqrt{di}$ and the denominator is negative, the case of Fig. 138*b* obtains. When v equals $\sqrt{gd}$, the value of $\delta d/\delta l$ is infinity and the water surface stands normal to the bed of the stream; this remarkable case can actually occur in two ways, and they will be discussed in Art. 139.

Prob. 138. Let the velocity of the stream be 20 feet per second, the value of c be 80, and the slope be 1 on 2000. Compute values of $\delta d/\delta l$ for depth of 12.2, 12.3, 12.4, 12.5, and 12.6 feet; then draw the surface curve.

Art. 139. The Jump and the Bore

A very curious phenomenon which sometimes occurs in shallow channels is that of the so-called "jump," as shown in Fig. 139*a*.

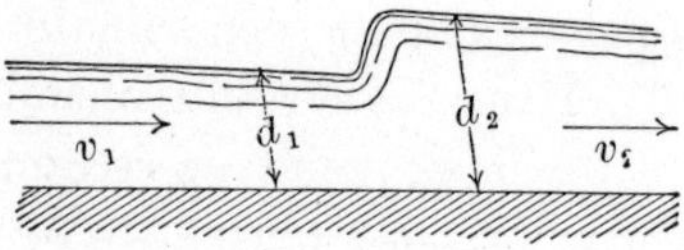

Fig. 139*a*.

This happens when the denominator in $(138)_3$ is zero; then $\delta d/\delta l$ is infinite, and the water surface stands normal to the bed. Placing that denominator equal to zero, there is found $v^2 = gd$. Now by further consideration it will appear that the varying denominator in passing through zero changes its sign. Above the jump where the depth is d_1 the velocity is slightly greater than $\sqrt{gd_1}$, and below it is less than $\sqrt{gd_2}$. The conditions for the occurrence of the jump are that an obstruction should be in the stream below, that the slope i should not be small, and that the velocity v_1 should be greater than $\sqrt{gd_1}$. To find the necessary slope, the algebraic conditions are

$$v_1 = c\sqrt{d_1 i} \quad \text{and} \quad v_1 > \sqrt{gd_1} \quad \text{whence} \quad i > g/c^2$$

and accordingly the jump cannot occur when i is less than g/c^2. For an unplaned planked trough c may be taken at about 100; hence the slope for this must be equal to or greater than 0.00322.

To find the depth d_2 when d_1 and v_1 are given, it will be assumed that the bed of the channel is horizontal, and that there are no frictional losses between the sections d_1 and d_2; then

$$d_1 + \frac{v_1^2}{2g} = d_2 + \frac{v_2^2}{2g}$$

where the first member is the total head in the section d_1 and the second is that in d_2. Inserting for v_2 its equivalent v_1d_1/d_2, letting h represent the velocity-head $v_1^2/2g$, and solving the equation for d_2, gives

$$d_2=\tfrac{1}{2}h+\sqrt{h(d_1+\tfrac{1}{4}h)} \qquad (139)$$

which is the formula first deduced by Belanger. The following is a comparison of the computed depths d_2 with those observed by Bidone in 1818 for four experiments, d_1 being in feet and v_1 in feet per second, g being taken as 32.19 feet per second per second for Paris, where Bidone made the experiments:

Velocity v_1	Observed d_1	Observed d_2	Computed d_2
4.47	0.155	0.423	0.424
4.59	0.149	0.423	0.438
5.59	0.208	0.613	0.642
6.39	0.242	0.764	0.811

It is seen that the computed values are all greater than those observed, which should be the case, as frictional resistances have been neglected, but on the whole the agreement is fair. Experiments made at Lehigh University in 1894 show also a fair agreement between computed and observed values.* The depths in these experiments were less than in those of Bidone, but higher relative jumps were obtained. For instance, for $v_1=4.33$ feet per second and $d_1=0.038$ feet, the observed value of d_2 was 0.167 feet, but the value computed from the above formula is 0.177 feet; here the height of the jump d_2-d_1 is more than three times the depth d_1, while it is usually about twice d_1 in the above records from Bidone. Again for $v_1=3.56$ feet per second and $d_1=0.036$ feet in the Lehigh experiments, the observed value of d_2 was 0.153 feet, while the computed value is 0.147 feet.

Another remarkable phenomenon is that of the so-called "bore," where a tidal wave moves up a river with a vertical front. It is also seen when a large body of water moves down a cañon after a heavy rainfall, or when a reservoir bursts and allows a large discharge suddenly to escape down a narrow valley. In the great flood of 1889 at Johnstown, Pa., such a vertical wall of water,

* Engineering News, 1895, vol. 34, p. 28.

variously estimated at from 10 to 30 feet in height, was seen to move down the valley, carrying on its front brush and logs mingled with spray and foam.* In 41 minutes it traveled a distance of 13 miles down the descent of 380 feet. The velocity was hence about 28 feet per second.

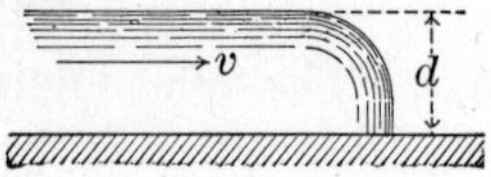

Fig. 139*b*.

Fig. 139*b* shows the form of surface curve for this case, and by reference to $(138)_3$ it is seen that $\delta d/\delta l$ must be negative and that it has the value ∞ at the vertical front. The conditions for the occurrence of the bore then are

$$v = \sqrt{gd} \quad \text{and} \quad v > c\sqrt{di} \quad \text{whence } i < g/c^2$$

For the Johnstown flood, taking v as 28 feet per second, the value of d found from this equation is 24 feet; it was probably greater than this in the upper part of the valley and less in the lower part. Since the value of i is about 1/180, it follows that c must have been less than 76. The conditions here established show that the flood bore will occur when the velocity becomes equal to $\sqrt{gd}$, provided c is less than $\sqrt{g/i}$. It appears, therefore, that roughness of surface is an essential condition for the formation of the bore in a steep valley.

The bore can also occur in a canal with horizontal bed when a lock breaks above an empty level reach, provided v becomes equal to $\sqrt{gd}$. No case of this kind appears to be on record, and there seems to be no way of ascertaining whether the actual velocity will reach the limit $\sqrt{gd}$. If the bore occurs and the depth of the vertical wall be d_2, its distance from a point where the depth is d_1 is found from $(139)_2$ by inserting in it the value of g corresponding to the critical velocity v. Thus may be shown that for c = 80 and $d_1 = \frac{1}{2}d_1$ the length l is $275d_1$.

The tidal bore, which occurs in many large rivers when the tide flows in at their mouths, obeys similar laws. Here the slope i may be taken as zero, while c is probably very large, so that roughness of surface is not an essential condition. The great bore at Hangchow, China, which occurs twice a year, is said to travel up the river at a rate of from 10 to 13 miles per hour, the height of the vertical front being

* Transactions American Society of Civil Engineers, 1889, vol. 21, p 564.

from 10 to 20 feet.* From $v = \sqrt{gh}$, the velocity corresponding to a depth of 10 feet is 12.6 miles per hour, while that corresponding to a depth of 20 feet is 17 miles per hour, so that the statements have a fair agreement with the theoretical law. This investigation indicates that the velocity of the tidal bore depends mainly upon the depth of the tidal wave above the river surface, but it may be noted that other discussions† regard the depth of the river itself as an element of importance, and Art. 191 considers this with respect to common waves.

Prob. 139. When the height of the jump is three times the depth d_1, show that the velocity v_1 must be $2\sqrt{2gd_1}$. Also show that $0.414d_1$ is the minimum height of a jump.

Art. 140. The Backwater Curve

When a dam is built across a channel the water surface is raised for a long distance up-stream. This is a fruitful source of contention, and accordingly many attempts have been made to discuss it theoretically, in order to be able to compute the probable increase in depth at various distances back from a proposed dam. None of these can be said to have been successful except for the simple case where the slope of the bed of the channel is constant and its cross-section such that the width may be regarded as uniform and the hydraulic radius be taken as equal to the depth. These conditions are closely fulfilled for some streams, and an approximate solution may be made by the formula $(137)_2$. It is desirable, however, to obtain an exact equation of the surface curve.

For this purpose take the differential equation of the surface curve given in $(138)_2$, and let the independent variable d/D be represented by x. Then it may be put into the more convenient form

$$\frac{\delta l}{\delta x} = \frac{D}{i}\left(1 + \frac{1 - c^2 i/g}{x^3 - 1}\right) \qquad (140)_1$$

in which l is the abscissa and Dx the ordinate of any point of the curve. The general integral of this is

$$l = \frac{Dx}{i} - D\left(\frac{1}{i} - \frac{c^2}{g}\right)\left(\frac{1}{6}\log_e \frac{x^2 + x + 1}{(x-1)^2} - \frac{1}{\sqrt{3}} \text{ arc cot } \frac{2x+1}{\sqrt{3}}\right) + C$$

* Skidmore's China, the Long-lived Empire (New York), 1900, p. 294.

† G. H. Darwin, The Tides, p. 65; Century Magazine, vol. 34, p. 903.

which is the equation of the surface curve, C being the constant of integration. To use this let the logarithmic and circular function in the second parenthesis of the second member be designated by $\phi(x)$ or $\phi(d/D)$, namely,

$$\phi(x) = \phi(d/D) = \frac{1}{6}\log_e \frac{x^2 + x + 1}{(x-1)^2} - \frac{1}{\sqrt{3}} \text{ arc cot } \frac{2x+1}{\sqrt{3}}$$

Then the above value of l may be written

$$l = \frac{Dx}{i} - D\left(\frac{1}{i} - \frac{c^2}{g}\right)\phi\left(\frac{d}{D}\right) + C$$

Now let d_2 be the depth at the dam and let l be measured up-stream from that point to a section where the depth is d_1. Then, taking the integral between these limits the constant C disappears, and

$$l = \frac{d_2 - d_1}{i} + D\left(\frac{1}{i} - \frac{c^2}{g}\right)\left[\phi\left(\frac{d_1}{D}\right) - \phi\left(\frac{d_2}{D}\right)\right] \qquad (140)_2$$

which is the practical formula for use. In like manner d_2 may represent a depth at any given section and d_1 any depth at the distance l up the stream.

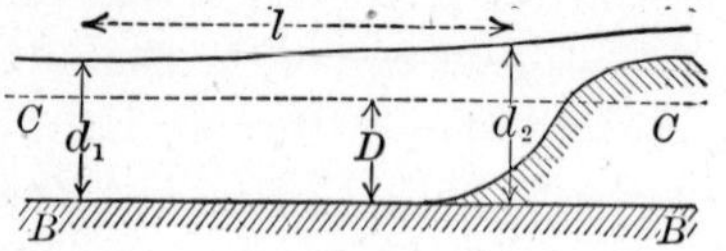

Fig. 140a.

When $d = D$, the depth of the backwater becomes equal to that of the previous uniform flow, x is unity, and hence l is infinity. The slope CC of uniform flow is therefore an asymptote to the backwater curve. Accordingly the depth d_1 is always greater than D, although practically the difference may be very small for a long distance l.

In the investigation of backwater problems by the above formula there are two cases: first, d_2 and d_1 may be given and l is to be found; and second, l and one of the depths are given and the other depth is to be found. To solve these problems the values of the backwater function $\phi(d/D)$ computed by Bresse are given in Table 140.* The argument of the table is D/d, which, being always less than unity, is more convenient for tabular purposes than d/D, since the values of the latter range from 1 to ∞. By the help of Table 140 practical problems may be discussed and the following examples will illustrate the method of procedure.

* Bresse's Mécanique appliqués (Paris, 1868), vol. 2, p. 556.

TABLE 140. VALUES OF THE BACKWATER FUNCTION

$\frac{D}{d}$	$\phi\left(\frac{d}{D}\right)$	$\frac{D}{d}$	$\phi\left(\frac{d}{D}\right)$	$\frac{D}{d}$	$\phi\left(\frac{d}{D}\right)$	$\frac{D}{d}$	$\phi\left(\frac{d}{D}\right)$
1.	∞	0.954	0.9073	0.845	0.5037	0.61	0.2058
0.999	2.1834	.952	.8931	.840	.4932	.60	.1980
.998	1.9523	.950	.8795	.835	.4831	.59	.1905
.997	1.8172	.948	.8665	.830	.4733	.58	.1832
.996	1.7213	.946	.8539	.825	.4637	.57	.1761
.995	1.6469	.944	.8418	.820	.4544	.56	.1692
.994	1.5861	.942	.8301	.815	.4454	.55	.1625
.993	1.5348	.940	.8188	.810	.4367	.54	.1560
.992	1.4902	.938	.8079	.805	.4281	.53	.1497
.991	1.4510	.936	.7973	.800	.4198	.52	.1435
.990	1.4159	.934	.7871	.795	.4117	.51	.1376
.989	1.3841	.932	.7772	.790	.4039	.50	.1318
.988	1.3551	.930	.7675	.785	.3962	.49	.1262
.987	1.3284	.928	.7581	.780	.3886	.48	.1207
.986	1.3037	.926	.7490	.775	.3813	.47	.1154
.985	1.2807	.924	.7401	.770	.3741	.46	.1102
.984	1.2592	.922	.7315	.765	.3671	.45	.1052
.983	1.2390	.920	.7231	.760	.3603	.44	.1003
.982	1.2199	.918	.7149	.755	.3536	.43	.0955
.981	1.2019	.916	.7069	.750	.3470	.42	.0909
.980	1.1848	.914	.6990	.745	.3406	.41	.0865
.979	1.1686	.912	.6914	.740	.3343	.40	.0821
.978	1.1531	.910	.6839	.735	.3282	.39	.0779
.977	1.1383	.908	.6766	.730	.3221	.38	.0738
.976	1.1241	.906	.6695	.725	.3162	.37	.0699
.975	1.1105	.904	.6625	.720	.3104	.36	.0660
.974	1.0974	.902	.6556	.715	.3047	.35	.0623
.973	1.0848	.900	.6489	.710	.2991	.34	.0587
.972	1.0727	.895	.6327	.705	.2937	.33	.0553
.971	1.0610	.890	.6173	.70	.2883	.32	.0519
.970	1.0497	.885	.6025	.69	.2778	.30	.0455
.968	1.0282	.880	.5884	.68	.2677	.28	.0395
.966	1.0080	.875	.5749	.67	.2580	.25	.0314
.964	0.9890	.870	.5619	.66	.2486	.20	.0201
.962	.9709	.865	.5494	.65	.2395	.15	.0113
.960	.9539	.860	.5374	.64	.2306	.10	.0050
.958	.9376	.855	.5258	.63	.2221	.05	.0015
.956	.9221	.850	.5146	.62	.2138	.00	.0000

A stream of 5 feet depth is to be dammed so that the water shall be 10 feet deep a short distance up-stream from the dam. The uniform slope of its bed and surface is 0.000189, or a little less than one foot per mile, and its channel is such that the coefficient c is 65. It is required to find at what distance up-stream the depth of water is 6 feet. Here $D = 5$, $d_2 = 10$, $d_1 = 6$ feet, $1/i = 5291$, and $c^2/g = 131$. Now $D/d_2 = 0.5$, for which the table gives $\phi(d_2/D) = 0.1318$, and $D/d_1 = 0.833$, for which the table gives $\phi(d_1/D) = 0.4792$. These values inserted in $(140)_2$ give

$$l = 5291(10 - 6) + 5(5291 - 131)(0.4792 - 0.1318)$$

from which $l = 30\,125$ feet $= 5.70$ miles. In this case the water is raised one foot at a distance 5.7 miles up-stream from the dam.

The inverse problem, to compute d_2 or d_1, when one of these and l are given, can only be solved by repeated trials by the help of Table 140. For example, let $l = 30\,125$ feet, the other data as above, and let it be required to determine d_2 so that d_1 shall be only 5.2 feet, or 0.2 greater than the original depth of 5 feet. Here $D/d_1 = 0.962$, for which the table gives $\phi(d_1/D) = 0.9709$. Then $(140)_2$ becomes

$$30\,125 = 5291(d_2 - 5.2) + 25\,800[0.9709 - \phi(d_2/D)]$$

which is easily reduced to the simpler form

$$32\,590 = 5291\,d_2 - 25\,800\,\phi(d_2/D)$$

Values of d_2 are now to be assumed until one is found that satisfies this equation. Let $d_2 = 8$ feet, then $(D/d_2) = 0.625$ and, from the table, $\phi(d_2/D) = 0.2180$; substituting these, the second member becomes 36 700, which shows that the assumed value is too large. Again, take $d_2 = 7$ feet, then $D/d_2 = 0.714$, for which $\phi(d_2/D) = 0.3047$, whence the second member is 29 200, showing that 7 feet is too small. If $d_2 = 7.4$ feet, then $D/d_2 = 0.675$ and $\phi(d_2/D) = 0.2629$, and with these values the equation is nearly satisfied, but 7.4 is still too small. On trying 7.5 it is found to be too large. The value of d_2 hence lies between 7.4 and 7.5 feet, which is as close a solution as will generally be required. The height of dam required to maintain this depth may now be computed from Art. 136.

If the slope, width, or depth of the stream changes materially, the above method, in which the distance l is measured from the dam as an origin, cannot be used. In such cases the stream should be divided into reaches, for each of which the slope, width, and depth can be regarded as constant. The formula can then be used for the first reach and the depth of its upper section be determined; then the application can be made to the next reach, and so on in order. For common rivers and for shallow canals it will probably be a good plan to determine D by actual measurement of the area and wetted perimeter of the cross-section, the hydraulic radius computed from these being taken as the value of D. Strictly speaking, the coefficient c varies with the slope and with D, and its values may be found by Kutter's formula, if it be thought worth the while. Even if this be done, the results of the computations must be regarded as liable to considerable uncertainty. In computing depths for given lengths an uncertainty of 10 percent or more in the value of $d_2 - d_1$ should be expected.

The following method of computation is readily applicable to cases of backwater and gives results which are often sufficiently satisfactory. The distance l between two sections does not appear in the formulas, but it is essential that this distance shall be small enough so that the water surface between them may be regarded as a straight line. In some streams the distance apart of sections may be as high as 1000 feet, in others smaller. Let Fig. 140b represent the case of a stream where an obstruction, which is some distance down-stream from the station M, causes a rise of the original surface. At the several stations

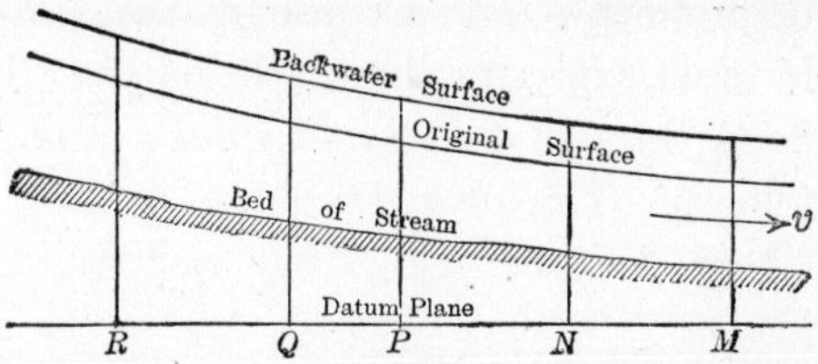

Fig. 140b

M, N, P, Q, R, etc., elevations of the original surface above a datum plane are taken. A cross-section of the stream is also made at each station, the levels being extended upward on the banks so that for any water level the area a and the wetted perimeter p may be ascertained from a drawing. At the first station M the elevation of the backwater is known, it being either assumed or computed from Art. 136. The problem then is to determine the elevation of the backwater at each of the stations up-stream from M.

Fig. 140*c* shows on a larger scale the profile between M and N and also the two cross-sections at M which are drawn from the given data. In this diagram the elevations of M_1, M_2, and N_1 are known, and it is required to find that of N_2. Let a_1 and a_2

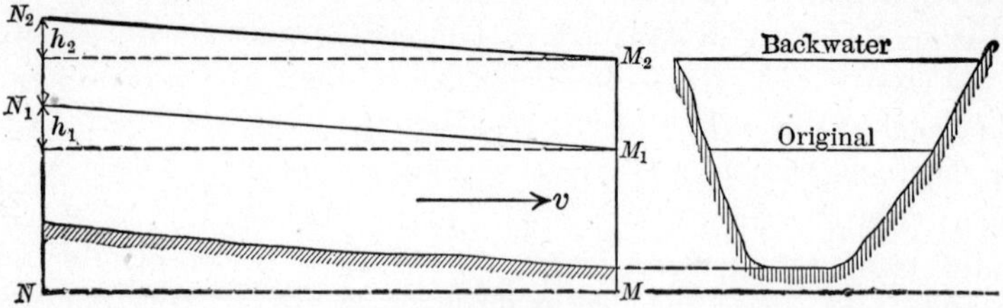

Fig. 140*c*.

denote the areas of the cross-section at M, the first for the original flow and the second for the backwater, and let p_1 and p_2 be the corresponding wetted perimeters. Let h_1 be the known difference of the elevations of M_1 and N_1, and h_2 the unknown difference of the elevations of M_2 and N_2. Then the formula

$$h_2 = h_1 \frac{a_1^3 p_2}{a_2^3 p_1} \qquad (140)_3$$

determines h_2, and accordingly the elevation of N_2 is known. This formula expresses the condition that the same quantity of water flows through the cross-sections a_1 and a_2, and it is deduced as follows. The mean discharges in these two sections are, from the Chezy formula, $c_1 a_1 \sqrt{r_1 s_1}$ and $c_2 a_2 \sqrt{r_2 s_2}$. Equating these, replacing r_1 and r_2 by a_1/p_1 and a_2/p_2, squaring, and making the coefficients c_1 and c_2 equal, gives the equation $s_1 a_1^3/p_1 = s_2 a_2^3/p_2$. Now $s_1 = h_1 l$ and $s_2 = h_2 l$ where l is the distance between the two sections. Hence $h_1 a_1^3/p_1 = h_2 a_2^3/p_2$, from which the above formula $(140)_3$ at once results.

As an example, take the case of four stations on Coal River, W.Va., data for the original water surface being as follows:

Station	=	M	N	P	Q	R
Elevation	=	10.05	11.53	11.95	13.44	14.39 ft.
Rise	h_1 =		1.48	0.42	1.49	0.95 ft.
Area	a_1 =	3034	3012	3210	2749	2340 sq. ft.
Perimeter	p_1 =	255	260	280	204	192 ft.

and let it be required to find the elevations of the backwater surface when an obstruction down-stream from M raises the water to elevation 12.05 at M_2. Drawing the water level in the cross-section at M, there are found $a_2 = 3533$ square feet and $p_2 = 260$ feet. Then

$$h_2 = 1.48 \frac{3034^3 \times 260}{3533^3 \times 255} = 0.95 \text{ feet},$$

and hence the elevation at N_2 is $12.05 + 0.95 = 13.00$ feet. For this water-level the cross-section for station N gives 3390 square feet area and 264 feet wetted perimeter for the backwater condition. Then the backwater rise at station P is

$$h_2 = 0.42 \frac{3012^3 \times 280}{3390^3 \times 264} = 0.30 \text{ feet},$$

which gives 13.30 feet for the elevation of the backwater surface at P. The results for the five stations are arranged as follows, the last line showing the required elevations of the backwater surface:

Station		= M	N	P	Q	R
Area	a_2 =	3533	3390	3580	2940	2492 sq. ft.
Perimeter	p_2 =	260	264	286	209	197 ft.
Rise	h_2 =		0.95	0.30	1.10	0.80 ft.
Elevation		= 12.05	13.00	13.30	14.40	15.20 ft.

While there are several assumptions and limitations in this method, it does not appear that they introduce more error than that which obtains when the formula $(140)_2$ is applied to a stream of irregular section. By the exercise of much judgment in selecting the stations, and by taking the data for a cross-section as the mean of several on both sides of a station, it is believed that the method can be used with much confidence in all cases where extreme conditions do not obtain. If the Chezy coefficients at a station can be found, then the formula $(140)_3$ may be written in the more exact form

$$h_2 = h_1 \, c_1^2 a_1^3 p_2 / c_2^2 a_2^3 p_1 \qquad (140)_4$$

Prob. 140. A stream, having a cross-section of 2400 square feet and a wetted perimeter of 300 feet, has a uniform slope of 2.07 feet per mile, and its channel is such that c = 70. It is proposed to build a dam to raise the water 6 feet above the former level, without increasing the width. Compute the rise of the backwater at a distance of one mile up-stream.

Art 141. The Drop-down Surface Curve

When a sudden fall occurs in a stream, the water surface for a long distance above it is concave to the bed, as seen in Fig. 138*b* or in Fig. 141. This case also occurs when the entire discharge of a canal is allowed to flow out through a fore-bay *F* to supply a water-power plant. Let *D* be the original uniform depth of water having its surface parallel to the bed, the slope of both being *i*. Let d_1 and d_2 be two of the depths after the steady non-uniform flow has been established by letting water out at *F*, and let d_1 be greater than d_2, the distance between them being *l*. The investigation of the last article applies in all respects to this form of surface curve, and

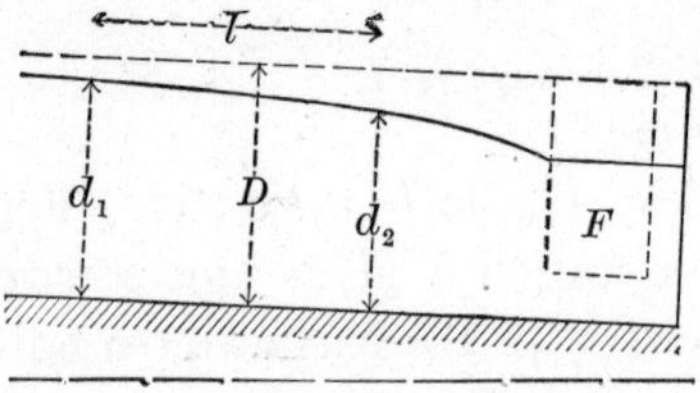

Fig. 141.

$$l = -\frac{d_1 - d_2}{i} + D\left(\frac{1}{i} - \frac{c^2}{g}\right)\left[\phi\left(\frac{d_1}{D}\right) - \phi\left(\frac{d_2}{D}\right)\right] \qquad (141)$$

is the equation for practical use, in which c is the coefficient in the Chezy formula $v = c\sqrt{rs}$, and *g* is the acceleration of gravity. Table 140 cannot, however, be used for this case because d/D in that table is greater than unity, while here it is less than unity.

The function $\phi(d/D)$ with values of d/D less than unity is here called the "drop-down function," in order to distinguish it from the backwater function of the last article, although the algebraic expression for the two functions is the same. Table 141, due also to Bresse, gives values of this drop-down function for values of the argument d/D, ranging from 0 to 1, and by its use approximate solutions of practical problems can be made. For example, take a canal 10 feet deep, having a coefficient c equal to 80, and let the slope of its bed be 1/5000 and its surface slope be the same when the water is in uniform flow. Here $D = 10$ feet, $c^2/g = 200$, and $1/i = 5000$. Then

$$l = -5000(d_1 - d_2) + 48\,000\left[\phi\left(\frac{d_1}{D}\right) - \phi\left(\frac{d_2}{D}\right)\right]$$

Now suppose that a break occurs in the bank of the canal out of which rushes more water than that delivered in normal flow when the depth is 10 feet, and let it be required to find the distance between two points where the depths of water are 8 and 7 feet. Here $d_1/D = 0.8$, for which

TABLE 141. VALUES OF THE DROP-DOWN FUNCTION

$\frac{d}{D}$	$\phi\left(\frac{d}{D}\right)$	$\frac{d}{D}$	$\phi\left(\frac{d}{D}\right)$	$\frac{d}{D}$	$\phi\left(\frac{d}{D}\right)$	$\frac{d}{D}$	$\phi\left(\frac{d}{D}\right)$
1.	∞	0.954	0.8916	0.845	0.4478	0.61	0.0454
0.999	2.1831	.952	.8767	.840	.4353	.60	.0325
.998	1.9517	.950	.8624	.835	.4232	.59	.0199
.997	1.8162	.948	.8487	.830	.4114	.58	+0.0074
.996	1.7206	.946	.8354	.825	.3988	.57	−0.0050
.995	1.6452	.944	.8226	.820	.3886	.56	− .0172
.994	1.5841	.942	.8102	.815	.3776	.55	− .0293
.993	1.5324	.940	.7982	.810	.3668	.54	− .0412
.992	1.4876	.938	.7866	.805	.3562	.53	− .0530
.991	1.4486	.936	.7753	.800	.3459	.52	− .0647
.990	1.4125	.934	.7643	.795	.3357	.51	− .0763
.989	1.3804	.932	.7537	.790	.3258	.50	− .0878
.988	1.3511	.930	.7433	.785	.3160	.49	− .0991
.987	1.3241	.928	.7332	.780	.3064	.48	− .1104
.986	1.2990	.926	.7234	.775	.2970	.47	− .1216
.985	1.2757	.924	.7138	.770	.2877	.46	− .1327
.984	1.2538	.922	.7045	.765	.2785	.45	− .1438
.983	1.2323	.920	.6953	.760	.2696	.44	− .1547
.982	1.2139	.918	.6864	.755	.2607	.43	− .1656
.981	1.1955	.916	.6776	.750	.2520	.42	− .1765
.980	1.1781	.914	.6691	.745	.2434	.41	− .1872
.979	1.1615	.912	.6607	.740	.2350	.40	− .1980
.978	1.1457	.910	.6525	.735	.2260	.39	− .2086
.977	1.1305	.908	.6445	.730	.2184	.38	− .2192
.976	1.1160	.906	.6366	.725	.2102	.37	− .2298
.975	1.1020	.904	.6289	.720	.2022	.36	− .2403
.974	1.0886	.902	.6213	.715	.1943	.35	− .2508
.973	1.0757	.900	.6138	.710	.1864	.34	− .2612
.972	1.0632	.895	.5958	.705	.1787	.33	− .2716
.971	1.0512	.890	.5785	.70	.1711	.32	− .2819
.970	1.0396	.885	.5619	.69	.1560	.30	− .3025
.968	1.0174	.880	.5459	.68	.1413	.28	− .3230
.966	0.9965	.875	.5305	.67	.1268	.25	− .3536
.964	.9767	.870	.5156	.66	.1127	.20	− .4042
.962	.9580	.865	.5012	.65	.0987	.15	− .4544
.960	.9402	.860	.4872	.64	.0851	.10	− .5046
.958	.9233	.855	.4737	.63	.0716	.05	− .5546
.956	.9071	.850	.4605	.62	.0584	.00	− .6046

$\phi(d_1/D) = 0.3459$, and $d_2/D = 0.7$, for which $\phi(d_2/D) = 0.1711$. Inserting these values in the equation, there is found $l = 7890$ feet.

In this case there is a certain limiting depth below which the above formula is not valid. This limit is the value of x for which $\delta l/\delta x$ becomes zero or the value of x where the surface curve is vertical and the bore occurs (Art. 139). From $(140)_1$ this happens when

$$x^3 = c^2 i/g \quad \text{or} \quad d = D(c^2 i/g)^{\frac{1}{3}}$$

and for the above example this limiting depth is found to be 3.4 feet. Near this limit, however, the velocity becomes large, so that there is much uncertainty regarding the value of the coefficient c.

When a given discharge per second is taken out of a forebay at the end of a canal having its bed on a slope i, the above formula must be modified. Let q be the discharge and let D_1 be the depth at a section where the slope is s, then q equals $cbD_1\sqrt{D_1 s}$. If this value of q be substituted in the equation $(138)_1$ and then the same reasoning be followed as at the beginning of Art. 140, it will be found that formula (141) will apply to this case if $D_1(s/i)^{\frac{1}{3}}$ be used instead of D. For example, let $q = 3000$ cubic feet per second, $D_1 = 10$ feet, $i = 1/10\,000$, $c = 80$, and the width $b = 100$ feet. Then

$$s = q^2/c^2b^2D_1^3 = 1/7100 \qquad D = D_1(s/i)^{\frac{1}{3}} = 11.2 \text{ feet.}$$

Now if it be required to find the distance between two points where the depths of water are 10 and 9 feet, formula (141) can be directly applied, and accordingly there is found, by the help of Table 141,

$$l = -10\,000(10-9) + 109\,800(0.578-0.355) = 14\,400 \text{ feet,}$$

and hence a forebay admitting the given discharge will not draw down the water to a depth less than 9 feet if it be located 14 400 feet downstream from the section where the mean depth is 10 feet.

Navigation canals are often built with the bed horizontal between locks, and here $i=0$. The above formula cannot be applied to this case because the differential equation $(138)_2$ vanishes when i is zero. To discuss it, equation $(138)_1$ must be resumed, and, inverting the same,

$$\frac{\delta l}{\delta d} = -\frac{c^2b^2d^3}{q^2} + \frac{c^2}{g}$$

The integration of this between the limits d_1 and d_2 gives

$$l = \frac{c^2b^2}{4q^2}(d_1^4 - d_2^4) - \frac{c^2}{g}(d_1 - d_2) \qquad (141)_2$$

from which l may be computed when q is known. As an example, take a rectangular trough for which $q = 20$ cubic feet per second, $b = 5$ feet, $c = 89$, and let $d_1 = 2.00$ feet and $d_2 = 1.91$ feet. Then from the formula l is found to be 317 feet. This is the reverse of the example at the end of Art. 137, where l was given as 333 feet, so that the agreement is very good.

To compare a canal having a level bed with the one previously considered, the same data will be used, namely, $d_1 = 10$ feet, $d_2 = 9$ feet, $b = 100$ feet, $c = 80$, and $q = 3000$ cubic feet per second. Then from $(141)_2$ there is found

$$l = 1.778(10^4 - 9^4) - 200(10 - 9) = 5920 \text{ feet},$$

and accordingly the water level is drawn down in one-third of the distance of that of the previous case. The quantity of water that can be obtained from a navigation canal is always less than from one having a sloping bed, and it has frequently happened, when such a canal is abandoned for navigation purposes and is used to furnish water for power or for a public supply, that the quantity delivered is very much smaller than was expected.

The method of computation explained at the end of Art. 140 may be used also to determine the drop-down curve. Referring to Fig. 140*b* the upper curve will be the original one and the lower one that which is obtained by computation. The formula $(140)_3$ is to be used by taking h_1, a_1, p_1 for the upper curve and h_2, a_2, p_2 for the lower one. For example, let the data for a station on the upper original curve be $a_1 = 600$ square feet and $p_1 = 80$ feet, $a_2 = 480$ square feet and $p_2 = 66$ feet. Let the elevations of two points on the upper curve be 18.26 and 16.68 feet so that $h_1 = 1.58$ feet, then the fall in the lower curve is

$$h_2 = 1.58\,\frac{600^3 \times 66}{480^3 \times 80} = 2.57 \text{ feet},$$

and hence when the elevation of the first station on the lower curve is 16.26 feet, the probable elevation of the second station on that curve is 13.69 feet. The fall 2.57 feet is here probably liable to a considerable error, since the application of $(141)_1$ to these data gives a much smaller result for h_2. Experiments are greatly needed in order to test the comparative value of these two methods of computation, and these, on a small scale, might well be undertaken in the hydraulic laboratory of an engineering college.

Prob. 141*a*. A canal from a river to a power house is two miles long, its bed is on a slope of 1/10 000, and c is 70. When the water is in uniform flow, the depth D is 6.0 feet, and the discharge is 800 cubic feet per second. If there be a power house which takes 1000 cubic feet per second, find the probable depth of water at the entrance to its forebay.

Prob. 141*b*. Show that the last formula in Art. 135, when reduced to the metric system, becomes $v = v' + 6.1\sqrt{rs}$.

Prob. 141*c*. A stream 181 meters wide and 5 meters deep has a discharge of 1318 cubic meters per second. Find the height of backwater when the stream is contracted by piers and abutments to a width of 96 meters.

Prob. 141*d*. Which has the greater discharge, a stream 1.2 meters deep and 20 meters wide on a slope of 3 meters per kilometer, or a stream 1.6 meters deep and 26 meters wide on a slope of 2 meters per kilometer?

Prob. 141*e*. A stream 2 meters deep is to be dammed so that water shall be 4 meters deep at the dam. Its slope is 0.0002 and its channel is such that the metric value of c is 39. Compute the distance to a section up-stream where the depth of water is 3.6 meters.

CHAPTER 11

WATER SUPPLY AND WATER POWER

Art. 142. Rainfall

All the water that flows in a stream has at some previous time been precipitated in the form of rain or snow. The word "rainfall" means the total rain and melted snow, and it is usually measured in vertical inches of water. The annual rainfall is least in the frigid zone and greatest in the torrid zone; at the equator it is about 100 inches, at latitude 40° about 40 inches, and at latitude 60° about 20 inches. There are, however, certain places where the annual rainfall is as high as 500 inches, and others where no rain ever falls. In the United States the heaviest annual rainfall is near the Gulf of Mexico, where 60 inches is sometimes registered, and near Puget Sound, where 90 inches is not uncommon. In that large region, formerly called the Great American Desert, which lies between the Rocky and Sierra Nevada mountains, the mean annual rainfall does not exceed 15 inches, and in Nevada it is only about $7\frac{1}{2}$ inches. The amount of rainfall in any locality depends upon the winds and upon the neighboring mountains and oceans.

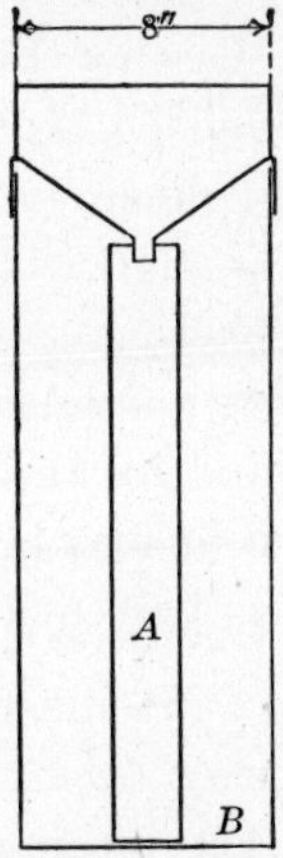

Fig. 142*a*.

The standard type of rain gage used by the U. S. Weather Bureau has a diameter of 8 inches. The rain falling into the gage passes down through the funnel shown in Fig. 142*a* and into the small cylinder *A*, the area of which is one-tenth that of the gage. One inch of rainfall therefore will give a depth of 10 inches in the cylinder *A* and small falls can thus be accurately measured. As the cylinder *A* fills it overflows into the body of the gage *B*, and when measured is simply poured into the cylinder *A* after the water it contains has been measured and poured out. These gages should be read each day in order that the loss due to evaporation may not become excessive and introduce material errors. Other forms of rain gages which record on a chart each one-hundredth of an inch of rainfall at the time when it falls are made. Such gages are of particular use in determining the rate of rainfall and the time of the fall rather than its total quantity.

At any place the rainfall in a given year may vary considerably from the mean derived from the observations of several years. Thus, at Philadelphia, Pa., the mean annual rainfall is about 42 inches, but in 1890 it was 50.8 inches and in 1885 it was only 33.4 inches. Similarly at Denver, Col., the mean is about 14 inches, but the extremes are about 20 and 9 inches. When a very low rainfall occurs, that of the year preceding or following is also apt to be low, and estimates for the water supply of towns must take into account this minimum annual rainfall. The distribution of rainfall throughout the year must also be considered, and for this purpose the rainfall records of the given locality should be obtained from the publications of the U. S. Weather Bureau as well as from all other available sources and be carefully discussed. In making plans for a water supply it should be the aim to store a sufficient quantity so that an ample amount will be available at the end of the driest period which is likely to occur. In Table 142 are shown the average rainfalls at a number of places in the United States for the four seasons and for the year; in estimates for very wet years about 25 percent may be added to these values, while for very dry years about 25 percent may be subtracted.

As illustrating the variations from the mean rainfall which may be expected at any place the following example is given. The mean rainfall at Philadelphia is about 42 inches, and the following are some of the values for various years: 29.6 inches for 1825, 30.2 inches for 1881, 61.3 inches for 1867, and 55.5 inches for 1840.

TABLE 142. RAINFALL IN THE UNITED STATES *

City	Length of Record. Years	Rainfall in Inches				
		Spring	Summer	Autumn	Winter	Annual
Vicksburg	32	15.9	12.0	10.3	15.6	53.8
Charleston	33	10.6	20.1	12.5	10.2	53.4
Little Rock	24	14.5	11.2	10.5	13.4	49.6
Portland	32	10.7	3.0	11.9	20.0	45.6
New York	33	10.6	12.3	10.8	11.1	44.8
Boston	31	11.2	10.5	11.1	10.9	43.7
Cairo	22	11.4	10.4	9.1	10.7	41.6
Cincinnati	33	9.9	10.9	7.9	9.7	38.4
Key West	33	5.5	12.6	14.5	5.3	37.9
Cleveland	33	8.5	10.2	9.0	7.9	35.6
Chicago	33	8.7	10.1	8.2	6.4	33.4
Detroit	33	7.9	10.1	7.6	6.6	32.2
Omaha	33	8.8	13.3	6.4	2.3	30.8
St. Paul	31	7.4	11.4	7.0	2.8	28.6
San Antonio	18	7.7	8.4	7.0	5.3	28.4
San Francisco	32	5.7	0.2	4.4	12.2	22.5
Bismarck	29	5.8	8.3	2.7	2.0	18.8
Spokane	23	4.1	2.7	4.7	6.8	18.3
Salt Lake City	30	5.9	2.0	3.8	4.1	15.8
Los Angeles	28	1.7	0.0	5.6	8.1	15.4
Santa Fé	30	2.7	6.2	3.3	2.0	14.2
Denver	31	5.4	4.4	2.2	1.7	13.7
Helena	24	4.0	3.9	2.8	2.6	13.3
Yuma	28	0.4	0.4	0.6	1.3	2.7

The annual rainfall at any locality seems to vary in cycles, but no law of such variation, if any there be, has yet been discovered. The manner of variation at Philadelphia and New York is shown in Fig. 142*b*, the curves being obtained by plotting for each year a value for the rainfall which is one-third of the sum of the rainfalls for that year, the preceding year, and the following year. The curves are not drawn to exactly follow the plotted points, but are smoothed out in order to better illustrate the probable variations.

* From Records of U. S. Weather Bureau to 1910.

The distribution of rainfall from place to place is also subject to many variations, some local and others general in their nature. Among them may be mentioned both the topography and the

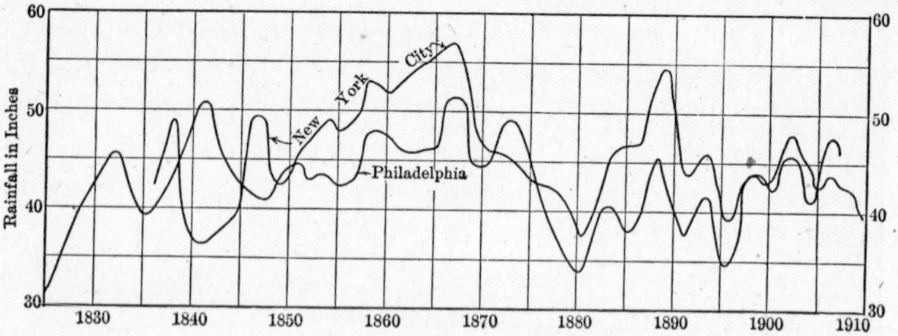

Fig. 142*b*.

altitude of the country and their relation to the prevailing wind direction. The presence of large bodies of water in the neighborhood also has its influence.

As examples of such variations in rainfall there may be mentioned the Esopus and Catskill watersheds in New York.* Their areas are nearly the same, they both drain into the Hudson River from the west, and their centers are not more than 25 miles apart, yet the rainfall on the former is about 20 percent greater than on the latter. As one other example there may be mentioned the rainfall at "Number 4" in northern New York in the Western Adirondacks and Avon on the Genessee River 23 miles south of Lake Ontario. These two stations are but 145 miles apart, yet the average yearly rainfall at the former is 50.4 inches, while at the latter it is only 27.0 inches. In determining the rainfall at any point or for any given area all available records must be examined and all other collateral evidence carefully analyzed, particularly in cases where estimates of the stream flow are to be based on estimates of the rainfall.

Prob. 142. Consult the "Instructions for Voluntary Observers," published by the United States Weather Bureau, and describe a method of determining the amount of rainfall contained in a given depth of snowfall. In making reports how much rainfall on the average is to be taken as representing a snowfall of 12 inches?

* Monthly Weather Review, March, 1907.

Art. 143. Evaporation

After rain has fallen evaporation from both land and water surfaces at once begins and continues until all of the rainfall has passed off into the atmosphere, where it is condensed into clouds and again falls as rain, thus completing the cycle. Like rainfall the evaporation is to be measured in inches of depth. Various experiments on the evaporation from water surfaces have been made, and a number of the results which have been derived are shown in Table 143*a*.

Table 143*a*. Monthly and Yearly Evaporation from Water Surfaces

Place	Evaporation in Inches												
	Jan.	Feb.	Mar.	April	May	June	July	Aug.	Sept.	Oct.	Nov.	Dec.	Year
Boston, Mass.*	0.96	1.05	1.70	2.97	4.46	5.54	5.98	5.50	4.12	3.16	2.25	1.51	39.20
Rochester, N.Y.†	0.52	0.54	1.33	2.62	3.93	4.94	5.47	5.30	4.15	3.16	1.45	1.13	34.54
Emdrup, Denmark ‡	0.70	0.50	0.90	2.00	3.70	5.40	5.20	4.40	2.60	1.30	0.70	0.50	27.90
Lee Bridge, England §	0.75	0.60	1.07	2.10	2.75	3.14	3.44	2.85	1.61	1.06	0.67	0.57	20.61
GraniteReef, Arizona ¶	4.25	4.40	5.25	7.00	9.50	12.00	12.75	12.50	11.00	8.31	6.56	4.22	97.74
Birmingham, Ala.¶	1.50	1.50	2.25	4.45	5.91	7.28	7.36	7.34	6.00	4.00	2.25	1.50	51.34
Klamath, Oregon ¶	0.50	1.25	3.57	6.64	7.15	6.99	8.01	9.21	6.13	2.50	1.00	0.50	53.45

Evaporation from land surfaces is dependent on the character of the soil, on the extent and character of the forestation and cultivation, and in a considerable measure on the general steepness of the surface, for on this is dependent the time in which evaporation can act. In a steep country the rainfall rapidly runs into

* Transactions, American Society of Civil Engineers, vol. 15.
† Annual Reports, Rochester, N.Y., Board of Water Commissioners.
‡ Hydrology, Beardmore, London, 1862.
§ Proceedings, Institution Civil Engineers, vol. 45.
¶ Engineering News, June 16, 1910.

the streams, while in a flat country it passes off more slowly, and the amount of the evaporation is thus increased.

Experiments on the evaporation from earth, from short grass and long grass surfaces have been made, and some results are shown in Table 143*b*.

TABLE 143*b*. MONTHLY AND YEARLY EVAPORATION FROM LAND SURFACES

Place	Evaporation in Inches												
	Jan.	Feb.	Mar.	April	May	June	July	Aug.	Sept.	Oct.	Nov.	Dec.	Year
Lancashire, England,* from earth	0.64	0.95	1.59	2.59	4.38	3.84	4.02	3.16	2.02	1.28	0.81	0.47	25.65
Cumberland, England,† from earth	0.95	1.01	1.77	2.71	4.11	4.25	4.13	3.29	2.96	1.76	1.25	1.02	29.21
Emdrup, Denmark,* from short grass	0.70	0.80	1.20	2.60	4.10	5.50	5.20	4.70	2.80	1.30	0.70	0.50	30.10
Emdrup, Denmark,* from long grass	0.90	0.60	1.40	2.60	4.70	6.70	9.30	7.90	5.20	2.90	1.30	0.50	44.00
Rothamsted, England,‡ from earth	0.45	0.60	0.88	1.53	1.69	1.92	2.26	1.95	2.11	1.70	0.98	0.61	16.68

The evaporation from any particular watershed is dependent on the temperature, the humidity, the altitude, the area of the watershed, and the area of the water surface on it. The evaporation is dependent also on the wind velocity, the inclination or slope of the watershed, its geological character, its forest cover, and its state as regards cultivated areas. The total amount of evaporation is also dependent on the rainfall, and varies with it. The distribution of the rainfall throughout the year greatly influences the evaporation; a heavy winter and a light summer rainfall will together show a small annual evaporation.

* Hydrology, Beardmore, London.

† Fanning, Treatise on Water Supply Engineering, New York, 1878.

‡ Proceedings Institution Civil Engineers, vol. 105.

In the Atlantic States it may be said that the annual evaporation from land surfaces is about 45 percent and that from water surfaces about 60 percent of the annual rainfall, so that about one-half of the rainfall reaches the streams and may be utilized. In the arid regions west of the Rocky Mountains the percentages of evaporation are much higher, as indicated in Table 143*a*.

Many attempts to deduce a formula which will take account of the various factors which influence evaporation have been made but without definite success. The problem is a very complicated one. Vermeule has deduced the formula

$$E = (15.5 + 0.16\,R)(0.05\,T - 1.48)$$

where R is the annual rainfall and E the annual evaporation in inches, and T is the mean annual temperature in Fahrenheit degrees.* If $T = 49°.6$, this becomes $E = 15.5 + 0.16\,R$, which is a mean value for New Jersey and neighboring states; if T be 47°, the evaporation is 10 percent less, and if T be 52°, it is 10 percent more, than this mean. The evaporation in different months varies greatly, the mean monthly temperature being the controlling factor. The following are average values given by Vermeule for the vicinity of New Jersey, where the mean annual temperature is 49°.6; r representing mean monthly rainfall and e mean monthly evaporations in inches:

Jan.,	$e = 0.27 + 0.10r$	July,	$e = 3.00 + 0.30r$
Feb.,	$e = 0.30 + 0.10r$	Aug.,	$e = 2.62 + 0.25r$
March,	$e = 0.48 + 0.10r$	Sept.,	$e = 1.63 + 0.20r$
April,	$e = 0.87 + 0.10r$	Oct.,	$e = 0.88 + 0.12r$
May,	$e = 1.87 + 0.20r$	Nov.,	$e = 0.66 + 0.10r$
June,	$e = 2.50 + 0.25r$	Dec.,	$e = 0.42 + 0.10r$

To obtain the monthly evaporations for places of mean annual temperature T, the values found for e are to be multiplied by $0.05T - 1.48$. Thus, if there be 8 inches of rain in July, $e = 5.40$ inches, and if the mean annual temperature be 56°, this is to be increased by 32 percent. Vermeule's formulas for evaporation were deduced from a consideration of the relation between the rainfall and the observed flows of a number of streams in the New England and Middle States. They take account of the effect of unequal distribution of the rainfall

* U. S. Geological Survey of New Jersey (Trenton, 1894), vol. 3, p. 76.

throughout the year and give results which agree well with actual gagings if care be taken to determine a proper factor for each watershed to which they are applied.*

Like rainfall the evaporation varies greatly, even in regions not widely separated. In Art. 142 the difference in the rainfall on the Esopus and Schoharie watersheds in New York State was referred to. The evaporation on the Esopus will probably average about 15 inches per year, while on the Catskill it is not far from 19 inches, a difference of over 20 percent in a distance of less than 30 miles.

Experiments on evaporation are of interest and value, but the best results as to its amount are determined by taking the difference between the amount of the rainfall and the results of measured stream flows. In this manner all of the factors are taken account of and the most accurate results obtained. Experiments made by collecting the rainfall in pans and measuring the depth of water from time to time are not highly reliable, since the size of the pan influences the results. It has been shown by the U. S. Department of Agriculture that the evaporation from a pan 2 feet in diameter is about 75 percent, that from a pan 4 feet in diameter is about 50 percent, and that from a pan 6 feet in diameter is about 30 percent greater than the evaporation from a large pond or lake.†

Prob. 143. The rainfall on a watershed of 850 square miles is 44.8 inches. Assuming a seasonal distribution as at New York (Table 142) compute the evaporation by Vermeule's formula.

Art. 144. Ground Water and Runoff

When the ground is frozen and the precipitation does not accumulate in the form of ice and snow, the runoff from a watershed is closely equal to the rainfall minus the evaporation. If three inches of rain falls per month and one-third of this evaporates, the runoff will be nearly 2 cubic feet per second for each square mile of the watershed. The discharge due to a heavy rainfall occurring in a short period or to the melting of snow may be twenty or thirty times as great. A rainfall of 10 inches occurring in two days, if three-fourths of it is delivered at once to the streams, will give a flood discharge of about 100 cubic feet per

* Monthly Weather Review, March, 1907.

† American Civil Engineers' Pocket Book, 1911, p. 1286.

second per square mile of watershed area. It is not usually necessary to consider these flood discharges in estimates for water supply and water power, except in order to take precautions against the damage they may cause.

In Table 144*a* are shown some observed flood flows of various small and large streams in the United States.

TABLE 144*a*. OBSERVED MAXIMUM FLOOD FLOWS *

Stream and Place	Watershed Area Square Miles	Cubic Feet per Second per Square Mile
Starch Factory Creek, New Hartford, N.Y.	3.4	209
Mad Brook, Sherburne, N.Y.	5.0	262
Mill Brook, Edmeston, N.Y.	9.4	241
Sawkill, near mouth, N.J.	35.0	229
Rock Creek, Washington, D.C.	77.5	126
Ramapo River, Mahwah, N.J.	118.0	105
Esopus, Olive Bridge, N.Y.	238.0	110
Great River, Westfield, Mass.	350.0	152
Raritan River, Bound Brook, N.J.	879	59
Mora River, La Cueva, N.M.	159	140
Delaware River, Lambertville, N.J.	6 500	54
Susquehanna River, Harrisburg, Pa.	24 030	19

Data such as those in Table 144*a* are of use in proportioning overflows and waste-weirs for reservoirs and in fixing on the length of overfall dams in rivers. Numerous formulas have been proposed, but data such as actual observations are to be preferred in making designs of this character. In each particular case all available information must be considered, including the traditions as to the past highest water, and then after making due allowance for all of the conditions which influence the rapidity of runoff from the watershed, a liberal factor of safety must be applied.

Runoff may be defined as the difference between the rainfall and the evaporation if in the latter be included all of the water which fails to reach the streams. The runoff of a stream can

* Taken largely from American Civil Engineers' Pocket Book, New York, 1911.

be determined by measuring the flow over a weir (Chap. 6) or by daily gage height readings in connection with a discharge curve which has been determined by gagings of the flow at various water stages (Art. 131). The runoff is usually expressed as a percentage of the rainfall, thus if F be the rainfall, E the evaporation, and R the runoff, all in inches, then $R = F - E$, and as a percentage of the rainfall the runoff is $100(F - E)/F$.

In Table 144*b* are shown some observed values of the rainfall and runoff on a number of streams in the United States.

TABLE 144*b*. OBSERVED RAINFALL AND RUNOFF *

Stream and Place	Area of Watershed Square Miles	Rainfall in Inches	Runoff	
			Percent of Rainfall	Cubic Feet per Second per Square Mile
Sudbury, Boston, Mass.	75.2	45.77	48.6	1.64
Connecticut, Hartford, Conn.	10 234.0	44.69	56.5	1.86
Croton, Old Croton Dam, N.Y.	338.0	48.38	50.8	1.81
Upper Hudson, Mechanicsville, N.Y.	4 500.0	39.70	59.0	1.72
Perkiomen, Philadelphia, Pa.	152.0	47.98	49.2	1.74
Potomac, Point of Rocks, Md.	9 650.0	36.86	38.6	1.05
Savannah, Augusta, Ga.	7 294.0	45.41	48.9	1.63
Upper Mississippi, Pokegama Falls	3 265.0	26.57	18.4	0.36

The gagings which have been made and are being continued by the U. S. Geological Survey on many streams all over this country furnish a vast fund of information concerning the runoff of streams. The results of these gagings are published in the various Water Supply and Irrigation Papers of the Survey, and are to be consulted wherever questions involving the runoff of streams are being considered.

During the spring the ground is filled with water which is slowly flowing toward the streams, and this ground water is the main source of the runoff from a watershed during the dry months. The velocity of flow of this ground water varies directly as the slope of its surface, for this velocity is so slow that no losses

* From American Civil Engineers' Pocket Book, New York, 1911.

occur in impact (Art. 90). When the slope of the surface of the ground water becomes zero, the streams are dry if there be no rainfall. The discharge of a stream in a dry season hence depends upon the depth and slope of the ground water, and this in turn depends upon the previous rainfall, the topography of the country, and the character of the soil.

While data regarding rainfall and evaporation will furnish valuable information regarding the mean annual flow of a stream, they will usually fail to indicate the mean discharge during different months. For this purpose the study of discharge curves and gage heights (Art. 134) is important, and if there be none for the stream in hand, it will be necessary to make a few gagings at different stages of water and to collect information regarding the lowest stages that have been observed in dry years.

In irrigation work quantities of water are often estimated in terms of a convenient unit called the acre-foot, which is the quantity which will cover one acre to a depth of one foot, namely, 43 560 cubic feet. The discharge of a stream is often stated in acre-feet per day. One acre-foot per day is 0.5042 cubic feet per second, or one cubic foot per second is 1.983 acre-feet per day. One acre-foot of water is 325 851 U. S. gallons, and 1 000 000 gallons is 3.0689 acre-feet. One inch of rainfall per month is, very closely, 0.9 cubic feet per second per square mile.

In irrigation estimates the "duty" of water is to be regarded. This is defined as the number of acres that can be irrigated by a supply of one cubic foot per second, and it usually ranges from 60 to 100 acres. An inverse measure of duty is the number of vertical inches of water required to irrigate any area, this usually ranging from 18 to 24 inches per year. The acre-foot is also frequently used in statements of duty of water. The methods of measuring the water by orifices and modules in terms of the miner's inch unit have been explained in Art. 55.

The hydraulics of irrigation engineering differs in no respect from that of water supply and water power. Water is collected in reservoirs or obtained by damming a river, and it is led by a main canal to the area to be irrigated, and there it is distributed through smaller lateral canals to the fields. The smaller the canal or ditch, the steeper becomes its slope, and in the final application to the crops the flow in the furrows is often normal to the contours of the surface. In a river system the brooks feed the creeks, and the creeks feed the river, the flow being from the smaller to the larger; in an artificial irrigation system, however, the flow is from the larger to the smaller channel.

Seepage into the earth from an irrigation canal constantly goes on, unless its bed be puddled with clay or lined with concrete, and this loss of water is often very heavy. For new canals it is often as high as 50 percent of the water, but for old canals it may become lower than 10 percent. In making estimates for an irrigation supply it is hence necessary to take into account this seepage loss, and also to consider that due to evaporation.

Prob. 144. If all the rainfall that does not evaporate flows into the stream, find the runoff in cubic feet per second from a watershed of 1225 square miles during a month when the rainfall is 3.6 inches, the mean annual temperature being 48°.5 Fahrenheit. Also for the temperature of 49°.5.

Art. 145. Estimates for Water Supply

The consumption of water in American cities is, on the average, about 100 gallons per person per day, the large cities using more and the small ones less than this amount. The daily consumption in July and August is from 15 to 20 percent greater than the mean, owing to the use of water for sprinkling, while during January and February it is also greater than the mean in the colder localities, owing to the large amount that is allowed to run to waste in houses in order to prevent the freezing of the pipes. On Mondays, in small towns when every household is at work on the weekly washing, the consumption may be put at 50 percent higher than the mean for the week. Accordingly if the yearly mean be 100 gallons per person per day, the Monday consumption during very hot or very cold weather may be as high as 150 gallons per person per day. When a large fire occurs, the hourly consumption for this purpose alone in a fire district of 10 000 people may be at the rate of 175 gallons per person per day. In general the maximum available hourly supply should be from three to four times as great as the mean daily consumption.

When water is to be pumped from a river directly into the pipes, without tank or reservoir storage, the capacity of the pumps should be such that during the occurrence of fires at least three times the mean daily consumption may be furnished. When a pump delivers water to a distributing reservoir, its capacity need not be so high as in the case of direct pumping, for the reservoir storage can be drawn upon in case of fire. When the reservoir is large, the pump capacity need be only sufficient to lift the annual consumption during the time when it is in operation. The subject of pumping is an extensive one, but it will be briefly treated from a hydraulic standpoint in Arts. 192–201.

Gravity supplies are those obtained by impounding the runoff of a watershed at an elevation sufficiently high so that the water will flow without pumping to the places where it is to be consumed. Pumped supplies are obtained either from a stream which lies too low to furnish the water by gravity or from the ground from water-bearing strata which may be termed natural underground reservoirs. Such areas in a sandy country may yield as high as 1 000 000 gallons per day per square mile. The borough of Brooklyn of the City of New York obtains its water from the sands of Long Island, and a good example of the methods to be followed in estimating on such a supply is to be found in a report by Burr, Hering, and Freeman.*

In estimating on the safe yield of a surface watershed a study of the existing rainfall and stream flow data should be made. In the absence of the latter, estimates of the flow may be made by considering the rainfall records and computing the evaporation after allowing for all of the causes by which it is influenced. In some cases it will be found that even few rainfall data are available, and it then becomes necessary to consider the records at the nearest points where such observations have been made, and deduce values for the rainfall in the locality being considered.† In making estimates of this character all evidence should be carefully considered in order to avoid errors.

* Report on Additional Water Supply, New York, 1903.
† Monthly Weather Review, March, 1907.

When gagings of the stream being studied are available,* the problem is a simpler one, but the period during which the gagings were taken must be examined with reference to its relation with the rainfall cycle (Art. 142). The results shown by such a series of gagings during a period of high rainfall would differ materially from those during a low cycle. This consideration is of particular importance when determining on the storage required for a water supply or for a power plant on a stream of moderate size, while on larger streams the controlling factor is often simply the quantity and duration of the minimum flow. This minimum is generally less dependent on the rainfall cycle than is the total yearly yield of the stream.

Having determined on the quantity of water to be supplied and on the flow for a series of years of the stream from which the water is to be obtained, it becomes necessary to fix on the volume of storage which will be necessary to tide over the driest period which is likely to occur. For this purpose the method proposed by Rippl † is a convenient one. It consists essentially in determining the net available stream flow for each month, after making allowances for evaporation from the reservoir surfaces which will result from the new construction and for all other possible losses. The total flow for each month is then added to the total of the months preceding and since the beginning of the period being studied. The total flow from the beginning of the period to the end of each month is thus determined and may be plotted as in Fig. 145*a*. The inclination of the curve *AM* joining the points so plotted thus represents the rate of net available stream flow, and may on occasion have a negative value as at *EI*, when the evaporation, leakage, and other losses are larger than the quantity of water available in the stream.

The amount of water to be used is now plotted as the line *AB*, it being assumed that the use is at a practically constant rate. Wherever the inclination of the curve is greater than that of the line *AB*, the net stream flow is greater than the draft, and wherever

* Transactions American Society Civil Engineers, vol. 59.

† Proceedings Institution Civil Engineers, vol. 71.

it is less the draft is in excess of the available water. To determine the amount of storage necessary to tide over such a period of deficiency, *EI*, if the line *EF* be drawn parallel to *AB* and tangent to the curve at *E*, the maximum ordinate *HI* will, on the scale

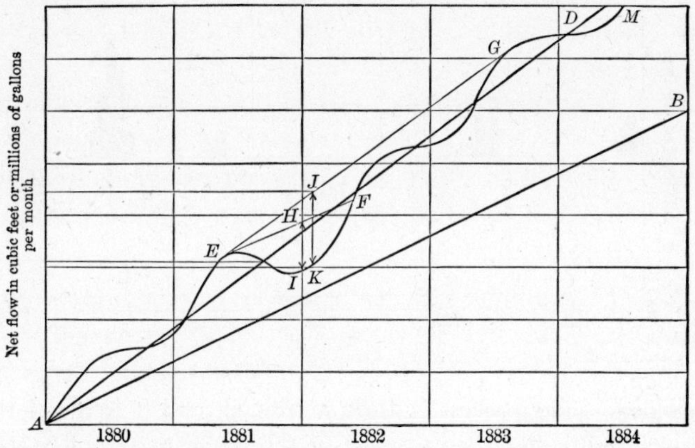

Fig. 145*a*.

of the diagram, indicate the amount of water which would have been necessary to maintain the uniform rate of draft as indicated by the line *AB*. Similarly if *AD* were the uniform rate of draft, the maximum ordinate *JK* between *EG*, drawn parallel to *AD*, and the curve would represent the storage volume necessary to maintain the draft *AD* from *A* to *G*. The maximum uniform rate of draft which could be obtained from *A* to *G* would be represented by the inclination of the line *AG*, but this rate, as also *AB* and *AD*, could not be constantly maintained unless the necessary storage was available at the beginning of the period at *A*. In case the tangent to any summit of the curve and parallel to the assumed rate of draft should fail to intersect the curve, it would be indicated that the draft was in excess of the total yield for the period under consideration.

Another graphical method is to plot the summation of the monthly differences between the net stream flow and the assumed uniform draft. In Fig. 145*b* if the reservoir be assumed to be full at the beginning of the period, then for the next three months the stream flow exceeds the draft and an overflow occurs as indicated above the zero line.

Above this line the actual amount of overflow in each month is plotted. At the end of the three months the draft begins to exceed the net stream flow and the reservoir level falls, as indicated by the continuous line. By the early part of the year 1891 the reservoir has

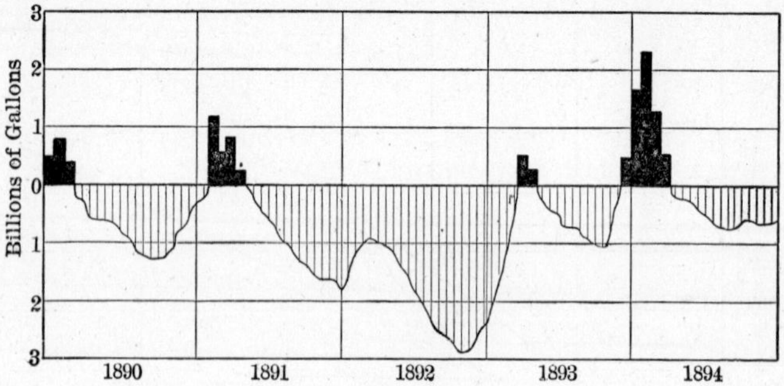

Fig. 145*b*.

again filled. The process is thus continued, and it is found that to tide over the period 1890 to 1894, if the reservoir be full at the beginning, a storage capacity of 3 billions of gallons is required.

The necessary volume of storage having thus been determined, it is usual in proportioning the reservoir to make an allowance to cover the uncertainties in the data as well as to provide a factor of safety against the occurrence of drier years than those covered by the records. Such an allowance may range from 10 to 50 percent of the storage as determined by the methods of Figs. 145*a* and 145*b*.

The quantity of storage necessary is dependent on the proposed rate of draft, but in general it may be said in the northeastern part of the United States, on rainfalls of from 38 to 50 inches, that a storage capacity of 250 000 000 gallons per square mile of watershed will permit of a safe uniform draft of from 600 000 to 900 000 gallons per square mile per day, the smaller figure being applicable to flat watersheds of low rainfall and the larger to those which are steep in slope and have higher rainfall.

After the height of the water level in the reservoir has been fixed, the dimensions of its waste weir or spillway are to be determined. This is a most important problem, for on its proper solution depends the safety and security of the dams and structures which form the reservoir. The spillway must be of sufficient size to safely discharge the largest flood which will come down the valley. Numerous formulas for maximum flood discharge have been derived, but in general they give results which are too small and which represent average flood conditions more nearly than the maximum which the spillway must carry. Records of the actual greatest floods should be procured when possible,* and higher records of discharge than those hitherto observed are liable to occur. The history of the disastrous floods of 1913 in Ohio and Indiana is still fresh in the memory. Generalities and lack of thorough investigation merely lead to failure when the day of the real test arrives.

Prob. 145. How many cubic feet per second per square mile are equivalent to a rainfall of one inch per month?

Art. 146. Estimates for Water Power

The methods of estimating the water power that can be derived by damming a stream are to some extent similar to those for water supply. In the absence of gagings the records of rainfall and evaporation are to be collected and discussed, but a few gagings will probably give more definite information if records of water stages during several years can be had. A method of determining the advisable extent of a water power development when records of stream flow are available has been developed by Herschel.†

In nearly every situation the stream flow in connection with the storage which can be obtained at a reasonable expense is not sufficient to continuously generate the power which is required. In such cases it is necessary to supplement the water power with an auxiliary steam plant located at some point within the territory to be served where fuel can be obtained most economically. In order to determine on the capacity of such an auxiliary plant the general method shown in Fig. 145*a* may be used. With the known volume of available storage and net flow of the stream the maximum uniform rate of draft can be determined. The capacity of the auxiliary steam plant may then be considered as the difference between the power capacity required and that furnished by the minimum flow of the stream; while the advisable extent of the water power development will depend upon considerations of the river discharge, the cost of

* American Civil Engineers Pocket Book, Second Edition, pp. 904–906.

† Transactions American Society of Civil Engineers, 1907, vol. 58, p. 29.

the development, and the cost of installation and operation of the auxiliary steam plant. No definite rules are to be laid down in this regard, as the exact proportion to be finally decided upon depends on many factors which vary in every locality.

The power needed to be generated by a plant varies from hour to hour. The greatest demand is called the "peak." A peak load is one of very short duration and can be met by installing an excess of turbine and generator capacity and by providing storage in a pond of adequate size. It is probable, however, that in many cases the auxiliary heat engines already installed to meet low water conditions will more economically supply the power for the peak loads than would the necessary excess turbine, generator, power house and storage capacity.

At times of high water the head on the wheels is often reduced, due to the change in slope of the river, and the normal output of the plant is thus diminished. The "fall increaser" (Art. 181) will operate to increase the available head, or where this is not provided the auxiliary steam plant must be called on to supply the deficiency.

Let W be the weight of water delivered per second to a hydraulic motor, and h be its effective head as it enters the motor, h being due either to pressure (Art. 11), or to velocity (Art. 22), or to pressure and velocity combined (Art. 24). The theoretic energy per second of this water is

$$K = Wh \qquad (146)_1$$

and if W be in pounds and h in feet, the theoretic horse-power of the water as it enters the motor is

$$\overline{HP} = Wh/550 \qquad (146)_2$$

and this is the power that can be developed by a motor of efficiency unity. The work k delivered by the motor is, however, always less than K, owing to losses in impact and friction, and the horse-power $\overline{hp}$ of the motor is less than $\overline{HP}$. The efficiency of the motor is

$$e = k/K = k/Wh \quad \text{or} \quad e = \overline{hp}/\overline{HP} \qquad (146)_3$$

and the value of this for turbine wheels is usually about 0.80; that is, the wheel transforms into useful work about 80 percent of the energy of the water that enters it.

In designing a water-power plant it should be the aim to arrange the forebays and penstocks which lead the water to the wheel so that the losses in these approaches may be as small as possible. The entrance from the head race into the forebay, from the forebay into the penstock, and from the penstock to the motor should be smooth and well rounded; sudden changes in cross-section should be avoided, and all velocities should be low except that at the motor. If these precautions be carefully observed, the loss of head outside of the motor can be made very small. Let H be the total head from the water level in the head race to that in the tail race below the motor. The total available energy per second is WH, and it should be the aim of the designer to render the losses of head in the approaches as small as possible so that the effective head h may be as nearly equal to H as possible. Neglect of these precautions may render the effective power less than that estimated.

The efficiency e_1 of the approaches is the ratio of the energy K of the water as it enters the wheel to the maximum available energy WH, or $e_1 = K/WH$. The efficiency E of the entire plant, consisting of both approaches and wheel, is the ratio of the work k delivered by the wheel to the energy WH, or

$$\text{E} = k/WH = eK/WH = ee_1$$

or, the final efficiency is the product of the separate efficiencies. If the efficiency of the wheel be 0.75 and that of the approaches 0.96, the efficiency of the plant as a whole is 0.72, or only 72 percent of the theoretic energy is utilized. Usually the efficiency of the approaches can be made higher than 96 percent.

In making estimates for a proposed plant, the efficiency of turbine wheels may generally be taken at 80 percent; the effective work is then $0.80Wh$, and accordingly if the wheels are required to deliver the work k per second, the approaches are to be so arranged that Wh shall not be less than $1.25k$. Especially when the water supply is limited it is important to make all efficiencies as high as possible.

Prob. 146. A stream delivers 500 cubic feet of water per second to a canal which terminates in a forebay where the water level is 8.1 feet above the tail race. The wheels deliver 335 horse-power and their efficiency is known to be 75 percent. How much power is lost in the forebay and penstock?

Art. 147. Water delivered to a Motor

To determine the efficiency of a hydraulic motor by formula $(146)_3$ the effective work k is to be measured by the methods of Art. 149, and the head h to be ascertained by Art. 148. In order to find the weight W that passes through the wheel in one second, there must be known the discharge per second q and the weight w of a cubic unit of water; then

$$W = wq$$

Here w may be found by weighing one cubic foot of the water, or when the water contains few impurities its temperature may be noted and the weight be taken from Table 3. In approximate computations w may be taken at 62.5 pounds per cubic foot. In precise tests of motors, however, its actual value should be ascertained as closely as possible.

The measurement of the flow of water through orifices, weirs, tubes, pipes, and channels has been so fully discussed in the preceding chapters, that it only remains here to mention one or two simple methods applicable to small quantities, and to make a few remarks regarding the subject of leakage. In any particular case that method of determining q is to be selected which will furnish the required degree of precision with the least expense.

For a small discharge the water may be allowed to fall into a tank of known capacity. The tank should be of uniform horizontal cross-section, whose area can be accurately determined, and then the heights alone need be observed in order to find the volume. These in precise work will be read by hook gages, and in cases of less accuracy by measurements with a graduated rod. At the beginning of the experiment a sufficient quantity of water must be in the tank so that a reading of the gage can be taken; the water is then allowed to flow in, the time between the beginning and end of the experiment being determined by a stop-watch, duly tested and rated. This time must not be short, in order that the slight errors in reading the watch may not affect the result. The gage is read at the close of the test after the surface of the water becomes quiet, and the difference of the gage readings gives the depth which has flowed in during the observed time. The depth multiplied by the area of the cross-section of the tank gives the volume, and this divided by the number of seconds during which the flow has occurred furnishes the discharge per second q.

If the discharge be very small, it may be advisable to weigh the water rather than to measure the depths and cross-sections. The total weight divided by the time of flow then gives directly the weight W. This has the advantage of requiring no temperature observation, and is probably the most accurate of all methods, but unfortunately it is not possible to weigh a considerable volume of water except at great expense.

When water is furnished to a motor through a small pipe, a common water meter may often be advantageously used to determine the discharge (Art. 38). No water meter, however, can be regarded as accurate until it has been tested by comparing the discharge as recorded by it with the actual discharge as determined by measurement or weighing in a tank. Such a test furnishes the constants for correcting the result found by its readings, which otherwise is liable to be 5 or 10 percent in error. The Venturi meter (Art. 38) furnishes an accurate method of measuring large quantities.

The leakage which occurs in the flume or penstock before the water reaches the wheel should not be included in the value of W, which is used in computing its efficiency, although it is needed in order to ascertain the efficiency of the entire plant. The manner of determining the amount of leakage will vary with the particular circumstances of the case in hand. If it be small, it may be caught in pails and directly weighed. If large in quantity, the gates which admit water to the wheel may be closed, and the leakage being then led into the tail race, it may be there measured by a weir, or by allowing it to collect in a tank. The leakage from a vertical penstock whose cross-section is known may be ascertained by filling it with water, the wheel being still, and then observing the fall of the water level at regular intervals of time. In designing constructions to bring water to a motor, it is best, of course, to arrange them so that all leakage will be avoided, but this cannot always be fully attained, except at great expense.

The most common method of measuring q is by means of a weir placed in the tail race below the wheel. This has the disadvantage that it sometimes lessens the fall which would be otherwise available, and that often the velocity of approach is high. It has, however, the advantage of cheapness in construction and operation, and for any considerable discharge appears to be almost the only method which is both economical and precise. If the weir is placed above the wheel, the leakage of the penstock must be carefully ascertained.

Prob. 147. A weir with end contractions and no velocity of approach has a length of 1.33 feet, and the depth on the crest is 0.406 feet. The same water passes through a small turbine under the effective head 10.49 feet. Compute the theoretic horse-power.

Art. 148. Effective Head on a Motor

The total available head H between the surface of the water in the reservoir or head race and that in the lower pool or tail race is determined by running a line of levels from one to the other. Permanent bench marks being established, gages can then be set in the head and tail races and graduated so that their zero points will be at some datum below the tail-race level. During the test of a wheel each gage is read by an observer at stated intervals, and the difference of the readings gives the head H. In some cases it is possible to have a floating gage on the lower level, the graduated rod of which is placed alongside a glass tube that communicates with the upper level; the head H is then directly read by noting the point of the graduation which coincides with the water surface in the tube. This device requires but one observer, while the former requires two; but it is usually not the cheapest arrangement unless a large number of observations are to be taken.

From this total head H are to be subtracted the losses of head in entering the forebay and penstock, and the loss of head in friction in the penstock itself, and these losses may be ascertained by the methods of Chaps. 8 and 9. Then

$$h = H - h' - h''$$

is the effective head acting upon the wheel. In properly designed approaches the lost heads h' and h'' are very small.

When water enters upon a wheel through an orifice which is controlled by a gate, losses of head will result, which can be estimated by the rules of Chaps. 5 and 6. If this orifice is in the head race, the loss of head should be subtracted together with the other losses from the total head H. But if the regulating gates are a part of the wheel itself, as is the case in a turbine, the loss of head should not be subtracted, because it is properly chargeable to the construction of the wheel, and not to the arrangements which furnish the supply of water. In any event that head should be determined which is to be used in the subsequent discussions: if the efficiency of the fall is desired, the total available head is required; if the efficiency of the motor, that effective head is to be found which acts directly upon it (Art. 146).

When water is delivered through a nozzle or pipe to an impulse wheel, the head h is not the total fall, since a large part of this may be lost in friction in the pipe, but is merely the velocity-head $v^2/2g$ of the issuing jet. The value of v is known when the discharge q and the area of the cross-section of the stream have been determined, and

$$h = v^2/2g = (q/a)^2/2g$$

In the same manner when a stream flows in a channel against the vanes of an undershot wheel the effective head is the velocity-head, and the theoretic energy is

$$K = Wh = Wv^2/2g = wq^3/2ga^2$$

If, however, the water in passing through the wheel falls a distance h_0 below the mouth of the nozzle, then the effective head which acts upon the wheel is given by

$$h = v^2/2g + h_0$$

In order to fully utilize the fall h_0 it is plain that the wheel should be placed as near the level of the tail race as possible.

Lastly, when water enters a turbine wheel through a pipe, a piezometer may be placed near the wheel entrance to register the pressure-head during the flow; if this pressure-head, measured upon and from the water level in the tail race, be called h_1 and if the velocity in the pipe be v, then

$$h = h_1 + v^2/2g$$

is the effective head acting on the wheel. It is here supposed that the turbine has a draft tube leading below the water level in the tail race; if this is not the case, h_1 should be measured upward from the lowest part of the exit orifices.

Prob. 148. A pressure gage at the entrance of a nozzle registers 116 pounds per square inch, and the coefficient of velocity of the nozzle is 0.98. Compute the effective velocity-head of the issuing jet.

Art. 149. Measurement of Effective Power

The effective work and horse-power delivered by a water-wheel or hydraulic motor is often required to be measured. Water power may be sold by means of the weight W, or quantity q, furnished under a certain head, leaving the consumer to provide his own motor; or it may be sold directly by the number of horse-power. In either case tests must be made from time to time in order to insure that the quantity contracted for is actually delivered and is not exceeded. It is also frequently required to measure effective work in order to ascertain the power and efficiency of the motor, either because the party who buys it has bargained for a certain power and efficiency, or because it is desirable to know exactly what the motor is doing in order to improve if possible its performance.

The test of a hydraulic motor has for its object: first, the determination of the effective energy and power; second, the determination of its efficiency; and third, the determination of that speed which gives the greatest power and efficiency. If the wheel be still, there is no power; if it be revolving very fast, the water is flowing through it so as to change but little of its energy into work: and in all cases there is found a certain speed which gives the maximum power and efficiency. To execute these tests, it is not at all necessary to know how the motor is constructed or the principle of its action, although such knowledge is very valuable, and is in fact indispensable to enable the engineer to suggest methods by which its operation may be improved.

A method in which the effective work of a small motor may be measured is to compel it to exert all its power in lifting a weight. For this purpose the weight may be attached to a cord which is fastened to the horizontal axis of the motor, and around which it winds as the shaft revolves. The wheel then expends all its power in lifting this weight W_1 through the height h_1 in t_1 seconds, and the work performed per second then is $k = W_1h_1/t_1$. This method is rarely used in practice on account of the difficulty of measuring t_1 with precision.

The usual method of measuring the effective work of a hydraulic motor is by means of the friction brake or power dynamometer invented by Prony about 1780. In Fig. 149 is illustrated a simple method of applying the apparatus to a vertical shaft, the upper diagram being a plan and the lower an elevation. Upon the vertical shaft is a fixed pulley, and against this are seen two rectangular pieces of wood hollowed so as to fit it, and connected by two bolts. By turning the nuts on these bolts while the pulley is revolving, the friction can be increased at pleasure, even so as to stop the motion; around these bolts between the blocks are two spiral springs (not shown in the diagram) which press the blocks outward when the nuts are loosened. To one of these blocks is attached a cord which runs horizontally to a small movable pulley over which it passes, and supports a scale-pan in which weights are placed. This cord runs in a direction opposite to the motion of the shaft, so that when the brake is tightened, it is prevented from revolving by the tension caused

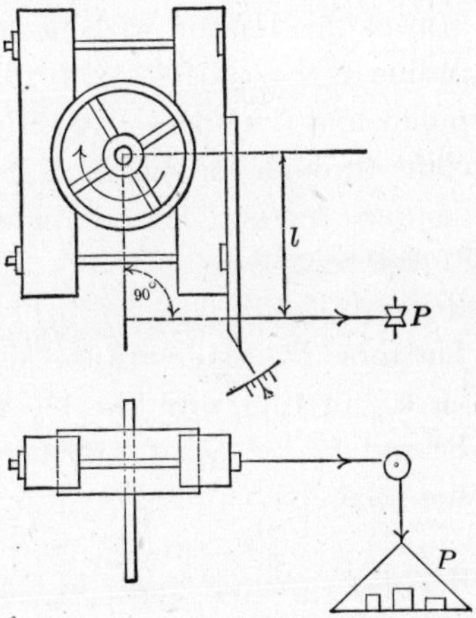

Fig. 149.

by the weights. The direction of the cord in the horizontal plane must be such that the perpendicular let fall upon it from the center of the shaft, or its lever-arm, is constant; this can be effected by keeping the small pointer on the brake at a fixed mark established for that purpose.

To measure the work done by the wheel, the shaft is disconnected from the machinery which it usually runs, and allowed to revolve, transforming all its work into heat by the friction between the revolving pulley and the brake, which is kept stationary by tightening the nuts, and at the same time placing sufficient weights in the scale-pan to hold the pointer at the fixed mark. Let n be the number of revolutions per second as determined by a counter attached to the shaft, P the tension in the cord which is equal to the weight of the scale-pan and its loads, l the lever-arm of this tension with respect to the center of the shaft, r the radius of the pulley, and F the total force of friction between the pulley and the brake. Now in one revolution the force F is overcome through the distance $2\pi r$, and in n revolutions through the distance $2\pi rn$. Hence the effective work done by the wheel in one second is

$$k = F \cdot 2\pi rn = 2\pi n \cdot Fr$$

The force F acting with the lever-arm r is exactly balanced by the force P acting with the lever-arm l; accordingly the moments Fr and Pl are equal, and hence the work done by the wheel in one second is

$$k = 2\pi nPl \qquad (149)_1$$

If P is in pounds and l in feet, the effective horse-power of the wheel is given by

$$\overline{hp} = 2\pi nPl/550$$

As the number of revolutions in one second cannot be accurately read, it is usual to record the counter readings every minute or half-minute; if N be the number of revolutions per minute,

$$\overline{hp} = 2\pi NPl/33\,000 \qquad (149)_2$$

It is seen that this method is independent of the radius of the pulley, which may be of any convenient size; for a small motor the brake may be clamped directly upon the shaft, but for a large one a pulley of considerable size is needed, and a special arrangement of levers is used instead of a cord.

The efficiency of the motor is now found by dividing the effective work per second by the theoretic work per second. Let K be this theoretic work, which is expressed by Wh, where W and h are determined by the methods of Arts. 147 and 148; then

$$e = k/K \quad \text{or} \quad e = \overline{hp}/\overline{HP}$$

The work measured by the friction brake is that delivered at the circumference of the pulley, and does not include that power which is required to overcome the friction of the shaft upon its bearings. The shaft or axis of every water-wheel must have at least two bearings, the friction of which consumes probably about 2 or 3 percent of the power. The hydraulic power and efficiency of the wheel, regarded as a user of water, are hence 2 or 3 percent greater than the values computed from above formulas. For example, let $P = 12.5$ pounds, $l = 14.31$ feet, and $N = 635$, then 21.6 horse-powers are in total delivered by the wheel, of which about 0.6 horse-power is consumed in shaft friction.

There are in use various forms and varieties of the friction brake, but they all act upon the principle and in the manner above described. For large wheels they are made of iron, and almost completely encircle the pulley; while a special arrangement of levers is used to lift the large weight P.* If the work transformed into friction be large, both the brake and the pulley may become hot, to prevent which a stream of cool water is allowed to flow upon them. To insure steadiness of motion, it is well that the surface of the pulley should be lubricated, which for a wooden brake is well done by the use of soap. It is important that the connection of the cord to the brake should be so made that the lever-arm l increases when the brake moves slightly with the wheel; if this is not done, the equilibrium will be unstable and the wheel will be apt to cause the brake to revolve with it.

Prob. 149. Find the power and efficiency of a motor when the theoretic energy is 1.38 horse-power, which makes 670 revolutions per minute, the weight on the brake being 2 pounds 14 ounces and its lever-arm 1.33 feet.

* Thurston, in Transactions American Society of Mechanical Engineers, 1886, vol. 8, p. 359.

Art. 150. Tests of Turbine Wheels

The following description of a test of a 6-inch Eureka turbine, made in 1888 at the hydraulic laboratory of Lehigh University, may serve to exemplify the methods of the preceding articles. The water was measured by a weir from which it ran into a vertical penstock 15.98 square feet in horizontal cross-section. This plan of having the weir above the wheel is not a good one, but it was here adopted on account of lack of room below the turbine. When a constant head was maintained in the penstock, the quantity of water flowing through the wheel was the same as that passing the weir; if, however, the head in the penstock fell x feet per minute, the flow through the wheel in cubic feet per minute was $60q + 15.98x$, in which q is the discharge per second over the weir. As the supply of water was very limited, the wheel could not be run to its fully capacity. The level of water in the penstock was read upon a head gage consisting of a glass tube behind which a graduated scale was fixed, the zero of which was a little above the water level in the tail race. The latter level was read upon a fixed graduated scale having its zero in the same horizontal plane as the first; these readings were hence essentially negative. The head upon the wheel is then found by adding the readings of the two gages.

The vertical shaft of the turbine, being about 15 feet long, was supported by four bearings, and to a small pulley upon its

Time on April 13, 1888	Depth on Weir Crest Feet	Penstock Gage Feet	Tail-race Gage Feet	Revolutions in One Minute	Weight on Brake Pounds	Remarks
$3^h\ 17^m$	0.288	11.25	−0.21	635	2.5	Length of weir,
18	0.289	11.17	0.20	625	2.5	$b = 1.909$ feet.
19	0.289	11.13	0.21	635	2.5	Length of lever-arm on brake,
20	0.288	11.10	0.21		2.5	$l = 1.431$ feet.
$3^h\ 22^m$	0.287	10.81	−0.20	535	3.0	Gate of wheel $\frac{3}{4}$
23	0.287	10.69	0.20	540	3.0	open during all experiments.
24	0.287	10.62	0.21	535	3.0	
25	0.286	10.57	0.21		3.0	

upper end was attached the friction dynamometer, as described in the last article. The number of revolutions was read from a counter placed in the top of this shaft. The observations were taken at minute intervals, electric bells giving the signals, so that precisely at the beginning of each minute simultaneous readings were taken by observers at the weir, at the head gage, at the tail gage, and at the counter, the operator at the brake continually keeping it in equilibrium with the resisting weight in the scale-pan by slightly tightening and loosening the nuts as required. The above shows notes of all the observations of two sets of tests, each lasting three minutes, the weight in the scale-pan being different in the two sets.

The following are the results of the computations made from the above notes for each minute interval. The second column is derived from formula $(63)_1$, using the coefficient corresponding to the given length of weir and depth on crest. The third column is obtained by taking the differences of the observed readings of the penstock head gage. The fourth column gives the discharge

Interval of Time	Discharge over Weir Cubic Feet per Minute	Fall in Penstock Feet	Flow through Wheel Cubic Feet per Minute	Head on Wheel Feet	Theoretic Horse-power of the Water	Effective Horse-power of the Wheel	Efficiency of the Wheel Percent
17^m to 18^m	58.49	+0.08	59.77	11.41	1.290	0.433	33.6
18 to 19	58.66	+0.04	59.30	11.36	1.274	0.426	33.4
19 to 20	58.49	+0.03	58.97	11.32	1.262	0.433	34.3
22^m to 23^m	58.05	+0.13	60.13	10.95	1.245	0.437	35.1
23 to 24	58.05	+0.07	59.17	10.86	1.215	0.441	36.3
24 to 25	57.88	+0.05	58.68	10.80	1.198	0.437	36.5

Q through the wheel found as above explained. The fifth column is the mean head h on the wheel during the minute, as derived from the observed readings of head and tail gage. The sixth column is found by formula $(146)_2$, using for W its value $\frac{1}{60}wQ$, in which w is taken at 62.4 pounds per cubic foot. The seventh column is computed from formula $(149)_2$; and the last column is found by dividing the numbers in the seventh by those in the sixth column.

These results show that the mean efficiency of the wheel and shaft under the conditions stated was about 35 percent; this low figure being due to the circumstance that the gate was not fully opened. It is also seen that the mean efficiency of the second set is 2.2 percent greater than that of the first set; this is due to the lower speed, and with still lower speeds the efficiency was found to be lower, so that a speed of about 535 revolutions per minute gives the maximum efficiency.

The work of Francis on the experiments made by him at Lowell, Mass., will always be a classic in American hydraulic literature, for the methods therein developed for measuring the theoretic power of a waterfall and the effective power utilized by the wheel are models of careful and precise experimentation.* In determining the speed of the wheel he used a method somewhat different from that above explained, namely, the counter attached to the shaft was connected with a bell which struck at the completion of every 50 revolutions; the observer at the counter had then only to keep his eye upon the watch, and to note the time at certain designated intervals, say at every sixth stroke of the bell. The number of revolutions per second was then obtained by dividing the number of revolutions in the interval by the number of seconds, as determined by the watch. This method requires a stop-watch in order to do good work, unless the observer be very experienced, as an error of one second in an interval of one minute amounts to 1.7 percent.

At Holyoke, Mass., there is a permanent flume for testing turbines arranged with a weir which can be varied up to lengths of 20 feet, so as to test the largest wheels which are constructed. As the expense of fitting up the apparatus for testing a large turbine at the place where it is to be used is often great, it is sometimes required in contracts that the wheel shall be sent to a place where a special outfit for such work exists. The wheel is mounted in the testing flume, and there, by the methods explained in the

* Lowell Hydraulic Experiments, 1st Edition, 1855; 4th, 1883.

preceding articles, it is run at different speeds in order to determine the speed which gives the maximum efficiency as well as the effective power developed at each speed. As the efficiency of a turbine varies greatly with the position of the gate which admits the water to it, tests are made with the gate fully opened and at various partial openings. The results thus obtained are not only valuable in furnishing full information concerning the effective power and efficiency of the wheel, but they also convert the turbine into a water meter, so that when running under the same head as during the tests, the quantity of water which passes through it per second can at any time be closely ascertained by noting the number of revolutions per second.

The following gives the results of the tests of an 80-inch outward-flow Boyden turbine, made at Holyoke in 1885, the gate being fully opened in each experiment. The heads in the second column were derived from the head and tail race gages, these being arranged so

Number	Head in Feet	Revolutions per Minute	Discharge Cubic Feet per Second	Horse-power	Efficiency Percent
21	17.16	63.5	117.01	172.57	75.85
20	17.27	70.0	118.37	177.41	76.60
19	17.33	75.0	119.53	178.63	76.11
18	17.34	80.0	121.15	178.32	74.92
17	17.21	86.0	122.41	178.57	74.81
16	17.21	93.2	124.74	176.44	72.54
15	17.19	100.0	127.73	167.94	67.51

that one observer could directly read the difference. The numbers in the third column were found by dividing the total number of revolutions during the experiment by its length in minutes; those in the fourth by the weir formula $(63)_1$; those in the fifth by $(149)_2$ from the records of the friction dynamometer; and those in the last column were computed by $(146)_3$. It is seen that the discharge always increased with the speed of the wheel, and the reason for this is explained in Art. 166. The maximum efficiency of 76.6 percent occurred at 70 revolutions per minute; and for 100 revolutions per minute the efficiency was lowered to 67.7 percent, notwithstanding that the quantity of water passing through the wheel was much greater.

Prob. 150. Compute the theoretic horse-power and the efficiency for the above experiments, Nos. 15 and 21, on the large Boyden outward-flow turbine.

Art. 151. Facts concerning Water Power

The number of horse-powers generated by water-wheels and turbines and used in manufacturing establishments in the United States was 1 130 431 in 1870, 1 225 379 in 1880, 1 263 343 in 1890, and 1 727 258 in 1900; these figures do not include the electric power derived from water. In 1908* the total development was 5 356 680 horse-powers in 52 827 wheels and turbines. Since 1890 there has been a large development of water power in connection with electric light and trolley service, and this development promises to attain great proportions during the twentieth century. It has been estimated that the rivers of the United States can furnish about 212 000 000 horse-powers, so that the possibilities for the future are almost unlimited.

Water power is sometimes sold by what is called the "mill power," which may be roughly supposed to be such a quantity as the average mill requires, but which in any particular case must be defined by a certain quantity of water under a given head. Thus at Lowell the mill power is 30 cubic feet per second under a head of 25 feet, which is equivalent to 85.2 theoretic horse-power. At Minneapolis it is 30 cubic feet per second, under 22 feet head, or 75 theoretic horse-power. At Holyoke it is 38 cubic feet per second under 20 feet head, or 86.4 theoretic horse-power. This seems an excellent way to measure power when it is to be sold or rented, as the head in any particular instance is not subject to much variation; or if so liable, arrangements must be adopted for keeping it nearly constant, in order that the machinery in the mill may be run at a tolerably uniform rate of speed. Thus nothing remains for the water company to measure except the water used by the consumer. The latter furnishes his own motor, and is hence interested in securing one of high efficiency, that he may derive the greatest power from the water for which he pays. The perfection of American turbines is undoubtedly largely due

* Water Supply and Irrigation Paper, No. 234.

to this method of selling power, and the consequent desire of the mill owners to limit their expenditure for water. The turbine itself, when tested and rated, becomes a meter by which the company can at any time determine the quantity of water that passes through it.

A common method of selling the power which is generated by turbines is by the nominal horse-power of the wheel as stated in the catalogue of the manufacturer. The seller fixes a price per annum for one horse-power on this basis, and the buyer furnishes his own wheel. By this method no controversy can arise regarding the amount of water used, for the purchaser has the right to use all that can pass through the turbine. The head to be used for finding the nominal horse-power is the mean head which can be utilized by the wheel, and this must be agreed upon in advance between the parties.

The power of electric generators is usually expressed in kilowatts. One English horse-power is 0.746 kilowatts, and one metric horse-power is 0.736 kilowatts. One kilowatt is 1.340 English horse-powers or 1.360 metric horse-powers. The efficiency of a good electric generator is about 95 percent, so that it delivers 95 percent of the work imparted to it by the turbine wheel; if the efficiency of this wheel is 75 percent, the combined efficiency of the hydraulic and electric plant is 71 percent. Electric power is usually sold by the kilowatt-hour, this being measured by a wattmeter.

The available power of natural waterfalls is very great, but it is probably exceeded by that which can be derived from the tides and waves of the ocean. Twice every day, under the attraction of the sun and moon, an immense weight of water is lifted, and it is theoretically possible to derive from this a power due to its weight and lift. Continually along every ocean beach the waves dash in roar and foam, and energy is wasted in heat which by some device might be utilized in power. The expense of deriving power from these sources is indeed greater than that of the water wheel under a natural fall, but the time may come when the profit will exceed the expense, and then it will certainly be done. Coal and wood and oil may become exhausted, but as long as the force of gravitation exists, and the ocean remains upon which it can act, power, heat, and light can be generated in unlimited quantities.

Prob. 151*a*. Deduce the simple and useful rule that one inch of rainfall per hour is, very nearly, equivalent to one cubic foot per second per acre.

Prob. 151*b*. Find the theoretic horse-power of a plant where 1200 cubic feet of water per second is used under a total head of 49.5 feet. If the efficiency of the approaches is 99 per cent, the efficiency of the turbines 76 percent, and the efficiency of the dynamos 96 percent, what power in kilowatts is delivered?

Prob. 151*c*. What is the theoretic metric horse-power of a plant where 112 cubic meters of water per second are used under a head of 23.5 meters? If the efficiencies of the approaches, turbines, and electric generators are 98.5, 74.3, and 97.5 percent, respectively, compute the number of metric horse-powers delivered, and also the power in kilowatts.

Prob. 151*d*. When a turbine is tested by a friction dynamometer, show that its power in kilowatts is $0.00103NPl$, if P be the load on the brake in kilograms, l its lever-arm in meters, and N the number of revolutions per minute. When $N = 200$, $P = 250$ kilograms, and $l = 2.01$ meters, what electric power is delivered by a dynamo attached to the turbine when the efficiency of the dynamo is 97.2 percent?

Prob. 151*e*. The hectare-meter is a convenient unit for estimating large quantities of water in irrigation and water-supply work. Show that one hectare-meter is 10 000 cubic meters. Show that 100 centimeters of rainfall falling in one month is, very nearly, 0.004 cubic meters per second per hectare.

CHAPTER 12

DYNAMIC PRESSURE OF WATER

Art. 152. Definitions and Principles

The pressures exerted by moving water against surfaces which change its direction or check its velocity are called dynamic, and they follow very different laws from those which govern the static pressures that have been discussed and used in the preceding chapters. A static pressure due to a certain head may cause a jet to issue from an orifice; but this jet in impinging upon a surface may cause a dynamic pressure less than, equal to, or greater than that due to the head. A static pressure at a given point in a mass of water is exerted with equal intensity in all directions; but a dynamic pressure is exerted in different directions with different intensities. In the following chapters the words "static" and "dynamic" will generally be prefixed to the word "pressure," so that no confusion may result.

The dynamic pressure exerted by a stream flowing with a given velocity against a surface at rest is evidently equal to that produced when the surface moves in still water with the same velocity. This principle was applied in Art. 40 in rating the current meter, the vanes of which move under the impulse of the impinging water. The dynamic pressure exerted upon a moving body by a flowing stream depends upon the velocity of the body relative to the stream.

The "impulse" of a jet or stream of water is defined as the dynamic pressure which it is capable of producing in the direction of its motion when its velocity is entirely destroyed in that direction. This can be done by deflecting the jet normally sidewise by a fixed surface; when the surface is smooth, so that no energy is lost in frictional resistances, the actual velocity remains unaltered, but the velocity in the original direction has been rendered null. In Art. 27 it is shown that the theoretic force of impulse of a stream of cross-section a and velocity v is

$$F = W\frac{v}{g} = wq\frac{v}{g} = 2wa\,\frac{v^2}{2g} \tag{152}$$

in which W and q are the weight and volume delivered per second, and w is the weight of one cubic unit of water. This equation shows that the dynamic pressure that may be produced by impulse is equal to the static pressure due to twice the head corresponding to the velocity v. It would then be expected, when two equal orifices or tubes are placed exactly opposite, as in Fig. 125, and a loose plate is placed vertically against one of them, that the dynamic pressure upon the plate caused by the impulse of the jet issuing from A under the head h would balance the static pressure caused by the head $2h$. This conclusion has been confirmed by experiment, for a tube A which has a smooth inner surface and rounded inner edges so that its coefficient of discharge is unity.

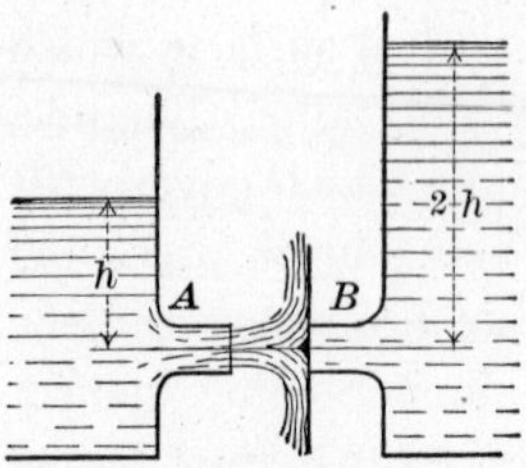

Fig. 152.

The reaction of a jet or stream is the backward dynamic pressure, in the line of its motion, which is exerted against a vessel out of which it issues, or against a surface away from which it moves. This is equal and opposite to the impulse, and the equation above given expresses its value and the laws which govern it. The expression for the reaction or impulse F in (152) may be also proved as follows: The definition by which forces are compared with each other is, that forces are proportional to the accelerations which they can produce. The weight W, if allowed to fall, acquires the acceleration g; the force F which can produce the acceleration v is hence related to W and g by the equation $F/W = v/g$, and accordingly $F = W \cdot v/g$.

The forces of impulse and reaction do not really exist in a stream flowing with constant velocity and direction, although F indicates the force that was exerted in putting the stream into motion and the force that is required to stop it. When the direction of the stream is changed by opposing obstacles, the impulse and reaction produce dynamic pressure; if, in making this change, the absolute velocity is retarded, energy is converted into work. Impulse and reaction are of practical value, because the resulting dynamic pressures may be utilized for the production of work. For this purpose water is made to impinge upon moving vanes, which alter both its direction and velocity, thus producing a dynamic pressure P, which overcomes in each second an equal resisting force through the space u. The work done per second is then $k = Pu$, and it is the object in designing a hydraulic motor to make this work as large as possible; for this purpose, the most advantageous values of P and u are to be selected.

The word "impact" is sometimes popularly used to designate impulse or pressure, but in hydraulics it refers to those cases where energy is lost in eddies and foam, as when a jet impinges into water or upon a rough plane surface. Impact is not defined in algebraic terms, but the energy lost in impact may be so defined and computed. When the energy of a stream of water is to be utilized, losses due to impact should be avoided. Whenever impact occurs, kinetic energy is transformed into heat.

Prob. 152. When a jet is one inch in diameter, how many gallons per second must it deliver in order that its impulse may be 100 pounds?

Art. 153. Experiments on Impulse and Reaction

A simple device by which the dynamic pressure P exerted upon a surface by the impulse and reaction of a jet that glides over it can be directly weighed is shown in Fig. 153*a*. It consists merely of a bent lever supported on a pivot at O, and having a plate A attached at the lower end of the vertical arm upon which the stream impinges, while weights applied at the end of the other arm measure the dynamic pressure produced by the impulse. By means of an apparatus of this nature, experiments have been made by Bidone, Weisbach, and others, the results of which will now be stated.

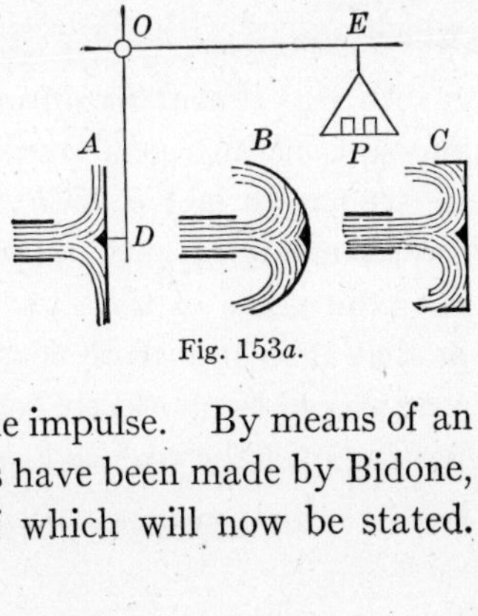

Fig. 153*a*.

When the surface upon which the stream impinges is a plane normal to the direction of the stream, as shown at A, the dynamic pressure P closely agrees with that given by the theoretic formula for F in the last article, namely,

$$P = W\frac{v}{g} = 2wa\frac{v^2}{2g} \tag{153}$$

being about 2 percent greater according to Bidone, and about 4 percent less according to Weisbach. The actual value of P was found to vary somewhat with the size of the plate, and with its distance from the end of the tube from which the jet issued.

When the surface upon which the stream impinges is curved, as at B, or so arranged that the water is turned backward from the surface, the value of the dynamic pressure P was found to be always greater than the theoretic value, and that it increased with the amount of backward inclination. When a complete reversal of the original direction of the water was obtained, as at C, it was found that P, as measured by the weights, was nearly double the value of that against the plane. This is explained by stating that as long as the direction of the flow is toward the surface the dynamic pressure of its impulse is exerted upon it, but when the water flows backward away from the surface, the dynamic pressure due to both impulse and reaction is then exerted upon it. The sum of these is

$$P = F + F = 2W\frac{v}{g} = 4wa\frac{v^2}{2g}$$

which agrees with the results experimentally obtained.

An experiment by Morosi * shows clearly that the dynamic pressure against a surface may be increased still further by the device shown in Fig. 153*b*, where the stream is made to perform two complete reversals upon the surface. He found that in this case the value of the dynamic pressure was 3.32 times as great as that against a plane, for $P = 3.32\,F$, whereas theoretically the 3.32 should be 4. In this case, as in those preceding, the water in passing over the surface loses energy in friction and foam, so that

* Ruhlman's Hydromechanik (Hannover, 1879), p. 586.

its velocity is diminished, and it should hence be expected that the experimental values of the dynamic pressures would be less than the theoretic values, as in general they are found to be.

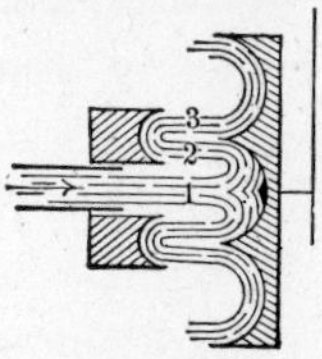

Fig. 153*b*.

While the experiments here briefly described thoroughly confirm the results of theory, they further show it is the change in direction of the velocity when in contact with the surface which produces the dynamic pressure. If the stream strikes normally against a plane, the direction of its velocity is changed 90°, and this is the same as the entire destruction of the velocity in its original direction, so that the dynamic pressure P should agree with the impulse F. This important principle of change in direction will be theoretically exemplified later.

The dynamic pressure which is produced by the direct reaction of a stream of water when issuing from a vertical orifice in the side of a vessel was measured by Ewart with the apparatus shown in Fig. 153*c*, which will be readily understood without a detailed description. The discussion of these experiments made by Weisbach * shows that the measured values of P were from 2 to 4 per cent less than the theoretic value F as given by (153), so that in this case, also, theory and observation are in accordance.

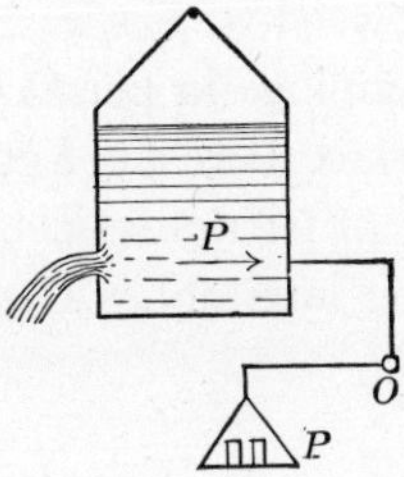

Fig. 153*c*.

An experiment by Unwin,† illustrated in Fig. 153*d*, is very interesting, as it perhaps explains more clearly than formula (152) why it is that the dynamic pressure due to impulse is double the static pressure. Two vessels having converging tubes of equal size were placed so that the jet from A was directed exactly into B. The head in A was kept uniform at $20\frac{1}{2}$ inches,

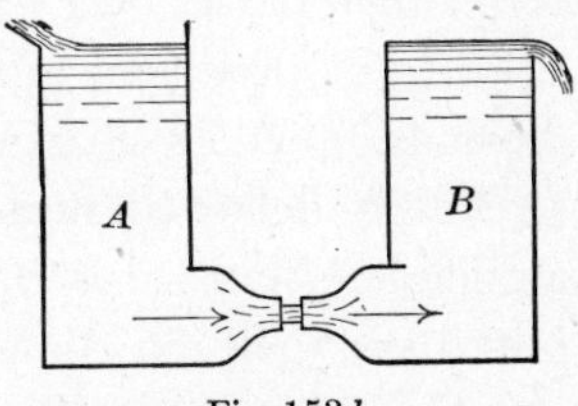

Fig. 153*d*.

* Theoretical Mechanics, Coxe's translation, vol. 1, p. 1004.
† Encyclopedia Britannica, 9th Edition, vol. 12, p. 467.

when it was found that the water in B continued to rise until a head of 18 inches was reached. All the water admitted into A was thus lifted in B by the impulse of the jet, with a loss of $2\frac{1}{2}$ inches of head, which was caused by foam and friction. If such losses could be entirely avoided, the water in B might be raised to the same level as that in A. In the case shown in the figure where the water overflows from B, the impulse of the jet has not only to overcome the static pressure due to the head h, but also to furnish the dynamic pressure equivalent to a second head h in order to raise the water through that height. But the level in B can never rise higher than in A, for the velocity-head of the jet cannot be greater than that of the static head which generates it.

Prob. 153. Accepting as an experimental fact that the force of impulse or reaction is double the static pressure, show that the theoretic velocity of flow is $\sqrt{2gh}$.

Art. 154. Surfaces at Rest

Let a jet of water whose cross-section is a impinge in permanent flow with the uniform velocity v upon a surface at rest. Let the surface be smooth, so that no resisting force of friction exists, and let the stream be prevented from spreading laterally. The

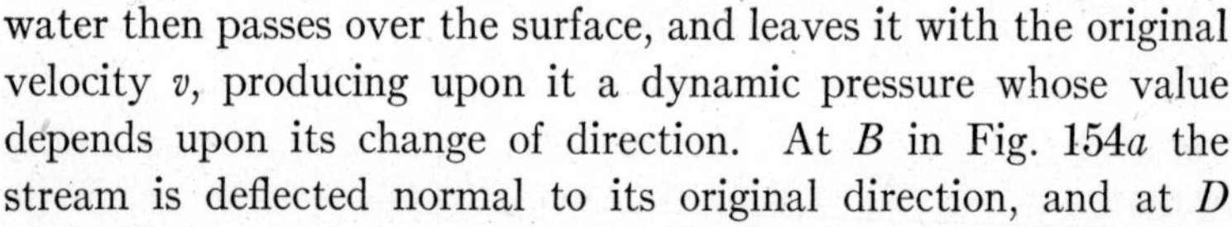

Fig. 154a.

water then passes over the surface, and leaves it with the original velocity v, producing upon it a dynamic pressure whose value depends upon its change of direction. At B in Fig. 154a the stream is deflected normal to its original direction, and at D a complete reversal is effected. Let θ be the angle between the initial and final directions, as shown. It is required to determine the dynamic pressure exerted upon the surface in the same direction as that of the jet. In the above figures, as in those that follow, the stream is supposed to lie in a horizontal plane, so that no acceleration or retardation of its velocity will be produced by the action of gravity.

The stream entering upon the surface exerts its impulse F in the same direction as that of its motion; leaving the surface, it exerts its reaction F in opposite direction to that of its motion. Let P be the dynamic pressure thus produced in the direction of the initial motion, F_1 the component of the reaction F in the same direction. Then

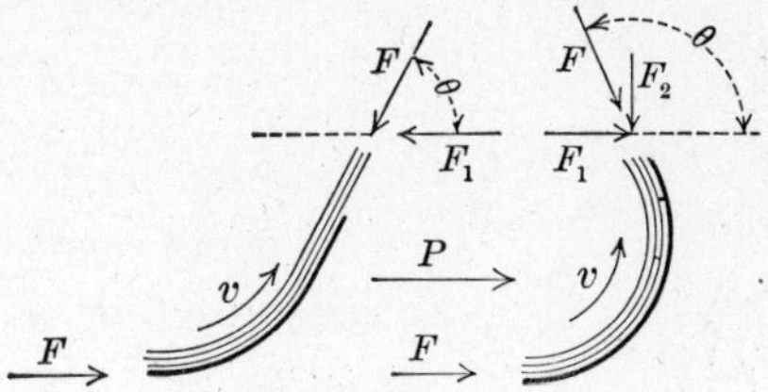

Fig. 154*b*.

$$P = F - F_1 = F(1 - \cos\theta)$$

and inserting for F its value as given by (152),

$$P = (1 - \cos\theta)\, W \frac{v}{g} \qquad (154)_1$$

which is the formula for the dynamic pressure in the direction of the impinging jet. If in this $\theta = 0°$, the stream glides along the surface without changing its direction, and P becomes zero; if θ is 90°, the resulting dynamic pressure is

$$P = F = W \frac{v}{g}$$

and if θ becomes 180°, a complete reversal of direction is obtained, and the resulting dynamic pressure that is exerted by the jet against the surface is

$$P = 2F = 2W \frac{v}{g}$$

These theoretic conclusions agree with the experimental results described in the last article. In the deduction of $(154)_1$ the angle θ has been regarded as less than 90°, but the same formula results if θ be considered greater than 90°, since then the sign of the reaction F_1 is positive.

The resultant dynamic pressure exerted upon the surface is found by combining by the parallelogram of forces the impulse F

and the equal reaction F. In Fig. 154b it is seen that this resultant bisects the angle $180 - \theta$, and that its value is

$$P' = 2F \cos\tfrac{1}{2}(180 - \theta) = 2 \sin\tfrac{1}{2}\theta \cdot W\frac{v}{g}$$

It is usually, however, more important to ascertain the pressure in a given direction than the resultant. This can be found by taking the component of the resultant in that direction, or by taking the algebraic sum of the components of the initial impulse and the final reaction.

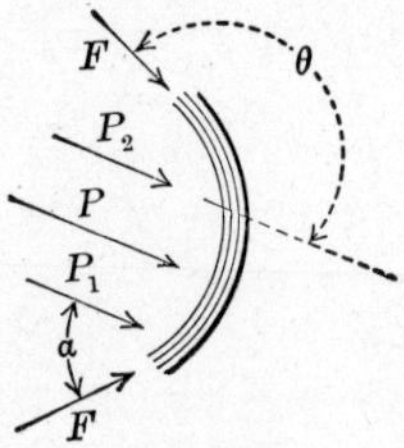

Fig. 154c.

To find the dynamic pressure P in a direction which makes an angle α with the entering and the angle θ with the departing stream, the components in that direction are

$$P_1 = F \cos\alpha \qquad P_2 = -F \cos\theta$$

and the algebraic sum of these two components is

$$P = F(\cos\alpha - \cos\theta) = (\cos\alpha - \cos\theta)\, W\frac{v}{g} \qquad (154)_2$$

This becomes equal to F when $\alpha = 0$ and $\theta = 90°$, as at B in Fig. 154a, and also when $\alpha = 90°$ and $\theta = 180°$. When $\alpha = 0°$ and $\theta = 180°$ the entering and departing streams are parallel, as at D in Fig. 154a, so that the value of P is $2F$, which in this case is the same as the resultant pressure.

The formulas here deduced are entirely independent of the form of the surface, and of the angle with which the jet enters upon it. It is clear, however, if, as in the planes in Fig. 154a, this angle is such as to allow shock to occur, that foam and changes in cross-section may result which will cause energy to be dissipated in heat. These losses will diminish the velocity v and decrease the theoretic dynamic pressure. These effects cannot be formulated, but it is a general principle, which is confirmed by experiment, that they may be largely avoided by allowing the jet to impinge tangentially upon the surface.

In all the foregoing formulas the weight W which impinges upon the surface per second is the same as that which issues from the orifice or nozzle that supplies the stream, or

$$W = wq = wav$$

To find W it is hence necessary to use the methods of the preceding chapters to determine either the discharge q or the mean velocity v.

Prob. 154. If F is 10 pounds, $\alpha = 0°$, and $\theta = 60°$, show that the pressure parallel to the direction of the jet is 5 pounds, that the pressure normal to that direction is 8.66 pounds, and that the resultant dynamic pressure is 10 pounds.

Art. 155. Immersed Bodies

When a body is immersed in a flowing stream, or when it is moved in still water, so that filaments are caused to change their direction, a dynamic pressure is exerted by the stream or overcome

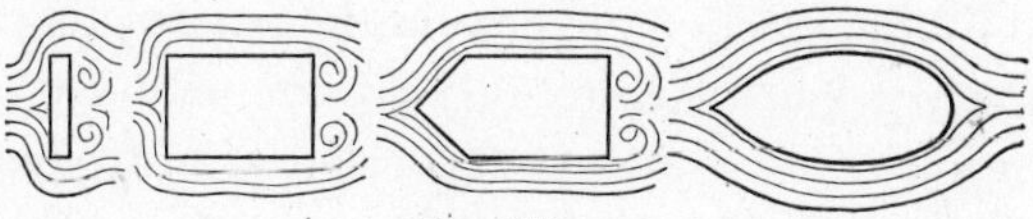

Fig. 155.

by the body. It is to be inferred from what has preceded that the dynamic pressure in the direction of the motion is proportional to the force of impulse of a stream which has a cross-section equal to that of the body, or

$$P = m \cdot wa \frac{v^2}{2g}$$

in which m is a number depending upon the length and shape of the immersed portion, and whose value is 2 for a jet impinging normally upon a plane.

Experiments made upon small plates held normally to the direction of the flow show that the value of m lies between 1.25 and 1.75, the best determinations being near 1.4 and 1.5. It is to be expected that the dynamic pressure on a plate in a stream would be less than that due to the impulse of a jet of the same cross-section, as the filaments of water near the outer edges are crowded sideways in the latter case and hence do not impinge with full normal effect, and the above results confirm this supposition. The few experiments on record were made with small plates, mostly less than 2 square feet in area, and they seem to indicate that the value of the coefficient m is greater for large surfaces than for small ones.

The determination of the dynamic pressure upon the end of an immersed cylinder or prism is difficult because of the resisting friction of the sides; but it is well ascertained to be less than that upon a plane of the same area, and within certain limits to decrease with the length. For a conical or wedge-shaped body the dynamic pressure is less than that upon the cylinder, and it is found that its intensity is much modified by the shape of the rear surface of the body.

When a body is so shaped as to gradually deflect the filaments of water in front, and to allow them to gradually close in again upon the rear, the impulse of the front filaments upon the body is balanced by the reaction of those in the rear, so that the resultant dynamic pressure is zero. The forms of boats and ships should be made so as to obtain this result as nearly as possible, and then the propelling force has only to overcome the frictional resistance of the surface upon the water. A body so shaped is said to have a "fair form" (Art. 183).

The dynamic pressure produced by the impulse of ocean waves striking upon piers or lighthouses is often very great. The experiments of Stevenson on Skerryvore Island, where the waves probably acted with greater force than usual, showed that during the summer months the mean dynamic pressure per square foot was about 600 pounds, and during the winter months about 2100 pounds, the maximum observed value being 6100 pounds. At the Bell Rock lighthouse the greatest value observed was about 3000 pounds per square foot. The observations were made by allowing the waves to impinge upon a circular plate about 6 inches in diameter, and the pressure produced was registered by the compression of a spring. Such high unit-pressures do not probably act upon large areas of masonry which are exposed to wave action.*

Prob. 155. Compute the probable dynamic pressure upon a surface 1 foot square when immersed in a current whose velocity is 9 feet per second, the direction of the current being normal to the surface.

* Cooper on Ocean Waves, in Transactions American Society Civil Engineers, 1896, vol. 36, p. 150.

Art. 156. Curved Pipes and Channels

The dynamic pressures discussed in the preceding article have been those caused by jets, or isolated streams, of water. There is now to be considered the case of dynamic pressures caused by streams flowing in pipes, conduits, or channels of any kind; these are sometimes called limited or bounded streams, the boundary being the surface whose cross-section is the wetted perimeter. When such a stream is straight and of uniform section, and all its filaments move with the same velocity v, the impulse, or the pressure which it can produce, is the quantity F given by the general expression in Art. 152; under these conditions it exerts no dynamic pressure, but if a body be immersed and

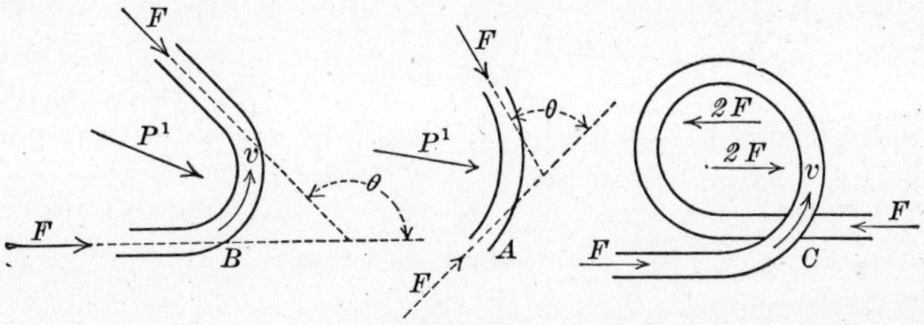

Fig. 156*a*.

held stationary, pressure is produced upon it. If its direction changes in an elbow or bend, pressure upon the bounding surface is produced; if its cross-section increases or decreases, pressure is developed or absorbed.

The resultant dynamic pressure P' upon a curved pipe which runs full of water with the uniform velocity v depends upon the angle θ between the initial and final directions, and must be the same as that produced upon a surface by an impinging jet which passes over it without change in velocity. The formula of Art. 154 then directly applies, and

$$P' = 2 \sin\tfrac{1}{2}\theta \cdot F = 2 \sin\tfrac{1}{2}\theta \cdot W \frac{v}{g}$$

if $\theta = 0°$, there is no bend, and $P' = 0$; if $\theta = 180°$, the direction of flow is reversed, and $P' = 2F$. If the direction is twice reversed, as at C in Fig. 156*a*, the value of θ is $360°$, and the resultant is the initial impulse F minus the final reaction F, or simply zero; in this case, however, there may be a couple which tends to twist the pipe, unless the impulse and reaction lie in the same straight line.

The dynamic pressure developed in a unit of length of the curve will now be found. Let the pipe at A in Fig. 156*a* have the length δl, and let θ be nearly 0°, so that its value is the elementary angle $\delta\theta$. Then in the above formula P' becomes the elementary radial pressure δP_1, and

$$\delta P_1 = 2 \sin \tfrac{1}{2}\,\delta\theta \cdot F = F\delta\theta$$

Now since $\delta\theta = \delta l/R$, where R is the radius of the curve, the dynamic pressure developed in the distance δl is $F\delta l/R$, and that for a unit of length is F/R. Accordingly, by Art. 153, this pressure is

$$P_1 = \frac{F}{R} = \frac{2wa}{R}\,\frac{v^2}{2g}$$

The unit-pressure p' is found by dividing P_1 by a, and the corresponding head h_1 is found by dividing p' by w; hence

$$p' = \frac{2\,w}{R}\,\frac{v^2}{2g} \qquad \text{and} \qquad h_1 = \frac{2}{R}\,\frac{v^2}{2g}$$

are the values for one unit of length of the curve. The dynamic pressure-head h_1 is developed in every unit of length of the pipe. It is not known how these influence the static pressure or how they affect piezometers. Nor is it known whether they combine so that the dynamic pressure becomes greater with the distance from the beginning of the curve. Undoubtedly, however, a part of h_1 is expended in causing cross-currents whereby impact results and some of the static head is lost. This loss should be proportional to h_1 and proportional to the length l of the curve, or, if d is the diameter of the pipe,

$$h''' = m_1 \frac{l}{R}\,\frac{v^2}{2g} = m_1 \frac{d}{R} \cdot \frac{l}{d}\,\frac{v^2}{2g} = f_1 \frac{l}{d}\,\frac{v^2}{2g}$$

in which the curvature factor f_1 depends upon the ratio R/d. This investigation appears to indicate that pipes of the same diameter and of different curvatures give the same loss of head, if the central angle is the same; but, as seen in Art. 91, certain experiments seem to point to the conclusion that the loss per linear unit is greatest in the pipe having the longest radius.

The same reasoning applies approximately to the curves of conduits, canals, and rivers. In any length l there exists a radial dynamic pressure P_1, acting toward the outer bank and causing currents in that direction, which, in connection with the greater velocity that naturally there exists, tends to deepen the channel on that side. This may help to explain the reason why rivers run in winding courses. At first the curve may be slight, but the radial flow due to the dynamic pressure causes the outer bank to scour away; this increases the velocity v_2 and decreases v_1 (Fig. 156*b*), and this in turn hastens the scour on the outer and allows material to be deposited on the inner side. Thus the process continues until a state of permanency is reached, and then the existing forces tend to maintain the curve. The cross-currents which the radial pressure produces have been actually seen in experiments devised by Thomson,* and it is found that they move in the manner shown in the above figure, the motion toward the outer bank being in the upper part of the section, while along the wetted perimeter they flow toward the inner bank. When the slope is small and the mean velocity low, the influence of the cross-currents is relatively greater than for higher slopes, and this is probably one of the reasons why the sharpest curves are found in streams of slight slope. Perhaps another reason for this is that at very low velocities the law of flow is different, the head varying as the first power of the velocity (Art. 124).

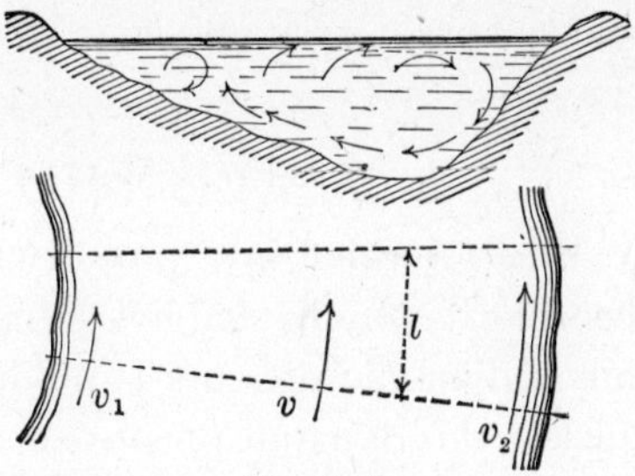

Fig. 156*b*.

The elevation of the water on the outer bank of a bend is higher than on the inner. This is only a partial consequence of the radial dynamic pressure, as in straight streams it is also seen that the water surface is curved, the highest elevation being where the velocity is greatest. In this case cross-currents are also ob-

* Proceedings Royal Society of London, 1878, p. 356.

served which move near the surface toward the center of the stream, and near the bottom toward the banks, their motion being due to the disturbance of the static pressure consequent upon the varying water level.

Prob. 156. The mean velocity in a pipe is 9 feet per second. If it be laid on a curve of 3 feet radius, show that the dynamic pressure-head for each foot in length of the pipe is 0.84 feet. If the radius of the curve be 6 feet, what is the dynamic pressure-head? What is the dynamic pressure-head for each case when the mean velocity is 3 feet per second?

Art. 157. Water Hammer in Pipes

When a valve in a pipe is closed while the water is flowing, the velocity of the water is retarded as the valve descends, and thus a dynamic pressure is produced. When the valve is closed quickly, this dynamic pressure may be much greater than that due to the static pressure, and it is then called "water hammer" or "water ram." Pipes have often been known to burst under this cause, and hence the determination of the maximum dynamic pressure of the water hammer is a matter of importance. Fig. 157*a* illustrates the phenomena of water hammer for the closing

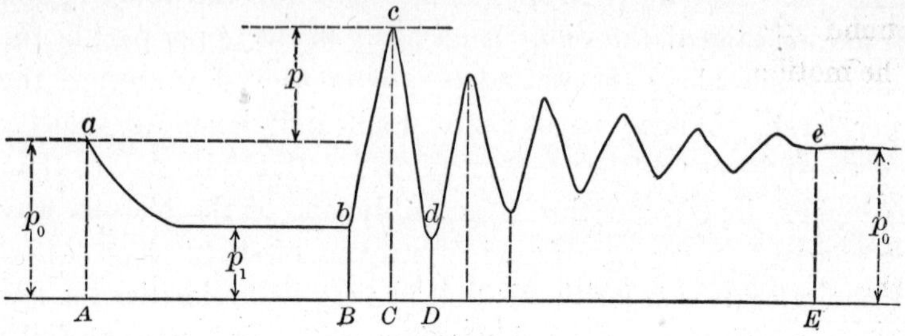

Fig. 157*a*.

of a valve at the end of a pipe where the water issues through a nozzle. At the entrance there is supposed to be a gage which registers the static unit-pressure p_1 while the flow is in progress, and the static unit-pressure p_0 when there is no flow. The abscissas represent time, and at *B* the valve begins to close. After a short interval of time *BC* the gage registers the unit-pressure *Cc*; after another short interval the unit-pressure has decreased to *Dd*, and a series of oscillations follows until finally the disturbance ceases. A diagram of this kind may be autographically drawn by suitable mechanism connected with the pressure gage, and such were made in the experiments conducted by Carpenter,* as also in those of Fletcher.†

Let p represent the excess of maximum dynamic unit-pressure over the static unit-pressure when there is no flow; that is, the difference of the ordinates *Cc* and *Ee*. This is the excess unit-pressure due to the water hammer, and it is required to determine an expression for its value. It is first to be noted that the actual dynamic unit-pressure produced by the retardation of the velocity is the difference of the ordinates *Cc* and *Bb* and this difference is $p + p_0 - p_1$, or simply $p + p_0$ when there is no unit-pressure while the flow is in progress; let this be denoted by S. Let a be the area of cross-section of the pipe, or the weight of a cubic unit of water, l' a short length of the pipe, and v the velocity of the water during the flow. The kinetic energy of the water in motion is $wal'v^2/2g$. When this water is brought to rest under the unit-stress S, its stress energy ‡ is $al'S^2/2E$, if E be the modulus of elasticity of the water (Art. 5). Supposing all the kinetic energy to be expended in stress energy, these expressions are equal, whence $S = v(Ew/g)^{\frac{1}{2}}$, or

$$p = v(Ew/g)^{\frac{1}{2}} + p_1 - p_0 \qquad (157)_1$$

which is the formula for the maximum excess unit-pressure over the static pressure when there is no flow in the pipe.

The time t which elapses between the instant when the valve begins to close and the instant when this pressure p is felt at the gage must be equal to or less than $2l/u$, where l is the length of the pipe and u is the velocity of sound in water. For the time l/u must elapse after the valve begins to close before the velocity begins to be checked at the upper end of the pipe, and the further time of l/u must elapse before the pressure can be transmitted back to the valve. Hence the pressure at the valve

* Transactions American Society of Mechanical Engineers, 1894, vol. 15.

† Engineering News, 1898, vol. 39, p. 323.

‡ Merriman's Mechanics of Materials (New York, 1905), p. 306.

is less than that given by $(157)_1$ when the valve closes in a time greater than $2l/u$. The velocity ur for water is about 4670 feet per second (Art. 5).

When v is in feet per second, and p_0, p_1, and p are in pounds per square inch, the above formula becomes

$$p = 63v + p_1 - p_0 \qquad (157)_2$$

which applies when the valve is closed in a time equal to or less than $2l/u$. To prevent the effects of water hammer it is customary to arrange valves so that the time of closing is greater than $2l/u$.

The elaborate experiments of Joukowsky at Moscow in 1898 * have fully confirmed the truth of formula $(157)_2$. Horizontal pipes of 2, 4, and 6 inches diameter, with lengths of 2494, 1050, and 1066 feet, were used, and the valve at the end was closed in 0.03 seconds. Ten autographic recording gages were placed along the length of a pipe, and it was found that substantially the same dynamic pressure was produced at each, but that the time length of a wave was the shorter the farther the distance of a gage from the valve; this wave length is shown in the above figure by the distance BD. The following is a comparison of the observed values

For the 4-inch Pipe			For the 6-inch Pipe		
Velocity	Observed	Computed	Velocity	Observed	Computed
0.5	31	31	0.6	43	38
1.9	115	118	1.9	106	118
2.9	168	183	3.0	173	189
4.1	232	258	5.6	369	353
9.2	519	580	7.5	426	472

of $p + p_0 - p_1$ for a few of these experiments with the values computed from $(157)^2$. It is seen that the observed are less than the computed values except in one instance, and Joukowsky concludes that, owing to the influence of the metal of the pipes, the velocity u with which stress is transmitted in the water is about 4200 instead

* Stoss in Wasserleitungsröhren, St. Petersburg, 1900. Translation from the Memoirs of the St. Petersburg Academy of Sciences.

of 4670 feet per second. This conclusion may be applied in practice by using $59v$ instead of $63v$ in $(157)_2$.

In computing the thickness of water pipes it is customary to add 100 pounds per square inch to the static pressure in order to allow for the influence of water hammer. This is equivalent, if p_1 is zero, to making $p_0 + 100$ equivalent to $63v$; when v is 3 feet per second, then p_0 is 89 pounds per square inch. Since these values of v and p are larger than the usual ones for a city water supply, the customary practice is on the safe side for this case, but it would not give sufficient security for the high velocities often used in pipe lines for power plants. When a wave of dynamic pressure travels toward a dead end of a pipe, the water hammer at that end may be two or three times as great as the maximum pressure given by the formula.

In the above no consideration has been given to the energy expended in stretching the metal of the pipe. Let d be the diameter and b the thickness of the pipe; the volume of metal in a length l' is then closely $\pi dbl'$, the tensile unit-stress in this is $Sd/2b$ (Art. 16) and the stress energy is $\pi dbl'(Sd/\frac{1}{2}b)^2/2E_1$, where E_1 is the modulus of elasticity of the metal. Adding this to the stress energy above found for the water, equating the sum to the kinetic energy, and noting that $a = \frac{1}{4}\pi a^2$, there is found a value of S, from which

$$p = v\sqrt{\frac{Ew/g}{1 + (E/E_1)\ (d/b)}} + p_1 - p_0 \qquad (157)_3$$

as was first shown by Frizell,* and this gives a smaller value of p than $(157)_1$. For example let a cast-iron pipe be 24 inches in diameter and 0.9 inch thick; here

$$E/E_1 = 300\,000/15\,000\,000 = 1/50$$

and $d/b = 24/0.9 = 27$, so that in $(157)_2$ the number 63 is to be replaced by 51. There is, however, some uncertainty regarding the transmission of stress through pipe joints, and hence it is well to regard $(157)_2$ as a limit which may be approached but never be exceeded.

A surge tank or stand-pipe is a vertical, open cylinder connected near the gate of a power plant, with the feeding pipe

*Transactions American Society Civil Engineers, 1898, p. 1.

or penstock. When the gate is quickly closed the water rises in the surge tank instead of expending its energy in causing water ram (Fig. 157*c*). The kinetic energy of the water in the feeding pipe of length l and area a is $walv^2/2g$. When the gate closes the water rises in the vertical surge tank to a height h; let A be its section area and D its diameter, then the weight

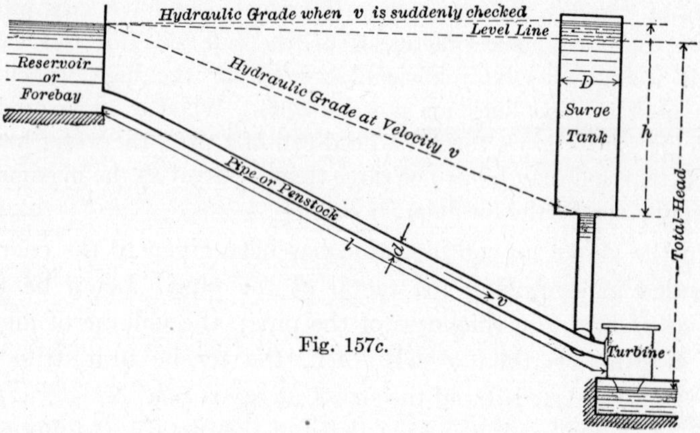

Fig. 157*c*.

wAh is raised to the height $\frac{1}{2}h$, so that $\frac{1}{2}wAh^2$ is the energy of the water in it. Equating these two energies there is found

$$h = v\sqrt{al/Ag} \qquad \text{or} \qquad h = v(d/D)\sqrt{l/g}$$

for the height of the surge. Friction is here neglected, and in fact, the full discussion of the phenomena in the surge tank is very complicated. A design based on the above formula would be on the safe side, since friction and foam will decrease the theoretic height of the surge. From this formula the diameter D may be also computed when the height h is given.

A surge tank with open top must have that top higher than the water level in the reservoir, or else overflow will occur when the plant is not running. When circumstances do not allow a tank of this height to be built, a so-called "differential surge tank" having a closed top may be used.* The surge tank, or stand-pipe, as it is often called, also serves the useful purpose of furnishing a supply of water which can be quickly drawn upon, and of preventing sudden changes in pressure due to changes in load on the wheels.

* Transactions American Society of Civil Engineers, 1915, vol. 78, p. 760.

Prob. 157*a*. The pressure-head at the entrance to a nozzle is 230 feet when there is no flow and 50 feet when the water is flowing. The pipe is 1500 feet long and the velocity in it is 4.2 feet per second when the nozzle is in operation. Compute the maximum excess dynamic pressure.

Prob. 157*b*. A turbine operating under a total head of 50 feet discharges 200 cubic feet per second. The penstock or feeding pipe is 6 feet in diameter and its length is 2000 feet. If the diameter of the surge tank is to be made 18 feet, find the height of its top above the reservoir level.

Art. 158. Moving Vanes

A vane is a plane or curved surface which moves in a given direction under the dynamic pressure exerted by an impinging jet or stream. The direction of the motion of the vane depends upon the conditions of its construction; for example, the vanes of a water wheel can only move in a circumference around its axis. The simplest case for consideration, however, is that where the motion is in a straight line, and this alone will be considered in this article. The plane of the stream and vane is to be taken as horizontal, so that no direct action of gravity can influence the action of the jet.

Let a jet with the velocity v impinge upon a vane which moves in the same direction with the velocity u, and let the velocity of the jet relative to the surface at the point of exit make an angle β with the reverse direction of u, as shown in Fig. 158*a*. The velocity of the stream relative to the surface is $v - u$, and the dynamic pressure is the same as if the surface were at rest and the stream moving with the absolute velocity $v - u$. Hence formula $(154)_1$ directly applies, replacing v by $v - u$ and θ by $180° - \beta$, and the dynamic pressure is

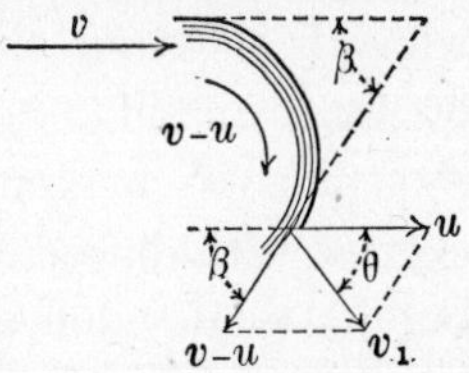

Fig. 158*a*.

$$P = (1 + \cos\beta)\, W \frac{v - u}{g}$$

In this formula W is not the weight of the water which issues from the nozzle, but that which strikes and leaves the vane, or $W = wa(v - u)$; for under the condition here supposed the vane moves continually away from the nozzle, and hence does not receive all the water which it delivers.

Another method of deducing the last equation is as follows: At the point of exit let lines be drawn representing the velocities $v - u$ and u; then, completing the parallelogram, the line v_1 is the absolute velocity of the departing jet (Art. 28). Let θ be the angle which v_1 makes with the direction of u, and β as before the angle between $v - u$ and the reverse direction of u. Then the dynamic pressure on the vane is that due to the absolute impulse of the entering and departing streams: the former of these is $W \cdot v/g$ and the latter is $W \cdot v_1 \cos\theta/g$. Hence the resultant dynamic pressure in the direction of the motion of the vane is the difference of these impulses, or

$$P = W\frac{v - v_1 \cos\theta}{g}$$

But from the triangle between v_1 and u

$$v_1 \cos\theta = u - (v - u) \cos\beta$$

Inserting this, the value of the dynamic pressure is

$$P = (1 + \cos\beta) W \frac{v - u}{g}$$

which is the same as that found before. If $\beta = 180°$, there is no pressure, and if $\beta = 0°$, the stream is completely reversed, and P attains its maximum value. The dynamic pressure may be exerted with different intensities upon different parts of the vane, but its total value in the direction of the motion is that given by the formula.

Usually the direction of the motion is not the same as that of the jet. This case is shown in Fig. 158*b*, where the arrow marked F designates the direction of the impinging jet, and that marked P the direction of the motion of the vane, α being the angle between them. The jet having the velocity v impinges upon the vane at A, and in passing over it exerts a dynamic pressure P which causes it to move with the velocity u. At A let lines be drawn representing the intensities and directions of v and u, and let the parallelogram of velocities be formed as shown; the line

V then represents the velocity of the water relative to the vane at A. The stream passes over the surface and leaves it at B with the same relative velocity V, if not retarded by friction or foam. At B let lines be drawn to represent u and V, and let β be the angle which V makes with the reverse direction of u; let the parallelogram be completed, giving v_1 for the absolute velocity of the departing water, and let θ be the angle which it makes with u. The total pressure in the direction of the motion is now to be regarded as that caused by the components in that direction of the initial and the final impulse of the water. The impulse of the stream before striking the vane is $W \cdot v/g$ and its component in the direction of the motion is $W \cdot v \cos\alpha/g$. The impulse of the stream as it leaves the vane is $W \cdot v_1/g$ and its component in the direction of the motion is $W \cdot v_1 \cos\theta/g$. The difference of these components is the resultant dynamic pressure in the given direction, or

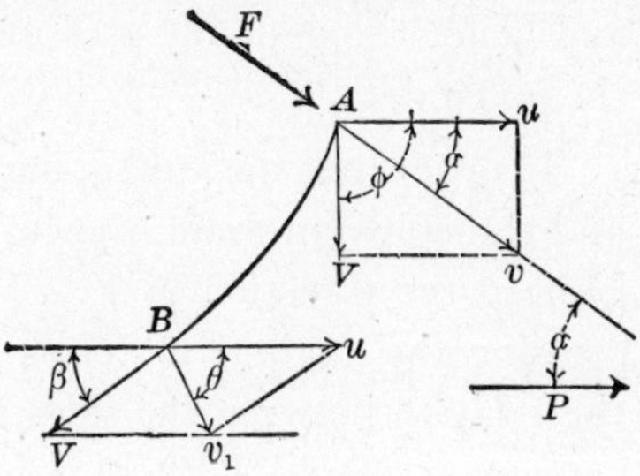

Fig. 158*b*.

$$P = W\frac{v \cos\alpha - v_1 \cos\theta}{g} \tag{158}$$

This is a general formula for the dynamic pressure in any given direction upon a vane moving in a straight line, if α and θ be the angles between that direction and those of v and v_1. If the surface be at rest, v and v_1 are equal and the formula reduces to $(154)_2$.

If it be required to find the numerical value of P, the given data are the velocities v and u and the angles α and β. The term $v_1 \cos\theta$ is hence to be expressed in terms of these quantities. From the triangle at B between v_1 and u, there is found

$$v_1 \cos\theta = u - V \cos\beta$$

and substituting this, the formula becomes

$$P = W\frac{v \cos\alpha - u + V \cos\beta}{g}$$

which is often a more convenient form for discussion. The value of V is found from the triangle at A between u and v, thus:

$$V^2 = u^2 + v^2 - 2uv \cos\alpha$$

and hence the dynamic pressure P is fully determined in terms of the given data.

In order that the stream may enter tangentially upon the vane, and thus prevent foam, the curve of the vane at A should be tangent to the direction of V. This direction can be found by expressing the angle ϕ in terms of the given angle α. Thus from the relation between the sides and angles of the triangle included between u, v, and V there is found

$$\sin(\phi - \alpha)/\sin\phi = u/v$$

which is easily reduced to the form

$$\cot\phi = \cot\alpha - \frac{u}{v \sin\alpha}$$

from which ϕ can be computed when u, v, and α are given. For example, if u be equal to $\frac{1}{2}v$, and if α be 30°, then $\cot\phi$ is 0.732, whence the angle ϕ should be $53\frac{3}{4}°$, in order that the jet may enter without impact. If the angle made by the vane with the direction of motion be greater or less than this value, some loss due to impact will result at the given speed.

Prob. 158. Given $u = 86.6$ and $v = 100.0$ feet per second, and $\alpha = 30°$. What should be the value of the angle ψ in order that no loss by impact may occur? Draw the parallelogram showing the velocities u, v, and V.

Art. 159. Work derived from Moving Vanes

The work imparted to a moving vane by the energy of the impinging water is equal to the product of the dynamic pressure P, which is exerted in the direction of the motion and the space through which it moves. If u be the space described in one second, or the velocity of the vane, the work per second is

$$k = Pu$$

This expression is now to be discussed in order to determine the value of u which makes k a maximum.

When the vane moves in a straight line in the same direction as the impinging jet and the water enters it tangentially, as shown in Fig. 154*b*, the work imparted is found by inserting for P its value from $(154)_1$. If a be the area of the cross-section of the jet and w the weight of a cubic unit of water, the weight W is $wa(v-u)$, and then

$$k = (1+\cos\beta)\,W\frac{(v-u)u}{g} = (1+\cos\beta)\,wa\frac{(v-u)^2u}{g}$$

The value of u which renders k a maximum is obtained by equating to zero the derivative of k with respect to u, or

$$\frac{\delta k}{\delta u} = (1+\cos\beta)\frac{wa}{g}(v^2-4vu+3u^2)=0$$

from which the value of u is $\frac{1}{3}v$, and accordingly

$$k = \tfrac{8}{27}(1+\cos\beta)\,wa\frac{v^3}{2g}$$

is the maximum work that can be done by the vane in one second. The theoretic energy of the impinging jet is

$$K = W\frac{v^2}{2g} = wa\frac{v^3}{2g}$$

and the efficiency of the vane is the ratio of the effective work of the vane to the theoretic energy of the water, or

$$e = k/K = \tfrac{8}{27}(1+\cos\beta)$$

If $\beta = 180°$, the jet glides along the vane without producing work and $e = 0$; if $\beta = 90°$, the water departs from the vane normal to its original direction and $e = \frac{8}{27}$; if $\beta = 0°$, the direction of the stream is reversed and $e = \frac{16}{27}$.

It appears from the above that the greatest efficiency which can be obtained by a vane moving in a straight line under the impulse of a jet of water is $\frac{16}{27}$; that is, the effective work is only about 59 percent of the theoretic energy attainable. This is due to two causes: first, the quantity of water which reaches and leaves the vane per second is less than that furnished by the nozzle or mouthpiece from which the water issues; and, secondly, the water leaving the vane still has an absolute velocity of $\frac{1}{3}v$. A vane moving in a straight line is therefore a poor arrangement for utilizing energy, and it will also be seen upon reflection that it would be impossible to construct a motor in which a vane would move continually in the same direction away from a fixed nozzle. The above discussion therefore gives but a rude approximation to the results obtainable under practical conditions. It shows truly, however, that the efficiency of a jet which is deflected normally from its path is but one-half of that obtainable when a complete reversal of direction is made.

Water wheels which act under the impulse of a jet consist of a series of vanes arranged around a circumference which by the motion are brought in succession before the jet. In this case the quantity of water which leaves the wheel per second is the same as that which enters it, so that W does not depend on the velocity of the vanes, as in the preceding case, but is a constant whose value is wq, where q is the quantity furnished per second. A close estimate of the efficiency of a series of such vanes can be made by considering a single vane and taking W as a constant. The water is supposed to impinge tangentially and the vane to move in the same line of direction as the jet (Fig. 158*a*). Then the work which is imparted in one second by the water to the moving vane is

$$k = (1 + \cos\beta)\, W \frac{(v - u)\, u}{g}$$

This becomes zero when $u = 0$ or when $u = v$, and it is a maximum when $u = \frac{1}{2}v$, or when the vane moves with one-half the velocity of the jet. Inserting this value of u,

$$k = \tfrac{1}{2}(1 + \cos\beta)\, W \frac{v^2}{2g}$$

and, dividing this by the theoretic energy of the jet, the efficiency of the vane is found to be

$$e = \tfrac{1}{2}(1 + \cos\beta)$$

When $\beta = 180°$, the jet merely glides along the surface without performing work and $e = 0$; when $\beta = 90°$, the jet is deflected normally to the direction of the motion and $e = \frac{1}{2}$; when $\beta = 0°$, a complete reversal of direction is obtained and the efficiency attains its maximum value $e = 1$.

These conclusions apply closely to the vanes of a water wheel which are so shaped that the water enters upon them tangentially in the direction of the motion. If the vanes are plane radial surfaces, as in simple paddle wheels, the water passes away normally to the circumference, and the highest obtainable efficiency is about 50 percent. If the vanes are curved backward, the efficiency becomes greater, and, neglecting losses in impact and friction, it might be made nearly unity, and the entire energy of the stream be realized, if the water could both enter and leave the vanes in a direction tangential to the circumference. The investigation shows that this is due to the fact that the water leaves the vanes without velocity; for, as the advantageous velocity of the vane is $\frac{1}{2}v$, the water upon its surface has the relative velocity $v - \frac{1}{2}v = \frac{1}{2}v$; then, if $\beta = 0°$, its absolute velocity as it leaves the vane is $\frac{1}{2}v - \frac{1}{2}v = 0$. If the velocity of the vanes is less or greater than half the velocity of the jet, the efficiency is lessened, although slight variations from the advantageous velocity do not practically influence the value of e.

Prob 159. A nozzle 0.125 feet in diameter, whose coefficient of discharge is 0.95, delivers water under a head of 82 feet against a series of small vanes on a circumference whose diameter is 18.5 feet. Find the most advantageous velocity of revolution of the circumference.

Art. 160. Revolving Vanes

When vanes are attached to an axis around which they move, as is the case in water wheels, the dynamic pressure which is effective in causing the motion is that tangential to the circumferences of revolution; or at any given point this effective pressure is normal to a radius drawn from the point to the axis. In Fig. 160 are shown two cases of a rotating vane; in the first the water passes outward or away from the axis, and in the second it passes inward or toward the axis. The reasoning, however, is general and will apply to both cases. At A, where the jet enters upon the vane, let v be its absolute velocity, V its velocity relative to the vane, and u the velocity of the point A; draw u normal to the radius r and construct the parallelogram of velocities as shown, α being the angle between the directions of u and v, and ϕ that between u and V. At B, where the water leaves the vane, let u_1 be the velocity of that point normal to the radius r_1, and V_1 the velocity of the water relative to the vane; then constructing

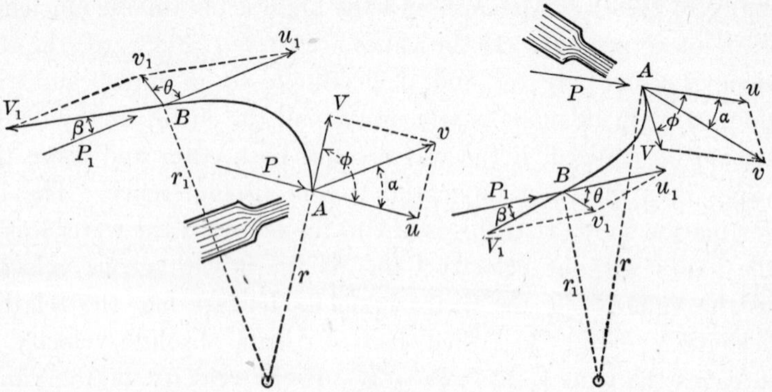

Fig. 160.

the parallelogram, the resultant of u_1 and V_1 is v_1, the absolute velocity of the departing water. Let β be the angle between V_1 and the reverse direction of u_1, and θ be the angle between the directions of v_1 and u_1.

The total dynamic pressure exerted in the direction of the motion will depend upon the values of the impulse of the entering and departing streams. The absolute impulse of the water before entering is $W \cdot v/g$, and that of the water after leaving is $W \cdot v_1/g$, Let the components of these in the directions of the motion of the vane at entrance and departure be designated by P and P_1; then

$$P = W\frac{v\cos\alpha}{g} \qquad P_1 = W\frac{v_1\cos\theta}{g}$$

These, however, cannot be subtracted to give the resultant dynamic pressure, as was done in the case of motion in a straight line, because their directions are not parallel, and the velocities of their points of application are not equal. The resultant dynamic pressure is not important in cases of this kind, but the above values will prove useful in the next article in investigating the work that can be delivered by the vane.

If n be the number of revolutions around the axis in one second, the velocities u and u_1 are

$$u = 2\pi rn \qquad u_1 = 2\pi r_1 n$$

and accordingly the relation obtains

$$u_1/u = r_1/r \qquad \text{or} \qquad u_1 r = u r_1$$

which shows that the velocities of the points of entrance and exit are directly proportional to their distances from the axis. If r and r_1 are infinity, u equals u_1 and the case is that of motion in a straight line as discussed in Art. 158.

The relative velocities V_1 and V are connected with the velocities of rotation u_1 and u by a simple relation. To deduce it, imagine an observer standing on the outward-flow vane and moving with it; he sees a particle of weight w at A which to him appears to have the velocity V, while the same particle at B appears to have the velocity V_1; the difference of their kinetic energies, or $w(V_1^2 - V^2)/2g$, is the apparent gain of the wheel-energy. Again, consider an observer standing on the earth and looking down upon the vane; from his point of view the energy gained is $w(u_1^2 - u^2)/2g$. Now these two expressions for the gain of the wheel in energy must be equal, or

$$V_1^2 - V^2 = u_1^2 - u^2 \qquad (160)$$

and this is the formula by which V_1 is to be computed when V and the velocities of rotation are known. The same reasoning applies to the inward-flow vane by using the word "loss" instead of "gain," and the same formula results.

The given data for a revolving vane are the angles ϕ and β, the radii r and r_1, the velocity v, the number of revolutions per second, and the weight of water delivered to the vane per second. The value of $v \cos\alpha$, and hence that of P_1, is immediately known. From the speed of revolution the velocities u and u_1 are found. The relative velocity V is, from the triangle between u and v,

$$V = v \sin\alpha / \sin\phi$$

and by (160) the relative velocity V_1 is then found from

$$V_1^2 = u_1^2 - u^2 + V^2$$

Lastly, the value of $v_1 \cos\theta$, from the triangle between u_1 and V_1, is

$$v_1 \cos\theta = u_1 - V_1 \cos\beta$$

and accordingly the values of the dynamic pressures P and P_1 are fully determined. Numerical values of these, however, are never needed, but the work due to them is of much importance, as will be explained in the next article.

Prob. 160. Given $r = 2$ feet, $r_1 = 3$ feet, $\alpha = 45°$, $\psi = 90°$, $v = 100$ feet per second, and $n = 6$ revolutions per second. Compute the velocities u, u_1, V, and V_1.

Art. 161. Work derived from Revolving Vanes

The investigation in Art. 159 on the work and efficiency of a revolving vane supposes that all its points move with the same velocity, and that the water enters upon it in the same direction as that of its motion, or that $\alpha = 0$. This cannot in general be the case in water motors, as then the jet would be tangential to the circumference and no water could enter. To consider the subject further the reasoning of the last article will be continued, and, using the same notation, it will be plain that the work of a series of vanes arranged around a wheel may be regarded as that due to the impulse of the entering stream in the direction of the motion around the axis minus that due to the impulse of the departing stream in the same direction, or

$$k = Pu - P_1 u_1$$

Here P and P_1 are the pressures due to the impulse at A and B (Fig. 160), and inserting their values as found,

$$k = W \frac{uv \cos\alpha - u_1 v_1 \cos\theta}{g} \qquad (161)_1.$$

This is a general formula applicable to the work of all wheels of outward or inward flow, and it is seen that the useful work k consists of two parts, one due to the entering and the other to the departing stream.

Another general expression for the work of a series of vanes may be established as follows: Let v and v_1 be the absolute velocities of the entering and departing water; the theoretic energy of this water is $W \cdot v^2/2g$, and when it leaves the wheel it still has the energy $W \cdot v_1^2/2g$. Neglecting losses of energy in impact and friction the work that can be derived from the wheel is

$$k = W\frac{v^2 - v_1^2}{2g} \qquad (161)_2$$

This is a formula of equal generality with the preceding, and like it is applicable to all cases of the conversion of energy into work by means of impulse or reaction. In both formulas, however, the plane of the vane is supposed to be horizontal, so that no fall occurs between the points of entrance and exit.

Formula (160) may be demonstrated in another way by equating the values of k in the preceding formulas; thus

$$uv\cos\alpha - u_1v_1\cos\theta = \tfrac{1}{2}(v^2 - v_1^2)$$

Now from the triangle at A between u and v

$$v^2 = V^2 - u^2 + 2\,uv\cos\alpha$$

and from the triangle at B between u_1 and v_1

$$v_1^2 = V_1^2 - u_1^2 + 2\,u_1v_1\cos\theta$$

Inserting these values of v^2 and v_1^2 the equation reduces to

$$V_1^2 - V^2 = u_1^2 - u^2$$

This shows that if u_1 be greater than u, as in the outward-flow vane, then V_1 is greater than V; if u_1 is less than u, as in an inward-flow vane, then V_1 is less than V.

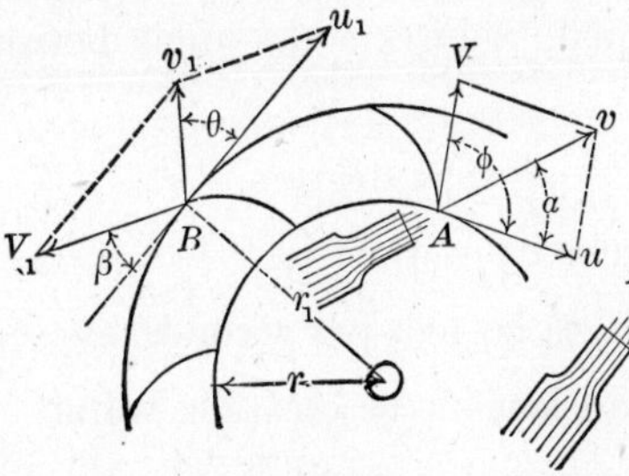

Fig. 161*a*.

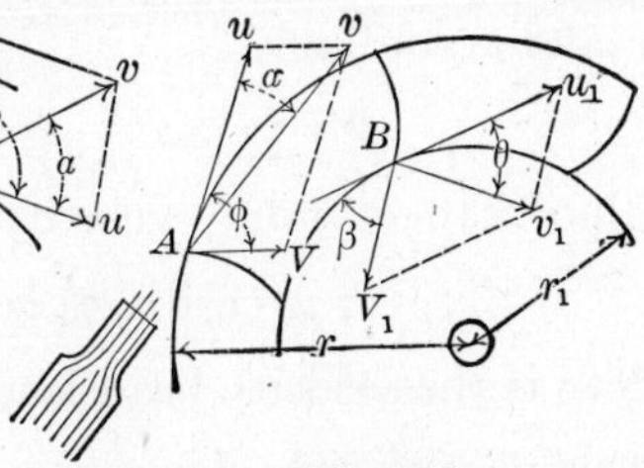

Fig. 161*b*.

The above principles will now be applied to the simple case of an outward-flow wheel driven by a fixed nozzle, as in Fig. 161*a*.

The wheel is so built that $r = 2$ feet, $r^1 = 3$ feet, $\alpha = 45°$, $\phi = 90°$, and $\beta = 30°$. The velocity of the water issuing from the nozzle is $v = 100$ feet per second, and the discharge per second is 2.2 cubic feet. It is required to find the work of the wheel and the efficiency when its speed is 337.5 revolutions per minute.

The theoretic work of the stream per second is the weight delivered per second multiplied by its velocity-head, or

$$k = 62.5 \times 2.2 \times 0.01555 \times 100^2 = 21\,380 \text{ foot-pounds}$$

which gives 38.9 theoretic horse-powers. The actual work of the wheel, neglecting losses in foam and friction, can be computed either from $(161)_1$ or $(161)_2$. In order to use the first of these, however, the velocities u, u_1, v_1, and the angle θ must be found, and to use the second, v_1 must be found; in each case V and V_1 must be determined.

The velocities u and u_1 are found from the given speed of 5.625 revolutions per second, thus:

$$u = 2 \times 3.1416 \times 2 \times 5.625 = 70.71 \text{ feet per second;}$$

$$u_1 = 1\tfrac{1}{2} \times 70.71 = 106.06 \text{ feet per second.}$$

The relative velocity V at the point of entrance is found from the triangle between V and v, which in this case is right-angled;

$$V = v \cos(\phi - \alpha) = v \cos 45° = 70.71 \text{ feet per second.}$$

The relative velocity V_1 at the point of exit is found from the relation (160), which gives $V_1 = u_1 = 106.06$ feet per second. And since u_1 and V_1 are equal, v_1 bisects the angle between V_1 and u_1, and accordingly

$$\theta = \tfrac{1}{2}(180° - \beta) = 75 \text{ degrees.}$$

The value of the absolute velocity v_1 then is

$$v_1 = 2\,u_1 \cos\theta = 54.90 \text{ feet per second,}$$

and $v_1^2/2g$ is the velocity-head lost in the escaping water.

The work of the wheel per second, computed either from $(161)_1$ or $(161)_2$, is now found to be $k = 14\,934$ foot-pounds or 27.2 horse-powers, and hence the efficiency, or the ratio of this work to the theoretic work, is $e = 0.699$. Thus 30.1 percent of the energy of the water is lost, owing to the fact that the water leaves the wheel with such a large absolute velocity.

In this example the speed given, 337.5 revolutions per minute, is such that the direction of the relative velocity V is tangent to the vane at the point of entrance. For any other speed this will not be the case, and thus work will be lost in shock and foam. It is observed also that the approach angle α is one-half of the entrance angle ϕ; with this arrangement the velocities u and V are equal, as also u_1 and V_1. Had the angle β been made smaller the efficiency of the wheel would have been higher.

Prob. 161. Compute the power and efficiency for the above example if the angle β be 15° instead of 30°. Explain why β cannot be made very small.

Art. 162. Revolving Tubes

The water which glides over a vane can never be under static pressure, but when two vanes are placed near together and connected so as to form a closed tube, there may exist in it static pressure if the tube is filled. This is the condition in turbine wheels, where a number of such tubes, or buckets, are placed around an axis and water is forced through them by the static pressure of a head. The work in this case is done by the dynamic pressure exactly as in vanes, but the existence of the static pressure renders the investigation more difficult.

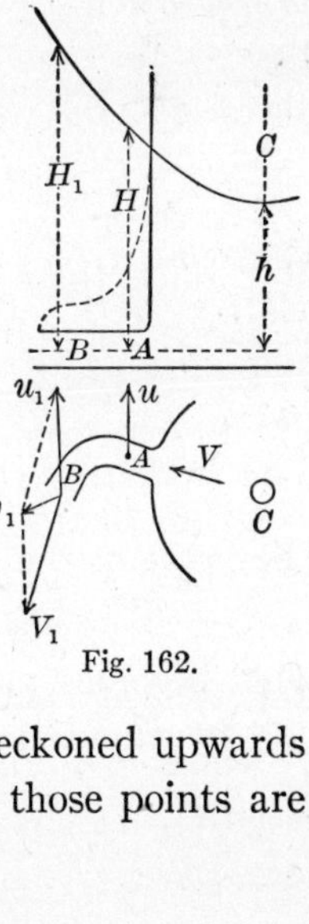

Fig. 162.

The simplest instance of a revolving tube is that of an arm attached to a vessel rotating about a vertical axis, as in Fig. 162. It was shown in Art. 29 that the water surface in this case assumes the form of a paraboloid, and if no discharge occurs, it is clear that the static pressures at any two points B and A are measured by the pressure-heads H_1 and H reckoned upwards to the parabolic curve, and, if the velocities of those points are u_1 and u, that

$$H_1 - \frac{u_1^2}{2g} = H - \frac{u^2}{2g} = h$$

Now suppose an orifice to be opened in the end of the tube and the flow to occur, while at the same time the revolution is continued. The velocities V_1 and V diminish the pressure-heads so that the piezometric line is no longer the parabola, but some curve represented by the lower broken line in the figure. Then, according to the theorem of Art. 31, that pressure-head plus velocity-head remains constant during steady flow, if no loss of energy occurs,

$$H_1 + \frac{V_1^2}{2g} - \frac{u_1^2}{2g} = H + \frac{V^2}{2g} - \frac{u^2}{2g} = h \qquad (162)$$

in which H_1 and H are the heads due to the actual static pressures. This is the theorem which gives the relation between pressure-head, velocity-head, and rotation-head at any point of a revolving tube or bucket. If the tube is only partly full, so that the flow occurs along one side, like that of a stream upon a vane, then there is no static pressure, and the formula becomes the same as (160).

An apparatus like Fig. 162, but having a number of arms from which the flow issues, is called a reaction wheel, since the dynamic pressure which causes the revolution is wholly due to the reaction of the issuing water. To investigate it, the general formula $(161)_1$ may be used. Making $u = 0$, the work done upon the wheel by the water is

$$k = W\frac{-u_1 v_1 \cos\theta}{g} = W\frac{u_1 V_1 \cos\beta - u_1^2}{g}$$

But since there is no static pressure at the point B, the value of V_1 is, from (162), or also from Art. 29,

$$V_1 = \sqrt{2gh + u_1^2}$$

The work that can be derived from the wheel now is

$$k = W\frac{u_1 \cos\beta\sqrt{2gh + u_1^2} - u_1^2}{g}$$

This becomes nothing when $u_1 = 0$, or when $u_1^2 = 2gh \cot^2\beta$, and by equating the first derivative to zero it is found that k becomes a maximum when the velocity is given by

$$u_1^2 = \frac{gh}{\sin\beta} - gh$$

Inserting this advantageous velocity, the maximum work is

$$k = Wh(1 - \sin\beta)$$

and therefore the efficiency of the reaction wheel is

$$e = 1 - \sin\beta$$

When $\beta = 90°$, both u_1 and e become 0, for then the direction of the stream is normal to the circumference and no reaction can occur in the direction of revolution. When $\beta = 0$, the efficiency becomes unity, but the velocity u_1 becomes infinity. In the reaction wheel, therefore, high efficiency can only be secured by making the direction of the issuing water directly opposite to that of the revolution, and by having the speed very great. If $\beta = 19°.5$ or $\sin \beta = \frac{1}{3}$, the advantageous velocity u_1 becomes $\sqrt{2gh}$ and e becomes 0.67. The effect of friction of the water on the sides of the revolving tube is not here considered, but this will be done in Art. 172.

Prob. 162*a*. Compute the theoretic efficiency of the reaction wheel when $\theta = 180°$, $\beta = 0°$, and $u_1 = \sqrt{2gh}$.

Prob. 162*b*. A reaction wheel has $\beta = 30°$, $r_1 = 0.302$ meters, and $h = 4.5$ meters. Compute the most advantageous number of revolutions per minute. If the quantity of water delivered to the wheel is 1600 liters per minute, compute the power of the wheel in metric horse-powers and in kilowatts.

Prob. 162*c*. When l is in meters, v in meters per second, and p, p_1, and p_0 are in kilograms per square centimeter, the formulas $(157)_3$ for water hammer become

$$p = 0.0204\,(l/t)\,v + p_1 - p_0 \qquad p = 14.5\,v + p_1 - p_0$$

the first of which is to be used when t is greater than $0.001404l$ and the second when t is equal to or less than it, l being in meters.

CHAPTER 13

WATER WHEELS

Art. 163. Conditions of High Efficiency

A hydraulic motor is an apparatus for utilizing the energy of a waterfall. It generally consists of a wheel which is caused to revolve either by the weight of water falling from a higher to a lower level, or by the dynamic pressure due to the change in direction and velocity of a moving stream. When the water enters at only one part of the circumference, the apparatus is called a water wheel; when it enters around the entire circumference, it is called a turbine. In this chapter and the next these two classes of motors will be discussed in order to determine the conditions which render them most efficient. Overshot wheels, which move under the weight of water caught in their buckets, and undershot wheels, which move under the impact of a flowing stream, are forms that have been used for many centuries. Impulse wheels, which owe their motion to a jet of water striking their vanes with high velocity, were perfected in the nineteenth century.

The efficiency e of a motor ought, if possible, to be independent of the amount of water used, or if not, it should be the greatest when the water supply is low. This is very difficult to attain. It should be noted, however, that it is not the mere variation in the quantity of water which causes the efficiency to vary, but it is the losses of head which are consequent thereon. For instance, when water is low, gates must be lowered to diminish the area of orifices, and this produces sudden changes of section which diminish the effective head h. A complete theoretic expression for the efficiency will hence not include W, the weight of water supplied per second, but it should, if possible, include the losses of energy or head which result when W varies. The actual efficiency of a motor can only be determined by tests with the friction brake (Art. 149); the theoretic efficiency, as deduced from formulas like those of the last chapter, will as a rule be higher than the actual, because it is impossible to formulate accurately all the sources of loss. Nevertheless the deduction and discussion of formulas for theoretic efficiency are very important for the correct understanding and successful construction of all kinds of hydraulic motors.

When a weight of water W falls in each second through the height h, or when it is delivered with the velocity v, its theoretic energy per second is

$$K = Wh \qquad \text{or} \qquad K = W\frac{v^2}{2g}$$

The actual work per second equals the theoretic energy minus all the losses of energy. These losses may be divided into two classes: first, those caused by the transformation of energy into heat; and second, those due to the velocity v_1 with which the water reaches the level of the tail race. The first class includes losses in friction, losses in foam and eddies consequent upon sudden changes in cross-section or from allowing the entering water to dash improperly against surfaces; let the loss of work due to this be Wh', in which h' is the head lost by these causes. The second loss is due merely to the fact that the departing water carries away the energy $W \cdot v_1^2/2g$. The work per second imparted by the water to the wheel then is

$$k = W\left(h - h' - \frac{v_1^2}{2g}\right)$$

and dividing this by the theoretic energy the efficiency is,

$$e = 1 - \frac{h'}{h} - \left(\frac{v_1}{v}\right)^2 \qquad (163)$$

in which v is the velocity due to the head h. This formula, although very general, must be the basis of all discussions on the theory of water wheels and motors. It shows that e can only become unity when $h' = 0$ and $v_1 = 0$, and accordingly the two following fundamental conditions must be fulfilled in order to secure high efficiency:

1. The water must enter and pass through the wheel without losing energy in friction and foam.
2. The water must reach the level of the tail race without absolute velocity.

These two requirements are expressed in popular language by the well-known maxim "the water should enter the wheel without shock and leave without velocity." Here the word "shock" means that method of introducing the water upon the wheel which produces foam and eddies.

The friction of the wheel upon its bearings is included in the lost work when the power and efficiency are actually measured as described in Art. 149. But as this is not a hydraulic loss it should not be included in the lost work k' when discussing the wheel merely as a user of water, as will be done in this chapter. The amount lost in shaft and journal friction in good constructions may be estimated at 2 or 3 percent of the theoretic energy, so that in discussing the hydraulic losses the maximum value of e will not be unity, but about 0.98 or 0.97. This will usually be rendered considerably smaller by the friction of the wheel upon the air or water in which it moves, and which will here not be regarded. The efficiency given by (163) is called the hydraulic efficiency to distinguish it from the actual efficiency as determined by the friction brake.

Prob. 163. A wheel using 70 cubic feet of water per minute under a head of 12.4 feet has an efficiency of 63 percent. What effective horse-power does it deliver?

Art. 164. Overshot Wheels

In the overshot wheel the water acts largely by its weight. Figure 164 shows an end view or vertical section, which so fully illustrates its action that no detailed explanation is necessary. The total fall from the surface of the water in the head race or flume to the surface in the tail race is called h, and the weight of water delivered per second to the wheel is called W. Then the theoretic energy per second imparted to the wheel is Wh. It is required to determine the conditions which will render the effective work of the wheel as near to Wh as possible.

The total fall may be divided into three parts: that in which the water is filling the buckets, that in which the water is descending in the filled buckets, and that which remains after the buckets are emptied. Let the first of these parts be called h_0, and the last h_1. In falling the distance h_0 the water acquires a velocity v_0 which is approximately equal to $\sqrt{2gh_0}$, and then, striking the buckets, this is reduced to u, the tangential velocity of the wheel, whereby a loss of energy in impact occurs. It then descends through the distance $h - h_0 - h_1$, acting by its weight alone, and finally, dropping out of the buckets, reaches the level of the tail race with a velocity which causes a second loss of energy. Let h' be the head lost in entering the buckets, and let v_1 be the velocity of the water as it reaches the level of the tail race. Then the hydraulic efficiency of the wheel is given by the general formula (163), or

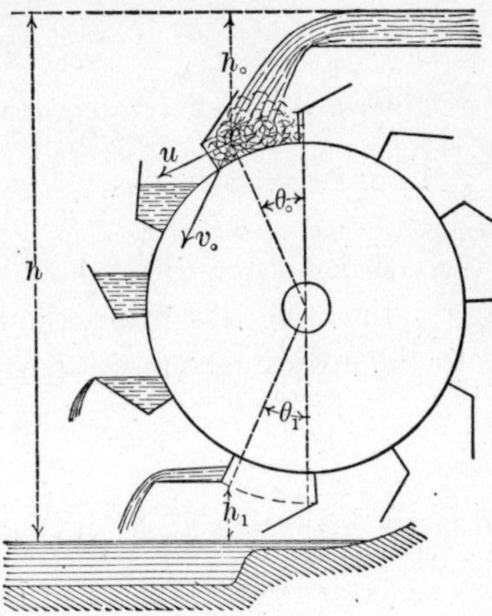

Fig. 164.

$$e = 1 - \frac{h'}{h} - \frac{v_1^2}{v^2}$$

and to apply it, the values of h' and v_1 are to be found. In this equation v is the velocity duc to the head h, or $v = \sqrt{2gh}$.

The head lost in impact when a stream of water with the velocity v_0 is enlarged in section so as to have the smaller velocity u, is, as proved in Art. 76,

$$h' = \frac{(v_0 - u)^2}{2g} = \frac{v_0^2 - 2\,v_0 u + u^2}{2g}$$

The velocity v_1 with which the water reaches the tail race depends upon the velocity u and the height h_1. Its kinetic energy as it leaves the buckets is $W \cdot u^2/2g$, the potential energy of the fall h_1 is Wh_1, and the resultant kinetic energy as it reaches the tail race is $W \cdot v_1^2/2g$; hence the value of v_1 is

$$v_1 = \sqrt{u^2 + 2\,gh_1}$$

Inserting these values of h' and v_1 in the formula for e, and placing for v^2 its equivalent $2gh$, there is found

$$e = 1 - \frac{v_0^2 - 2v_0u + 2u^2 + 2gh_1}{2gh}$$

The value of u which renders e a maximum is found by equating the first derivative to zero, which gives

$$u = \tfrac{1}{2}v_0$$

or the velocity of the wheel should be one-half that of the entering water. Inserting this value, the hydraulic efficiency corresponding to the advantageous velocity is

$$e = 1 - \frac{\frac{1}{2}v_0^2 + 2gh_1}{2gh}$$

and lastly, replacing v_0^2 by its value $2gh_0$, it becomes

$$e = 1 - \frac{1}{2}\frac{h_0}{h} - \frac{h_1}{h} \qquad (164)$$

which is the maximum efficiency of the overshot wheel.

This investigation shows that one-half of the entrance fall h_0 and the whole of the exit fall h_1 are lost, and it is hence plain that in order to make e as large as possible both h_0 and h_1 should be as small as possible. The fall h_0 is made small by making the radius of the wheel large; but it cannot be made zero, for then no water would enter the wheel; it is generally taken so as to make the angle θ_0 about 10 or 15 degrees. The fall h_1 is made small by giving to the buckets a form which will retain the water as long as possible. As the water really leaves the wheel at several points along the lower circumference, the value of h_1 cannot usually be determined with exactness.

The practical advantageous velocity of the overshot wheel, as determined by the method of Art. 149, is found to be about $0.4v_0$, and its efficiency is found to be high, ranging from 70 to 90 percent. In times of drought, when the water supply is low, and it is desirable to utilize all the power available, its efficiency is the highest, since then the buckets are but partly filled and h_1 becomes small. Herein lies the great advantage of the overshot wheel; its disadvantage is in its large size and the expense of construction and maintenance.

The number of buckets and their depth are governed by no laws except those of experience. Usually the number of buckets is about $5r$ or $6r$, if r is the radius of the wheel in feet, and their radial depth is from 10 to 15 inches. The breadth of the wheel parallel to its axis depends upon the quantity of water supplied, and should be so great that the buckets are not fully filled with water, in order that they may retain it as long as possible and thus make h_1 small. The wheel should be set with its outer circumference at the level of the tail water.

Prob. 164. Estimate the horse-power and efficiency of an overshot wheel which uses 1080 cubic feet of water per minute under a head of 26 feet, the diameter of the wheel being 23 feet, and the water entering 15° from the top and leaving 12° from the bottom.

Art. 165. Breast Wheels

The breast wheel is applicable to small falls, and the action of the water is partly by impulse and partly by weight. As represented in Fig. 165 water from a reservoir is admitted through an orifice upon the wheel under the head h_0 with the velocity v_0; the water being then confined between the vanes and the curved breast acts by its weight through a distance h_2, which is approximately equal to $h - h_0$, until finally it is released at the level of the tail race and departs with the velocity u, which is the same as that of the circumference of the wheel. The total energy of the water being Wh, the work of the wheel is eWh, if e be its efficiency.

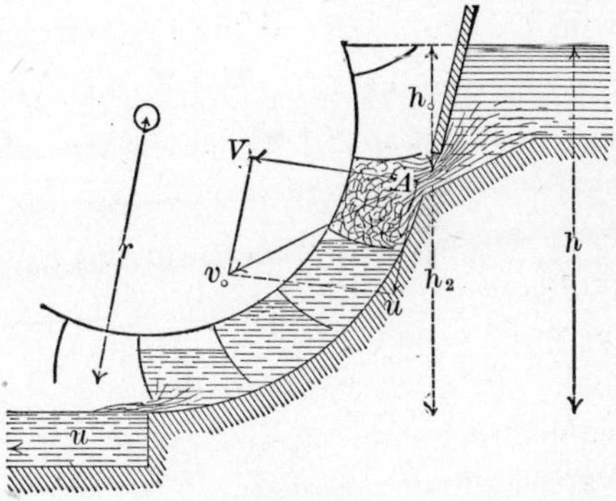

Fig. 165.

The reasoning of the last article may be applied to the breast wheel, h_1 being made equal to zero, and the expression there deduced for e may be regarded as an approximate value of its theoretic efficiency. It appears, then, that e will be the greater the smaller the fall h_0; but owing to leakage between the wheel and the curved breast, which cannot be theoretically estimated, and which is less for high velocities than for low ones, it is not desirable to make v_0 and h_0 small. The efficiency of the breast wheel is hence materially less than that of the overshot, and usually ranges from 50 to 80 percent, the lower values being for small wheels.

Another method of determining the theoretic efficiency of the breast wheel is to discuss the action of the water in entering and leaving the vanes as a case of impulse. Let at the point of entrance Av_0 and Au be drawn parallel and equal to the velocities v_0 and u, the former being that of the entering water and the latter that of the vanes. Let α be the angle between v_0 and u, which may be called the angle of approach. Then the dynamic pressure exerted by the water in entering upon and leaving the vanes is, from Art. 158,

$$P = W\frac{v_0 \cos\alpha - u}{g}$$

and the work performed by it per second is

$$k_0 = W\frac{(v_0 \cos\alpha - u)u}{g}$$

This expression has its maximum value when

$$u = \tfrac{1}{2}v_0 \cos\alpha$$

which gives the advantageous velocity of the wheel circumference, and the corresponding work of the dynamic pressure is

$$k_0 = W\frac{v_0^2 \cos^2\alpha}{4g}$$

Adding this to the work Wh_2 done by the weight of the water, the total work of the wheel when running at the advantageous velocity is found to be

$$k = W\left(\frac{v_0^2 \cos^2\alpha}{4g} + h_2\right)$$

or, if v_0^2 be replaced by its value $c_v^2 \cdot 2gh_0$, where c_v is the coefficient of velocity for the stream as it leaves the orifice of the reservoir,

$$k = W(\tfrac{1}{2}c_v^2 \cos^2 \alpha \cdot h_0 + h_2)$$

whence the maximum hydraulic efficiency of the wheel is

$$e = \tfrac{1}{2}c_v^2 \cos^2 \alpha \cdot \frac{h_0}{h} + \frac{h_2}{h} \qquad (165)$$

If in this expression h_2 be replaced by $h - h_0$, and if $c_v = 1$ and $\alpha = 0°$, this reduces to the same value as found for the overshot wheel. The angle α, however, cannot be zero, for then the direction of the entering water would be tangential to the wheel, and it could not impinge upon the vanes; its value, however, should be small, say from 10° to 25°. The coefficient c_v is to be rendered large by making the orifice of the discharge with well-rounded inner corners so as to avoid contraction and the losses incident thereto. The above formulas cannot be relied upon in practice to give close values of k and e, on account of losses by foam and leakage along the curved breast, which of course cannot be algebraically expressed.

Prob. 165. A breast wheel is 10.5 feet in diameter, and has $c_1 = 0.93$, $h_0 = 4.2$ feet, and $\alpha = 12$ degrees. Compute the most advantageous number of revolutions per minute.

Art. 166. Undershot Wheels

The common undershot wheel has plane radial vanes, and the water passes beneath it in a direction nearly horizontal. It may then be regarded as a breast wheel where the action is entirely by impulse, so that in the preceding equations h_2 becomes 0, h_0 becomes h, and α will be 0°. The theoretic efficiency then is $e = \frac{1}{2}c_v^2$. In the best constructions the coefficient c_v is nearly unity, so it may be concluded that the maximum efficiency of the undershot wheel is about 0.5. Experiments show that its actual efficiency varies from 0.20 to 0.40, and that the advantageous velocity is about $0.4v_0$ instead of $0.5v_0$. The lowest efficiencies are obtained from wheels placed in an unlimited flowing current, as upon a scow anchored in a stream; and the highest from those where the stream beneath the wheel is confined by walls so as to prevent the water from spreading laterally.

The Poncelet wheel, so called from its distinguished inventor, has curved vanes, which are so arranged that the water leaves them tangentially, with its absolute velocity less than that of the velocity of the wheel. If in Fig. 165 the fall h_2 be very small, and the vanes be curved more than represented, it will exhibit the main features of the Poncelet wheel. The water entering with the absolute velocity v_0 takes the velocity u of the vane and the velocity V relative to the vane. Passing then under the wheel, its dynamic pressure performs work; and on leaving the vane its relative velocity V is probably nearly the same as that at entrance. Then if V be drawn tangent to the vane at the point

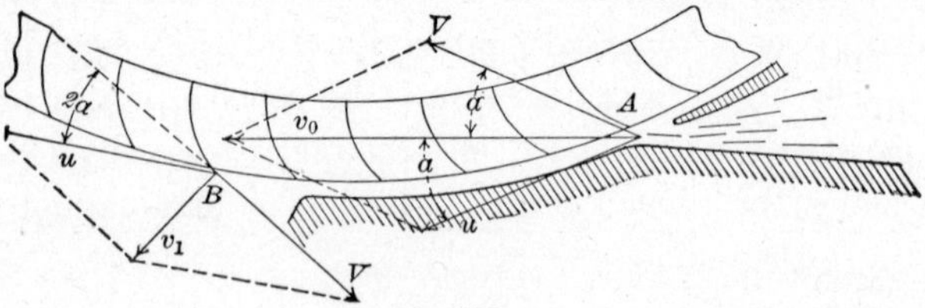

Fig. 166.

of exit, and u tangent to the circumference, their resultant will be v_1, the absolute velocity of exit, which will be much less than u. Consequently the energy carried away by the departing water is less than in the usual forms of breast and undershot wheels, and it is found by experiment that the efficiency may be as high as 60 percent.

In Fig. 166 is shown a portion of a Poncelet wheel. At A the water enters the wheel through a nozzle-like opening with the absolute velocity v_0 and at B it leaves with the absolute velocity v_1. In the figure A and B have the same elevation. At A the entering stream makes the approach angle α with the circumference of the wheel and the same angle with the vane, so that the relative velocity V is equal to the velocity of the outer circumference u. If h be the head on A, the theoretic work of the water is Wh, and the work of the wheel is

$$k = W\frac{v_0^2 - v_1^2}{2g}$$

and the efficiency, neglecting friction and leakage, is

$$e = \frac{v_0^2 - v_1^2}{2gh}$$

Now, let c_v be the coefficient of velocity of the entrance orifice, then $v_0 = c_v \sqrt{2gh}$. From the parallelograms of velocity at A and B, there are found

$$u = \frac{v_0}{2 \cos\alpha} \qquad v_1 = 2\, u \sin\alpha = v_0 \tan\alpha$$

and for this velocity u the efficiency of the wheel is

$$e = c_v^2(1 - \tan^2\alpha) \tag{166}$$

If $c_v = 1$ and $\alpha = 0$, the efficiency becomes unity. In the best constructions c_v may be made from 0.95 to 0.98, but α cannot be a very small angle, since then no water could enter the wheel. If $\alpha = 30°$ and $c_v = 0.95$ the efficiency is 0.60, which is probably a higher value than usually attained in practice. If the velocity be greater or less than $\frac{1}{2}v_0/\cos\alpha$, the efficiency will be lowered on account of shock and foam at A.

Prob. 166. Estimate the horse-power that can be obtained from an undershot wheel with plane radial vanes placed in a stream having a mean velocity of 5 feet per second, the width of the wheel being 15 feet, its diameter 8 feet, and the maximum immersion of the vanes being 1.33 feet. How many revolutions per minute should this wheel make in order to furnish the maximum power?

Art. 167. Vertical Impulse Wheels

A vertical wheel like Fig. 166, but having smaller vanes against which the water is delivered from a nozzle, is often called an impulse wheel, or a "hurdy-gurdy" wheel. The Pelton wheel, the Cascade wheel, and other forms can be purchased in several sizes and are convenient on account of their portability. Figure 167a shows an outline sketch of such a wheel with the vanes somewhat exaggerated in size. The simplest vanes are radial planes as at A, but these give a low efficiency. Curved vanes, as at B, are generally used, as these cause the water to turn backward, opposite to the direction of the motion, and thus to leave the wheel with a low absolute velocity (Art. 159). In the plan

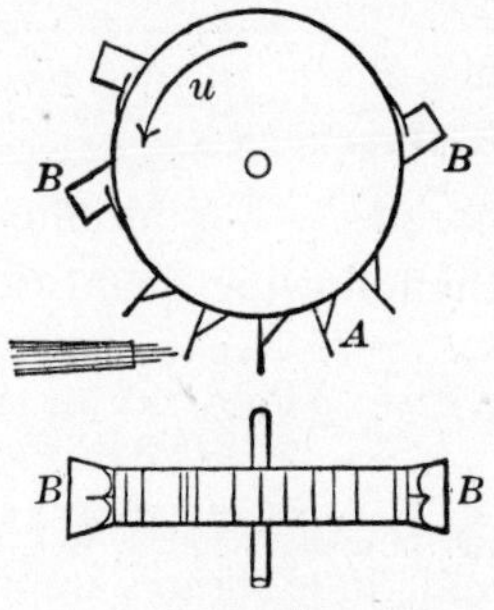

Fig. 167a.

of the wheel it is seen that the vanes may be arranged so as also to turn the water sidewise while deflecting it backward. The experiments of Browne * show that with plane radial vanes the highest efficiency was 40.2 percent, while with curved vanes or cups 82.5 percent was attained. The velocity of the vanes which gave the highest efficiency was in each case almost exactly one-half the velocity of the jet.

The Pelton wheel is used under high heads, and also being of small size it has a high velocity. The effective head is that measured at the entrance of the nozzle by a pressure gage, corrected for velocity of approach and the loss in the nozzle by formula $(83)_1$. These wheels are wholly of iron, and are provided with a casing to prevent the spattering of the water. Fig. 167*b* shows a form with three nozzles, by which three streams are applied at different parts of the circumference, in order to obtain a greater power than by a single nozzle, or to obtain a greater speed by using smaller nozzles. For an effective head of 100 feet and a single nozzle the following quantities are given by the manufacturers:

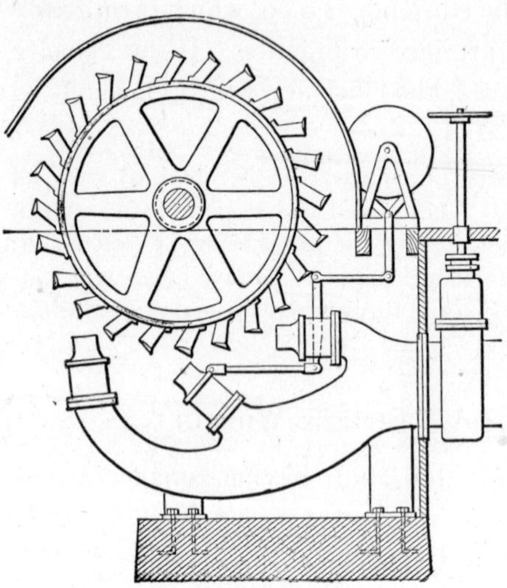

Fig. 167*b*.

Diameter in feet,	1	2	3	4	6
Cubic feet per minute,	8.29	44.19	99.52	176.7	398.1
Revolutions per minute,	726	363	242	181	121
Horse-powers,	1.40	7.49	16.84	29.93	67.3

and these figures imply an efficiency of 85 percent.

The general theory of these vertical impulse wheels is the same as that given for moving vanes in Art. 158. Owing to the high

* Bowie's Treatise on Hydraulic Mining (New York, 1885), p. 193.

velocity, more or less shock occurs at entrance, and as the angle of exit β cannot be made small, the water leaves the vanes with more or less absolute velocity. The advantageous velocity of the vanes or cups is between 40 and 50 percent of that of the entering jet.

Prob. 167. The diameter of a hurdy-gurdy wheel is 12.5 feet between centers of vanes, and the impinging jet has a velocity of 58.5 feet per second and a diameter of 0.182 feet. The efficiency of the wheel is 44.5 percent, when making 62 revolutions per minute What effective horse-power does it furnish?

Art. 168. Horizontal Impulse Wheels

When a wheel is placed with its plane horizontal and is driven by a stream of water from a nozzle, it is called a horizontal impulse wheel. There are two forms, known as the outward-flow and the inward-flow wheel. In the former, shown in Fig. 168*a*, the water enters the wheel upon the inner and leaves it upon the

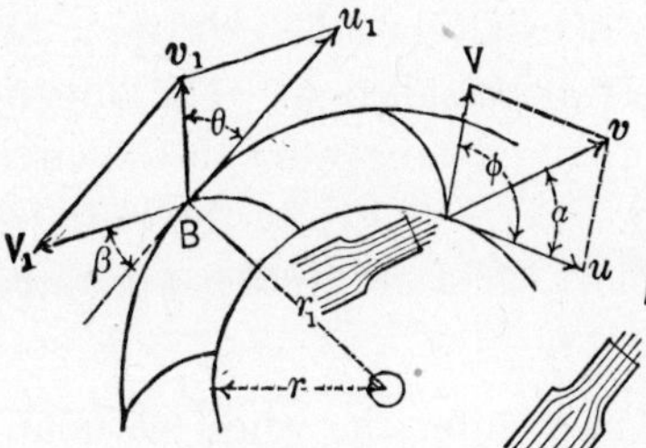

Fig. 168*a*.

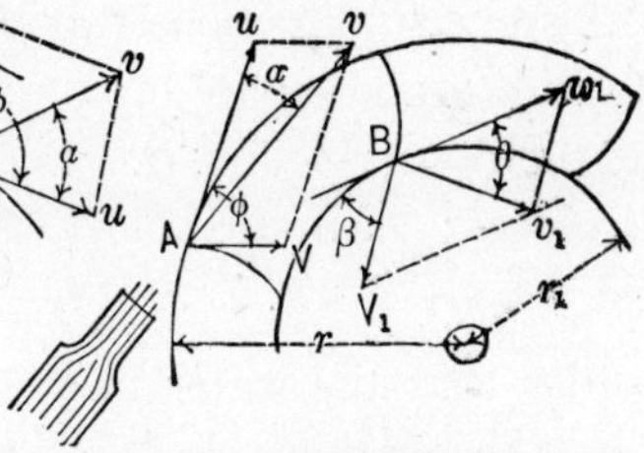

Fig. 168*b*.

outer circumference; in the latter, shown in Fig. 168*b*, the water enters upon the outer and leaves upon the inner circumference. The water issuing from the nozzle with the velocity v impinges upon the vanes, and in passing through the wheel alters both its direction and its absolute velocity, thus transforming its energy into useful work. The energy of the entering water is $W \cdot v^2/2g$ and that of the departing water is $W \cdot v_1^2/2g$. Neglecting frictional resistances, the work imparted to the wheel by the water is

$$k = W\left(\frac{v^2}{2g} - \frac{v_1^2}{2g}\right)$$

and dividing this by the theoretic energy, the efficiency is

$$e = 1 - (v_1/v)^2$$

This is the same as the general formula (163) if $h' = 0$; that is, if losses in foam and friction are disregarded, and if the wheel is set at the level of the tail race. It is now required to state the conditions which will render these losses and also the velocity v_1 as small as possible. The reasoning will be general and applicable to both outward and inward-flow wheels.

At the point A where the water enters the wheel let the parallelogram of velocities be drawn, the absolute velocity of entrance being resolved into its two components, the velocity u of the wheel at that point, and the velocity V relative to the vane; let the approach angle between u and v be called α, and the entrance angle between u and V be called ϕ. At the point B where the water leaves the wheel let V_1 be its velocity relative to the vane, and u_1 the velocity of the wheel at that point; then their resultant is v_1, the absolute velocity of exit. Let the exit angle between V_1 and the reverse direction of u_1 be called β. The directions of the velocities u and u_1 are of course tangential to the circumferences at the points A and B. Let r and r_1 be the radii of these circumferences; then the velocities of revolution are directly as the radii, or $ur_1 = u_1 r$.

In order that the water may enter the wheel without shock and foam, the relative velocity V should be tangent to the vane at A, so that the water may smoothly glide along it. This will be the case if the wheel is run at such speed that the parallelogram at A can be formed, or when the velocities u and v are proportional to the sines of the angles opposite them in the triangle Auv. The velocity v_1 will be rendered very small by running the impulse wheel at such speed that the velocities u_1 and V_1 are equal, since then the parallelogram at B becomes a rhombus and the diagonal v_1 is very small. Hence

$$\frac{u}{v} = \frac{\sin(\phi - \alpha)}{\sin\phi} \qquad \text{and} \qquad u_1 = V_1 \qquad (168)_1$$

are the two conditions of maximum hydraulic efficiency.

Now, referring to the formula (160), which expresses the relation between the velocities of rotation and the relative velocities of the water for revolving vanes, it is seen that if $u_1 = V_1$, then also $u = V$. But u cannot equal V unless $\phi = 2\alpha$, and then $u = v/2 \cos\alpha$, which is the advantageous velocity of the circumference at A. Therefore the two conditions above reduce to

$$\phi = 2\alpha \qquad \text{and} \qquad u = \frac{v}{2 \cos\alpha} \qquad (168)_2$$

which show how the wheel should be built and what speed it should have to secure the greatest efficiency. When this speed obtains, the absolute velocity v_1 is

$$v_1 = 2u_1 \sin \tfrac{1}{2}\beta = 2u\frac{r_1}{r} \sin \tfrac{1}{2}\beta = v\frac{r_1}{r}\frac{\sin \frac{1}{2}\beta}{\cos\alpha}$$

and the corresponding hydraulic efficiency is

$$e = 1 - \left(\frac{r_1}{r}\frac{\sin \frac{1}{2}\beta}{\cos\alpha}\right)^2 \qquad (168)_3$$

by the discussion of which proper values of the approach angle α and the exit angle β can be derived.

This formula shows that both the approach angle α and the exit angle β should be small in order to give high efficiency, but they cannot be zero, as then no water could pass through the wheel; values of from 15° to 30° are usual in practice. It also shows that β is more important than α, and if β be small, α may sometimes be made 40° or 45°. It likewise shows that for given values of α and β the inward-flow wheel, in which r_1 is less than r, has a higher efficiency than the outward-flow wheel.

The condition $V_1 = u_1$ renders the absolute exit velocity v_1 very small, but it does not give its true minimum. This will be obtained by making $V_1 = u_1 \cos \beta$, so that the direction of v_1 is normal to that of V_1, and thus $v_1 = u_1 \sin \beta$. The discussion of water wheels and turbines under this condition of the true minimum leads to very complex formulas, and hence in this book, as in many others, the simpler condition $V_1 = u_1$ is used.

Prob. 168. Compute the maximum efficiency of an outward-flow impulse wheel when $r_1 = 3$ feet, $r = 2$ feet, $\alpha = 45°$, $\phi = 90°$, $\beta = 30°$, and find the number of revolutions per minute required to secure such efficiency when the velocity of the entering stream is v = 100 feet per second.

Art. 169. Downward-flow Impulse Wheels

In the impulse wheels thus far considered the water leaves the vanes in a horizontal direction. Another form used less frequently is that of a horizontal wheel driven by water issuing from an inclined nozzle so that it passes downward along the vanes without approaching or receding from the axis. Figure 169 shows an outline plan of such an impulse wheel and a development of a part of a cylindrical section. Let v be the velocity of the entering stream, u that of the wheel at the point where it strikes the vanes, and v_1 the absolute velocity of the departing water. At the entrance A the direction of v makes with that of u the approach angle α, and the direction of the relative velocity V makes with that of u the entrance angle ϕ. The water then passes over the vane, and, neglecting the influence of friction and gravity, it issues at B with the same relative velocity V, making the exit angle β with the plane of motion.

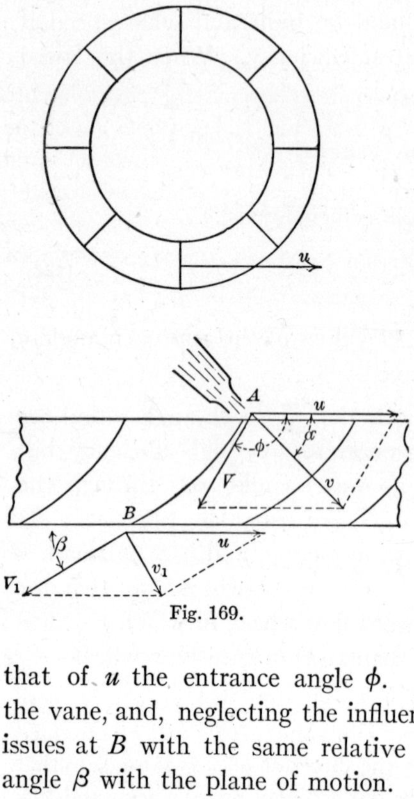

Fig. 169.

The condition that impact and foam shall be avoided at A is fulfilled by making the relative velocity V tangent to the vane, and the condition that the absolute velocity v_1 shall be small is fulfilled by making the velocities u and V equal at B. Hence, as in the last article, the best construction is to make $\phi = 2\alpha$, and the best speed of the wheel is $u = v/2\cos\alpha$. Also by the same reasoning the efficiency under these conditions is

$$e = 1 - (\sin \tfrac{1}{2}\beta/\cos\alpha)^2$$

which shows that α, and especially β, should be a small angle to give a high numerical value of e. For instance, if both these angles are 30°, the efficiency is 0.92, but if $\alpha = 45°$ and $\beta = 10°$, the efficiency is 0.94.

Although these wheels are but little used, there seems to be no hydraulic reason why they should not be employed with a success equal to or greater than that attained by vertical impulse wheels. It will be possible to arrange several nozzles around the circumference and thus to secure a high power with a small wheel. The fall of the water through the vertical distance between A and B will also add slightly to the power of the wheel, and if this be taken into account, the above values of advantageous velocity and efficiency will be modified, both being slightly increased, as the following investigation shows.

Let h_1 be the vertical fall between A and B; then the theoretic energy of the water with respect to B is

$$K = W\left(h_1 + \frac{v^2}{2g} - \frac{v_1^2}{2g}\right)$$

and the hydraulic efficiency of the wheel is

$$e = 1 - \frac{v_1^2}{v^2 + 2gh_1}$$

Here the relative velocity V_1 at B is greater than V, or

$$V_1^2 = V^2 + 2\,gh_1$$

and since u should equal V_1, this equation becomes, after inserting for V its value in terms of u, v, and α,

$$u = \frac{v}{2\cos\alpha}\left(1 + \frac{2gh_1}{v^2}\right)$$

which gives the advantageous velocity of the wheel. Since

$$v_1 = 2u \sin \tfrac{1}{2}\beta,$$

the above expression for the theoretic hydraulic efficiency reduces to

$$e = 1 - \left(1 + \frac{2gh_1}{v^2}\right)\left(\frac{\sin \frac{1}{2}\beta}{\cos\alpha}\right)^2$$

For this case the approach angle ϕ must be a little greater than 2α, and its value can be found by

$$\cot\phi = \cot\alpha - \frac{v^2 + 2gh_1}{v^2 \sin 2\alpha}$$

and by using this angle ϕ, losses due to impact will be avoided when the wheel is run at the advantageous speed. For example, if $v = 50$ feet per second, and $h_1 = 1$ foot, and $\alpha = 30°$, the value of ϕ is about 63° instead of 60° as the simpler condition requires, while the increase in the advantageous speed is about 2 percent over the former value.

Prob. 169. A wheel like Fig. 169 is driven by water which issues from a nozzle with a velocity of 100 feet per second. If the diameter is 3 feet, the efficiency 0.90, and the approach angle $\alpha = 45°$, find the best value of the entrance and exit angles and the best speed.

Art. 170. Nozzles for Impulse Wheels

Impulse wheels are driven by the dynamic pressure of water issuing from nozzles attached to the end of a pipe which conducts the water from a reservoir. It is shown in Art. 101 that the greatest velocity is secured when the diameter of the nozzle is as small as possible and that the greatest discharge occurs when there is no nozzle. To secure the greatest power, however, there is a certain diameter of nozzle which will now be determined, and it is advisable for economical reasons to use a nozzle of this size and adjust the speed of the wheel thereto.

Let h be the hydrostatic head on the nozzle, l the length, and d the diameter of the pipe, and D the diameter of the nozzle. Let all the resistances except that due to friction in the pipe and nozzle be neglected; then from Art. 101 the velocity of the jet from the nozzle is

$$V = \sqrt{\frac{2gh}{f(l/d)(D/d)^4 + (1/c_v)^2}}$$

in which f is the friction factor for the pipe and c_v is the coefficient of velocity for the nozzle. Let w be the weight of a cubic foot of water; then the theoretic energy of the jet per second is

$$K = w \cdot \tfrac{1}{4}\pi D^2 V \cdot \frac{V^2}{2g} = \frac{\pi w}{8g}\left(\frac{2gc_v{}^2 hd^5 D^{\frac{4}{3}}}{fc_1{}^2 lD^4 + d^5}\right)^{\frac{3}{2}}$$

and the value of D which renders this a maximum is, by the usual method of differentiation, ascertained to be

$$D = (d^5/2fc_v^2l)^{\frac{1}{4}} \qquad (170)_1$$

and for a nozzle of this size the velocity of the jet is

$$V = 0.816c_v\sqrt{2gh}$$

or, since c_v is about 0.97, the velocity of the jet when leaving the nozzle is about 80 percent of the theoretic velocity due to the head on the nozzle.

As an example let a pipe be 1200 feet long and 1 foot in diameter; then, taking for f the mean value 0.02 and using $c_v = 0.97$, there is found $D = 0.39$ feet, and hence a nozzle $4\frac{5}{8}$ inches in diameter is required to give the maximum power. This result may be revised, if thought necessary, by finding the velocity in the pipe and thus getting a better value of f from Table 90*a*. If the head be 100 feet, this velocity is found to be 9.2 feet per second, whence $f = 0.018$, and on repeating the computation there is found $D = 0.40$ feet $= 4.8$ inches. If the pipe be 12 000 feet long, the advantageous diameter of the nozzle will be found to be much smaller, namely, $2\frac{1}{4}$ inches.

When there is more than one nozzle at the end of the pipe, the above investigation must be modified. Let there be two nozzles with the diameters D_1 and D_2, each having the coefficient c_v Then the discharge $\frac{1}{4}\pi d^2v$ through the pipe equals the discharge $\frac{1}{4}\pi(D_1^2V_1 + D_2^2V_2)$. But the velocities V_1 and V_2 are equal if the tips of the nozzles are on the same elevation, and hence d^2v equals $(D_1^2 + D_2^2)V$, where V is the velocity of flow from each nozzle. Now, referring to Art. 101 and to the proof of $(170)_1$, it is seen that it applies to this case provided D^2 be replaced by $D_1^2 + D_2^2$, and accordingly

$$D_1^2 + D_2^2 = (d^5/2fc_v^2l)^{\frac{1}{2}} \qquad (170)_2$$

is the formula for determining the sizes of the two nozzles which will furnish the maximum power; if D_1 be assumed, the value of D_2 can be computed. The area of the circle of diameter D found from $(170)_1$ is equal to the sum of the areas of the two circles found from $(170)_2$. If there be three or more nozzles, the sum of their areas is equal to that corresponding to the diameter D as computed from

$(170)_1$. For example, let there be a pipe 1200 feet long and one foot in diameter to which three nozzles of equal size are attached. The diameter found above for one nozzle is 4.80 inches, and the corresponding area is 18.10 square inches; hence the area of the cross-section of the tip of each of the three nozzles is 6.03 square inches, which corresponds to a diameter of 2.77 inches.

Prob. 170. A pipe 15 000 feet long and 18 inches in diameter runs from a mountain reservoir to a power plant, where the water is to be delivered through two nozzles against a hurdy-gurdy wheel. If the diameter of one nozzle is 2 inches, find the diameter of the other in order that the maximum power may be developed. If the head on the nozzles is 623 feet and the efficiency of the wheel 79 percent, compute the horse-power that may be expected.

Art. 171. Special Forms of Wheels

Numerous varieties of the water wheels above described have been used, but the variation lies in mechanical details rather than in the introduction of any new hydraulic principles. In order that a wheel may be a success it must furnish power as cheap as or cheaper than steam or other motors, and to this end compactness, durability, and low cost of installation and maintenance are essential.

A variety of the overshot wheel, called the back-pitch wheel, has been built, in which the water is introduced on the back instead of on the front of the wheel. The buckets are hence differently arranged from those of the usual form, and the wheel revolves also in an opposite direction. One of the largest overshot wheels ever constructed is at Laxey, on the east coast of the Isle of Man. It is $72\frac{1}{2}$ feet in diameter, about 10 feet in width, and furnishes about 150 horse-power, which is used for pumping water out of a mine.

A breast wheel with very long curved vanes extending over nearly a fourth of the circumference has been used for small falls, the water entering directly from the penstock without impulse, so that the action is that of weight alone. This form is made of iron and gives a high efficiency.

Undershot wheels with curved floats for use in the open current of a river have been employed, but in order to obtain much power they require to be large in size, and hence have not been able to compete with other forms. The great amount of power wasted in all rivers should, however, incite inventors to devise wheels that can economically utilize it. Currents due to the movement of the tides also afford opportunity for the exercise of inventive talent.

The conical wheel, or danaïde, is an ancient form of downward-flow impulse wheel, in which the water approaches the axis as it descends, and thus its relative motion is decreased by the centrifugal force. The theory of this is almost precisely the same as that of an inward-flow impulse wheel, and there seems to be no hydraulic reason why it should not give a high efficiency. Another form of danaïde has two or more vertical vanes attached to an axis, which are inclosed in a conical case to prevent the lateral escape of the water.

A water-pressure engine is a hydraulic motor which moves under the static pressure of water acting against a piston or a revolving disk. The piston forms are reciprocating in motion like the steam-engine and operate in the same way, the water entering and leaving through ports which are opened and closed by a link motion connected with the piston-rod. The other forms give rotary motion directly from the revolving vanes or disks. The piston engine has been employed in Germany to a considerable extent to drive pumps for draining mines, but the rotary engine has not been widely used, and it cannot be advantageously arranged to deliver a high power. On account of the incompressibility of water, special devices for regulating the opening and closing of the valves are necessary.

Numerous other special devices for utilizing the energy of water by means of water wheels have been invented, but they do not introduce any new hydraulic principle. The efficiency of these special forms is often low on account of the imperfections of the apparatus, but it should be borne in mind that high efficiency is only obtained after trials extending over much time, such trials enabling the imperfections to be discovered and removed. The formulas for hydraulic efficiency deduced in the preceding pages do not include losses due to friction, and these may often amount to 10 or 20 percent of the theoretic energy, so that due allowance for them should be made in estimating the power which a proposed design may deliver.

Power may be obtained from the ocean waves, which are constantly rising and falling, by a suitable arrangement of wheels and levers, and some inventions in this direction have given fair promise of success. One in operation on the coast of England about 1890 consisted of a large buoy which rose and fell with the waves on a fixed vertical shaft fastened in the rock bottom. As the buoy moved up and down it operated a system of levers and wheels which drove an air-compressor, and this in turn ran a dynamo that generated electric power. The rise of the ocean tide also affords opportunity for impounding water which may be used to generate power when the tide falls. Plants for this purpose are to be located along tidal rivers where opportunities for impounding occur, the wheels being idle during the rise of the tide, and in operation during its fall. Owing to this intermittent generation of power, it will be necessary to provide for its storage, so that industries using it may be in continuous operation.

Prob. 171*a*. A wheel using 10.5 cubic meters of water per minute under an effective head of 23.4 meters has an efficiency of 75 percent. What metric horse-power does it deliver? What is its power in kilowatts?

Prob. 171*b*. A breast wheel has $c_1 = 0.95$, $h_0 = 1.3$ meters, and $\alpha = 12°$. If its diameter is 3.5 meters, compute the most advantageous number of revolutions per minute.

Prob. 171*c*. An inward-flow impulse wheel has $\phi = 104°$, $\alpha = 52°$, and $\beta = 12°$, its inner diameter being 0.82 meters and its outer diameter 1.22 meters. If this wheel uses 0.86 cubic meters of water per second under an effective head of 7.9 meters, compute its efficiency and its probable effective horse-power.

Prob. 171*d*. A pipe 3200 meters long and 40 centimeters in diameter delivers water through two nozzles against a hurdy-gurdy wheel. When the diameter of one nozzle is 5 centimeters, find the diameter of the other nozzle in order that the energy of the two jets may be a maximum. If the head on the nozzles is 107 meters and the efficiency of the wheels is 81 percent, compute the horse-power which the wheels will deliver.

CHAPTER 14

TURBINES

Art. 172. The Reaction Wheel

The reaction wheel, invented by Barker about 1740, consists of a number of hollow arms connected with a hollow vertical shaft, as shown in Fig. 172. The water issues from the ends of the arms in a direction opposite to that of their motion, and by the dynamic pressure due to its reaction the energy of the water is transformed into useful work. Let the head of water CC in the shaft be h; then the pressure-head BB which causes the flow from the arms is greater than h, on account of the centrifugal force due to the rotation of the wheel. Let u_1 be the absolute velocity of the exit orifices, and V_1 be the velocity of discharge relative to the wheel; then, as shown in Art. 29, and also in Art. 162,

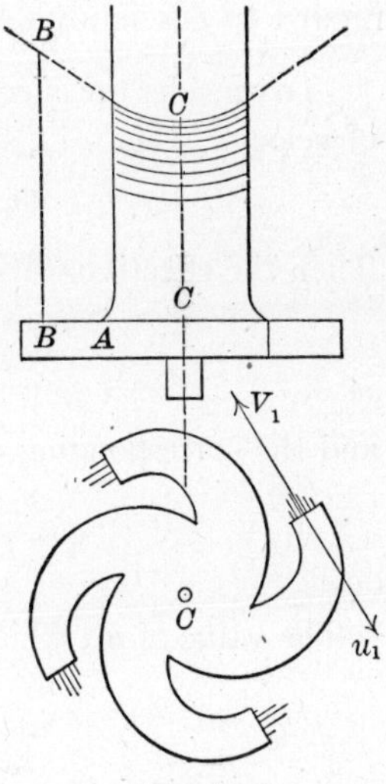

Fig. 172.

$$V_1 = \sqrt{2gh + u_1^2}$$

The absolute velocity v_1 of the issuing water now is

$$v_1 = V_1 - u_1 = \sqrt{2gh + u_1^2} - u_1$$

It is seen at once that the efficiency can never reach unity unless $v_1 = 0$, which requires that $V_1 = u_1$. This, however, can only occur when $u_1 = \infty$, since the above formula shows that V_1 must be greater than u_1 for any finite values of h and u_1. To deduce an expression for the efficiency the work of the wheel

$W(h - v_1^2/2g)$ is to be divided by the theoretic energy of the water Wh, and this gives

$$e = 1 - \frac{v_1^2}{2gh} = 1 - \frac{(V_1 - u_1)^2}{V_1^2 - u_1^2} = \frac{2u_1}{V_1 + u_1} \qquad (172)_1$$

which shows, as before, that e equals unity when $V_1 = u_1 = \infty$. If $V_1 = 2u_1$, the value of e is 0.667; if $V_1 = 3u_1$, the value of e is reduced to 0.50.

This investigation indicates that the efficiency of a reaction wheel increases with its speed. If a_1 be the area of the exit orifices and w the weight of a cubic unit of water, the weight of the water discharged in one second is wa_1V_1, which becomes infinite when $V_1 = u_1 = \infty$. Nothing approaching this can be realized, and on account of losses due to friction, a very high speed is impracticable. The reaction wheel, indeed, is like the jet propeller in regard to efficiency (Art. 186).

To consider the effect of friction in the arms, let c_v be the coefficient of velocity (Chap. 7), so that

$$V_1 = c_v\sqrt{2gh + u_1^2}$$

Then the effective work of the wheel is

$$k = W\frac{(c_v\sqrt{2gh + u_1^2} - u_1)u_1}{g}$$

and the corresponding efficiency of the wheel is

$$e = \frac{c_v u_1\sqrt{2gh + u_1^2} - u_1^2}{gh}$$

The value of u_1, which renders this a maximum, is

$$u_1^2 = \frac{gh}{\sqrt{1 - c_v^2}} - gh$$

and this reduces the value of the efficiency to

$$e = 1 - \sqrt{1 - c_v^2} \qquad (172)_2$$

If $c_v = 1$, there is no loss in friction, and $u_1 = \infty$ and $e = 1$, as before deduced. If $c_v = 0.94$, the advantageous velocity u_1 is very nearly $\sqrt{2gh}$, and e is 0.66; hence the influence of friction in diminishing the efficiency is very great. In order to make c_v large, the end of the arm where the water enters must be well rounded to prevent contraction, and the interior surface must be smooth. If the inner end has sharp, square edges, as in a standard tube (Art. 78), c_v is 0.82, and e is 0.43.

The reaction wheel is not now used as a hydraulic motor on account of its low efficiency. Even when run at high speeds the efficiency is low on account of the greater friction and resistance of the air. By experiments on a wheel one meter in diameter under a head of 1.3 feet Weisbach found a maximum efficiency of 67 percent when the velocity of revolution u_1 was $\sqrt{2gh}$. When u_1 was $2\sqrt{2gh}$, the efficiency was nothing, or all the energy was consumed in frictional resistances.

The reaction wheel is here introduced at the beginning of the discussion of turbines mainly to call attention to the fact that the discharge varies with the speed. Although sometimes called a turbine, it can scarcely be properly considered as belonging to that class of hydraulic motors.

Prob. 172. The sum of the exit orifices of a reaction wheel is 4.25 square inches, their radius is 1.75 feet, and their velocity 32.1 feet, per second. Compute the head necessary to furnish 1.6 horse-powers, when $c_v = 0.95$.

Art. 173. Classification of Turbines

A turbine wheel may be defined as one in which the water enters around the entire circumference instead of upon one portion, so that all the moving vanes are simultaneously acted upon by the dynamic pressure of the water as it changes its direction and velocity. The turbine was invented by Fourneyron in 1827, and owing to its compactness, cheapness, and high efficiency, it has largely replaced the older forms of water wheels. Turbines are usually horizontal wheels, and like the impulse wheels of the last chapter, they may be outward-flow, inward-flow, or downward-flow, with respect to the manner in which the water passes through them. In the outward-flow type the water enters the wheel around the entire inner circumference and passes out around the entire outer circumference (Fig. 174*b*). In the inward-flow type the motion is the reverse (Fig. 174*c*). In the downward-flow type the water enters around the entire upper annular openings, passes downward between the moving vanes, and leaves through the lower annulus (Fig. 179*a*). In all cases the water in leaving the wheel should have a low absolute velocity, so that most of its energy may be surrendered to the turbine in the form of useful work.

The supply of water to a turbine is regulated by a gate or gates, which can partially or entirely close the orifices where the water enters or leaves. The guides and wheel, with the gates and the surrounding casings, are made of iron. Numerous forms with different kinds of gates and different proportions of guides and vanes are in the market. They are made of all sizes from 6 to 60 inches in diameter, and larger sizes are built for special cases. The great turbines at Niagara are of the outward-flow type, the inner diameter of a wheel being 63 inches and each twin turbine furnishing about 5000 horse-powers (Art. 182). The smaller sizes of turbines used in the United States are mostly of the inward-flow type or of a combined inward- and downward-flow type.

The three typical classes of turbines above described are often called by the names of those who first invented or perfected them; thus the outward-flow is called the Fourneyron, the inward-flow the Francis, and the downward-flow the Jonval turbine. There are also many turbines in the market in which the flow is a combination of inward and downward motion, the water entering horizontally and inward, and leaving vertically, the vanes being warped surfaces. The usual efficiency of turbines at full gate is from 70 to 85 percent, although 90 percent has in some cases been derived. When the gate is partly closed, the efficiency in general decreases, and when the gate opening is small, it becomes very low. This is due to the loss of head consequent upon the sudden change of cross-section; and therein lies the disadvantage of the turbine, for when the water supply is low, it is important that it should utilize all the power available. A compilation of turbine tests with descriptions of the various forms of wheels has been made by Horton and issued by the United States Geological Survey.*

Another classification is into impulse and reaction turbines.

* Water Supply and Irrigation Paper, No. 180, 1906.

In an impulse turbine the water enters the wheel with a velocity due to the head at the point of entrance, just as it does from the nozzle which drives an impulse wheel (Art. 168). In a reaction turbine, however, the velocity of the entering water may be greater or less than that due to the head on the orifices of entrance, and, as in the reaction wheel, it is also influenced by the speed. This is due to the fact that in a reaction turbine the static pressure of the water is partially transmitted into the moving wheel, provided that the spaces between the vanes are fully filled. Any turbine may be made to act either as an impulse or a reaction turbine. If it be arranged so that the water passes through the vanes without filling them, it is an impulse turbine; if it be placed under water, or if by other means the flowing water is compelled to completely fill all the passages, it acts as a reaction turbine. As will be seen later, the theory of the reaction turbine is quite different from that of the impulse turbine.

Prob. 173. If the efficiency of a turbine is 75 percent when delivering 5000 horse-powers under a head of 136 feet, how many cubic feet of water per minute pass through it?

Art. 174. Reaction Turbines

A reaction turbine is driven by the dynamic pressure of flowing water which at the same time may be under a certain degree of static pressure. If in the reaction wheel of Fig. 172 the arms be separated from the penstock at *A*, and be so arranged that *BA* revolves around the axis while *AC* is stationary, the resulting apparatus may be called a reaction turbine. The static pressure of the head *CC* can still be transmitted through the arms, so

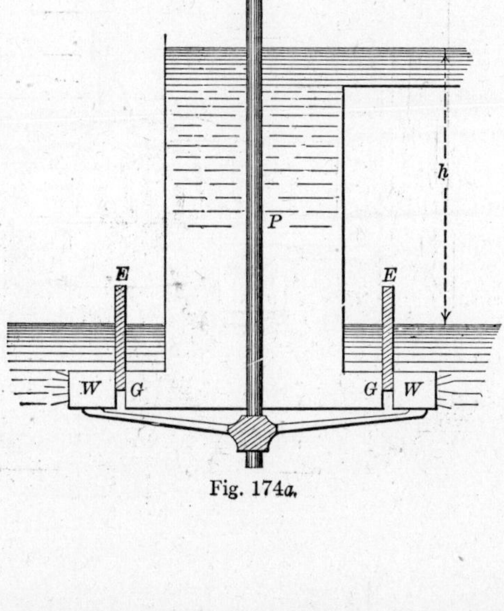

Fig. 174*a*.

that, as in the reaction wheel, the discharge will be influenced by the speed of rotation. The general arrangement of the moving part is, however, like that of an impulse wheel, the vanes being set between two annular frames, which are attached

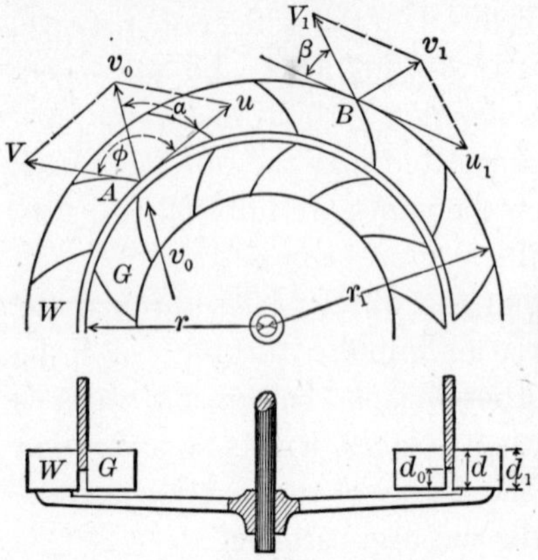

Fig. 174*b*.

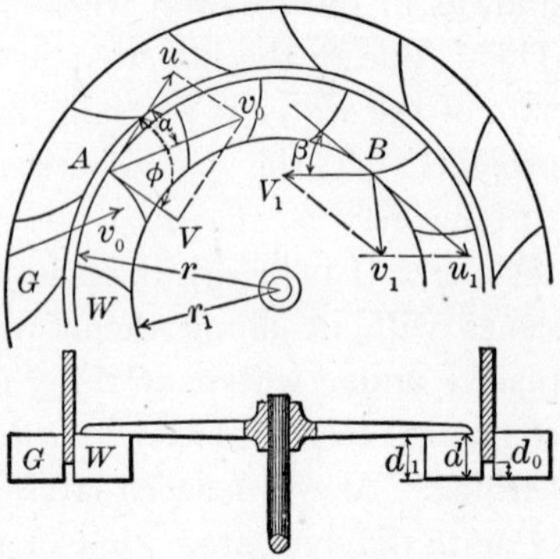

Fig. 174*c*.

by arms to a central axis. In Fig. 174*a* is a vertical section showing an outward-flow wheel *W* to which the water is brought by guides *G* from a fixed penstock *P*. Between the guides and the wheel there is an annular space in which slides

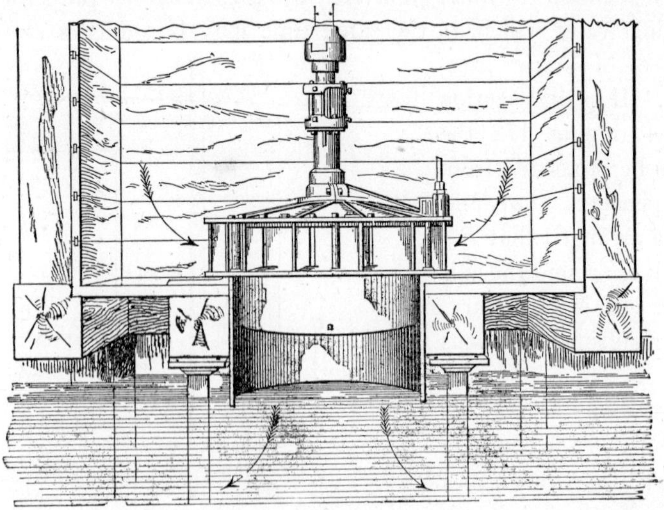

Fig. 174*d*.

an annular vertical gate E; this serves to regulate the quantity of water, and when it is entirely depressed, the wheel stops. Many other forms of gates are, however, used in the different styles of turbines found in the market.

In Figs. 174*b* and 174*c* are given horizontal and vertical sections of both the outward- and the inward-flow types, showing the arrangement of guides and vanes. The fixed guide passages which lead the water from the penstock are marked G, while the moving wheel is marked W. It is seen that the water is introduced around the entire circumference of the wheel, and hence the quantity supplied, and likewise the power, is far greater than in the impulse wheels of the last chapter.

In order that the static pressure may be transmitted into the wheel it is placed under water, as in Fig. 174*a*, or the exit orifices are partially closed by gates, or the air is prevented from entering them by some other device.

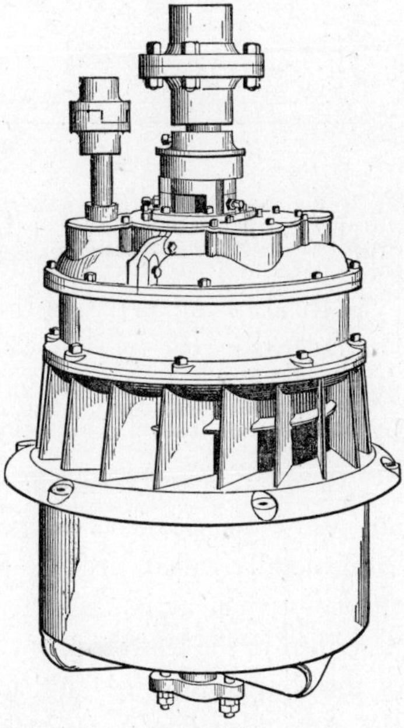

Fig. 174*e*.

In Fig. 174*d* a Leffel turbine of the inward-flow type is illustrated, the arrows showing the direction of the water as it enters and leaves. The wheel itself is not visible, it being within the inclosing case through which the water enters by the spaces between the guides. In Fig. 174*e* is shown a view of a Hunt turbine, which is also of the inward- and downward-flow type. In both cases the guides are seen with the small shaft for moving the gates, these being partly raised in Fig. 174*e*. The flange at the base of the guides serves to support the weight of the entire apparatus upon the floor of the inclosing penstock, which is filled with water to the level of the head bay. The cylinder below the flange, commonly called a draft-tube, carries away the water from the wheel, and the level of the tail water should stand a little higher than its lower rim in order to prevent the entrance of air and thus insure that the wheel may act as a reaction turbine. Iron penstocks are frequently used instead of wooden ones, and for the pure outward- and inward-flow types the wheel is often placed below the level of the tail race.

Turbines are sometimes placed vertically on a horizontal shaft. Fig. 174*f* shows twin Eureka turbines thus arranged in

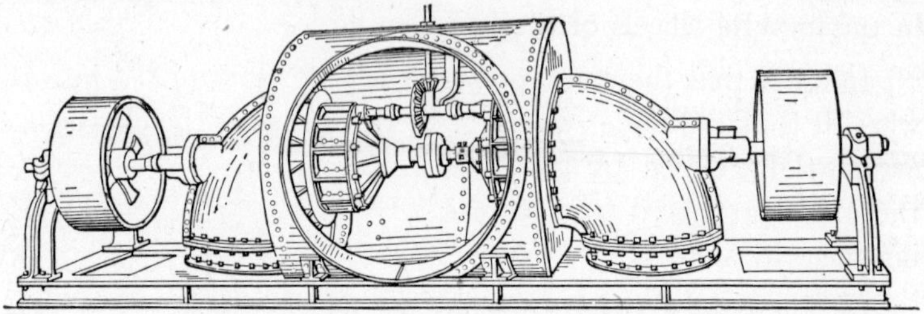

Fig. 174*f*.

an inclosing iron casing. The water enters through a large pipe attached to the cylinder opening, and having filled the cylindrical casing, it passes through the guides, turns the wheels, and escapes by the two elbows. Large twin vertical turbines furnishing 1200 horse-powers have been installed at Niagara Falls by the James Leffel Company.

All reaction turbines will act as impulse turbines when from any cause the passages between the vanes, or buckets, as they are generally called, are not filled with water. In this case the theory of their action is exactly like that of the impulse wheels described in the last chapter. In Arts. 175–178 reaction turbines of the simple outward- and inward-flow types will be discussed, the downward-flow type being reserved for special description in Art. 179.

Prob. 174. Consult Engineering Record, Feb. 5, 1898, and describe methods of regulating the speed of turbines.

ART. 175. FLOW THROUGH REACTION TURBINES

The discharge through an impulse turbine, like that for an impulse wheel, depends only on the area of the guide orifices and the effective head upon them, or $q = av = a\sqrt{2gh}$. In a reaction turbine, however, the discharge is influenced by the speed of revolution, as in the reaction wheel, and also by the areas of the entrance and exit orifices. To find an expression for this discharge let the wheel be supposed to be placed below the surface of the tail water, as in Fig. 175. Let h be the total head between the upper water level and that in the tail race, H_1 the pressure-head on the exit orifices, and H the pressure-head at the gate opening as indicated by a piezometer supposed to be there inserted. Let u_1 and u be the velocities of the wheel at the exit and entrance circumference, which have radii r_1 and r (Fig. 174*b*). Let V_1 and V be the relative velocities of exit and entrance, and v_0 be the absolute velocity of the water as it leaves the guides and enters the wheel; the entering velocity v_0 may be less or greater than $\sqrt{2gh}$, depending upon the value of the pressure-head H. Let a_1, a, and a_0 be the areas of the orifices normal to the directions of V_1, V, and v_0. Now, neglecting all losses of friction between the guides, the theorem of Art. 31, that pressure-head plus velocity-head equals the total head, gives the equation

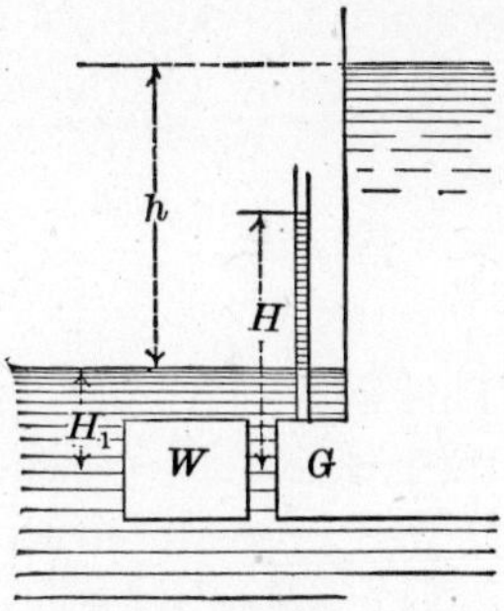

Fig. 175.

$$H + \frac{v_0^2}{2g} = h + H_1$$

Also, neglecting the friction and foam in the buckets, the corresponding theorem of Art. 162 gives

$$H_1 + \frac{V_1^2}{2g} - \frac{u_1^2}{2g} = H + \frac{V^2}{2g} - \frac{u^2}{2g}$$

Adding these equations, the pressure-heads H_1 and H disappear, and there results the formula

$$V_1^2 - V^2 + v_0^2 = 2gh + u_1^2 - u^2 \qquad (175)_1$$

Now, since the buckets are fully filled, the same quantity of water, q, passes in each second through each of the areas a_1, a, and a_0, and hence the three velocities through these areas have the respective values,

$$V_1 = \frac{q}{a_1}, \qquad V = \frac{q}{a}, \qquad v_0 = \frac{q}{a_0}$$

Introducing these values into the formula $(175)_1$, solving for q, and multiplying by a coefficient c to account for losses in leakage and friction, the discharge per second is

$$q = c\sqrt{\frac{2gh + u_1^2 - u^2}{\frac{1}{a_1^2} - \frac{1}{a^2} + \frac{1}{a_0^2}}} \qquad (175)_2$$

This is the formula for the flow through a reaction turbine when the gate is fully raised. The reasoning applies to an inward-flow as well as to an outward-flow wheel. In an outward-flow turbine u_1 is greater than u, and consequently the discharge increases with the speed; in an inward-flow turbine u_1 is less than u, and consequently the discharge decreases as the speed increases.

The value of the coefficient c will usually vary with the head, and also with the size of the areas a_1, a, and a_0. When a turbine has been tested by the methods of Arts. 147–150, and the areas have been measured, the values of c for different speeds may be computed. For example, take the outward-flow Boyden turbine, tests of which at full gate are given in Art. 150. The measured dimensions and angles of this wheel are as follows:

Outer radius of wheel	$r_1 = 3.3167$ feet
Inner radius of wheel	$r = 2.6630$ feet
Outer radius of guide case	$r_0 = 2.5911$ feet
Outer depth of buckets	$d_1 = 0.722$ feet
Inner depth of buckets	$d = 0.741$ feet
Outer area of buckets	$a_1 = 4.61$ square feet
Inner area of buckets	$a = 12.12$ square feet
Outer area of guide orifices	$a_0 = 4.76$ square feet
Exit angle of buckets	$\beta = 13.5$ degrees
Entrance angle of buckets	$\phi = 90$ degrees
Entrance angle of guides	$\alpha = 24$ degrees

Number of buckets 52, number of guides, 32

Inserting in the above formula the values of a_1, a, and a_0, placing for $u_1^2-u^2$ its value $(\frac{1}{30}\pi N)^2\,(r_1^2-r^2)$, where N is the number of revolutions per minute, it reduces to

$$q = 3.44c\sqrt{2gh + 0.04\ 8N^2}$$

From this the value of c may be computed for each of the seven experiments, and the following tabulation shows the results, the first four columns giving the number of the experiment, the observed head, number of revolutions per minute, and discharge in cubic feet per second. The fifth column gives the theoretic discharge computed from the above formula, taking the coefficient as unity, and the last column is derived by dividing the observed discharge q by the theoretic discharge Q. The discrepancy of 5 or 6 percent is smaller than might be expected, since the formula does not consider frictional resistances.

No.	h	N	q	Q	c
21	17.16	63.5	117.01	123.1	0.950
20	17.27	70.0	118.37	125.2	0.945
19	17.33	75.0	119.53	126.8	0.943
18	17.34	80.0	121.15	128.4	0.944
17	17.21	86.0	122.41	130.0	0.942
16	17.21	93.2	124.74	132.5	0.941
15	17.19	100.0	127.73	134.9	0.947

A satisfactory formula for the discharge through a turbine when the gate is partly depressed is difficult to deduce, because the loss of head which then results can only be expressed by the help of experimental coefficients similar to those given in Art. 92 for the sliding gate in a water pipe, and the values of these for turbines are not known. It is, however, certain that for each particular gate opening the discharge is given by

$$q = m\sqrt{2gh + u_1^2 - u^2}$$

in which m depends upon the areas of the orifices and the height to which the gate is raised. For instance, in the tests of the above Boyden turbine the mean value of m for full gate opening is 3.25, but when the gate was only six-tenths open, its value was 2.81, and when the gate was two-tenths open, its value was 1.36. Each form and size of reaction turbine has its own values of m, depending upon the area of its orifices, and when these have been determined, a turbine may be used as a water meter to measure the discharge with a fair degree of precision.

Prob. 175. Consult Francis' Lowell Hydraulic Experiments, pp. 67–75, and compute the coefficient m for experiments 30 and 31 on the center-vent Boott turbine.

ART. 176. THEORY OF REACTION TURBINES

The theory of reaction turbines may be said to include two problems: first, given all the dimensions of a turbine and the head under which it works, to determine the maximum efficiency, and the corresponding speed, discharge, and power; and second, having given the head and the quantity of water, to design a turbine of high efficiency. This article deals only with the first problem, and it should be said at the outset that it cannot be fully solved theoretically, even for the best-conditioned wheels, on account of losses in foam, friction, and leakage. The investigation will be limited to the case of full gate, since when the gate is partially depressed, a loss of energy results from the sudden expansion of the entering water.

The notation will be the same as that used in Chaps. 11 and 12, and as shown in Figs. 174*b* and 174*c*; the reasoning will apply to both outward- and inward-flow turbines. Let r be the radius of the circumference where the water enters the wheel and r_1 that of the circumference where it leaves, let u and u_1 be the corresponding velocities of revolution; then $ur_1 = u_1r$. Let v_0 be the absolute velocity with which the water leaves the guides and enters the wheel, and V its velocity of entrance relative to the wheel; let α be the approach angle and ϕ the entrance angle which these velocities make with the direction of u. At the exit circumference let V_1 be the relative velocity with which the water leaves the guides, and v_1 its absolute velocity; let β be the exit angle which V_1 makes with this circumference. Let a_0, a, and a_1 be the areas of the guide orifices, the entrance, and the exit orifices of the wheel, respectively, measured perpendicular to the directions of v_0, V, and V_1. Let d_0, d, and d_1 be the depths of these orifices; when the gate is fully raised, d_0 becomes equal to d.

The areas a_0, a, a_1, neglecting the thickness of the guides and vanes, and taking the gate as fully open, have the values

$$a_0 = 2\pi rd \sin\alpha \qquad a = 2\pi rd \sin\phi \qquad a_1 = 2\pi r_1 d_1 \sin\beta$$

and since these areas are fully filled with water,

$$q = v_0 \cdot 2\pi rd \sin\alpha = V \cdot 2\pi rd \sin\phi = V_1 \cdot 2r_1 d_1 \sin\beta \qquad (176)$$

These relations, together with the formulas of the last article and the geometrical conditions of the parallelograms of velocities, include the entire theory of the reaction turbine.

In order that the efficiency of the turbine may be as high as possible the water must enter tangentially to the vanes, and the absolute velocity of the issuing water must be as small as possible. The first condition will be fulfilled when u and v_0 are proportional to the sines of the angles $\phi - \alpha$ and ϕ. The second will be secured by making $u_1 = V_1$ in the parallelogram at exit, as then the diagonal v_1 becomes very small. Hence

$$\frac{u}{v_0} = \frac{\sin(\phi - \alpha)}{\sin\phi} \qquad u_1 = V_1 \qquad (176)_2$$

are the two conditions which should obtain in order that the hydraulic efficiency may be a maximum.

Now making $V_1 = u_1$ in the third quantity of $(176)_1$ and equating it to the first, there results

$$\frac{u_1}{v_0} = \frac{rd \sin\alpha}{r_1 d_1 \sin\beta} \qquad \text{and} \qquad \frac{u}{v_0} = \frac{r^2 d \sin\alpha}{r_1^2 d \sin\beta}$$

Also making $V_1 = u_1$ in $(175)_1$ and substituting for V^2 its value $u^2 + v_0^2 - 2uv_0 \cos\alpha$ from the triangle at A between u and v_0, there is found the important relation

$$uv_0 \cos\alpha = gh \qquad (176)_3$$

which gives another condition between u and v_0. The velocity v_0, with which the water enters, hence depends upon the speed of the wheel as well as upon the head h.

Thus three equations between two unknown quantities u and v_0 have been deduced for the case of maximum hydraulic efficiency, namely,

$$\frac{u}{v_0} = \frac{\sin(\phi - \alpha)}{\sin\phi} \qquad \frac{u}{v_0} = \frac{r^2 d \sin\alpha}{r_1^2 d_1 \sin\beta} \qquad uv_0 = \frac{gh}{\cos\alpha}$$

If the values of the velocities u and v_0 be found from the first and third equations, they are

$$u = \sqrt{\frac{gh \sin(\phi - \alpha)}{\cos\alpha \sin\phi}} \qquad v_0 = \sqrt{\frac{gh \sin\phi}{\cos\alpha \sin(\phi - \alpha)}} \qquad (176)_4$$

the first of which is the advantageous velocity of the circumference where the water enters, and the second is the absolute velocity with which the water leaves the guides and enters the wheel. In order, however, that these expressions may be correct, the first and second values of u/v_0 must also be equal, and hence

$$\frac{\sin(\phi - \alpha)}{\sin\phi} = \frac{r^2 d \sin\alpha}{r_1^2 d_1 \sin\beta} \qquad (176)_5$$

which is the necessary relation between the dimensions and angles of the wheel in order that this theory may apply.

For a turbine so constructed and running at the advantageous speed the theoretic hydraulic efficiency is

$$e = 1 - \frac{v_1^2}{2gh} = 1 - \frac{2u_1^2 \sin^2 \frac{1}{2}\beta}{gh}$$

and substituting for u_1 its value in terms of u from $(176)_4$, and having regard to $(176)_5$, this becomes

$$e = 1 - \frac{d}{d_1} \tan\alpha \tan\tfrac{1}{2}\beta \qquad (176)_6$$

The discharge under the same conditions is $q = a_0 v_0$, and lastly the work of the wheel per second is $k = wqhe$.

The result of this investigation is that the general problem of investigating a given turbine cannot be solved theoretically, unless it be so built as to approximately satisfy the condition in $(176)_5$. If this be the case, it may be discussed by the formulas deduced. Even then no very satisfactory conclusions can be drawn from the numerical values, since the formulas do not take into account the loss by friction and that of leakage. To determine the actual efficiency, best speed, and power of a given turbine, the only way is to actually test it by the method described in Art. 149. The above formulas are, however, of great value in the discussion of the design of turbines. More exact formulas, from a theoretical standpoint, may be derived by using the condition $V_1 = u_1 \cos\beta$ instead of $V_1 = u_1$ to determine the exit velocity v_1 (Art. 168), but these are very complex in form, and numerical values computed from them differ but little from those found from the formulas here established.

When the coefficient of discharge of a turbine is known (Art. 175), the advantageous speed and corresponding discharge may be closely computed. For this purpose the condition $u_1 = V_1 = q/a_1$ is to be used. Inserting in this the value of q from $(175)_2$ and solving for u_1, there is found

$$u_1^2 = \frac{c^2 \cdot 2gh}{1 + c^2 \frac{r^2}{r_1^2} + \frac{a_1^2}{a_0^2} - \frac{a_1^2}{a^2} - c^2}$$

which gives the advantageous velocity of the circumference where the water leaves the wheel, and then by $(175)_2$ the discharge can be obtained. As an example, take the case of Holyoke test No. 275, where $r_1 = 27\frac{1}{2}$ inches, $r = 21\frac{1}{2}$ inches, $h = 23.8$ feet, $a_0 = 2.066$, $a = 5.526$, $a_1 = 1.949$ square feet, $\alpha = 25\frac{1}{2}°$, $\phi = 90°$, $\beta = 11\frac{3}{4}°$. Assuming $c = 0.95$, as the turbine is similar to that investigated in the last article, the above formula gives $u_1 = 31.24$ feet per second, which corresponds to 130 revolutions per minute, and this agrees well with the actual number 138. The efficiency found by the test at that speed was 0.79, which is a very much less value than the above theoretic formula gives, since this formula was derived without taking into account the friction losses within and without the wheel.

Prob. 176. For the case of the last problem $r = 4.67$, $r_1 = 3.95$, $d = 1.01$, $d_1 = 1.23$, $h = 13.4$ feet, $\alpha = 9°.5$, $\phi = 119°$, $\beta = 11°$. Compute the areas a_0, a, a_1, and the advantageous speed. Compute also the velocity with which the water enters the wheel.

Art. 177. Design of Reaction Turbines

The design of an outward- or inward-flow turbine for a given head and discharge includes the determination of the dimensions r, r_1, d, d_1, and the angles α, β, and ϕ. These may be selected in very many different ways, and the formulas of the last article furnish a guide how to make a selection so as to secure a high degree of efficiency.

First, it is seen from $(176)_6$ that the approach angle α and the exit angle β should be small, but that, as in other wheels, β has a greater influence than α. However, β must usually be greater for an inward-flow than for an outward-flow wheel in order to make the orifices of exit of sufficient size. For the entrance angle ϕ a good value is 90°, and in this case the velocity u is always that due to one-half the head, as seen from $(176)_4$. The radii r and r_1

should not differ too much, as then the frictional resistance of the flowing water and the moving wheel would be large. It is also seen that the efficiency is increased by making the exit depth d_1 greater than the entrance depth d, but usually these cannot greatly differ, and are often taken equal.

Secondly, it is seen that the dimensions and angles should be such as to satisfy the formula $(176)_5$, since if this be not the case losses due to impact at entrance will occur which will render the other formulas of little value.

Most American reaction turbines are of a modified inward-flow type in which the direction of the entering water is at first inward and then downward as in Fig. 174*d*. The design of these can scarcely be made by theoretical rules, but must mostly depend upon the results of tests of wheels previously built, the effort in each improvement being to increase the efficiency. Such turbines are made by different manufacturers in many different types and sizes, and Art. 181 gives the practical method of selecting one to fulfil required conditions.

Prob. 177. To design an outward-flow turbine which shall use 120 cubic feet per second under a head of 18 feet and make 100 revolutions per minute, let the entrance angle ϕ be taken at 90°. Show that the advantageous velocity of the inner circumference of the wheel is 24 feet per second and hence that the inner radius should be 2.3 feet.

Art. 178. Downward-flow Turbines

Downward- or parallel-flow turbines are those in which the water passes through the wheel without changing its distance from the axis of revolution. In Fig. 178*a* is a semi-vertical section of the guide and wheel passages, and also a development of a portion of a cylindrical section showing the inner arrangement. The formula for the discharge can be adapted to this by making $u_1 = u$. In this turbine there is no action of centrifugal force,

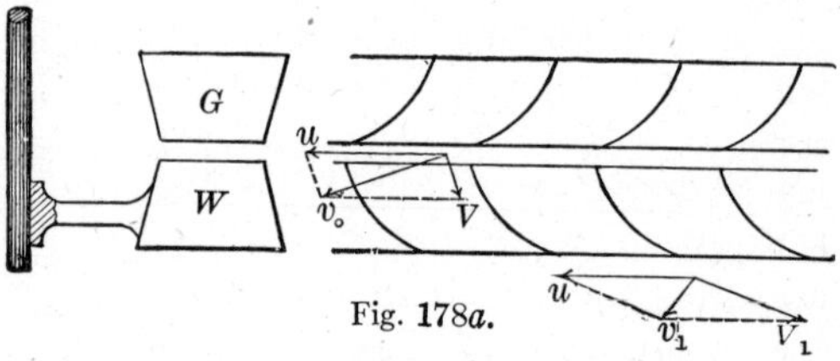

Fig. 178*a*.

so that the relative exit velocity V_1 is equal to the relative entrance velocity V.

The great advantage of this form of turbine is that it can be set some distance above the tail race and still obtain the power due to the total fall. This distance cannot exceed 34 feet, the height of the water barometer, and usually it does not exceed 25 feet. Fig. 178*b* shows in a diagrammatic way a cross-section of the penstock P, the guide passages G, the wheel W, and the air-tight draft tube T, from which the water escapes by a gate E to the tail race. The pressure-head H_1 on the exit orifice is here negative, so that the air pressure equivalent to this head is added to the water pressure in the penstock, and hence the discharge through the guides occurs as if the wheel were set at the level of the tail race. Strictly speaking, a vacuum, more or less complete, is formed just below the wheel into which the water drops with a low absolute velocity, having surrendered to the wheel nearly all its energy. Draft tubes are also often used with inward-flow turbines when these are set above the tail race.

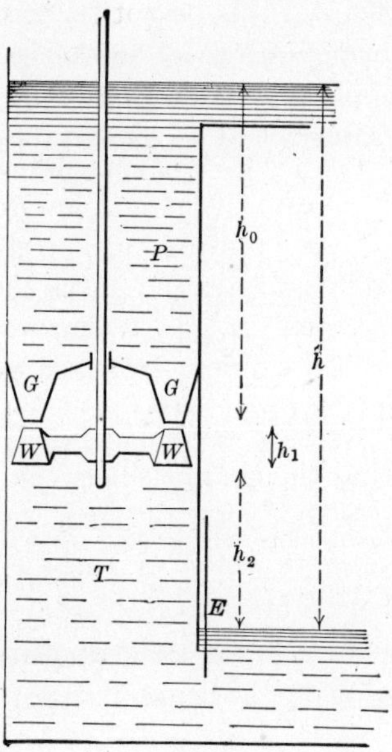

Fig. 178*b*.

Let h be the total head between the water levels in the head and tail races, h_0 the depth of the entrance orifices of the wheel below the upper level, h_1 the vertical height of the wheel, and h_2 the height of the exit orifices above the tail race; so that $h = h_0+h_1+h_2$. Let H and H_1 be the heads which measure the absolute pressures at the entrance and exit orifice of the wheel, and h_a the height of the water barometer. Let v_0 be the absolute velocity with which the water leaves the guides and enters the vanes, and V and V_1 the relative velocities at entrance and exit. Then from the theorem of energy in steady flow (Art. 31),

$$v_0^2 = 2g(h_a + h_0 - H)$$
$$V_1^2 = V^2 + 2g(h_1 + H - H_1)$$

Adding these two equations there results

$$v_0^2 - V^2 + V_1^2 = 2g(h_0 + h_1 + h_a - H_1)$$

But $h_a - H_1$ is equal to h_2, and hence

$$v_0^2 - V^2 + V_1^2 = 2gh$$

This formula is the same as $(175)_1$ if u be made equal to u_1, and hence all the formulas of the last three articles apply to the downward-flow reaction turbine by making equal the velocities u and u_1, as also the radii r and r_1.

Prob. 178. A downward-flow turbine with draft tube has its exit orifice 7.5 feet above the level of the tail race and it uses 92 cubic feet of water per second under a head h of 27 feet. What is its horse-power when the efficiency, as measured by the friction brake, is 78 percent?

Art. 179. Impulse Turbines

Whenever a turbine is so arranged that the channels between the vanes are not fully filled with water, it ceases to act as a reaction turbine and becomes an impulse turbine. A turbine set above the level of the tail race becomes an impulse turbine when the gate is partially lowered, unless the gates are arranged so as to cover the exit orifices instead of being, as usual, in front of the entrance orifices.

The theoretic velocity with which the water leaves the guides in an impulse turbine is simply $\sqrt{2gh_0}$, where h_0 is the head on the guide orifices. The rules and formulas in Art. 168 apply in all respects, and for a well-designed wheel the entrance angle ϕ is double the approach angle α, the advantageous speed and corresponding hydraulic efficiency are

$$u = \sqrt{\frac{gh_0}{2\cos^2\alpha}} \qquad e = 1 - \left(\frac{r_1 \sin\frac{1}{2}\beta}{r\cos\alpha}\right)^2$$

while the discharge is $q = a_0\sqrt{2gh_0}$, and the work of the turbine per second is $k = whq_0e$. Impulse turbines are but little used in comparison with reaction turbines.

Impulse turbines revolve more slowly than reaction turbines under the same head, but the relative entrance velocity V is greater, and hence more energy is liable to be spent in shock and foam. In impulse turbines the entrance angle ϕ should be double the approach angle α, but in reaction turbines it is often greater than 3α, and its value depends upon the exit angle β; hence the vanes in impulse turbines are of sharper curvature for the same values of α and β. In impulse turbines the efficiency is not lowered by a partial closing of the gates, whereas the sudden enlargement of section causes a material loss in reaction turbines. The advantageous speed of an impulse turbine remains the same for all positions of the gate, but with a reaction turbine it is very much slower at part gate than at full gate. For many kinds of machinery it is important to maintain a constant speed for different amounts of power, and with a reaction turbine this can only be done by a great loss in efficiency. When the water supply is low, the impulse turbine hence has a marked advantage in efficiency. A further merit of the impulse turbine is that it may be arranged so that water enters only through a part of the guides, while this is impossible in reaction turbines. On the other hand, reaction turbines can be set below the level of the tail race or above it, using a draft tube in the latter case, and still secure the power due to the total fall, whereas an impulse turbine must always be set above the tail-race level and loses all the fall between that level and the guide orifices.

Prob. 179. An outward-flow impulse turbine is to use 120 cubic feet per second under a head of 18 feet and make 77 revolutions per minute. Show that the entrance angle ϕ should be about 48° if the inner radius of the wheel is 2.3 feet.

Art. 180. Special Devices

Many devices to increase the efficiency of reaction turbines, particularly at part gate, have been proposed. In the Fourneyron turbine a common plan is to divide the wheel into three parts by horizontal partitions between the vanes, so that these are completely filled with water when the gate is either one-third or two-thirds closed (see Fig. 182*d*). The surface exposed to friction is thus, however, materially increased at full gate.

The Boyden diffuser is another device used with outward-flow reaction turbines. This consists of a fixed wooden annular frame D placed around the wheel W, through which the water must pass after exit from the wheel. Its width is about four or five times that of the wheel, and at the outer end its depth becomes about double that of the wheel. The effect of this is like a draft tube, and although the absolute velocity of the water when issuing from the wheel is greater than before, the absolute velocity of the water coming out of the diffuser is less, and hence a greater amount of energy is imparted to the turbine. It has been shown above that the efficiency of a reaction turbine is increased by making the exit depth d_1 greater than the entrance depth d, and the fixed diffuser produces the same result. By the use of this diffuser Boyden increased the efficiency of the Fourneyron reaction turbine several percent.

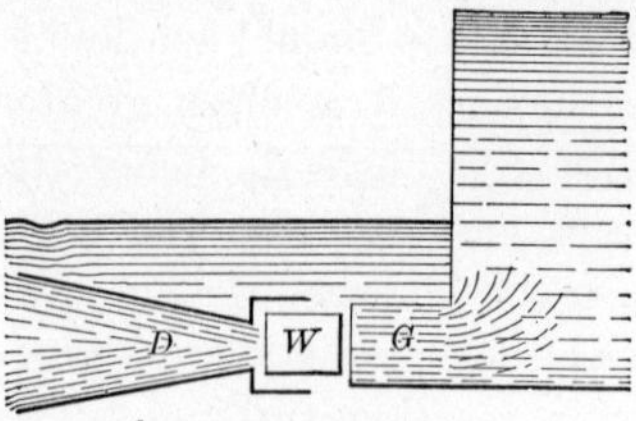

Fig. 180.

The pneumatic turbine of Girard was devised to overcome the loss in reaction turbines due to a partial closing of the gate. The turbine was inclosed in a kind of bell into which air could be pumped, thus lowering the tail-water level around the wheel. At part gate this pump is put into action, and as a consequence the air is admitted into the wheel, and the water flowing through it does not fill the spaces between the vanes. Hence the action becomes like that of an impulse turbine, and the full efficiency is maintained, although power is lost in compressing the air.

At a high stage of the stream, when water flows to waste over the dam, backwater usually lessens the available fall and power. To increase that fall and power, Herschel in 1908 devised and tested at the Holyoke testing flume the plan of connecting the lower end of the turbine draft tube to a chamber wherein a partial vacuum is produced by causing part of the waste to flow through a tube shaped like the Venturi meter, suitable connection being made between the throat of this tube and the vacuum chamber. This device, called "the fall increaser," gives greater available power at high-water stages, since the vacuum head h_0 is added to the head h between the upper and lower water levels and thus the discharge through the turbine is increased.*

The screw turbine consists of one or two turns of a helicoidal surface around a vertical shaft, the screw being inclosed in a cylindrical case. At a point where the water enters on the helicoidal surface its downward pressure can be resolved into two components, a relative velocity V parallel to the surface and a horizontal velocity u which corresponds to the velocity of the wheel. At the exit it can be resolved in like manner into V_1 and u_1. But, as in other cases, the condition for high efficiency is $u_1 = V_1$, and, since the water moves parallel to the axis $u_1 = u$. Applying the general formula of Art. 175, it is seen that this can only occur when the head h is zero or when the velocity u is infinite. The screw turbine is hence like a reaction wheel and high efficiency can never practically be obtained by its use.

Of all the special devices for increasing the power of turbines that of the draft tube has proved the most valuable. Increasing the depth of the exit orifices also increases the hydraulic efficiency of the outward- or inward-flow turbine, as formula $(176)_6$ shows. The common American reaction turbine is, however, of a mixed-flow type, the direction of flow of the water through it being first inward and then downward. In the more modern styles of these the area of the exit orifices is increased so that part of the water may turn outward at its exit as shown by the arrows in Fig. 174*d*; this is accomplished by proper curves of the buckets so that the lower part of the bucket case, or runner as it is often called, is larger in diameter at the exit than at the entrance, as seen in Fig. 182.

Turbines for ordinary requirements of power and speed are kept in stock by manufacturers and may be obtained at short notice; Art. 181 gives information with regard to the selection of such stock turbines. Very large turbines, however, are specially designed by experts for the data and requirements of each particular case; Art. 182 gives notes regarding some large turbines which have been erected since 1895.

* Harvard Engineering Journal, June, 1908.

Prob. 180. Consult Iron Age, March 13, 1913, and ascertain the special arrangements used for admitting the water to the great turbines of the plant at Keokuk on the Mississippi River.

Art. 181. Type Characteristics

Turbines are of the same type when they differ only in size, they being in all other respects geometrically similar. A turbine manufacturer usually has several different types, and of each type there are six or more sizes. The types may vary in number of guides and buckets, in their thickness, in their angles at entrance and exit, and in the ratio of entrance to exit orifices. But in all the sizes of a given type the number and angles of guides and buckets is the same, linear dimensions vary as the diameters, and areas of entrance and exit vary as the squares of the diameters. By the diameter of an outward- or inward-flow turbine is meant the diameter of the buckets where the water enters, or it is double the radius r of the preceding formulas. For a downward- or mixed-flow turbine the diameter may be any dimension connected with the radial direction, it being taken for a given type always between the same definite points. In turbine catalogs the word size is generally used instead of diameter.

The speed of a turbine is the number of revolutions per minute, and the best or advantageous speed is that which gives the maximum hydraulic efficiency. All turbines of the same type have the same advantageous speed and the same hydraulic efficiency under a given head; thus, for an outward- or inward-flow turbine, formula $(176)_4$ gives the same velocities for a given h, and formula $(176)_6$ gives the same efficiencies for all sizes of a given type.

The advantageous speeds of two turbines of the same type, under the same head, are inversely as their diameters. Let N' and N'' be the number of revolutions per minute, and D' and D'' the diameters. Then the velocities at the extremities of the diameters are

$$u' = 2\pi D'N'/60 \qquad u'' = 2\pi D''N''/60$$

Now from the formula $(176)_4$ the velocities u' and u'' are equal to the same constant function of h and the angles, hence $D'N' = D''N''$, or

$$N'/N'' = D''/D'$$

that is, under the same head, the speeds of different sizes of the same type are inversely as their diameters. Thus, if a 20-inch turbine has 320 revolutions per minute for its best speed under a head of 16 feet, then a 40-inch turbine of the same type under the same head will have 160 revolutions per minute for its best speed.

The discharges through two turbines of the same type under the same head are proportional to the squares of their diameters. For the discharge is $q = a_0v_0$ (Art. 176) in which v_0 is constant and a_0 varies as D^2, hence, under the best speed and the same head,

$$q'/q'' = (D'/D'')^2.$$

Thus, if a 20-inch turbine under a head of 16 feet uses 32 cubic feet of water per second, then a 40-inch turbine of the same type under the same head will require 128 cubic feet per second.

The horse-powers of two turbines of the same type under the same head are also proportional to the squares of their diameters, since the work is proportional to q when h is a constant; hence if $\overline{HP}'$ and $\overline{HP}''$ be the horse-powers,

$$\overline{HP}'/\overline{HP}'' = (D'/D'')^2$$

Thus, if a 20-inch turbine under a head of 16 feet delivers 12 horse-power, then a 40-inch turbine of the same type under the head of 16 feet will deliver 48 horse-power.

It is important now to determine how the speed N, discharge q, and horse-power $\overline{HP}$ vary with the head h for different diameters D of the same type. From $(176)_4$ the velocity u varies as $\sqrt{h}$, hence DN also varies as $\sqrt{h}$, and accordingly, if k_1 be a constant,

$$N = k_1\sqrt{h}/D \qquad (181)_1$$

From $q = a_0 v_0$, there is also found

$$q = k_2 D^2 \sqrt{h} \qquad (181)_2$$

where k_2 is another constant. From $\overline{HP} = wqhe$, the efficiency e being the same for all sizes of the same type, there results

$$\overline{HP} = k_3 D^2 h^{\frac{3}{2}} \qquad (181)_3$$

The three constants k_1, k_2, k_3 should be the same for all sizes of the same type. Hence by a test on one size of a given type the constants k_1, k_2, k_3 for that type may be found from the above equations. These formulas also show for any given diameter D, that the speed N varies as $\sqrt{h}$, that the discharge q also varies as $\sqrt{h}$, and that the horse-power $\overline{HP}$ varies as $h\sqrt{h}$ or $h^{\frac{3}{2}}$. Thus in order to double the speed or discharge of a given turbine the head must be quadrupled, and in order to double the horse-power the head must be increased 57.4 percent.

The specific speed, or characteristic speed as it is called by some writers, is the speed of a one horse-power turbine under a head of one foot. Eliminating D from $(181)_1$ and $(181)_3$ there results $N = k_1 k_3^{\frac{1}{2}} h^{\frac{5}{4}} / \overline{HP}^{\frac{1}{2}}$; now letting $h = 1$ and $\overline{HP} = 1$, it is seen that $k_1 k_3^{\frac{1}{2}}$ is the specific speed, which will be denoted by N_s; hence

$$N_s = N\,\overline{HP}^{\frac{1}{2}} / h^{\frac{5}{4}} \qquad (181)_4$$

is the formula for computing specific speed when N, $\overline{HP}$, h have been found by a test. For example, take the Boyden turbine of Art. 150, for which $N = 70$, $h = 17.27$, $\overline{HP} = 118.4$; from these the specific speed is $N_s = 21.6$. Each type of turbine has its own specific speed which is entirely independent of size, since the diameter D does not appear in $(181)_4$. For low-speed turbines the value of N_s ranges from 10 to 20, for medium-speed turbines from 30 to 50, for high-speed turbines from 60 to 80, and for very high-speed turbines from 90 to 100. The actual speed of any size depends of course upon its diameter, small diameters moving more rapidly than the larger ones.

The specific discharge is the discharge of a one horse-power turbine under a head of one foot. Eliminating D from $(181)_2$

and $(181)_3$ there results $q = (k_2/k_3)\overline{HP}/h$; now letting $h = 1$ and $HP = 1$, it is seen that k_2/k_3 is the specific discharge which will be denoted by q_s; hence

$$q_s = qh/\overline{HP} \qquad (181)_5$$

is the formula for computing specific discharge when q, h, $\overline{HP}$ have been found by a test. For example, take the Boyden turbine of Art. 150, for which $q = 118.4$, $h = 17.27$, $\overline{HP} = 177.4$; from these the specific discharge is $q_s = 10.4$ cubic feet per second. The specific discharge is characteristic of the efficiency of a given type and is the greater the lower the efficiency. For high efficiency the specific discharge is less than 10, for medium efficiency it ranges from 10.5 to 11.5, for low efficiency it is greater than 12. The specific speed does not depend at all upon the diameter.

The specific diameter of a given type is the diameter D_s corresponding to $h = 1$ and the specific speed N_s. Hence from $(181)_1$ $k_1 = ND$; thus when N and D are known from a test on one size the value of k_1 or N_sD_s is known for the type.

By means of a test on one size of a type the quantities N_s, q_s and k_1 can be computed. Accordingly for any other size of that type under any head h,

$$N = N_s h^{\frac{5}{4}}/\overline{HP}^{\frac{1}{2}} \qquad q = q_s\overline{HP}/h \qquad D = k_1\sqrt{h}/N \qquad (181)_6$$

The following table gives approximate values of N_s, q_s and k_1, which have been computed for a few different types from the performances given in the American Civil Engineers' Pocket Book, pages 882–883.

By the help of this table and the above formulas many practical problems relating to turbines can be solved. For example take the Smith type, for which N_s is 81; let it be required to find what size is needed to furnish 354 horse-powers under 35 feet head; here the best speed is $N = 81 \times 35^{\frac{5}{4}}/354^{\frac{1}{2}} = 366$ revolutions per minute, the quantity of water required is $q = 10.9 \times 354/35 = 110$ cubic feet per second, and the diameter of the wheel runner is

$$D = 1660 \times 35^{\frac{1}{2}}/366 = 27 \text{ inches.}$$

TABLE 181. CONSTANTS FOR REACTION TURBINES

Manufacturer	Type	Specific Speed N_s	Specific Discharge q_s	Specific Constant k_1
Allis-Chalmers Co.	A	13.4	11.6	1078
	B	20.4	11.6	1149
	C	29.4	11.6	1224
	D	40.6	11.1	1280
Ridson-Alcott Co.	Alcott	47	11.1	1250
	Ridson	47.5	10.4	1350
	Leviathan	74.1	11.0	1714
S. Morgan Smith Co.	McCormick	53	11.0	1260
	New Success	57	11.0	1350
	Smith	81	10.9	1660

Again let it be required to find the type to furnish 580 horse-powers under a head of 33 feet at 100 revolutions per minute; here

$$N_s = 100 \times 580^{\frac{1}{2}}/33^{\frac{5}{4}} = 30.5;$$

here the type **C** is the nearest in the table and the size D = 70 inches corresponds closely to that theoretically required. Again let it be required to find what turbine will furnish 28 horse-powers under 16 feet head at 1000 revolutions per minute; here

$$N_s = 1000 \times 28^{\frac{1}{2}}/16 = 165,$$

which shows that no turbine can fulfil this condition since N_s is never greater than 100; several different types will, however furnish 28 horse-powers under 16 feet head, but the speed will be much slower than 1000 revolutions per minute.

To make detailed comparisons between different types for a given case, catalogs of manufacturers must be obtained and the performances there given be carefully studied. Then questions of cost and installation must be taken up before a decision can be made as to the most advantageous type and size of turbine which should be used.

When a computed specific speed falls below 10, a turbine cannot be used. An impulse wheel driven by the discharge of a single nozzle has values of the specific speed ranging from 1 to 5, for two nozzles it ranges from 1.4 to 7, and for four nozzles from 2 to 10. However, performances of types of such wheels are less definitely known than those of reaction turbines, and the same is true of turbines which act by impulse only.

Prob. 181*a*. When a turbine has an efficiency of 0.80, what is its specific discharge? When the specific discharge is 10.4 cubic feet per second, what is the efficiency?

Prob. 181*b*. The catalog of a turbine manufacture gives, for the 48-inch size of a certain type, $\overline{HP} = 145$, $q = 175$ cubic feet per second, $N = 104$ revolutions per minute, all for 9 feet head. What are the values of $\overline{HP}$, q, and N for the 72-inch size of the same type under a head of 16 feet?

Art. 182. Large Reaction Turbines

In the eighth and ninth editions of this book the large Fourneyron turbines erected at Niagara Falls from 1894 to 1900 were fully described. There were ten of these wheels, each of 5000 nominal horse-powers, operated under a head of 136 feet at 250 revolutions per minute with a discharge of 450 cubic feet per second. These wheels have been removed since 1912 and hence the detailed description is here omitted. Fig. 182*a* is, however, retained in order to show how the water was carried by penstocks from the river to the wheels and how the vertical shafts of the turbines were connected at the top to the electric generators. A test of one of these turbines, made in 1895, showed that 5498 electrical horse-powers were developed by an expenditure of 447.2 cubic feet of water per second under a head of 135.1 feet; the efficiency of the dynamo being 97 percent, the efficiency of the turbine and approaches was $82\frac{1}{2}$ per cent. It will be seen, in Fig. 182*a*, that the water, after leaving the wheel, dropped several feet to the level of the tail water in the exit tunnel; hence this part of the fall was lost to the wheel. For this and for other reasons, these outward-flow turbines have been replaced by inward-flow Francis wheels, these being provided with draft tubes through which the water passes to the tunnel, the head being thus increased from 136 to 144 feet.

Draft tubes cannot easily be attached to outward-flow turbines and the use of these increases the power to such an

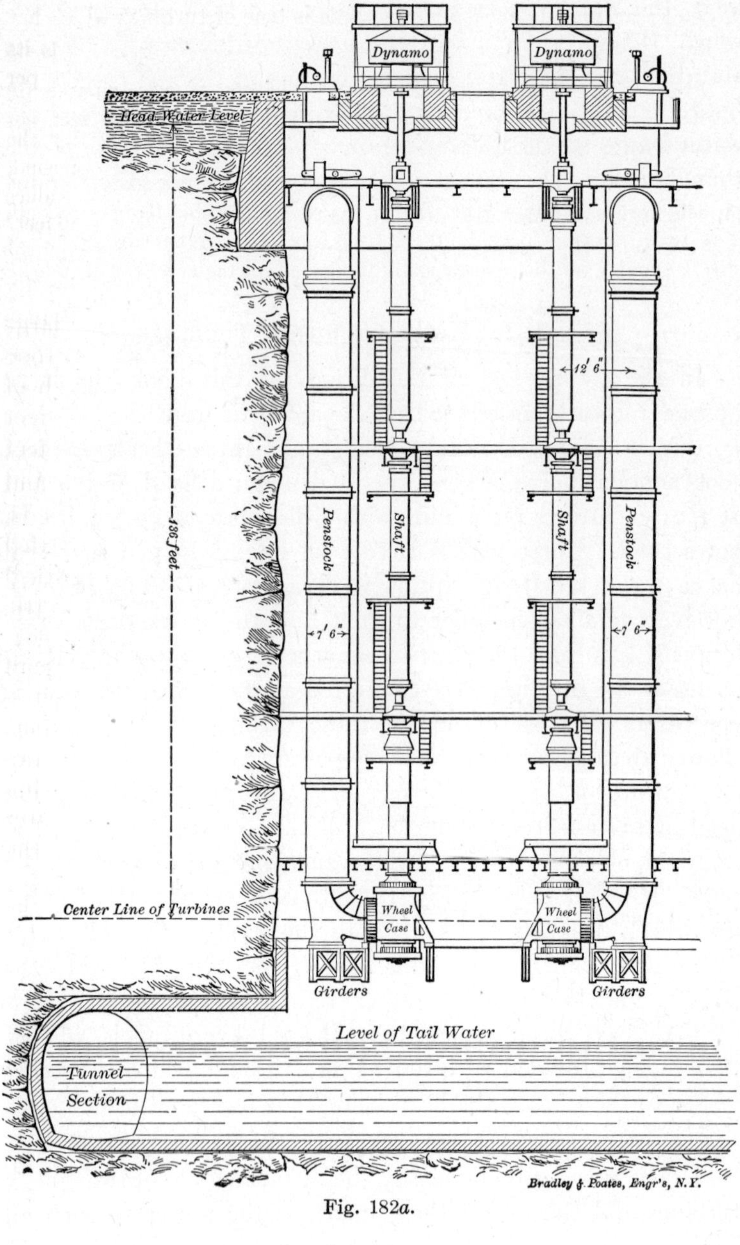
Dynamo
Dynamo
Head Water Level
12' 6"
136 feet
Penstock
Shaft
Shaft
Penstock
7' 6"
7' 6"
Center Line of Turbines
Wheel Case
Wheel Case
Girders
Girders
Level of Tail Water
Tunnel Section
Bradley & Poates, Engr's, N.Y.

Fig. 182*a*.

extent that nearly all modern turbines are of the inward-flow kind, the water entering horizontally and then passing downward. These draft tubes usually extend downward obliquely and discharge the water near the bottom of the tail race. The buckets of these turbines are usually flared outward where the water leaves, so as to increase the area of the exit orifices and thus diminish the absolute velocity of exit. Fig. 182*b* * shows on the left a runner for a large German turbine, while on the right is seen the fixed case containing the guides. The turbine

Fig. 182*b*.

is rendered complete by placing the guide annulus over the smaller part of the runner.

While the largest turbines at Niagara Falls revolve horizontally on vertical shafts, some smaller ones are placed on horizontal shafts in the manner seen in Fig. 174*f*. Many large turbines in other localities also revolve vertically on horizontal shafts; in such cases the wheel is placed in an enclosing case into one side of which the water enters through a penstock while it escapes through a draft tube attached to the case near the turbine axis. The enclosing case is not concentric with the wheel, but the space between is volute-shaped so that

* Camerer, Wasserkraftmaschinen (Berlin, 1914), plate 25.

the area between case and guide ring decreases with distance from the entrance. Fig. 128c * gives front and side outline views of a turbine of this kind; two of these turbines were installed in 1912 at the power development on the White River in California, each being rated as 22 500 horse-powers under 440 feet head at 360 revolutions per minute; this wheel has a double discharge from the enclosing case.†

Many other reaction turbines of a capacity of 10 000 horse-powers or higher have been installed since 1905. Of these can

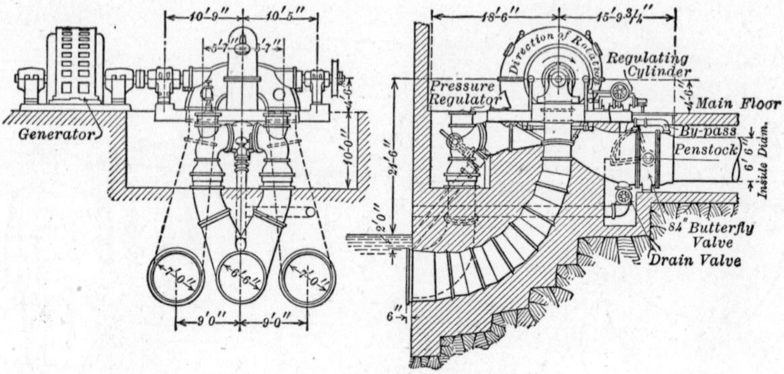

Fig. 182c.

only be mentioned here those of the great development at Keokuk on the Mississippi River, where 30 turbines, each of 10 000 horse-powers, will operate under about 32 feet head at 57.7 revolutions per minute, and those of the Cedar Rapids plant on St. Lawrence River, which have the largest dimensions of any built prior to 1915; these last are guaranteed to have a maximum efficiency of at least 87 percent when operating under an effective head of 30 feet at 55.6 revolutions per minute.

The following is a partial list of recent articles on water wheels, turbines, and water-power plants, especially those of large installations:

(1) A High-head Francis turbine. Engineering News, March 19, 1908, and Engineering Record, March 21, 1908.

* Courtesy of Allis-Chalmers Manufacturing Co., Milwaukee, Wis.

† Engineering News, April 18, 1912, p. 730.

(2) A theoretical article by Zowski on specific speed. Engineering News, January 28, 1909.

(3) Canadian Niagara Falls Plant by Van Cleve. Transactions American Society of Civil Engineers, 1909, Vol. 62, p. 199.

(4) A historical article giving facts regarding many installations. Engineering Magazine, March, 1910.

(5) A historical article. Transactions American Society of Civil Engineers, 1910, Vol. 66, p. 306.

(6) Turbines at Niagara. Electrical World, December 29, 1910.

(7) The Michocan Power Plant in Mexico. American Machinist, August 18, 1910.

(8) Theoretic Discussion of Specific Speedby Baashus. Engineering News, March 2, 1911.

(9) A Large Pelton Wheel in Brazil. London Engineering, September 13, 1912.

(10) The Great Plant at Keokuk, Iowa. Engineering Record, November 16, 1912, and Iron Age, March 13, 1913.

(11) New Turbines of the Niagara Falls Power Co. Engineering Record, October 18, 1913.

(12) A Large Turbine in Switzerland. London Engineering, November 8, 1913.

(13) Modern Reaction Turbines. General Electric Review, June, 1914.

(14) Turbines at Cedar Rapids on St. Lawrence River. Engineering News, April 1, 1915.

(15) Hydro-electric Power Development in Alabama. Transactions American Society Civil Engineers, 1915, Vol. 78, p. 1409.

(16) Design of Hydro-electric Power Plants. Transactions American Society Civil Engineers, 1915, Vol. 79, p. 100.

(17) The Large Burden Overshot Wheel at Troy, N. Y. (diameter = 57 feet). Transactions of American Society Civil Engineers, 1915, Vol. 79, p. 708.

Prob. 182*a*. Consult the above mentioned periodicals and describe power plants for the development of electrical energy which have been installed at Niagara Falls, especially that of the Canadian Niagara Power Company and that of the Ontario Power Company.

Prob. 182*b*. A dynamo delivering 4100 kilowatts has an efficiency of 97.5 percent, while the efficiency of the turbine is 81.3 percent and that of the approaches to the turbine is 99.7 per cent. The turbine is of the Jonval type, and the difference between the levels of head and tail race is 14.4 meters. How many cubic meters of water are used per second?

Prob. 182*c*. Consult the turbine performances given on pages 882–883 of the American Civil Engineers' Pocket Book, and compute therefrom some of the constants given in Table 181.

Prob. 182*d*. Compute the efficiency of a reaction wheel (Art. 172) for a head of 3.5 meters when the radius of the exit orifices is 0.64 meter and the number of revolutions per minute is 130, the coefficient of velocity being 0.95.

Prob. 182*e*. An electric generator delivering 4100 kilowatts has an efficiency of 97.5 percent, while the efficiency of the turbine is 81.3 percent, and that of the approaches to the turbine is 99.7 percent. The turbine is of the Jonval type, and the difference between the water levels of head and tail races is 14.4 meters. How many cubic meters of water per second are used?

182*f*. Consult Camerer's Wasserkraftmaschinen (Berlin, 1914) and ascertain facts regarding the large turbine shown in Fig. 182*b*.

182*g*. Consult Engineering News, April 18, 1912, and ascertain facts regarding the large turbine shown in Fig. 182*c*.

CHAPTER 15

NAVAL HYDROMECHANICS

Art. 183. General Principles

In this chapter is to be discussed in a brief and elementary manner the subject of the resistance of water to the motion of vessels, and the general hydrodynamic principles relating to their propulsion. The water may be at rest and the vessel in motion, or both may be in motion as in the case of a boat going up or down a river. In either event the velocity of the vessel relative to the water need only be considered, and this will be called v. The simplest method of propulsion is by the oar or paddle; then come the paddle wheel, and the jet and screw propellers. The action of the wind upon sails will not be here discussed, as it is outside of the scope of this book.

The unit of linear measure used on the ocean is generally the nautical mile, while one nautical mile per hour is called a knot. One nautical mile is about 6080 feet, so that knots may be transformed into feet per second by multiplying by 1.69, and feet per second may be transformed into knots by multiplying by 0.592. On rivers the speed is estimated in statute miles per hour, and the corresponding multipliers will be 1.47 and 0.682. One kilometer per hour equals 0.621 miles per hour or 0.91 feet per second. On the ocean the weight of a cubic foot of water is to be taken as about 64 pounds (it is often used as 64.32 pounds, so that the numerical value is the same as $2g$), and in rivers at 62.5 pounds.

The speed of a ship at sea was formerly roughly measured by observations with the log, which is a triangular piece of wood attached to a cord which is divided by tags into lengths of about $50\frac{2}{3}$ feet. The log being thrown into the water, it remains stationary, the ship moves away from it, and the number of tags run out in half a minute is counted; this number is the same as the number of knots per hour at which the ship is moving, since $50\frac{2}{3}$ feet is the same part of a knot that a half minute is of an hour. The patent log, which is a small self-recording current meter, drawn in the water behind the ship, is, however, now generally used, this being rated at intervals (Art. 40). In experimental work more accurate methods of measuring the velocity are necessary, and for this purpose the boat may run between buoys whose distance apart has been found by triangulation from measured bases on shore.

The Pitot tube has recently been applied to the determination of the velocity of a ship through the water. By the use in connection with this tube of a recording mechanism similar to that described in Art. 38 for the Venturi meter it would seem possible to automatically record on dials both the speed through the water as well as the total number of miles passed over. By the use of a chart an autographic record of variations in the speed could also be kept. Practical difficulties in the way of keeping the mouths of the Pitot tubes free from obstructions have already been to a certain extent overcome.*

When a boat or ship is to be propelled through water, the resistances to be overcome increase with its velocity, and consequently, as in railroad trains, a practical limit of speed is soon attained. These resistances consist of three kinds: the dynamic pressure caused by the relative velocity of the boat and the water, the frictional resistance of the surface of the boat, and the wave resistance. The first of these can be entirely overcome, as indicated in Art. 155, by giving to the boat a "fair" form; that is, such a form that the dynamic pressure of the impulse near the bow is balanced by that of the reaction of the water as it closes in around the stern. It will be supposed in the following pages that the boat has this form, and hence this first resistance need not be further considered. The second and third sources of resistance will be discussed later.

* Engineering News, May 4, 1911.

The total force of resistance which exists when a vessel is propelled with the velocity v can be ascertained by drawing it in tow at the same velocity, and placing on the tow line a dynamometer to register the tension. An experiment by Froude on the Greyhound, a steamer of 1157 tons, gave for the total resistance the following figures: *

Speed in knots,	4	6	8	10	12
Resistance in tons,	0.6	1.4	2.5	4.7	9.0

which show that at low speeds the resistance varies about as the square of the velocity, and at higher speeds in a faster ratio. For speeds of 15 to 25 knots, the usual velocity of ocean steamers, the law of resistance is not so well known, but as an approximation it is usually taken as varying with the square of the velocity.

Prob. 183. What horse-power was expended in the above test of the Greyhound when the speed was 12 knots per hour?

Art. 184. Frictional Resistances

When a stream or jet moves over a surface, its velocity is retarded by the frictional resistances, or if the velocity be maintained uniform, a constant force is overcome. In pipes, conduits, and channels of uniform section the velocity is uniform, and consequently each square foot of the surface or bed exerts a constant resisting force, the intensity of which will now be approximately computed. This resistance will be the same as the force required to move the same surface in still water, and hence the results will be directly applicable to the propulsion of ships.

Let F be the force of frictional resistance per square foot of surface of the bed of a channel, p its wetted perimeter, l its length, h its fall in that length, a the area of its cross-section, and v the mean velocity of flow. The force of friction over the entire surface then is Fpl, and the work per second lost in friction is $Fplv$. The work done by the water per second is Wh or $wavh$. Equating these two expressions for the work, there results

$$F = w(a/p)(h/l) = wrs$$

* Thearle's Theoretical Naval Architecture (London, 1876), p. 347.

in which r is the hydraulic radius and s the slope of the water surface. Now inserting for rs its value from formula (113), there results

$$F = wv^2/c^2$$

in which w is the weight of a cubic foot of water and c is the coefficient in the Chezy formula, the values of which are given in Chap. 9 and the accompanying tables. Inasmuch as the velocities along the bed of a channel are somewhat less than the mean velocity v, the values of F thus determined will probably be slightly greater than the actual resistance.

For smooth iron pipes the following are computed values of the frictional resistance in pounds per square foot of surface:

Velocity, feet per second =	2	4	6	10	15
for 1 foot diameter	F = 0.023	0.080	0.17	0.43	0.92
for 4 feet diameter	F = 0.015	0.053	0.11	0.28	0.59

These figures indicate that the resistance is subject to much variation in pipes of different diameters; it is not easy to conclude from them, or from formula (113), what the force of resistance is for plane surfaces over which water is moving.

Experiments made by moving flat plates in still water so that the direction of motion coincides with the plane of the surface have furnished conclusions regarding the laws of fluid friction similar to those deduced from the flow of water in pipes. It is found that the total resistance is approximately proportional to the area of the surface, and approximately proportional to the square of the velocity. Accordingly the force of resistance per square foot may be written

$$F = fv^2, \tag{184}$$

in which v is the velocity in feet per second and f is a number depending upon the nature of the surface. The following are average values of f for large surfaces, as given by Unwin: *

Varnished surface,	f = 0.00250
Painted and planed plank,	f = 0.00339
Surface of iron ships,	f = 0.00351
Fine sand surface,	f = 0.00405
New well-painted iron plate,	f = 0.00473

* Encyclopedia Britannica, 9th Ed., vol. 12, p. 483; 11th Ed., vol. 14, p. 57.

Undoubtedly the value of f is subject to variations with the velocity, but the experiments on record are so few that the law and extent of its variation cannot be formulated. It should, however, be remarked that the formulas and constants here given do not apply to low velocities, for the reasons given in Art. 124. At the same time they are only approximately applicable to high velocities. A low velocity of a body moving in an unlimited stream may be regarded as 1 foot per second or less, a high velocity as 25 or 30 feet per second.

It may be noted that the above-mentioned experiments indicate that the value of F is greater for small surfaces than for large ones. For instance, a varnished board 50 feet long gave $f = 0.00250$, while one 20 feet long gave $f = 0.00278$, and one 8 feet long gave $f = 0.00325$, the motion being in all cases in the direction of the length. The resistance is the same whatever be the depth of immersion, for the friction is uninfluenced by the intensity of the static pressure. This is proved by the circumstance that the flow of water in a pipe is found to depend only upon the head on the outlet end, and not upon the pressure-heads along its length.

The frictional resistance of a boat or ship may be roughly estimated by taking $0.004v^2$ and multiplying it by the immersed area. For instance, if this area be 8000 square feet, the frictional resistance at a velocity of 10 feet per second is 3200 pounds, but at a velocity of 20 feet per second it is 12 800 pounds; the horse-powers needed to overcome these resistances are 58 and 464, respectively. To these must be added the power necessary to overcome the friction of the air and that wasted in the production of waves.

The above discussion refers to the case of boats moving in the ocean and lakes or in a stream of large width and depth. In a canal the resistance is much greater, and it depends upon the ratio of the cross-section of the canal to that of the immersed portion of the boat. It depends also on the depth of the water. The "drag" of a ship in shoal water is very pronounced. For some experiments on the suction of vessels consult.* When the width of the canal is about five times that of the boat and the area of its cross-section about seven times that of the boat, the resistance is but slightly greater than in an

* Transactions American Society of Naval Architects and Marine Engineers, vol. 17, 1909.

unlimited stream. For smaller ratios the resistance rapidly increases, and when two boats pass each other in a small canal, the utmost power of the horses may be severely taxed. The reason for this increased resistance appears to be largely due to the fact that the velocity of the water relative to the boat increases with the diminution of the cross-section of the canal. Thus, if a and A be the areas of the cross-section of the canal and of the immersed part of the boat, the effective area of the water cross-section is $a - A$, and the water flowing backward through this area must have a higher relative velocity as A increases. The value of F given by formula (184) is accordingly increased to $fv^2/(1 - (A/a))^2$.

Prob. 184*a*. What horse-power is required to overcome the frictional resistance of a boat moving at the rate of 9 knots per hour when the area of its immersed surface is 320 square feet?

Prob. 184*b*. A canal has a cross-section of 360 square feet, while that of a canal boat is 60 square feet. Show that when two boats pass each other, the resistance of each is increased about 60 percent.

Art. 185. Work Required for Propulsion

When a boat or ship moves through still water with a velocity v, it must overcome the pressure due to impulse of the water and the resistance due to the friction of its surface on the water and air. If the surface be properly curved, there is no resultant pressure due to impulse, as shown in Art. 155. The resistance caused by friction of the immersed surface on the water can be estimated, as explained above. If A be the area of this surface in square feet, the work per second required to overcome this resistance is

$$k = AFv = fAv^3 \qquad (185)$$

The work, and hence the horse-power, required to move a boat accordingly varies approximately as the cube of its velocity. By the help of the values of f given in the last article an approximate estimate of the work can be made for particular cases. The resistance of the air, which in practice must be considered, will be here neglected.

To illustrate this law let it be required to find how many tons of coal will be used by a steamer in making a trip of 3000 miles in 6 days, when it is known that 800 tons are used in making the trip in 10 days. As the power used is proportional to the amount of coal, and as the distances traveled per day in the two cases are 500 miles and 300 miles, the law gives $T/480 = (5/3)^3$, whence $T = 2220$ tons. By the increased speed the expense for fuel is increased 277 percent, while the time is reduced 40 percent. If the value of wages, maintenance, interest, etc., saved on account of the reduction in time, will balance the extra expense for fuel, the increased speed is profitable. That such a compensation occurs in many instances is apparent from the constant efforts to reduce the time of trips of passenger steamers.

When a boat moves with the velocity v in a current which has a velocity u in the same direction, the velocity of the boat relative to the water is $v - u$, and the resistance is proportional to $(v - u)^2$ and the work to $(v - u)^3$. If the boat moves in the opposite direction to the current, the relative velocity is $v + u$, and of course v must be greater than u or no progress would be made. In all cases of the application of the formulas of this article and the last, v is to be taken as the velocity of the boat relative to the water.

Another source of resistance to the motion of boats and ships is the production of waves. This is due in part to a different level of the water surface along the sides of the ship due to the variation in static pressure caused by the velocity, and in part to other causes. It is plain that waves, eddies, and foam cause energy to be dissipated in heat, and that thus a portion of the work furnished by the engines of the boat is lost. This source of loss is supposed to consume from 10 to 40 percent of the total work, and it is known to increase with the velocity. On account of the uncertainty regarding this resistance, as well as those due to the friction of the water and air, practical computations on the power required to move boats at given velocities can only be expected to furnish approximate results.

The investigations of Rankine on this difficult subject led to the conclusion announced in 1858 in the anagram (20*a*, 4*b*, 6*c*, 9*d*, 34*e*, 8*f*, 4*g*, 16*h*, 10*i*, 5*l*, 3*m*, 15*n*, 14*o*, 4*p*, 3*q*, 14*r*, 13*s*, 25*t*, 4*u*, 2*v*, 2*w*, 1*x*, 4*y*).* The meaning of this anagram was published in 1861: "The resistance of a sharp-ended ship exceeds the resistance of a current of water of

* Philosophical Magazine, September, 1858.

the same velocity in a channel of the same length and mean girth by a quantity proportional to the square of the greatest breadth divided by the square of the length of the bow and stern."

Prob. 185. Compute the horse-power required to maintain a velocity of 18 knots per hour, taking $A = 7473$ square feet and $f = 0.004$.

Art. 186. The Jet Propeller

The method of jet propulsion consists in allowing water to enter the boat and acquire its velocity, and then to eject it backwards at the stern by means of a pump. The reaction thus produced propels the boat forward. To investigate the efficiency of this method, let W be the weight of water ejected per second, V its velocity relative to the boat, and v the velocity of the boat itself. The absolute velocity of the issuing water is then $V - v$, and it is plain without further discussion that the maximum efficiency will be obtained when this is 0, or when $V = v$, as then there will be no energy remaining in the water which is propelled backward. It is, however, to be shown that this condition can never be realized and that the efficiency of jet propulsion is low.

The effective work which is exerted on the boat by the reaction of the issuing water is

$$k = W\frac{(V-v)v}{g}$$

and the work lost in the absolute velocity of the water is

$$k' = W\frac{(V-v)^2}{2g}$$

The sum of these is the total theoretic work, or

$$K = W\frac{V^2 - v^2}{2g}$$

Therefore the efficiency of jet propulsion is expressed by

$$e = \frac{k}{K} = \frac{2v}{V+v}$$

This becomes equal to unity when $v = V$ as before indicated, but then it is seen that the work k becomes 0 unless W is infinite. The value of W is waV, if a be the area of the orifices through which the water is ejected; and hence in order to make e unity and at the same time perform work it is necessary that either V or a should be infinity. The jet propeller is therefore like a reaction wheel (Art. 172), and it is seen upon comparison that the formula for efficiency is the same in the two cases.

By equating the above value of the useful work to that established in the last article there is found

$$fgAv^2 = waV(V-v)$$

and if this be solved for V, and the resulting value be substituted in the formula for e, it reduces to

$$e = \frac{4}{3+\sqrt{1+(4fgA/wa)}}$$

which again shows that e approaches unity as the ratio of a to A increases. The area of the orifices of discharge must hence be very large in order to realize both high power and high efficiency. For this reason the propulsion of vessels by this method has not proved economical, although in the case of the boat Waterwitch, built in England about 1860, a fair speed was attained. In nature the same result is seen, for no marine animal except the cuttle-fish uses this principle of propulsion. Even the cuttle-fish cannot depend upon his jet to escape from his enemies, but for this relies upon his supply of ink with which he darkens the water about him.

Prob. 186. Compute the velocity and efficiency of a jet propeller driven by a 1-inch nozzle under a pressure of 150 pounds per square inch when $A =$ 1000 square feet and $f=0.004$. Compute also the efficiency when the diameter of the nozzle is 3 inches.

Art. 187. Paddle Wheels

The method of propulsion by rowing and paddling is well known to all. The power is furnished by muscular energy within the boat, the water is the fulcrum upon which the blade of the oar acts, and the force of reaction thus produced is transmitted to the boat and urges it forward. If water were an unyielding substance, the theoretic efficiency of the oar should be unity, or, as in any lever, the work done by the force at the rowlock should equal the work performed by the motive force exerted by the man on the handle of the oar. But as the water is yielding, some of it is driven backward by the blade of the oar, and thus energy is lost.

The paddle or side wheel so extensively used in river navigation is similar in principle to the oar. The power is furnished by motor within the boat, the blades or vanes of the wheel tend to drive the water backward, and the reaction thus produced urges the boat forward. On first though it might be supposed that the efficiency of the method would be governed by laws similar to those of the undershot wheel, and such would be the case if the vessel were stationary and the wheel were used as an apparatus for moving the water. In fact, however, the theoretic efficiency of the paddle wheel on a boat is much higher than that of the undershot motor.

The work exerted by the steam-engine upon the paddle wheels may be represented by PV, in which P is the pressure produced by the vanes upon the water, and V is their velocity of revolution; and the work actually imparted to the boat may be represented by Pv, in which v is its velocity with respect to the water. Accordingly the efficiency of the paddle wheel, neglecting losses due to foam and waves, is

$$e = \frac{v}{V} = \frac{v}{v + v_1}$$

in which v_1 is the difference $V - v$, or the so-called "slip." If the slip be o, the velocities V and v are equal, and the theoretic efficiency of the wheel is unity. The value of V is determined from the radius r of the wheel and its number of revolutions per second; thus $V = 2\pi rn$.

On account of the lack of experimental data it is difficult to give information regarding the practical efficiency of paddle wheels considered from a hydromechanic point of view. Owing to the water which is lifted by the blades, and to the foam and waves produced, much energy is lost. They are, however, very advantageous on account of the readiness with which the boat can be stopped and reversed. When the wheels are driven by separate engines, as is sometimes done on river boats, perfect control is secured, as they can be revolved in opposite directions when desired. Paddle wheels with feathering blades are more efficient than those with fixed radial ones, but practically they are found to be cumbersome, and liable to get out of order. In ocean navigation the screw has now almost entirely replaced the paddle wheel on account of its higher efficiency.

Prob. 187. The radius of the blades of a paddle wheel is 10.5 feet and the number of revolutions per minute is 24. If the efficiency is 75 percent, what is the velocity of the boat in miles per hour? Show that for this case the slip is 33 percent of the velocity of the boat.

Art. 188. The Screw Propeller

The screw propeller consists of several helicoidal blades attached at the stern of a vessel to the end of a horizontal shaft which is made to revolve by steam power. The dynamic pressure of the reaction developed between the water and the helicoidal surface drives the vessel forward, the theoretic work of the screw being the product of this pressure by the distance traversed. The pitch of the screw is the distance, parallel to the shaft, between any point on a helix and the corresponding point on the same helix after one turn around the axis, and the pitch may be constant at all distances from the axis, or it may be variable. If the water were unyielding, the vessel would advance a distance equal to the pitch at each revolution of the shaft; actually, the advance is less than the pitch, the difference being called the "slip." The effect thus is that the pressure P existing between the helical surfaces and the water moves the vessel with the velocity v, while the theoretic velocity which should occur is V, being the pitch of the screw multiplied by the number of revolutions per second. The work expended is hence PV or $P(v + v_1)$, if v_1 be the slip per second, and the work utilized is Pv. Accordingly the efficiency of screw propulsion is, approximately,

$$e = \frac{v}{v + v_1}$$

which is the same expression as before found for the paddle wheel. Here, as in the last article, all the pressure exerted by the blades upon the water is supposed to act backward in a direction parallel to the shaft of the screw, and the above conclusion is approximate because this is actually not the case, and also because the action of friction has not been considered. The practical advantage of the screw over the paddle wheel has been found to be very great, and this is probably due to the circumstance that less energy is wasted in lifting the water and in forming waves.

The pressure P which is exerted by the helicoidal blades upon the water is the same as the thrust or stress in the shaft, and the value of this may be approximately ascertained by regarding it as due to the reaction of a stream of water of cross-section a and velocity v, or

$$P = wa(v + v_1)v/g$$

Another expression for this may be found from the indicated work k of the steam cylinders of the engines; thus

$$P = k/v$$

Numerical values computed from these two expressions do not, however, agree well, the latter giving in general a much less value than the former.

In Art. 185 the work to be performed in propelling a vessel of fair form having the submerged surface A was found to be

$$k = fAv^3$$

If the value of v is taken from this equation and inserted in the expression for efficiency, there obtains

$$e = \frac{1}{1 + v_1(Af/k)^{\frac{1}{3}}}$$

which shows that e increases as v_1, f, and A decrease, and as k increases. Or for given values of f and A the efficiency decreases with the speed.

It has been observed in a few instances that the "slip" v_1 is negative, or that V, as computed from the number of revolutions and pitch of the screw, is less than v. This is probably due to the circumstance that the water around the stern is following the vessel with a velocity v', so that the real slip is $V - v + v'$ instead of $V - v$. The existence of negative slip is usually regarded as evidence of poor design.

Twin screws are frequently used, and since these revolve in opposite directions, the vessel can be more readily controlled. Fig. 188 shows the position of the twin screws with respect to the rudder. On some of the recent high-powered turbine-driven steamships two and three screws all mounted on a single shaft have been employed. Two sets of engines, and two shafts, one on each side of the rudder, are often employed as in Fig. 188, but a different arrangement of the shafts with respect to the hull of the ship permits the screws to be placed at considerable distances apart on the shafts, thus obtaining a greater efficiency than in the case of the single screw.

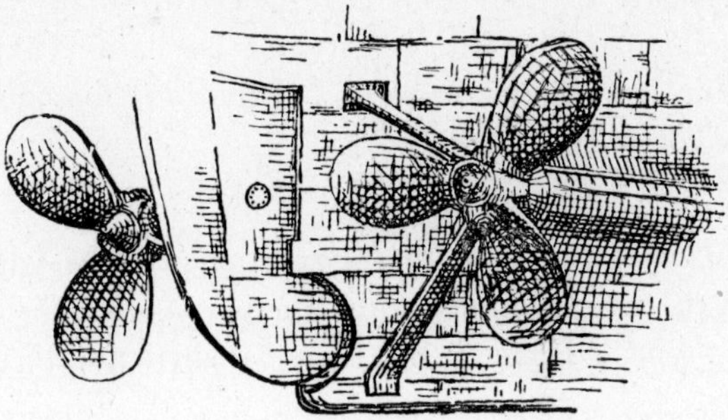

Fig. 188.

Prob. 188. A steamer having a submerged surface of 30 000 square feet is propelled at 18 knots per hour by an expenditure of 6000 horse-powers. If the pitch of the screw is 20 feet, its number of revolutions 120 per minute, and $f = 0.004$, compute the number of lost horse-powers.

Art. 189. Stability of a Ship

In Art. 14 the general principles regarding the stability of a floating body were stated, and these are of great importance in the design of ships. The center of gravity is, of course, always above the center of buoyancy, and the metacenter must be above the center of gravity in order to insure stability. The distance between the metacenter and the center of gravity is denoted by m, and if the body be inclined slightly to the vertical at the angle θ, the moment of the couple formed by the weight W of the body which acts downward through the center of gravity and the upward pressure W of the displaced water which acts through the center of buoyancy is $Wm \tan\theta$. Hence $m \tan\theta$ is a measure of the stability of the body, and the greater its value, the greater is the tendency of the body to return to the upright position.

The metacentric height m cannot, however, be made very great, for the rapidity of rolling increases with it. When a floating body or ship is displaced from its vertical position, it rolls to and fro with isochronous oscillations like those of a pendulum, and the time of one oscillation from port to starboard is given by the formula

$$t = \pi \sqrt{r^2/mg}$$

in which r is the radius of gyration of the weight of the ship about a horizontal longitudinal axis passing through its center of gravity. Hence if m is large t is small and the ship rolls quickly;

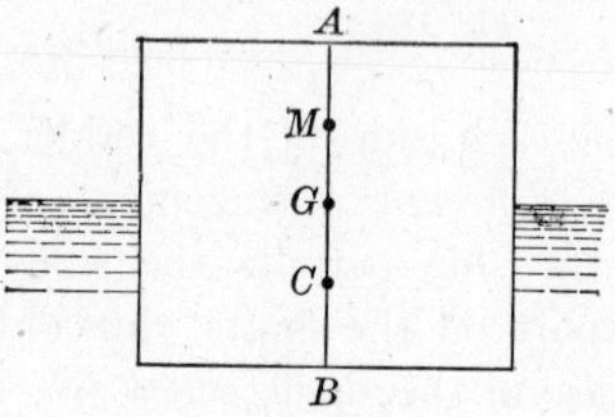

Fig. 189a.

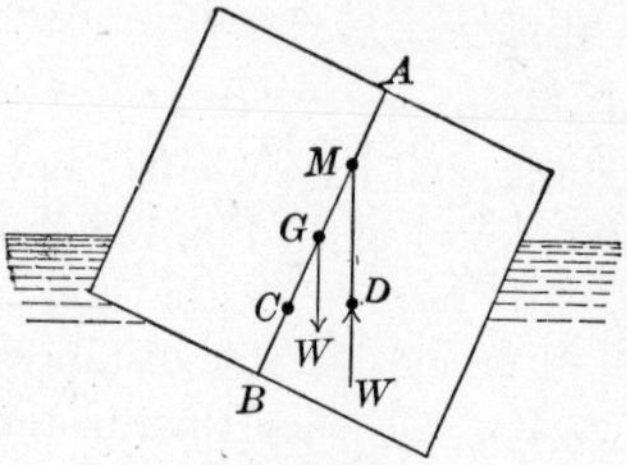

Fig. 189b.

but if m is small t is large and the ship rolls slowly. The metacentric height m for ocean vessels usually ranges from 2 to 15 feet, about 6 or 8 feet being the usual value.

The determination of the values of m and r for a ship is a laborious process, owing to its curved shape and the irregular distribution of its weight and cargo. The process will here be applied to the simple case of a rectangular prism of uniform density. Let h be the height and b the breadth of the prism, and l its length perpendicular to the plane of the drawing in Fig. 189*a*. When the prism is in the vertical position, its depth of flotation is sh, if s is its specific gravity (Art. 13), and this is also the length of the immersed portion of the axis AB when the prism is inclined to the vertical at the angle θ, as in Fig. 189*b*. In the latter position the center of buoyancy D, being the center of gravity of the displaced water, is easily located, and

$$x = \frac{b^2 \tan\theta}{12sh} \qquad y = \frac{sh}{2} + \frac{b^2 \tan^2\theta}{24sh}$$

are its coordinates with respect to B, x being measured normal and y

parallel to AB. The distance m from the center of gravity g to the metacenter M is then found to be

$$m = \frac{b^2}{12sh}(1 + \tfrac{1}{2}\tan^2\theta) - \tfrac{1}{2}h(1 - s)$$

If m is positive, the metacenter is above the center of gravity and the equilibrium is stable, for the moment $Wm \tan\theta$ restores the prism to the vertical position; if m is zero, the equilibrium is indifferent; if m is negative, the equilibrium is unstable, and the prism falls over.

The square of the radius of gyration of the prism with respect to a horizontal longitudinal axis through G is its polar moment of inertia $\frac{1}{12}l(bh^3+hb^3)$ divided by its volume lbd, whence $r^2 = \frac{1}{12}(h^2+b^2)$. For example, if h is 5 feet, b is 8 feet, and s is 0.5, the value of r^2 is 7.42 feet^2. The value of m to be used in the above formula for the time of one roll is that obtained by making θ equal to zero, since that formula is strictly true only for small deviations from the vertical. For the above data this value of m is $+0.88$ feet, the plus sign denoting stability, and hence the time of one oscillation from port to starboard is $t = 1.61$ seconds. It is seen that t can be increased either by increasing r^2 or by decreasing m; since a decrease in m is unfavorable to stability, it is usually preferable to increase r^2. For instance, in loading a ship the cargo may be placed along the sides rather than near the middle of the hold, and this will increase r^2, as the width of a ship is always greater than its depth. The general rule to promote stability and prevent quick rolling is hence to place the cargo as far as possible from the center of gravity.

The above formula for m shows that the moment $Wm \tan\theta$ which restores the floating prism to the vertical increases with the angle θ up to a maximum value, then decreases, and when D arrives vertically beneath G, it becomes zero and the prism upsets. For the case where $h = 5$ feet, $b = 8$ feet, and $s = 0.5$, the value of $m \tan\theta$ is 0.00 feet for $\theta = 0°$, 0.16 feet for $\theta = 10°$, 0.37 feet for $\theta = 20°$, and 0.72 feet for $\theta = 30°$; at $\theta = 32°$ the corner of the prism becomes immersed so that the formula no longer holds, but up to this point the moment constantly increases. From the above expression for m the solution of Prob. 14 is readily made.

Prob. 189*b*. An open rectangular wooden box caisson of length l, breadth b, and depth d has sides of mean thickness b_1 and a bottom of thickness d_1. Deduce formulas for the metacentric height m and the squared radius of gyration r^2. Compute m, r^2, and t for a numerical case.

Art. 190. Action of the Rudder

The action of the rudder in steering a vessel involves a principle that deserves discussion. In Fig. 190 is shown a plan of a boat with the rudder turned to the starboard side, at an angle θ with the line of the keel. The velocity of the vessel being v, the action of the water upon the rudder is the same as if the vessel were at rest and the water in motion with the velocity v. Let W be the weight of water which produces dynamic pressure against the rudder, due to the impulse $W \cdot v/g$ (Art. 152). The component of this pressure normal to the rudder is

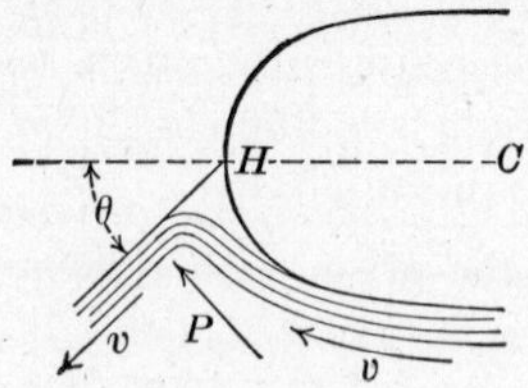

Fig. 190.

$$P = Wv \sin\theta / g$$

and its effect in turning the vessel about the center of gravity C is measured by its moment with reference to that point. Let b be the breadth of the rudder and d the distance CH between the center of gravity and the hinge of the rudder, then the lever arm of the force P is

$$l = \tfrac{1}{2}b + d \cos\theta$$

and accordingly the turning moment is

$$M = \tfrac{1}{2}W(b \sin\theta + d \sin 2\theta)v/g$$

To determine that value of θ which produces the greatest effect in turning the boat the derivative of M with respect to θ must vanish, which gives

$$\cos\theta = -\frac{b}{8d} + \sqrt{\frac{1}{2} + \frac{b^2}{64d^2}}$$

and from this the value of θ is found to be approximately 45°, since d is always much larger than b.

Values of the angle θ for several values of the ratio b/d may now be computed as follows:

$b/d =$	$\frac{1}{5}$	$\frac{1}{8}$	$\frac{1}{10}$	$\frac{1}{100}$	0
$\cos\theta =$	0.6825	0.6916	0.6947	0.7069	0.7071
$\theta =$	46° 58′	46° 15′	46° 00′	45° 01′	45°

which shows that about 45° is the advantageous angle. In practice it is usual to arrange the mechanism of the rudder so that it can only be turned to an angle of about 42° with the keel, for it is found that the power required to turn it the additional 3° or 4° is not sufficiently compensated by the slightly greater moment that would be produced. The reasoning also shows that intensity of the turning moment increases with v, so that the rudder acts most promptly when the boat is moving rapidly. For the same reason a rudder on a steamer propelled by a screw is not required to be so broad as one on a boat driven by paddle wheels, for the effect of the screw is to increase the velocity of the impinging water, and hence also to increase the dynamic pressure against the rudder.

Prob. 190. Explain how it is that a boat can sail against the wind. What is the influence of the keel in this motion?

Art. 191. Tides and Waves

The complete discussion of the subject of waves might, like many other branches of hydraulics, be expanded so as to embrace an entire treatise, while there can be here given only the briefest outline of a few of the most important principles. There are two classes or kinds of waves, the first including the tidal waves and those produced by earthquakes or other sudden disturbances, and the second those due to the wind. The daily tidal wave generated by the attraction of the moon and sun originates in the South Pacific Ocean, whence it travels in all directions with a velocity dependent upon the depth of water and the configuration of the continents, and which in some regions is as high as 1000 miles per hour. Striking against the coasts, the tidal waves cause currents in inlets and harbors, and if the circumstances were such that their motion could become uniform and permanent, these might be governed by the same laws which apply to the flow of water in channels. Such, however, is rarely the case; and accordingly the subject of tidal currents is one of much complexity and not capable of general formulation.

The velocity of a tidal wave on the ocean is $\sqrt{gD}$, where D is the depth of the water. When such a wave rolls over the land, the greatest velocity it can have is $\sqrt{gd}$, where d is its depth, this being the case of the bore (Art. 139). The velocity of a wave which is produced by a sudden disturbance in a channel of uniform width has also been found to be $\sqrt{gD}$, where D is the depth of the water.

Rolling waves produced by the wind travel with a velocity which is small compared with those above noted, although in water where the disturbance can extend to the bottom, it is generally supposed that their velocity is $\sqrt{gD}$. Upon the ocean the maximum length of such waves is estimated at 550 feet and their velocity at about 53 feet per second. For this class of waves it is found by observation that each particle of water upon the surface moves in an elliptic or circular orbit, whose time of revolution is the same as the time of one wave length.

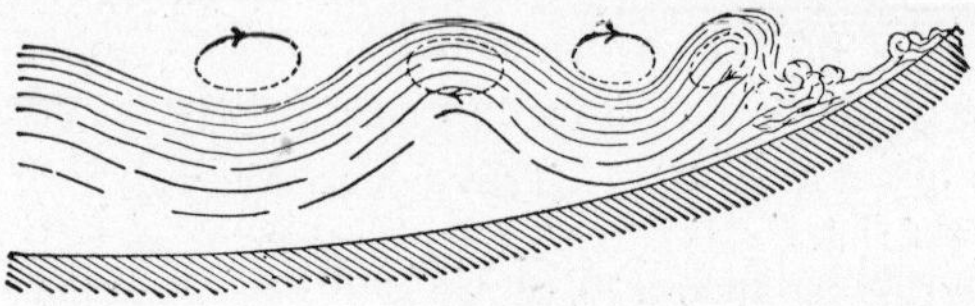

Fig. 191.

Thus the particles on the crest of a wave are moving forward in the direction of the motion of the wave, while those in the trough are moving backward. When such waves advance into shallow water, their length and speed decrease, but the time of revolution of the particles in their orbits remains unaltered, and as a consequence the slopes become steeper and the height greater, until finally the front slope becomes vertical and the wave breaks with roar and foam. Below the surface the particles revolve also in elliptic orbits, which grow smaller in size toward the bottom. The curve formed by the vertical section of the surface of a wave at right angles to its length is of a cycloidal nature.

The force exerted by ocean waves when breaking against sea walls is very great, as already mentioned in Art. 155, and often proves destructive. If walls can be built so that the waves are reflected without breaking, as is sometimes possible in deep water, their action is rendered less injurious. Upon the ocean waves move in the same direction as the wind, but along shore it is observed that they generally move normally toward it, whatever may be the direction in which the wind is blowing. The force of wave action is felt at depths of over 100 feet below the surface, for sand has been brought up from depths of 80 feet and dropped upon the decks of vessels. Shoals also cause a marked increase in the height of waves, even when such shoals are 500 feet or more below the water surface.

Prob. 191*a*. In a channel 6.5 feet wide, and of a depth decreasing 1.5 feet per 1000 feet, Bazin generated a wave by suddenly admitting water at the upper end. At points where the depths were 2.16, 1.85, 1.46, and 0.80 feet, the velocities were observed to be 8.70, 8.67, 7.80, and 6.69 feet per second. Do these velocities agree with the theoretic law?

Prob. 191*b*. Show that the values of f given in Art. 175 for use in the formula $F=fv^2$ are to be multiplied by 5.255 when v is in meters per second and F in kilograms per square meter.

Prob. 191*c*. Compute the metric horse-power required for a velocity of 25 kilometers per hour for a boat which has a submerged area of 237 square meters.

Prob. 191*d*. A ship rolls from starboard to port in 7.5 seconds. If the metacentric height m is 2.4 meters, what is the value of the transverse radius of gyration of the ship? How much must the radius of gyration be increased in order to increase the time of rolling 15 percent?

CHAPTER 16

PUMPS AND PUMPING

Art. 192. General Notes and Principles

Among the simple devices for raising water that have been used for many centuries, and which may be called lift pumps in a general way, are the sweep and windlass, buckets attached to a revolving wheel, the chain and bucket pump where the buckets move in a cylinder, and the Archimedian screw. The chain and bucket pump was probably first used by the Chinese in the form of an inclined trough in which moved the buckets attached to the endless chain, and this device in various forms has been used in all countries for lifting water from wells. The Archimedian screw, invented by the great engineer Archimedes when he was in Egypt, about 240 B.C., consists of a tube wound spirally around an inclined cylinder. When the lower end is placed under water and the cylinder revolved, the water is lifted and flows out of the upper end of the tube. This screw pump is still in use in northern Egypt, and it is said to be a satisfactory apparatus for a low lift.

The fact that water would sometimes rise into a space from which the air had been removed was known at a remote antiquity, and this was frequently explained by the statement that "nature abhors a vacuum." It was not until the middle of the seventeenth century that the true reason of this phenomenon was explained through the researches of Torricelli and Pascal (Art. 4), but prior to this time a rude form of suction pump, made by attaching a pipe to a bellows at the opening where the air usually enters, was used in both France and Germany. In 1732 the first true suction and lift pump was devised by Boulogne, and a little later the suction and force pump came into use.

The force pump is a device for raising water by means of pressure exerted on it by a piston. The syringe, which has been known from very early times, is an example of this principle, but the first true force pump was invented in Egypt about 120 B.C., by Ctesibius, a Greek hydraulician, and the description of it given by Vitruvius indicates that it was used to some extent by the Romans. The early force pumps were placed with their cylinders below the level of the water to be lifted, and had valves which closed under the back pressure of the water. By placing the cylinders above the water level and utilizing the principle of suction, the suction and force pump originated.

All devices for raising water may be classified under the three principles above mentioned: that of lifting in buckets, drawing it up by suction, or forcing it up by pressure, or under combinations of these. The lift or bucket principle is mainly employed for small quantities of water and has only a limited use in engineering practice. The suction principle, combined with lift or pressure, is extensively used, but in no event can the height of the suction exceed 34 feet, for it is the atmospheric pressure that causes the water to rise when the air above it is exhausted; under this principle also may be put injector pumps which operate under the action of negative pressure-head (Art. 31). The principle of direct pressure governs not only the force pump, but rotary and centrifugal pumps and also the devices for raising water by compressed air.

Whenever water is raised from a lower to a higher level, an amount of work must be expended greater than the theoretic work required to lift the given weight of water through the given height. The excess, called the lost work, is spent in overcoming resistances of friction and inertia. In designing pumps it is the object to reduce these losses to a minimum, so that the greatest economy in operation may result. The subject will here be mainly considered from a hydraulic standpoint, the object being to set forth the fundamental principles by which hydraulic losses may be avoided as far as possible.

Let W be the weight of water raised per second and h the height of the lift, then the useful work per second k is Wh. Let the total work expended per second be called K, then the efficiency of the apparatus is $e = k/K$. The work K to be considered here is that delivered to the pump and does not include that lost in transmission from the motor, since this, of course, is not fairly chargeable against the pump or lifting apparatus. If K be replaced by $W(h + h')$, where h' is the head lost in overcoming the frictional resistances, then the efficiency may be written

$$e = \frac{k}{K} = \frac{h}{h+h'} \qquad (192)$$

which is less than unity, since h' cannot be made zero.

The power required to operate a pump to raise the weight W of water per second through the height h is easily computed if the efficiency of the pump is known. For example, to raise 150 gallons per second through a height of 20 feet with a pump having an efficiency of 62 percent, the work which must be imparted to the pump per second is

$$K = k/e = (150 \times 8.335 \times 20)/0.62 = 40\ 340 \text{ foot-pounds,}$$

and this, divided by 550, gives 73.3 horse-powers.

Prob. 192. A pump raises 20.5 cubic feet of water per second through a height of 127.5 feet. The lost head in the pump and pipes amounts to 13.5 feet. Compute the efficiency of the pumping plant and the power required to operate it.

Art. 193. Raising Water by Suction

The term "suction" is a misleading one unless it be clearly kept in mind that water will not rise in a vacuum tube unless the atmospheric pressure can act underneath it. For example, no amount of rarefaction above the surface of the water in a glass bottle will cause that water to rise. When the tube is inserted into a river or pond, however, the water will rise in it when a partial vacuum is formed, since the atmospheric pressure which is transmitted through the water pushes it up until equilibrium is secured (Art. 4). The mean atmospheric pressure of 14.7 pounds per square inch at the sea level is equivalent to a height of water of 34 feet, and this is the limit of raising water by suction alone. In practice this height cannot be reached on account of the impossibility of producing a perfect vacuum, and it is found that about 28 feet is the maximum height of suction lift.

The height of the water barometer varies with the state of the weather, with the elevation above sea level, and with the temperature. The value of 34 feet is that corresponding to a reading of 30 inches on the mercury barometer at a temperature of 32° Fahrenheit. For higher temperatures more or less vapor is evaporated from the water surface and fills the suction tube, so that a complete vacuum cannot be formed. When the mercury barometer reads 30 inches, the water barometer is only 33.4 feet if the temperature of the water is 60° Fahrenheit, 32.4 feet at 90°, about 30 feet for 120°, about 23 feet for 160°, about 6 feet for 200°, and for 212° its height is zero, since the tube is then filled with steam. Hence water at the boiling-point cannot be raised by suction.

Fig. 193 gives two diagrams illustrating the principle of action of the common suction and lift pump. It consists of two vertical tubes *BD* and *BE*, the former being called the suction pipe and the latter the pump cylinder. The piston *A* in the pump cylinder has a valve opening upward, and the valve *B* at the top of the suction pipe also opens upward. In the left-hand diagram the piston is descending, the valve *A* being open and *B* being closed under the pressure of the air in the space between them. In the right-hand diagram the piston is ascending, the valve *A* being closed by the pressure of the air or water above it, while *B* is open, owing to the excess of atmos-

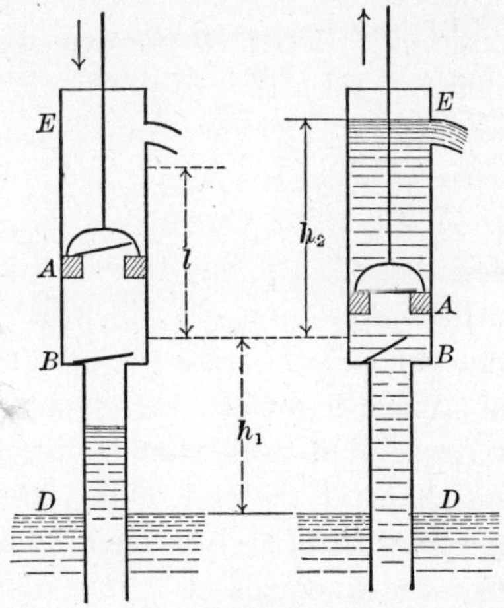

Fig. 193.

pheric pressure in BD above that in AB. In the first diagram the piston has made only one or two strokes, so that the water has risen but a short distance in the suction pipe. In the second diagram the piston has made a sufficient number of strokes so that the pump cylinder is full of water which is flowing out at the spout E.

Let h_1 be the distance from the water level D to the lowest position of the piston; this is called the height of lift by suction. Let h_2 be the height from the lowest position of the piston to the spout where the water flows out; this is called the height of lift by the piston. The distance $h_1 + h_2$ is the vertical height through which the water is raised, and if W be the weight of water raised in one second, the useful work per second is $W(h_1 + h_2)$. The energy imparted to the pump through the piston rod is always greater than this useful work, since energy is required to overcome the frictional resistances due to the motion of the water and piston, as also to overcome the resistance of inertia in putting them into motion.

To discuss the action of the pump in detail, let l be the stroke of the piston, that is, the distance between its highest and lowest positions. Let A be the area of the cross-section of the pump cylinder and a that of the suction pipe. Let the piston be supposed to be at its lowest position at the beginning of the operation when no water has been raised in the suction pipe above the level D in Fig. 193. On raising the piston through the stroke l it describes the volume Al, and the volume of air ah_1 now has the volume $Al + a(h_1 - x)$ in which x is the height through which the water rises during the upward stroke. Let h_a be the height of a water barometer corresponding to the air pressure above the water level at the beginning of the stroke, then $h_a - y$ is the pressure-head at the end of the stroke. Since, by Mariotte's law, the pressure of a given quantity of air is inversely as its volume, $(h_a - x)/h_a$ equals $ah_1/(Al + ah_1 - ax)$, whence,

$$x^2 - (rl + h_1 + h_a)x + rlh_a = 0$$

in which r represents the ratio A/a. For example, let A be 8 and a be 2 square inches, or $r = 4$, let h_1 be 20 and l be 1.5 feet;

then for $h_a = 34$ feet, the water rises during the first upward stroke to the height $x = 3.6$ feet. For the second upward stroke h_a is $34.0 - 3.6 = 30.4$ feet and h_1 is $20.0 - 3.6 = 16.4$ feet; then the formula gives $x = 3.7$ feet, so that the water level now stands 7.3 feet above its original level *D*. Proceeding in like manner, it is found that at the end of the third upward stroke the water stands at 11.2 feet above its original level. Similarly at the end of the fourth upward stroke it is found to be 15.3 feet above *D*, while at the end of the fifth upward stroke it has reached a height of 19.8 feet above its original level. During the progress of the sixth upward stroke the water enters the pump cylinder, during the next downward stroke it flows through the piston valve, and in the seventh upward stroke the water above the piston is lifted and flows out through the spout.

The preceding discussion supposes that there is no leakage of air through and around the piston, but this cannot be attained in practice; hence the degree of rarefaction below the piston is never so great as the above formula gives, and the number of strokes required to elevate the water above the valve *B* is larger than the computed number. When the suction height is greater than 25 feet, it becomes difficult to secure sufficient rarefaction to lift the water, and hence a foot valve, also opening upward, is placed in the suction pipe below the water level *D*. The pump cylinder and suction pipe can then be primed, or filled with water from above, and after this is done there will be no difficulty in operating the pump. If there is no foot valve, it will be necessary to have a very long piston stroke in order to start the pump, but with a foot valve the stroke of the piston may be any convenient length.

The action of this pump is intermittent, and water flows from the spout only during the upward stroke of the piston. When there are N upward strokes per minute, the discharge in one minute is NAl, if the piston and its valve be tight. The useful work per minute is $NwAl(h_1+h_2)$, if w be the weight of a cubic unit of water. When l and h_1+h_2 are in feet, A in square feet, and w in pounds per cubic foot, the horse-power expended in this useful work is

$$\overline{HP} = NwAl(h_1+h_2)/33\,000$$

and to this must be added the horse-power required to overcome the resistances of friction and inertia. This additional power often amounts to as much as that needed for the useful work, and in this case the efficiency of the pump is 50 percent. Suction and lift pumps are of numerous styles and sizes, the simplest being of square wooden tubes or of round tin-plate tubes with leather valves, and these can be readily made by a carpenter or tinsmith. They are mainly used for small quantities of water and for temporary purposes.

Prob. 193. The diameter of the pump cylinder is 8 inches and that of the suction pipe is 6 inches, while the vertical distance from the water level to the spout is 23 feet. If the pump piston makes 30 upward strokes per minute, each 9 inches long, what horse-power is required to operate the pump if its efficiency is 45 percent?

Art. 194. The Force Pump

A force pump is one that has a solid piston which can transmit to the water the pressure exerted by the piston rod and thus cause it to rise in a pipe. The early force pumps had little or no suction lift, as the pump cylinder was immersed in the body of water which furnished the supply, but the modern forms usually operate both by suction and pressure, the former occurring in a suction pipe and the latter in the pump cylinder. Fig. 194*a* shows the principle of action of the common vertical single-acting suction and force pump in which there is no water above the piston. In the left-hand diagram the piston is ascending, and the water is rising in the suction pipe BD under the upward atmospheric pressure; this ascent of the water occurs in exactly the same manner as explained in Art. 193, and after several strokes its level rises above the suction valve B. The right-hand diagram shows the piston descending and forcing the water up the discharge pipe CE. At C, where this pipe

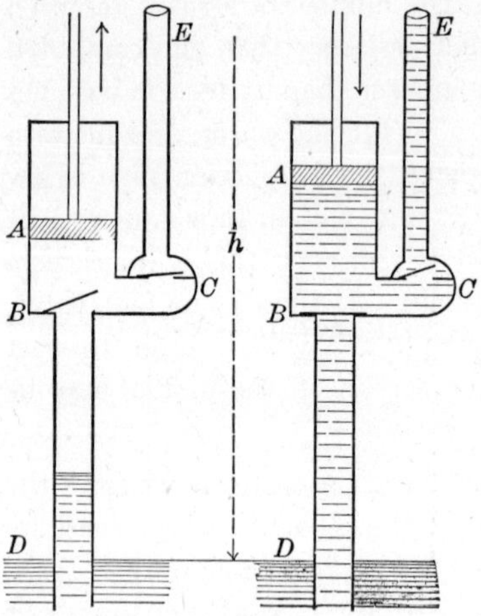

Fig. 194*a*.

joins the pump cylinder, is a check valve which closes on the upward stroke and thus prevents the water in *CE* from returning into the pump cylinder, while it opens on the downward stroke under the upward pressure of the water.

Let *A* be the area of the cross-section of the pump cylinder and *l* the length of the stroke of the piston. Then at each upward stroke a volume of water equal to *Al* is raised through the suction pipe, and in each downward stroke the same volume is raised in the discharge pipe. If *h* be the total lift above the water level *D* and *w* the weight of a cubic unit of water, the work done in each double stroke is *wAlh*. If there be made *N* double strokes per minute, the useful work per minute is *NwAlh*. When all dimensions are in feet, the horse-power required to do this useful work is found by dividing this quantity by 33 000, and the actual horse-power required to run the pump is greater than this by the amount needed to overcome the frictional resistances. This additional power will depend upon the length of the suction and discharge pipes, the speed at which the pump is operated, the friction along the sides of the piston, the losses of head in the passage of the water through the valve openings, and the losses of energy due to putting the water into motion at each stroke. The efficiency of single-acting suction and lift pumps hence varies between wide limits, 90 percent or more being obtained only for very low speeds and lifts, while for high speeds and lifts it may be 20 percent or less.

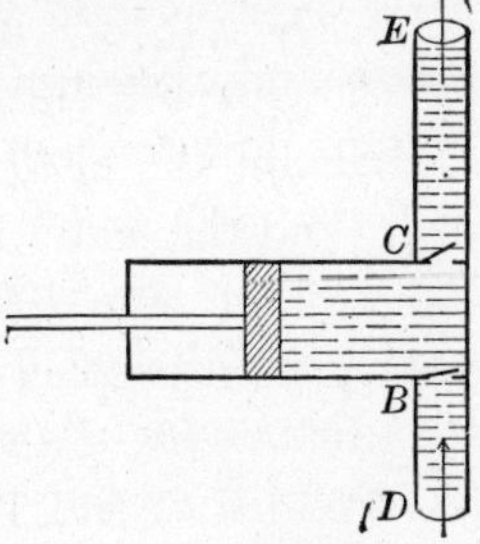

Fig. 194*b*.

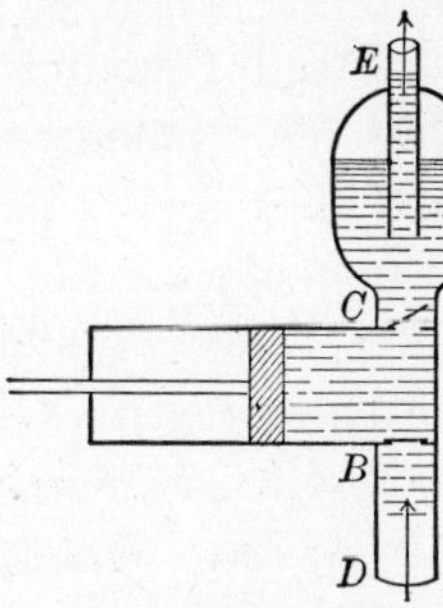

Fig. 194*c*.

The cylinder of the single-acting pump may be placed horizontal, as seen in Fig. 194*b*, where *BD* is the suction pipe and

CE the discharge pipe. When the piston moves toward the left, the suction valve *B* opens and the check valve *C* closes; when it moves toward the right, *B* closes and *C* opens. The discharge is intermittent, as in the previous case, but the horizontal position of the piston sometimes renders the connection of the piston rod to the motor more convenient. If the height of the suction lift be equal to that of the discharge lift, the force required to move the piston will be the same in each stroke and the pump will work with less shock than where the two lifts are unequal. Usually, however, the height of the discharge lift is greater than that of the suction lift, and the force required to move the piston is then the greatest when it moves from left to right in Fig. 194*b*. In order to equalize the forces exerted by the motor the duplex pump was devised; this consists of two single-acting cylinders placed side by side and connected to the same suction and discharge pipe, the pistons moving so that one exerts suction while the other is forcing the water upward. Three single-acting cylinders are also sometimes connected with the same suction and discharge pipe, in which case it is called the triplex pump. Duplex and triplex pumps give a more nearly continuous flow of water in both the suction and discharge pipes, and thus diminish the shocks that occur in a pump with one cylinder, while the efficiency is materially increased because the losses due to starting and stopping the columns of water are in large part avoided.

A double-acting pump is one having a single cylinder in which a solid piston or plunger exerts suction and pressure in both strokes and thus gives a nearly continuous flow through suction and discharge pipes. Fig. 194*d* shows the form known as the piston pump, while Fig. 194*e* is that called the plunger pump, the piston being replaced by a long cylinder moving in a short stuffing box *AA*. In both figures *D* is the suction pipe and *E* the discharge pipe. When the piston moves from left to right, the valves B_1 and C_2 open, while B_2 and C_1 close; when it moves in the opposite direction, B_2 and C_1 open, while B_1 and C_2 close. The plunger pump was invented in the seventeenth century, and its advantages over the piston type are so great that it is now extensively used for large pumping machinery. The cylinder of the piston pump must be bored to an exact and uniform size, and its piston must be carefully packed, while in the plunger pump only the short length of the stuffing box is bored and packed, the

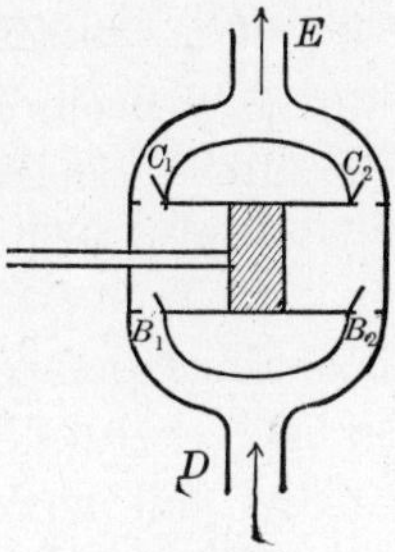

Fig. 194*d*.

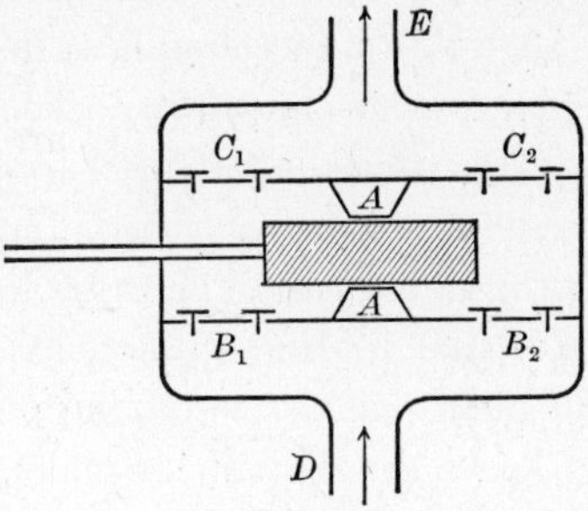

Fig. 194*e*.

plunger itself having no packing. The water lifted in one stroke of either pump is Al, where A is the area of the piston and l the length of its stroke, provided there is no leakage past the packing.

For all these forms of pumps a foot valve should be placed in the suction pipe, if the suction lift exceeds 20 feet, in order that the pump may be readily primed (Art. 193). To reduce the shocks that occur to a certain extent even in the double-acting pumps, an air chamber is frequently attached to the discharge pipe so that the confined air may distribute and lessen the shock that would otherwise be concentrated on the end of the discharge pipe. Fig. 194*c* shows such an air chamber attached to a single-acting pump; in the upper part of it is seen the compressed air which is receiving the pressure from the piston. After the check valve C closes the pressure of this air maintains the flow up the discharge pipe E, and hence the air chamber helps to avoid the losses due to intermittent flow. A duplex pump or a double-acting pump, when provided with an air chamber of proper size, will work very smoothly.

Prob. **194**. Consult Ewbanks' Hydraulics and Mechanics (New York, 1847), and describe a method of raising water through a low lift by means of a frictionless plunger pump. Ewbank notes that a stout young man weighing 134 pounds raised $8\frac{1}{3}$ cubic feet per minute with this machine to a height of $11\frac{1}{2}$ feet, and worked at this rate nine hours per day. If the efficiency of this pump was unity, what horse-power did the stout young man exert? Was his performance high or low?

Art. 195. Losses in the Force Pump

A reliable numerical computation of the hydraulic losses of energy in the force pump cannot be made without knowing the constants to use in finding the losses of head due to the valves (Art. 92), and these have been experimentally determined for only a few special forms. The valves shown in most of the figures of the preceding articles are simple flap valves, but poppet valves are more generally used, and Fig. 194*e* indicates such. In passing through a valve the water loses energy in friction, and also in impact due to the subsequent expansion. Since pumps are made in numerous forms having different details, general discussions of losses are difficult to make. The attempt will, however, be undertaken for the plunger force pump of Fig. 194*e*. Let h be the total height through which the water is lifted by both suction and pressure, and h' be the sum of all the hydraulic losses of head. Let K be the energy delivered per second to the piston rod, k' the energy expended in friction in the stuffing boxes of the piston rod and plunger, q the discharge per second, and w the weight of a cubic unit of water. Then

$$K = k' + wq\left(h + \frac{v_2^2}{2g} + h'\right)$$

and the pump should be so arranged as to make the losses k' and h' as small as possible. Only the hydraulic losses will be considered in the following discussion.

By means of the principles of Chap. 7 a rough formulation of the elements that make up the lost head h' can be effected, supposing the flow in the pipes to be steady. Let l_1 be the length, d_1 the diameter, and v_1 the velocity for the suction pipe, and l_2, d_2, and v_2 the same things for the discharge pipes. Let $2n$ be the number of valves in the suction and discharge chambers (Fig. 194*e*), all being taken of the same size, and let V denote the velocity of the water through each valve opening. Let these chambers be so large that the velocity of the water through them is very small compared to that in the pipes and valve openings. Then

$$h' = \left(m + f\frac{l_1}{d_1} + 1\right)\frac{v_1^2}{2g} + 2(m' + 1)\frac{V^2}{2g} + f_2\frac{l_2}{d_2}\frac{v_2^2}{2g} \tag{195}$$

gives all the hydraulic losses of head. In the first parenthesis m indicates the loss due to entrance at the foot of the suction pipe (Art. 89), fl_1/d_1 the friction loss in the suction pipe (Art. 90), and 1 the loss due to expansion (Art. 76) as the water enters the suction chamber B_1B_2. In the second parenthesis m' indicates the loss due to the open valves (Art. 92) and 1 that due to sudden expansion as the water enters the pump cylinder through the suction valves and the discharge chamber C_1C_2 through the discharge valves. The last term gives the loss due to friction in the discharge pipe. If there is an air chamber on the discharge pipe, another term might be introduced, but as the effect of the air chamber in reducing water hammer is a beneficial one, this term need not be used. The starting and stopping of the piston brings in other losses of energy, but as these are not hydraulic losses they will not be considered here.

When the pipes are long, the losses due to pipe friction will far exceed those in the pump, and are not fairly chargeable against it as a machine; hence in order to consider the pump alone the lengths l_1 and l_2 may be made equal to zero, as also m in the first parenthesis. Then formula (195) becomes

$$h' = \frac{v_1^2}{2g} + 2(m' + 1)\frac{V^2}{2g}$$

in which the first term of the second member gives the loss of head in entering the suction chamber, and the second those occurring in entering and leaving the pump cylinder. This equation appears, at first thought, to indicate that a suction chamber is not a hydraulic advantage, although it is known to afford a practical advantage in causing the valves to operate successfully, as also in permitting ready access to them. If a be the area of each valve opening, and a_1 that of the suction pipe, then a_1v_1 must equal $\frac{1}{2}naV$, since the same quantity of water passes per second through the suction pipe and through $\frac{1}{2}n$ valves. Accordingly the total loss of head in the pump may be written

$$h' = \frac{v_1^2}{2g} + 8(m' + 1)\left(\frac{a_1}{na}\right)^2 \frac{v_1^2}{2g}$$

which clearly shows that this loss decreases as the number of valves increases, when a is kept constant. Therefore the suction and discharge chambers may be made to give a hydraulic advantage, either by using many valves of a given size or by making the total valve area na sufficiently large, since h' is thus diminished. The number of valves will usually be 8, 12, or 16.

As a numerical example, take a plunger force pump, like Fig. 194e, having a piston area $A = 0.84$ square feet, and a stroke of 1.25 feet, the number of single strokes per minute being 30. The volume of water lifted per second is hence $30 \times 0.82 \times 1.25/60 = 0.525$ cubic feet. Let the diameter of the suction pipe be 10 inches and the area of its cross-section $a_1 = 0.545$ square feet. The mean velocity in the suction pipe is then $0.525/0.545 = 0.96$ feet per second. Let there be 12 valves in the suction chamber, so that $n = 6$, and let the area of each valve opening be $a = 8$ square inches $= 0.0556$ square feet. The velocity through each of the open valves is then $V = 0.525/3 \times 0.0556 = 3.15$ feet per second. As Art. 92 does not give the values of m' for poppet valves, it may be here noted that the experiments of Bach* indicate that they range from 1.1 to 2.8, depending upon the height of valve lift and the width of the seat. Taking 2 as a mean value of m', the lost head in the pump is

$$h' = 0.01555\left[1 + 8 \times 3\left(\frac{0.545}{6 \times 0.0556}\right)^2\right]0.96^2 = 0.96 \text{ feet.}$$

The useful head h, when the lengths of the suction and discharge pipes are disregarded, is probably about 3 feet, so that the hydraulic efficiency is $e = h/(h+h') = 0.75$. If the lengths of the vertical suction and discharge pipes be each 20 feet and their diameters be 10 inches, the useful head h is about 43 feet and from (195) the value of h' is found to be about one foot, so that the hydraulic efficiency is about 0.97. The velocity-head $v_2^2/2g$ which is lost at the top of the discharge pipe is here only 0.01 feet, so that it is unnecessary to consider it in determining the efficiency.

This discussion shows that the losses of head in force pumps may be made very slight by running them at low speeds in order that the velocity v_1 may be small. It shows that the losses decrease as the areas of the valve openings and their number are increased. It shows

* Zeitschrift deutscher Ingenieur Verein, 1886, p. 421.

that, for vertical suction and discharge pipes, the efficiency increases with the useful lift *h*, if the velocity in the pipes is the same for different lifts. These conclusions are verified by experiments, some of which will be noted in the next article. Since the flow through the valves and pump cylinder is not quite steady, numerical computations like the above cannot, however, be expected to give more than rough approximate results; nevertheless such results are useful in indicating the influence of the resistances upon the efficiency.

Prob. 195. For the above numerical example, compute the horse-power required to run the pump when the useful lift is 43 feet, assuming that 3 percent of that power is expended in overcoming friction in the stuffing boxes.

Art. 196. Pumping Engines

The steam engine was invented and perfected through the desire to devise methods of pumping water better than those in which the power of men and horses was used. Worcester in 1633, and Papin in 1695, used the direct pressure of steam upon water in a cylinder, and Savery in 1700 used both such pressure and the partial vacuum caused by the condensation of the steam. Newcomen in 1705 used a piston, on one side of which steam was applied and condensed, the motion of the piston being communicated by a walking beam to the piston rod of a pump. Watt, about 1775, introduced the crank, the parallel motion, the cut-off, the governor, and other improvements; he also brought the steam to both sides of the piston, thus making the engine double-acting. The first important application of the steam engine was in operating pumps to drain mines, but it soon came into use in all branches of industry where power was needed. Its influence on modern progress has been great.

The modern pumping engine consists of one or more steam cylinders connected to the same number of pump cylinders by piston rods, so that the steam pressure is directly transmitted through them to the water. It is important that the pressure in the water cylinder should be maintained nearly constant during the length of the stroke, and hence the steam should not be used expansively in the usual way; to insure constant steam pressure some form of compensator is used. The water cylinders are usually of the plunger type, and these are connected to the same suction and discharge pipes, an air chamber being placed on the latter to relieve the pump chambers of shock and to insure steady flow. The boilers, steam cylinders, and water cylinders constitute one machine or apparatus called a pumping engine. The efficiency of this apparatus is low, for it is equal to the product of the efficiencies of its separate parts. The efficiency of the furnace and boiler is about 75 percent in the best designs, the efficiency of the steam cylinders about 30 percent, and that of the water cylinders about 80 percent, so that the efficiency of the pumping engine as a whole is only 18 percent. This means that only 18 percent of the energy of the fuel is utilized in lifting the water, and this figure is, indeed, a high one, for many pumping plants are operated with an efficiency of less than 10 percent.

The term "duty" is often employed as a measure of the performance of a pumping engine, instead of expressing it by an efficiency percentage. This term was devised by Watt, who defined duty as the number of foot-pounds of useful work produced by the consumption of 100 pounds of coal. On account of the variable quality of coal a more precise definition of duty was introduced in 1890 by a committee of the American Society of Mechanical Engineers, namely, that duty should be the number of foot-pounds of work produced by the expenditure of 1 000 000 British thermal heat units. One British thermal heat unit is that amount of energy which will raise one pound of pure water one Fahrenheit degree in temperature when the water is at or near the temperature of maximum density (Art. 3); this amount of energy is 778 foot-pounds, and this constant is called the mechanical equivalent of heat. The duty of a perfect pumping engine, in which no losses of any kind occur, would be 778 000 000 foot-pounds. The highest duty obtained in a test is about 180 000 000 foot-pounds, and the efficiency of such an engine is $180/778 = 0.23$.* Common pumping engines have duties ranging from 120 000 000 to 60 000 000, the corresponding efficiencies being from 15 to 7.5 percent. The modern definition of duty

* Transactions American Society of Civil Engineers, vol. 73, 1911.

agrees with that of Watt, if the coal used be of such quality that one pound of it possesses a potential energy of 10 000 British heat units, which is somewhat less than that obtainable from average coal. The higher the duty of a pumping engine the greater is the amount of work that can be performed by burning a given quantity of coal. A high-duty engine is hence economical and a low-duty engine is wasteful in coal consumption, but the first cost of the former is much greater than that of the latter.

A duty test of a pumping engine consists in determining the number of heat units furnished by a given quantity of coal, the quantity of water lifted by the pump, the leakage past the piston packing, the pressure-heads in the suction and discharge pipes, the indicated horse-power of the steam cylinders, and many other minor quantities needed for estimating the efficiency of the boiler and steam part of the apparatus. The usual method of determining the discharge is by the displacement of the piston or plunger; if A be the area of its cross-section, l the length of the stroke, N the number of single strokes during the test, and T the number of seconds during which the test lasted, then NAl is the total quantity of water lifted, and

$$q = cNAl/T$$

is the quantity lifted per second, c being a coefficient which takes account of the leakage or slip past the plunger. The value of c is to be found by removing one of the cylinder heads and admitting water on the other side of the plunger, and its value is usually from 0.99 to 0.95 in new pumps, The total pressure-head H is found from

$$H = (h_2 \pm h_1 + d)$$

where h_1 and h_2 are the pressure-heads corresponding to the mean readings of the gages on the suction and discharge pipes and d the vertical distance between the centers of the gages; here the plus sign is to be used when the corresponding pressure is below and the minus sign when it is above that of the atmosphere. The total work done by the pump during the trial is then $cNAl \cdot H$ and then the duty of the pumping engine

$$\text{Duty} = 1\,000\,000\, cNAlH/\text{heat units},$$

in which the denominator is determined by the thermodynamic tests made on the boiler and steam engine. The capacity of the pump, or the quantity of water lifted in 24 hours, is $24 \times 3600 \times q$.

The efficiency of pump cylinders, which are tested in the above manner, is usually found by dividing the work wqH done by them in one second by that done by the steam as determined by indicator cards taken from the steam cylinders. This method differs from that used in the previous articles, and gives results too small from the standpoint of hydraulic losses. A discussion by Webber * of several tests shows that this efficiency increases with the lift as follows:

Lift in feet,	5	15	30	100	170	270
Efficiency,	0.30	0.45	0.65	0.85	0.91	0.88

The highest value of 91 percent was obtained from a test of a Leavitt pumping engine having a duty of 111 549 000 foot-pounds, and a capacity of 4 400 000 gallons per 24 hours; the duration of this test was 15.1 hours.

Prob. 196. In a test lasting 12 hours, 27 502 000 heat units were produced under the boiler. The area of the plunger was 172 square inches, the length of the stroke was 18.9 inches, the number of single strokes was 76 000, and the leakage past the plunger packing was 5900 cubic feet. The pressure gage on the force pipe read 100 and the vacuum gage on the suction pipe read 9.3 pounds per square inch, the distance between the centers of these gages being 8 feet. The mean indicated horse-power of the steam cylinders was 128. Compute the discharge of the pump in cubic feet per second and its capacity in gallons per day. Compute the total pressure-head H. Compute the duty of the pumping engine. Compute the efficiency of the pump cylinders.

Art. 197. The Centrifugal Pump

The centrifugal pump is the reverse of a turbine wheel, and any reaction turbine, when run backwards by power applied to its axle, will raise water through its penstock. The centrifugal pump, like the turbine, is of modern origin and development. A rude form, devised by Ledemour in 1730, consisted of an inclined tube attached by arms to a vertical shaft; the lower

* Transactions American Society Mechanical Engineers, 1886, vol. 7, p. 602.

end of the tube being immersed, the water flowed from its upper end when the shaft was rotated. It was not, however, until about 1840 that the first true centrifugal pumps came into use, and they have since been perfected so as to be of great value in engineering operations, especially for low lifts.

Fig. 197 shows the principle of the arrangement and action of the centrifugal pump. The power is applied through the axis A to rotate the wheel BB in the direction indicated by the arrow. This wheel is formed of a number of curved vanes like those in a turbine wheel (Art. 174). The revolving vanes produce a partial vacuum, and this causes the water to rise in the suction pipe DD which enters through the center of the wheel case and delivers the water at the axis of the wheel. The water is then forced outward through the vanes and passes into the volute chamber CC, which is of varying cross-section in order to accommodate the increasing quantity of water that is delivered into it, and all of which passes up the discharge pipe E. The rotation of the wheel hence produces a negative pressure at the upper end of the suction pipe and a positive pressure in the volute chamber, and the water rises in the pipes in the same manner as in those of a suction and force pump. The height of the suction lift cannot usually exceed about 28 feet.

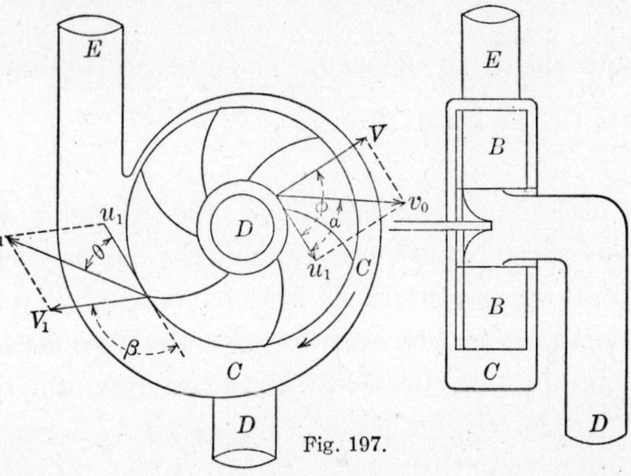

Fig. 197.

The parallelograms of velocity shown in Fig. 197 are the same as in the reaction turbine (Art. 174), and a similar notation will be used. The velocities of rotation of the inner and outer circumferences will be called u and u_1, the absolute velocities of the water as it enters and leaves the wheel are v_0 and v_1, and the corresponding relative velocities are V and V_1. The angles of entrance, approach, and exit are called ϕ, α, and β, while θ denotes the angle between v_1 and u_1. Let H_0 be the pressure-head at the top of the entrance pipe and H_1 that at the foot of the discharge pipe, while h_0 and h_1 are the heights of the suction and force lifts estimated downward and upward from the center of the wheel, and let h_a be the height of the water barometer. Then from formula (162)

$$V^2 - u^2 - V_1^2 + u_1^2 = 2g(H_1 - H_0)$$

and also from $(31)_2$, not considering frictional resistances,

$$H_1 = h_a + h_1 - \frac{v_1^2}{2g} \qquad H_0 = h_a - h_0 - \frac{v_0^2}{2g}$$

Combining these equations, and replacing $h_1 + h_0$ by h, where h is the total lift, the fundamental equation for the discussion of frictionless centrifugal pumps results. To introduce the frictional losses, however, $h + h'$ should be used instead of h, where h' is the total head lost in all the hydraulic resistances. Then

$$V^2 - V_1^2 - u^2 + u_1^2 + v_1^2 - v_0^2 = 2g(h + h') \qquad (197)_1$$

is the fundamental formula for the discussion of the centrifugal pump. Since there are no guides, the water enters the vanes radially, so that the approach angle α is a right angle, and hence $V^2 = u^2 + v_0^2$. Also the parallelogram of velocities at exit gives $V_1^2 = u_1^2 + v_1^2 - 2u_1v_1\cos\theta$. Inserting these values of V_2 and V_1^2 in $(197)_1$, it reduces to

$$u_1 v_1 \cos\theta = g(h + h')$$

which is a necessary relation connecting u_1 and v_1.

A centrifugal pump must be run at a certain velocity in order to overcome the pressure-head $h + h'$ by means of the velocity-head $v_1^2/2g$ of the issuing water. Hence $h + h' = v_1^2/2g$, and equating this to the value of $h + h'$ established by the above formula, there results $u_1 \cos\theta = \frac{1}{2}v_1$. It hence follows from the parallelogram of velocities that V_1 and u_1 must be equal. Then $\theta = 90° - \frac{1}{2}\beta$, and

$$u_1 = \frac{v_1}{2\sin\frac{1}{2}\beta} \quad \text{or} \quad u_1 = \frac{\sqrt{2g(h+h')}}{2\sin\frac{1}{2}\beta} \qquad (197)_2$$

gives the required velocity of the outer circumference of the wheel. This velocity decreases as the exit angle β increases; when β is very small, u_1 is very large; when the vanes are radial at the outer circumference, β is 90° and $u_1 = \sqrt{g(h + h')}$. Hence the speed of the pump must increase with the square root of the pressure-head $h + h'$. Since $v_1 = q/a_1$, where a_1 is the area of the exit orifices normal to v_1, the velocity is also $u_1 = q/2a_1 \sin \frac{1}{2}\beta$, and therefore the discharge q increases directly with the speed.

Since the speed must increase with the lift, and since the losses of head increase with the speed, it follows that the efficiency of the centrifugal pump in general decreases with the lift. This theoretic conclusion has been verified by practical tests. Webber, in his discussion cited in the last article, gives the following as the mean results derived from a number of experiments, the efficiency computed being the ratio of the work done by the pump to that obtained from indicator cards taken on the cylinders of the steam motor:

Lift in feet,	5	10	20	40	60
Efficiency,	0.56	0.64	0.68	0.58	0.40

For a low lift the centrifugal pump has a hydraulic efficiency higher than these figures indicate, but, as in the case of the force pump, it is difficult to determine reliable values by numerical computations.

The centrifugal pump possesses an advantage over the force pump in having no valves and in being able to handle muddy water, for even gravel may pass through the vanes without injuring them. The above figure represents the principle rather than the actual details of construction. Usually the suction pipe is divided into two parts which enter the axis upon opposite sides of the wheel, and the volute chamber is often made wider than the wheel case, thus forming what is called a whirlpool chamber, which prevents some of the losses of head due to impact. The vanes are sometimes curved in the opposite direction to that shown in the figure, as by so doing the angle β is made larger and the speed of the pump is lessened, as is seen from formula $(197)_2$. The theory of the centrifugal pump is, however, much less definite than that of the reaction turbine, and experiment is the best guide to determine the advantageous shape of the vanes.

Multiple stage centrifugal pumps for work against high heads are extensively used.*†

Prob. 197. A centrifugal pump lifts 120 cubic feet of water per minute through a discharge pipe having a diameter of 1 foot. The outer diameter of the wheel is 2 feet, the exit angle is 90°, the number of revolutions per second is 60, and the water is lifted 18 feet. Compute the horse-power of the pump, and its hydraulic efficiency.

Art. 198. The Hydraulic Ram

The hydraulic ram is an apparatus which employs the dynamic pressure produced by stopping a column of moving water to raise a part of this water to a higher level than that of its source. The principle of its action was recognized by Whitehurst in 1772,‡ but the credit of perfecting the machine is due to Montgolfier, who in 1796 built the first self-acting ram. It has since been widely used for pumping small quantities of water from streams to houses, but is not so well adapted to lifting a large quantity; many attempts have been made in this direction, some of which give promise of much usefulness.

The principle of the action of the hydraulic ram is shown in Fig. 198, where *A* is the reservoir that furnishes the supply, *BCD*

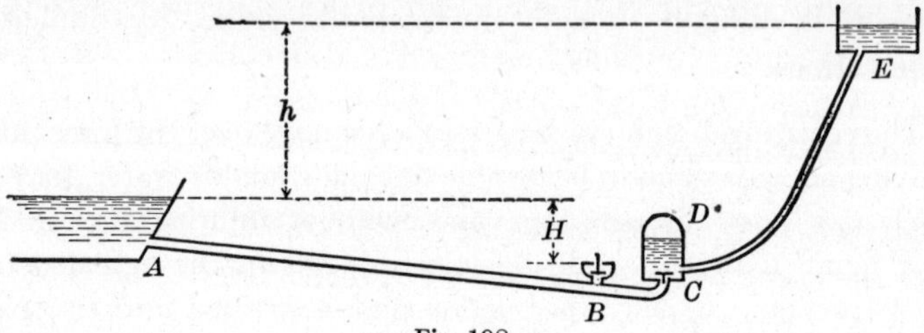

Fig. 198.

the ram, *AB* the drive pipe which carries the water to the ram, *DE* the discharge pipe through which a part of the water is raised to the tank *E*. The ram itself consists merely of the waste valve *B* through which a part of the water from the drive pipe

* Journal American Society of Mechanical Engineers, Jan. and March, 1910.
† Journal Western Society of Engineers, April, 1910.
‡ Transactions Royal Society, 1775, vol. 65, p. 277.

escapes, and the air vessel D which has a valve C that allows water to enter it through BC, but prevents its return. The waste valve B is either weighted or arranged with a spring so that it will open when acted upon by the static pressure due to the head H. As soon as it opens the water flows through it, but as the velocity increases the dynamic pressure due to the motion of the column AB (Art. 157) becomes sufficiently great to close the valve B. Then this dynamic pressure opens the valve C and compresses the air in the air chamber or forces water up the discharge pipe. A moment later when equilibrium has obtained in the air vessel, the valve C closes and the air pressure maintains the flow for a short period in the discharge pipe, while the water in the drive pipe comes to rest. Then the waste valve B opens again, and the same operations are repeated.

The algebraic discussion of the hydraulic ram is very difficult because it involves the time in which the waste valve closes and the law of its rate of closing. The investigation in Art. 157, however, clearly shows that the operations above described will take place if the drive pipe is long enough to produce a dynamic pressure sufficient to close the waste valve. Let l be the length of that pipe, v the velocity in it, p_0 the static unit pressure due to H, w the weight of a cubit unit of water, g the acceleration of gravity, and t the time in which the valve closes. Then, since there is no static pressure at the valve during the flow, the formula $(157)_1$ gives

$$p = 2wlv/gt - p_0$$

which is a good approximation to the excess of dynamic pressure over the static pressure p_0. It is seen that this excess p may be rendered very great by making l large and t small, and that its greatest value is

$$p = wuv/g - p_0$$

in which u is the velocity of sound in water. It is rare, however, that a drive pipe is sufficiently long to furnish the excess dynamic pressure given by the last formula.

The efficiency of the hydraulic ram is the ratio of the useful work done to the energy expended in the waste water. Let q be the quantity of water lifted per second through the height h

from the level of the reservoir A to that of the tank E. Let Q be the discharge per second through the waste valve and H the height through which it falls, then the efficiency of the ram and its pipes is

$$e = \frac{wqh}{wQH} = \frac{qh}{QH}$$

It is found by experiment that the efficiency decreases as the ratio h/H increases. Eytelwein found that e was 0.92 when h/H was unity, 0.67 when h/H was 5, and 0.23 when h/H was 20, but these values were probably derived by using a different formula for the efficiency.

Experiments in 1890 at Lehigh University on a Gould ram No. 2, in which the waste valve made 55 strokes per minute, gave a mean efficiency of 35 percent. The length of the supply pipe was 38 feet and its fall 12 feet, the length of the discharge pipe 60 feet, and the lift h was 12 feet, so that the ratio h/H was unity. These experiments showed also that the efficiency increased as the number of strokes per minute was decreased by lessening the weight on the waste valve. The maximum quantity of water raised per minute, however, occurred with a heavier waste valve than that which gave the maximum efficiency. The efficiency was also found to increase as the length of the stroke of the waste valve decreased.

The least possible fall in the drive pipe of the hydraulic ram is about 1½ feet and the least length of drive pipe about 15 feet. It is customary to make the area of the discharge pipe from one-third to one-fourth that of the drive pipe, and with these proportions a fall of 10 feet will force water to a height of nearly 150 feet. A common rule of manufacturers is that about one-seventh of the water flowing down the drive pipe may be raised to a height five times that of the fall in the drive pipe; this is a rough rule only, for the length of the discharge pipe is one of the controlling factors as well as its vertical rise.

The Rife hydraulic engine is a water ram on a large scale, two or more being connected to the same discharge pipe, so that the flow in it is nearly continuous.* Three of these engines are said to raise 864 000 gallons of water per day to an elevation of 150 feet, the fall in the drive pipe being 30 feet. The diameter of the drive pipe is 8 inches and that of the discharge pipe is 4 inches; the waste valve weighs

* Engineering News, 1896, vol. 36, p. 429.

50 pounds, and it is provided with an adjusting lever in order that its effective weight may be regulated so as to cause the maximum discharge to be delivered.

Prob. 198. A hydraulic ram raises $32\frac{1}{2}$ pounds of water in 5 minutes through a discharge pipe 60 feet long. The drive pipe is 38 feet long and the amount of water wasted in 5 minutes is $41\frac{1}{2}$ pounds. The fall of the drive pipe is 12 feet and the vertical rise of the discharge pipe above the ram is 24 feet. Compute the efficiency of the ram.

Art. 199. Other Kinds of Pumps

The lift and force pumps described in Arts. 193 and 194 are called displacement pumps, because the volume of water lifted in one stroke is that displaced by the piston or plunger. If there be no leakage past the piston packing, and if no air is mingled with the water, the discharge in a given time may be very accurately determined by counting the number of strokes and multiplying this number by the displacement in one stroke. On account of the reciprocating motion of the piston these forms are often called reciprocating pumps. There is always a loss of energy due to putting the piston into motion at the beginning of each stroke, and to avoid this many forms of rotary pumps have been devised; yet notwithstanding this loss the plunger force pump is probably the most efficient and economical of all kinds.

A rotary or impeller pump is one in which the moving parts have a circular motion only, and the centrifugal pump described in Art. 197 is of this kind. Numerous other rotary pumps have been invented, but none is widely used except the centrifugal one. Fig. 199*a* shows one where the moving parts consist of two wheels which are rotated in opposite directions as indicated by the arrows; this motion produces a partial vacuum whereby the water rises in the suction pipe D, and is then carried between the teeth and the case and forced up the discharge pipe E. Fig. 199*b* shows a form where the moving parts are two lobes in contact with each other and each in contact with the inclosing case. In the left-hand diagram the water rising in the pipe D is flowing toward the right, but a moment later the lobe B has assumed the position shown in the right-hand diagram, and the water is imprisoned between the lobe and the case. An instant later the two lobes are forcing this water up the pipe *E*, while the water coming in at *D* is flowing to the left. The greatest objection to

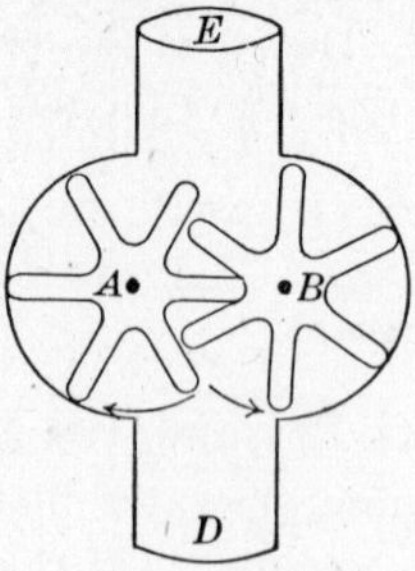

Fig. 199*a*.

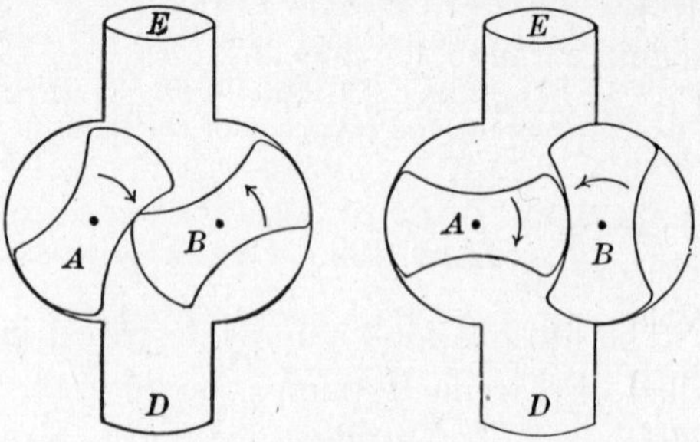

Fig. 199*b*.

these pumps is that it is difficult to maintain close contact between the case and the lobes or wheels, owing to wear, so that after being in use for some time there is much back leakage of water, and the capacity and efficiency of the pump are diminished. The only apparent advantage of the rotary pump is that it has no valves. Five rotary pumps of the type of Fig. 199*b* were installed in 1902 at a pumping station near Chicago, the lobes or impellers being 4 feet long and the distance between their centers 2.7 feet; these pumps run at 100 revolutions per minute, and each has a capacity of 6000 cubic feet per minute under the total lift of about 8 feet.*

The pumps thus far described, with the exception of the hydraulic ram, may be called mechanical pumps, because they act under energy communicated to them from motors. All mechanical pumps are reversible; that is, when the water moves in the opposite direction under a pressure-head, they become hydraulic motors. The reverse of the chain and bucket pump is the overshot or breast wheel, that of the suction and lift pump is the water-pressure engine, and that of the centrifugal pump is the turbine. The hydraulic ram does not operate under the action of a motor, and it does not appear to be reversible.

* Engineering News, 1903, vol. 49, p. 172.

Pumps which have no moving parts and which operate through the action of air suction and dynamic pressure constitute another class which will now be briefly considered. Here belong the jet or ejector pumps which act largely through suction, and the injector pump used on locomotives. The latter produces a vacuum through the flow of steam, and cannot be discussed here, as it involves principles of thermodynamics. The fundamental principle, however, is indicated in Fig. 199*c*, which shows the jet apparatus invented by James Thomson in 1850.* The water to be lifted is at *C*, and it rises by suction to the chamber *B*, from which it passes through the discharge pipe to the tank *D*. The forces of suction and pressure are produced by a jet of water issuing from a nozzle at the mouth of the discharge pipe, the nozzle being at the end of a pipe *AB* through which water is brought from a reservoir; or the water delivered from the nozzle may come from a hydrant or from a force pump. Let H be the effective head of the jet as it issues from the nozzle, h_1 the suction lift, and h_2 the lift above the tip of the nozzle; let q be the discharge through the nozzle and q_1 that through the suction pipe. Then, neglecting frictional resistances,

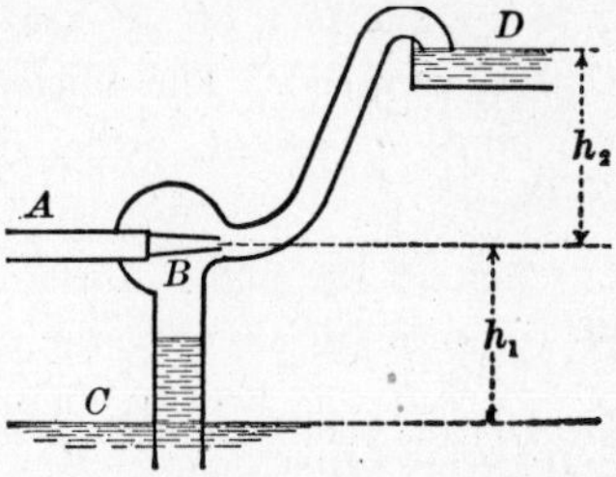

Fig. 199*c*.

$$qH = qh_2 + q_1(h_1 + h_2)$$
$$e = (qh_2 + q_1h_1 + q_1h_2)/qH$$

It is found by experiments that the efficiency of this jet pump is very low, usually not exceeding 20 percent, the highest efficiencies being for low ratios of $h_1 + h_2$ to H. This form of pump has, however, been found very convenient in keeping coffer dams and sewer trenches free from water, as it requires little or no attention and has no moving parts to get out of order.

Another class of pumps uses the pressure of air or of steam in order to elevate water. The idea of these pumps is old, yet it was not until 1875 that the steam pulsometer was perfected by Hall, while

* Report of British Association, 1852, p. 130.

the air-lift pump of Frizell dates from 1880. The air-lift pump is now extensively used for raising water from deep wells, the compressed air being forced down a vertical pipe in the well tube and issuing from its lower end. As it issues, bubbles are formed in the entire column of water in the well tube, and being lighter than a column of common water, it rises to a greater height under the atmospheric pressure, assisted by the upward impulse of the bubbles to a slight extent. In this manner water having a natural level 50 feet or more below the surface of the ground may be caused to rise above that surface. It has been found in practice that for lifts of 15 to 50 feet from 2 to 3 cubic feet of air are necessary for each cubic foot of water that is elevated. The efficiency of this form of pump is low, rarely reaching 30 percent, although a maximum of 50 percent has been claimed.*

Among the many forms of pumps operating under the pressure of compressed air only the ejector pump used in the Shone system of sewerage can here be mentioned. The sewage from a number of houses flows to a closed basin, called an injector, in which it continues to accumulate until a valve is opened by a float. The opening of this valve allows compressed air to enter, and this drives out the sewage through a discharge pipe to the place where it is desired to deliver it. In the installation of this system of sewerage at the World's Fair of 1893 in Chicago, there were 26 ejectors which lifted the sewage 67 feet, the total pressure-head being about 108 feet. Vacuum methods of moving sewage have also been used in Europe, but these cannot compete in efficiency with those using compressed air.

Prob. 199. For Fig. 199*c* let the diameter of the nozzle be 1 inch and that of the discharge pipe 4 inches. Let H be 64 feet, h_1 be 18 feet, h_2 be 3 feet, and the discharge from the nozzle be 0.25 cubic feet per second. Compute the greatest quantity of water that can be lifted per second through the suction pipe, and the efficiency of the apparatus when doing this work.

Art. 200. Pumping through Pipes

When water is pumped through a pipe from a lower to a higher level, the power of the pump must be sufficient not only to raise the required amount in a given time, but also to overcome the various resistances to flow. The head due to the resistances is

* Journal of Association of Engineering Societies, 1900, vol. 25, p. 173.

thus a direct source of loss, and it is desirable that the pipe should be so arranged as to render this as small as possible. The length of the pipe is usually much greater than the vertical lift, so that the losses of head in friction are materially higher than those indicated by the discussion of Art. 195, where vertical discharge pipes were alone considered.

Let w be the weight of a cubic foot of water and q the quantity raised per second through the height h, which, for example, may be the difference in level between a canal C and a reservoir R, as in Fig. 200*a*. The useful work done by the pump in each second is wqh. Let h' be the head lost in entering the pipe at the canal, h'' that lost in friction in the pipe, and h''' all other losses of head, such as those caused by curves, valves, and by resistances in passing through the pump cylinders. Then the total work performed by the pump per second is

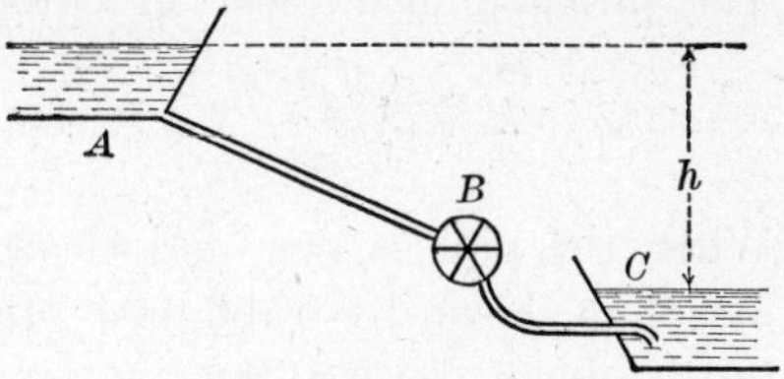

Fig. 200*a*.

$$k = wqh + wq(h' + h'' + h''') \tag{200$_1$}$$

Inserting the values of the lost heads from Arts. 89–92, this expression takes the form

$$k = wqh + wq\left(m + f\frac{l}{d} + m_2\right)\frac{v^2}{2g} \tag{200$_2$}$$

in which v is the velocity in the pipe, l its length, and d its diameter. In order, therefore, that the losses of work may be as small as possible, the velocity of flow through the pipe should be low; and this is to be effected by making the diameter of the pipe large. The size of the pipe is here regarded as uniform from the canal to the reservoir; in practice the suction pipe is usually larger in diameter than the discharge pipe, in order that the suction valves may receive an ample supply of water.

For example, let it be required to determine the horse-power of a pump to raise 1 200 000 gallons per day through a height of

230 feet when the diameter of the pipe is 6 inches and its length 1400 feet. The discharge per second is

$$q = \frac{1\ 200\ 000}{7.481 \times 24 \times 3600} = 1.86 \text{ cubic feet,}$$

and the velocity in the pipe is

$$v = \frac{1.86}{0.7854 \times 0.5^2} = 9.47 \text{ feet per second.}$$

The probable head lost in entering the pipe is, by Art. 89,

$$h' = 0.5 \frac{v^2}{2g} = 0.5 \times 1.39 = 0.7 \text{ feet.}$$

When the pipe is new and clean, the friction factor f is about 0.020, as shown by Table 90*a*; then the loss of head in friction in the pipe is, by Art. 90,

$$h'' = 0.020 \times \frac{1400}{0.5} \times 1.39 = 77.8 \text{ feet.}$$

The other losses of head depend upon the details of the pump cylinder and the valves; if these be such that $m_2 = 4$, then

$$h''' = 4 \times 1.39 = 5.6 \text{ feet.}$$

The total losses of head hence are

$$h' + h'' + h''' = 84.1 \text{ feet.}$$

The work to be performed per second by the pump now is

$$k = 62.5 \times 1.86 (230 + 84.1) = 36\ 510 \text{ foot-pounds,}$$

and the horse-power to be expended is 36 510/550 = 66.4. If there were no losses in friction and other resistances, the work to be done would be simply

$$k = 62.5 \times 1.86 \times 230 = 26\ 740 \text{ foot-pounds,}$$

and the corresponding horse-power would be 26 740/550 = 48.6. Hence 17.8 horse-power is wasted in injurious resistances, or the efficiency of the plant is only 73 percent.

For the same data let the 6-inch pipe be replaced by one 14 inches in diameter. Then, proceeding as before, the velocity of flow is found to be 1.74 feet per second, the head lost at entrance

0.03 feet, the head lost in friction 1.13 feet, and that lost in other ways 0.19 feet. The total losses of head are thus only 1.35 feet, as against 84.1 feet for the smaller pipe, and the horse-power required is 48.9, which is but little greater than the theoretic power. The great advantage of the larger pipe is thus apparent, and by increasing its size to 18 inches the losses of head may be reduced so low as to be scarcely appreciable in comparison with the useful head of 230 feet.

A pump is often used to force water directly through the mains of a water-supply system under a designated pressure. The work of the pump in this case consists of that required to maintain the pressure and that required to overcome the frictional resistances. Let h_1 be the pressure-head to be maintained at the end of the main, and z the height of the main above the level of the river from which the water is pumped; then h_1+z is the head H, which corresponds to the useful work of the pump, and, as before,

$$k = wqH + wq\,(h' + h'' + h''')$$

To reduce the injurious heads to the smallest limits the mains should be large in order that the velocity of flow may be small. In Fig. 200*b* is shown a symbolic representation of the case of pumping into a main, P being the pump, C the source of supply, and DM the pressure-head which is maintained upon the end of the pipe during the flow. At the pump the pressure-head is AP, so that AD represents the hydraulic gradient for the pipe from P to M. The total work of the pump may then be regarded as expended in lifting the water from C to A, and this consists of three parts corresponding to the heads CM or z, MD or h_1, and AB or $h' + h'' + h'''$, the first overcoming the force of gravity, the second maintaining the discharge under the required pressure, while the last is transformed into heat in overcoming friction and other resistances. In this direct method of water supply a standpipe, AP, is often erected near the pump, in which the water rises to a height corresponding to the required pressure, and which furnishes a supply when a temporary stoppage of the pumping engine

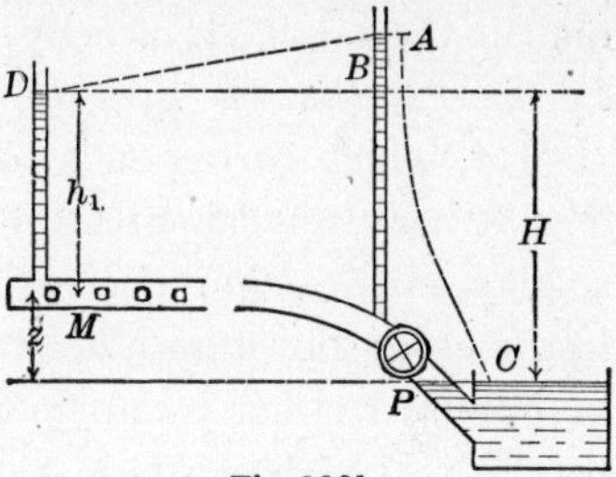

Fig. 200*b*.

occurs. This standpipe also relieves the pump to some extent from the shock of water hammer (Art. 157).

Prob. 200. Compute the horse-power of a pump for the following data, neglecting all resistances except those due to pipe friction: $q = 1.5$ cubic feet per second, which is distributed uniformly over a length $l_1 = 3000$ feet (Art. 104), the remaining length of the pipe being 4290 feet; $d = 10$ inches, $h_1 = 75.8$ feet, and $z = 10.6$ feet.

Art. 201. Pumping through Hose

In Art. 109 the flow of water through fire hose was briefly treated and the friction factors given for different kinds of hose linings. It was shown that the loss of head in a long hose line becomes so great, even under moderate velocities, as to consume a large proportion of the pressure exerted by the hydrant or steamer. As another example, let the pressure in the pump of the fire engine be 122 pounds per square inch, corresponding to a head of 281 feet, and let it be required to find the pressure-head in $2\frac{1}{2}$-inch rough rubber-lined cotton hose at 1000 feet distance, when a nozzle is used which discharges 153 gallons per minute, the hose being laid horizontal. The discharge is 0.341 cubic feet per second, which gives a velocity of 10.0 feet per second in the hose. Hence by (90) the loss of head in friction is 231 feet, so that the pressure-head at the nozzle entrance is only 50 feet, which corresponds to about 22 pounds per square inch. The remedy for this great reduction of pressure is to employ a smaller nozzle, thus decreasing the discharge and the velocity in the hose; but if both head and discharge are desired, they may be obtained either by an increase of pressure at the steamer or by the use of a larger hose.

Another method of securing both high velocity-head and quantity of water is by the use of siamesed hose lines, and this is generally used when large fires occur. This method consists in having several lines of hose, generally four, lead from the steamer to a so-called siamese connection, from which a short single line of hose leads to the nozzle. In Fig. 201 the pump or fire steamer is represented by A, the siamese joint by B, the nozzle entrance by C, and the nozzle tip by D. From A let n

lines of hose, each having the length l_1 and the diameter d_1, lead to B; and from B let there be a single line of length l_2 and diameter d_2 leading to the nozzle which has the diameter D. The hydraulic gradient (Art. 99) is shown by $abcD$, the pressure-heads

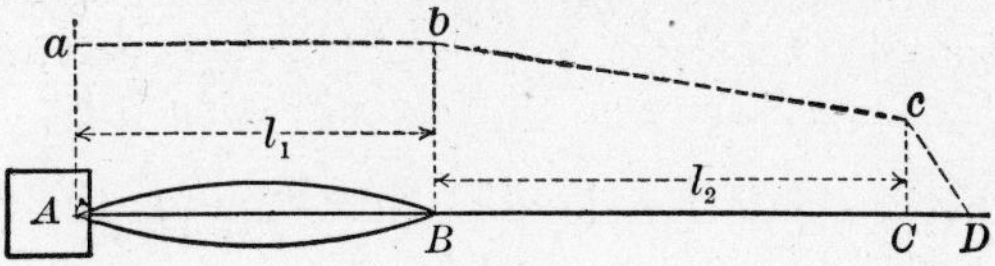

Fig. 201.

at A, B, C being represented by Aa, Bb, Cc. Let h be the pressure-head on the nozzle tip or the difference of the elevations of the points a and D. It is required to deduce a formula for the velocity at the nozzle tip and to determine the pressure-heads at B and C.

This case is one of diversions, already treated in Art. 105, and the same principles may be applied to its solution. Neglecting losses in entrance, in curvature, and in the siamese joint, the total head h is expended in friction in the hose lines and in the nozzle, or

$$h = f_1 \frac{l_1}{d_1}\frac{v_1^2}{2g} + f_2 \frac{l_2}{d_2}\frac{v_2^2}{2g} + \frac{1}{c_v^2}\frac{V^2}{2g}$$

in which v_1 and v_2 are the velocities in the lines l_1 and l_2, and V is that from the nozzle, while c_v is the coefficient of velocity of the nozzle (Art. 83). The first term of the second member is the head lost between A and B, and the algebraic expression for this is independent of the number of hose lines between those points; the velocity v_1 in these hose lines depends, indeed, upon their number, but the hydraulic gradient ab is the same for each and all of them. The law of continuity of flow (Art. 31) gives, however,

$$nd_1^2v_1 = d_2^2v_2 = D^2V$$

and, taking from these the values of v_1 and v_2 in terms of V and inserting them in the expression for h, there results

$$V^2 = \frac{2gh}{\frac{f_1l_1}{n^2d_1}\left(\frac{D}{d_1}\right)^4 + \frac{f_2l_2}{d_2}\left(\frac{D}{d_2}\right)^4 + \frac{1}{c_v^2}} \qquad (201)$$

from which the velocity V and the velocity-head $V^2/2g$ can be computed, while the discharge is given by $q = \frac{1}{4}\pi D^2 V$. The pressure-head h_2 at the nozzle entrance and the pressure-head h_1 at the siamese joint may then be found from

$$h_2 = \frac{1}{c_1^2}\frac{V^2}{2g} \qquad h_1 = \left[\frac{fl_2}{d_2}\left(\frac{D}{d_2}\right)^4 + \frac{1}{c_1^2}\right]\frac{V^2}{2g}$$

and, as a check, the latter should equal h minus the drop of the hydraulic gradient between a and b.

This discussion shows that, by increasing the number n, the loss of head between A and B may be made very small, the effect being practically the same as that of moving the steamer to B and using but a single hose line l_2. As a numerical example, let h = 230.4 feet, l_1 = 500 feet, l_2 = 60 feet, $d_1 = d_2$ = 2.5 inches, D = 1 inch, and c_1 = 0.975. Then, taking f as 0.03, the computed results for different values of n are as follows, V being in feet per second, $V^2/2g$ in feet, and q in gallons per minute. It is seen that

$n =$	1	2	3	4	6	∞
$V =$	68.9	92.2	99.8	10.3	105	107
$V^2/2g =$	73.7	132	155	165	173	180
$q =$	169	226	244	252	258	263

for four lines the velocity-head is more than double that for a single line and that the discharge is 50 percent greater. With more than four lines the velocity-head and discharge increase slowly, and for $n = \infty$ they are practically the same as for $n = 10$. The number of hose lines generally used is four, since the slight advantage of more lines is not sufficient to warrant their use.

Many other interesting problems relating to hose lines may be solved by using the same principles. If there are four lines of hose between the pump and the siamese joint, three having the diameter d_1 and one having the diameter d, it can be shown that the formula (201) applies, provided n be replaced by $3 + (d/d_1)^{\frac{5}{2}}$. For instance, if d be 3 inches and d_1 be $2\frac{1}{2}$ inches, this makes n^2 about 19. In deducing this expression for n it is assumed that the friction factors are the same for both sizes of hose, although in strictness the smaller hose has the higher value of f.

Another case is where two of the hose lines between A and B have the diameter d_1 and the length l_1, while the two other lines are of the length $l + l_3$, the length l having the diameter d and the length l_3 the diameter d_3. Here the principles regarding compound pipes (Art. 100) are also to be regarded, and formula (201) applies likewise to this case, if n be computed from

$$n = 2 + 2\left(\frac{d}{d_1}\right)^2 \sqrt{\frac{e_1}{e + e_3(d/d_3)^4}}$$

in which e represents $f(l/d)$, while e_1 and e_3 represent $f_1(l_1/d_1)$ and $f_3(l_3/d_3)$ respectively. For instance, if $l_1 = 100$, $l_3 = 100$, and $l = 50$ feet, while $d_1 = d_3 = 2\frac{1}{2}$ inches and $d = 3$ inches, then the value of n^2 is about 21, so that this arrangement is more effective than that of the preceding paragraph.

In the deduction of the above formulas losses of head at entrance and in the siamese joint have not been regarded, and it is unnecessary to consider these when the hose lines are long. For lines less than 100 feet in length the losses of head at entrance may be taken into account by adding the term $0.5(D/d_1)^2/n^2$ to the denominator of (201). The loss of head due to the siamese joint may, in the absence of experimental data, be approximately accounted for by adding about 0.02 to that denominator, thus considering its influence about one-half that of the nozzle. In a case like that of the last paragraph, where the length l in two of the hose lines is nearest the pumps, the values of e and e_1 may be increased by 0.5 in order to introduce the influence of the entrance heads. Errors of 5 percent or more are liable to occur in computations on pumping through short hose lines.

Prob. 201*a*. Three hose lines run from a pump to a siamese connection, each being 500 feet long and $2\frac{1}{2}$ inches in diameter, and from the siamese one line 50 feet long and $2\frac{1}{2}$ inches in diameter leads to a $1\frac{1}{2}$-inch nozzle having a velocity coefficient of 0.96. When the pressure at the pump is 100 pounds per square inch, what is the discharge from the nozzle and the velocity-head of the jet? What friction heads are lost in the hose and nozzle?

Prob. 201*b*. In a fire-engine test made in 1903, the lengths l_1 and l_2 were 50 feet, the length l was 12 feet, and l_2 was zero, as the nozzle was attached directly to the siamese joint. The diameter d_1 was 3 inches, while d and d_3 were $2\frac{1}{2}$ inches, and D was 2 inches. The pressure gage on the steamer read 90, while one on the siamese joint read 63 pounds per square inch. Compute the pressure-head at the siamese joint.

Prob. 201*c*. What is the efficiency of a bucket pump which lifts 2000 liters of water per minute through a height of 3.5 meters with an expenditure of 2.5 metric horse-powers?

Prob. 201*d*. When the height of the mercury barometer is 760 millimeters, water at a temperature of 0° centigrade is raised by suction in a perfect vacuum to a height of 10.33 meters (Art. 193). Under the same atmospheric pressure, how high can it be raised when the temperature is 32° centigrade?

Prob. 201*e*. What metric horse-power is required to raise 4 000 000 liters per day through a height of 75 meters when the diameter of the pipe is 20 centimeters and its length 500 meters?

Prob. 201*f*. The calorie is the metric thermal unit, this being the energy required to raise one kilogram of water one degree centigrade when the temperature of the water is near that of maximum density. How many calories are equivalent to 1 000 000 British thermal units?

APPENDIX

Art. 202. Hydraulic Machinery

Hydraulic presses, jacks, accumulators, elevators and other apparatus by which pressure and power are transmitted through water are frequently included under the term hydraulic machinery. In these the action of the water is mainly hydrostatic (Art. 10). Hydraulic motors convert the energy of water into useful work, pumps raise water by the work applied to them, but hydraulic machinery transmits energy through water from a point of application to a point where it is utilized in doing work.

The hydraulic press used in testing machines is very simple, consisting of a cylinder *C* into which water is forced through

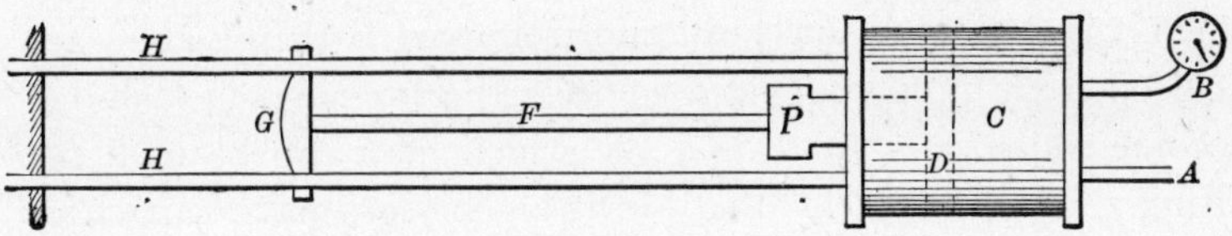

Fig. 202*a*.

the pipe *A* (Fig. 202*a*). The water pressure acts upon the piston *D* and is transmitted to the plunger *P* to one end of the bar *F* which is under test; the other end of the bar abuts against the tail piece *G* which can be fastened in any convenient position on the four guides *H*. If the diameter of the piston is *D* and the unit pressure behind the piston is p, then, neglecting friction, the force transmitted to the test bar is $\frac{1}{4}\pi D^2 p$, so that if the diameter of the bar is d the unit-stress in the bar is $(D/d)^2 p$. The unit-pressure p is measured either by a mercury column or by a spring gage *B*. The machine at Phoenixville has a capacity of 1200 tons, which is developed by a pressure of 800 pounds per square inch in the cylinder; the piston is 64 inches in diameter and has a 72-inch stroke, and the machine can be used for both compressive and tensile tests.

The hydraulic jack is a portable machine which is a combination of a force pump and hydraulic press. The common form, invented by Dudgeon about 1850, consists essentially of a fixed vertical column A (Fig. 202b) upon which moves the jack B, whose upper portion C is hollow and contains the operating fluid. By means of the handle H this fluid is forced by the piston P into the lower reservoir E where its pressure lifts the part B together with weight W. At V_1 is an inward-opening valve which admits the fluid beneath the piston when the handle H is raised, and at V_2 is a downward-opening valve through which the fluid passes when the handle is lowered;

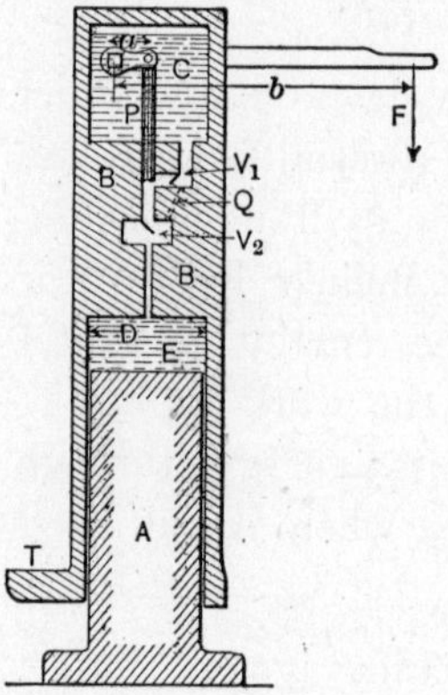

Fig. 202b.

when it is desired to lower the movable part B these valves are held open by proper devices so that the pressures in E and C become equalized. At T is a toe which may also be used for lifting. The large jacks used for lifting bridges have capacities of 600 tons. Neglecting friction, the mechanics of the jack is simple. Let W = load to be lifted, this including the weight of B, let F = force applied at end of handle, a and b = lever arms shown in Fig. 202b, d = diameter of piston P, D = diameter of reservoir E; then $W = (D/d)^2(a/b)F$. For example, if $a = 36$ inches, $b = 1\frac{1}{2}$ inches, $d = \frac{3}{4}$ inch, $D = 4$ inches, then a force F of 100 pounds will lift a load W of 68 300 pounds; when the force F falls 10 inches the weight W rises 0.0146 inch.

The accumulator is a device for storing energy by means of water under pressure in a tank. The water is forced into the tank C by pumps through the inlet pipe I (Fig. 202c) and its pressure lifts the plunger P and the attached loads W; when the plunger has reached the top of its travel it brings into action a mechanism which stops the pumps. The water under pressure passes out of the cylinder through the outlet pipe O, and, as the plunger nears the bottom of its travel, another mechanism starts the pumps. Let W be the total weight of plunger and loads, D = diameter of plunger, and p = unit-pressure in the water; then $p = W/\frac{1}{4}\pi D^2$, if friction of the packing be ignored. Let s = stroke of the piston, then Ws is the work that can be developed in one stroke. The accumulator is used for delivering energy to forging processes and other machinery whose action is variable. Let Q be the quantity of water required in the time t during which the machine is working, and T the time of a whole operation, that is, the period of working plus the time of rest. If an accumulator is not used the pump must be large enough to furnish Q/t per second while with an accumulator only Q/T is needed.

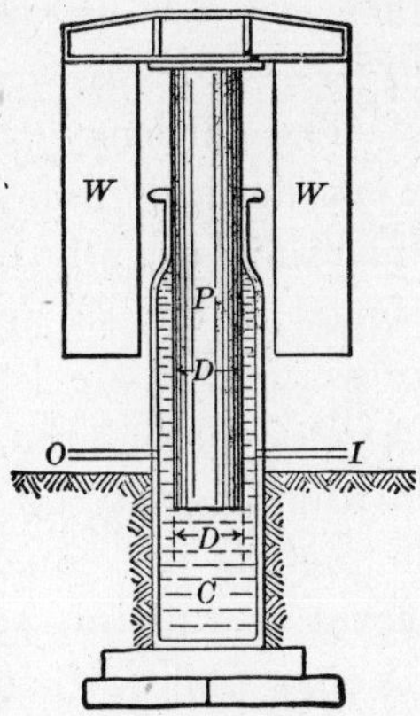

Fig. 202c.

The differental accumulator (Fig. 202*d*) enables a much higher pressure to be maintained with the same load W; here the plunger is fixed and is made of two diameters, the tank C being in the annular space above the larger diameter. If D and d be the two diameters, then $p = W/\frac{1}{4}\pi(D^2-d^2)$. Pressures as high as 2000 pounds per square inch have been developed and utilized by the differential accumulator. Let p be this unit-pressure, and the diameters be 7 and 5 inches; then $W = 2000\ (38.48 - 19.63) = 37\ 700$ pounds; if the stroke is 10 feet, the energy that can be developed in one stroke is 377 000 foot-pounds, which is equivalent to 11.4 horse-powers utilized in one minute. This result is slightly too large because friction losses have not been considered. The efficiency of an accumulator is usually about 98 percent. A large accumulator in London stores 2.8 horse-power-hours, or 168 horse-powers can be utilized in one minute.

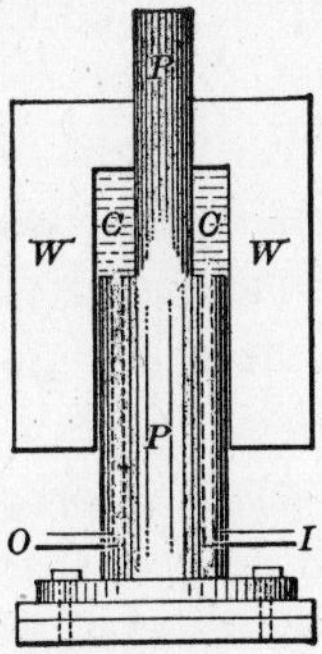

Fig. 202*d*.

Other hydraulic machines may be regarded as modifications of the pump, the hydraulic press and the accumulator. Among these are the water-pressure engine (Art. 171), hydraulic elevators, hoists, riveters, brakes and gate-operating devices. In all of these the water acts by its pressure and the efficiency of the operations depends upon the special pistons, packings, valves, and regulators which are used; these will not be considered here as their operation involves no hydraulic principles.

The efficiency of a hydraulic machine is the ratio of the work derived from it to the work applied to it. Thus, for a hydraulic elevator—let W_1 be the weight of the water consumed in one up-and-down trip, this water acting under the pressure-head h_1; let W be the total load which is lifted by the elevator through the height h; then the efficiency is $e = Wh/W_1h_1$ in which h_1 may be replaced by $2.3p$, if p is the water pressure in pounds per square inch and h is given in feet. Plunger elevators with a good counter-balancing arrangement give $e = 0.90$, while without such balancer e may be as low as 0.30. In general a reliable precise value of the efficiency of a hydraulic machine is difficult to determine.

Prob. 202*a*. An accumulator loaded to a pressure of 800 pounds per square inch has a plunger 18 inches in diameter and a stroke of 21 feet. What is the load W? What horse-power can be obtained for a period of 50 seconds?

Art. 203. Miscellaneous Problems

The following problems introduce subjects that have not been specifically treated in the preceding pages. Teachers who wish to offer prize problems to their classes may perhaps find some of these suitable for that purpose.

Prob. 203*a*. A wooden water tank 18 feet in diameter and 24 feet high is to be hooped with iron bands which may be safely spaced 6 inches apart at the middle of the height. How far apart should they be spaced at the bottom?

Prob. 203*b*. A house is 60 feet lower than a spring A and 30 feet higher than a spring B. A pipe from A to the house runs near B. Explain a method by which the water from B can be drawn into the pipe and be delivered at the house.

Prob. 203*d*. From a pumping station water is forced by direct pressure through a compound pipe, consisting of 7500 feet of 14-inch pipe, 4100 feet of 12-inch pipe, and 780 feet of 8-inch pipe, to a 6-inch pipe on which there are three hydrants *A*, *B*, and *C*. *A* is 133 feet from the end of the 8-inch pipe and 115 feet above the gage at the pumping station; *B* is 433 feet from the end of the 8-inch pipe and 135 feet above the gage; *C* is 733 feet from the end of the 8-inch pipe and 125 feet above the gage. To each of these hydrants is attached 50 feet of $2\frac{1}{2}$-inch rubber-lined hose with a 1-inch smooth nozzle at the end. When the gage at the pumping station reads 175 pounds per square inch, to what heights will the three streams be thrown from the three nozzles?

Prob. 203*e*. When a body falls vertically in water, its velocity soon becomes constant. For a smooth sphere an approximate formula for this velocity is $v\sqrt{2gd(s-1)}$, in which d is the diameter of the sphere and s its specific gravity. Compute the velocity v for a sphere having a diameter of 0.001 feet and a specific gravity of 1.25.

Prob. 203*f*. The velocity with which water flows through a sand filter bed varies directly as the head (Art. 110). If V is the velocity in meters per day, d the effective size of the sand grains in millimeters, h the head, l the thickness of the sand bed, and t the centigrade temperature,

$$V = 1000\,(0.70 + 0.03t)\,(h/l)d^2$$

is the formula deduced by Hazen.* When $t=32^\circ.4$ centigrade, $d=0.4$ millimeters, $l=4$ feet, and $h=0.4$ feet, find how many million gallons per day will pass through one acre of filter beds.

Prob. 203*g*. A bent U tube of uniform size is partly filled with water. Let the water in one leg be depressed a certain distance, causing that in the other to rise the same distance. When the depressing force is removed, the water oscillates up and down in the legs of the tube, the times of oscillation being isochronous. If l be the entire length of the water in the tube, show that the time of one oscillation is $\pi\sqrt{l/2g}$. If the legs are inclined to the horizontal at the angles θ and ϕ, show that the time of one oscillation is $\pi\sqrt{l/g\,(\sin\theta + \sin\phi)}$.

Prob. 203*h*. The bottom of a canal has the width $2b$, and it is desired to shape the banks so that the hydraulic radius of the cross-section may be constant. Show that the equation of the curve is

$$y = r\log_e (x + \sqrt{x^2 - r^2})/(b + \sqrt{b^2 - r^2})$$

in which y is the depth of the water, x the half width of the water surface, and r the constant hydraulic radius.

Prob. 203*i*. A river having a slope of 1 on 2500 runs due east. A line drawn due north at a point A on the river strikes at B, 5000 feet from A,

* Report Massachusetts State Board of Health, 1892, p. 553.

the edge of a large swamp which it is desired to drain. The level of the watei in this swamp is 0.5 feet below the river surface at A, and it is desired to lower that level 1.5 feet more. For this purpose a ditch is to be dug running from A in a straight line on a uniform slope until it joins the river at a point C eastward from A. The discharge of this ditch, in order to properly drain the swamp, will be 25 cubic feet per second, its side slopes are to be 1 on 1, the mean velocity is not to exceed 2.5 feet per second, and the coefficient c in the Chezy formula is estimated at 70. Find the length and width of the most economical ditch.

Art. 204. Answers to Problems

Below will be found answers to some of the problems given in the preceding pages, the numbers of the problems being placed in parentheses. In general it is not a good plan for a student to solve a problem in order to obtain a given answer. One object of solving problems is, of course, to obtain correct results, but the correctness of those results should be established by methods of verification rather than by the authority of a given answer. It is more profitable that a number of students should obtain different answers to a problem and engage in a discussion as to the correctness of their solutions than that all discussion should be stopped because a certain answer is given in the text. However satisfactory it may be to know in advance the result of the solution of an exercise, let the student bear in mind that after commencement day answers to problems will not be given.

(1) One horse-power. (3) 147.2 pounds. (4) See Table 4. (7) See Index. (8) 29.56 inches. (9*b*) 9.54 kilograms per square centimeter. (9*d*) 5575 kilograms. (12) 40.6, 1.56, 2.65. (15) 28 300 pounds. (17) 4.01 feet. (20*b*) 3.07. (20*c*) 2945 kilograms. (21) 56.9 feet per second. (25) $v = 32.1$ feet per second. (27) 19.3 pounds. (32) 24.9 seconds. (33*c*) 0.73. (35) 1.96 and 166 cubic feet. (36) 0.017 inches. (37) 1.15 feet. (39) $v = 4.00$ feet per second. (41) See Engineering News, May 4, 1911. (45) $c = 1.06$. (48) $c = 0.605$. (49) 17.2 feet. (50) 10.5 cubic feet per second. (51) 0.034 cubic feet per second. (55) 103. (59*a*) $c_1 = 0.98$. (60) 0.361 feet per second. (62) 0.0109 feet. (67) 7.10 and 6.97 cubic feet per second. (71) 0.74 percent. (72) 0.581. (72*a*) 1.30 centimeters. (75) 0.126 feet. (76) 0.13 and 7.60 feet. (77) 0.28 feet. (78) $c = 0.90$ and $h_1 = 0.70$. (80) $c = 0.802$. (81) 6.67 feet. (83) 0.963. (84) 1.06. (89) 0.29 feet. (95) 3.06 and 4.94 inches. (98) About 6 cubic feet per second. (112) 1.4 feet. (114) 4.4 feet. (115) 7.32 feet per second. (116)

1.28 × 0.64 feet. (118) 57 400 000 gallons. (120) $d = 3.09$ feet. (127*b*) 0.48 meters. (129) 546 cubic feet per second. (132) 1.76 feet per second. (134) 760 cubic feet per second. (140) $d_1 = 12.5$ feet. (141*d*) $H = 0.41$ meters. (145) 0.9. (146) 13.5 horse-powers. (147) 1.32 horse-powers. (148) 257 feet. (149) 35.4 percent. (151*c*) 18 400 kilowatts. (152) 3.96 gallons. (155) About 120 pounds. (159) 34.5 feet per second. (162*a*) $e = 0.83$. (164) From 48 to 50 horse-powers. (165) 13.6. (171*a*) 30.1 kilowatts. (172) 16 feet. (175) 4.117 and 4.120. (178) 167. (182*e*) 27.0 cubic meters. (183) 743 horse-powers. (185) 1530 horse-powers. (191*d*) $r = 11.6$ meters. (198) $e = 0.78$. (200) 17.8 horse-powers. (201*d*) $9\frac{1}{4}$ meters.

Evolvi varia problemata. In scientiis enim ediscendis prosunt exempla magisquam præcepta. Qua de causa in his fusius expatiatus sum. — NEWTON.

ART. 205. MATHEMATICAL TABLES

Tables A, B, C, D give constants often needed in computations.

Table E gives squares of numbers from 1.00 to 9.99, the arrangement being the same as that of the logarithmic table. By properly moving the decimal point, four-place squares of other numbers are also readily taken out. For example, the square of 0.874 is 0.7639, and that of 87.4 is 7639, correct to four significant figures.

Table F gives areas of circles for diameters ranging from 1.00 to 9.99, arranged in the same manner, and by properly moving the decimal point, four-place areas for all circles can be found. For instance, if the diameter is 4.175 inches, the area is 13.69 square inches; if the diameter is 0.535 feet, the area is 0.2248 square feet.

Table G gives trigonometric functions of angles and Table H the logarithms of these functions. The term "arc" means the length of a circular arc of radius unity, while "coarc" is the complement of the arc, or a quadrant minus the arc. If θ is the number of degrees in any angle, the value of arcθ is $\pi\theta/180$.

Table J gives four-place common logarithms of numbers, and these are of great value in hydraulic computations (Art. 8). Table K, taken from the author's "Elements of Precise Surveying and Geodesy," gives nine-place constants and their logarithms.

For other tables used in hydraulic computations see American Civil Engineers' Pocket Book (New York, 1912). Barlow's Tables (London, 1907) give eight-place values of squares, cubes, square roots, cube roots, and reciprocals of numbers from 1 to 10 000.

Table A. Fundamental Hydraulic Constants

English Measures

Name	Symbol	Number	Logarithm
Pounds of water in one cubic foot	w	62.5	1.7959
Pounds of water in one U. S. gallon	$w/7.481$	8.355	0.9220
Pounds per square inch due to one atmosphere		14.7	1.1673
Pounds per square inch due to one foot of head	$w/144$	0.434	$\bar{1}.6375$
Feet of head for pressure of one pound per square inch	$144/w$	2.304	0.3625
Cubic feet in one U. S. gallon	$231/1728$	0.1337	$\bar{1}.1261$
U. S. gallons in one cubic foot	$1728/231$	7.481	0.8739
Acceleration of gravity in feet per second per second	g	32.16	1.5073
	$\sqrt{2g}$	8.020	0.9042
	$\frac{2}{3}\sqrt{2g}$	5.347	0.7281
	$1/2g$	0.01555	$\bar{2}.1916$
	$\frac{1}{4}\pi\sqrt{2g}$	6.299	0.7993

Table B. Fundamental Hydraulic Constants

Metric Measures

Name	Symbol	Number	Logarithm
Kilograms of water in one cubic meter	w	1000	3.0000
Kilograms of water in one liter	$w/1000$	1	0.0000
Kilograms per square centimeter due to one atmosphere		1.033	0.0142
Kilograms per square centimeter due to one meter head	$w/10000$	0.1	$\bar{1}.0000$
Meters of head for pressure of one kilogram per square centimeter	$10000/w$	10	1.0000
Cubic meters in one liter	$1/1000$	0.001	$\bar{3}.0000$
Liters in one cubic meter	$1000/1$	1000	3.0000
Acceleration of gravity in meters per second per second	g	9.800	0.9912
	$\sqrt{2g}$	4.427	0.6461
	$\frac{2}{3}\sqrt{2g}$	2.951	0.4700
	$1/2g$	0.05104	$\bar{2}.7077$
	$\frac{1}{4}\pi\sqrt{2g}$	3.477	0.5412

TABLE C. METRIC EQUIVALENTS OF ENGLISH UNITS

English Unit	Metric Equivalent	Logarithm
1 Inch	2.5400 centimeters	0.40483
1 Foot	0.3048 meters	$\bar{1}.48402$
1 Square Inch	6.4520 square centimeters	0.80969
1 Square Foot	0.09290 square meters	$\bar{2}.96803$
1 Cubic Foot	0.02832 cubic meters	$\bar{2}.45209$
1 U. S. Gallon	3.7854 liters	0.57812
1 Imperial Gallon	4.5438 liters	0.65742
1 Pound	0.4536 kilograms	$\bar{1}.65667$
1 Pound per Square Inch	0.07030 kilograms per square centimeter	$\bar{2}.84697$
1 Pound per Cubic Foot	16.017 kilograms per cubic meter	1.20457
1 Foot-pound	0.1383 kilogram-meters	$\bar{1}.14069$
1 Horse-power	1.0139 cheval-vapeur	0.00599
Fahrenheit Temperature F°	Centigrade temperature $C° = \frac{5}{9}(F° - 32°)$	

TABLE D. ENGLISH EQUIVALENTS OF METRIC UNITS

Metric Unit	English Equivalent	Logarithm
1 Centimeter	0.3937 inches	$\bar{1}.59517$
1 Meter	3.2808 feet	0.51598
1 Square Centimeter	0.1550 square inches	$\bar{1}.19031$
1 Square Meter	10.764 square feet	1.03197
1 Cubic Meter	35.314 cubic feet	1.54791
1 Liter	0.2642 U. S. gallons	$\bar{1}.42188$
1 Liter	0.2201 imperial gallons	$\bar{1}.34258$
1 Kilogram	2.2046 pounds	0.34333
1 Kilogram per Square Centimeter	14.224 pounds per square inch	1.15303
1 Kilogram per Cubic Meter	0.06244 pounds per cubic foot	$\bar{2}.79543$
1 Kilogram-meter	7.2329 foot-pounds	0.85931
1 Cheval-vapeur	0.9863 horse-powers	$\bar{1}.99041$
Centigrade Temperature C°	Fahrenheit temperature $F° = 32° + 1.8\ C°$	

Table E. Squares of Numbers

n	0	1	2	3	4	5	6	7	8	9	Diff.
1.0	1.000	1.020	1.040	1.061	1.082	1.103	1.124	1.145	1.166	1.188	22
1.1	1.210	1.232	1.254	1.277	1.300	1.323	1.346	1.369	1.392	1.416	24
1.2	1.440	1.464	1.488	1.513	1.538	1.563	1.588	1.613	1.638	1.664	26
1.3	1.690	1.716	1.742	1.769	1.796	1.823	1.850	1.877	1.904	1.932	28
1.4	1.960	1.988	2.016	2.045	2.074	2.103	2.132	2.161	2.190	2.220	30
1.5	2.250	2.280	2.310	2.341	2.372	2.403	2.434	2.465	2.496	2.528	32
1.6	2.560	2.592	2.624	2.657	2.690	2.723	2.756	2.789	2.822	2.856	34
1.7	2.890	2.924	2.958	2.993	3.028	3.063	3.098	3.133	3.168	3.204	36
1.8	3.240	3.276	3.312	3.349	3.386	3.423	3.460	3.497	3.534	3.572	38
1.9	3.610	3.648	3.686	3.725	3.764	3.803	3.842	3.881	3.920	3.960	40
2.0	4.000	4.040	4.080	4.121	4.162	4.203	4.244	4.285	4.326	4.368	42
2.1	4.410	4.452	4.494	4.537	4.580	4.623	4.666	4.709	4.752	4.796	44
2.2	4.840	4.884	4.928	4.973	5.018	5.063	5.108	5.153	5.198	5.244	46
2.3	5.290	5.336	5.382	5.429	5.476	5.523	5.570	5.617	5.664	5.712	48
2.4	5.760	5.808	5.856	5.905	5.954	6.003	6.052	6.101	6.150	6.200	50
2.5	6.250	6.300	6.350	6.401	6.452	6.503	6.554	6.605	6.656	6 708	52
2.6	6.760	6.812	6.864	6.917	6.970	7.023	7.076	7.129	7.182	7.236	54
2.7	7.290	7.344	7.398	7.453	7.508	7.563	7.618	7.673	7.728	7.784	56
2.8	7.840	7.896	7.952	8.009	8.066	8.123	8.180	8.237	8.294	8.352	58
2.9	8.410	8.468	8.526	8.585	8.644	8.703	8.762	8.821	8.880	8.940	60
3.0	9.000	9.060	9.120	9.181	9.242	9.303	9.364	9.425	9.486	9.548	62
3.1	9.610	9.672	9.734	9.797	9.860	9.923	9.986	10.05	10.11	10.18	6
3.2	10.24	10.30	10.37	10.43	10.50	10.56	10.63	10.69	10.76	10.82	7
3.3	10.89	10.96	11.02	11.09	11.16	11.22	11.29	11.36	11.42	11.49	7
3.4	11.56	11.63	11.70	11.76	11.83	11.90	11.97	12.04	12.11	12.18	7
3.5	12.25	12.32	12.39	12.46	12.53	12.60	12.67	12.74	12.82	12.89	7
3.6	12.96	13.03	13.10	13.18	13.25	13.32	13.40	13.47	13.54	13.62	7
3.7	13.69	13.76	13.84	13.91	13.99	14.06	14.14	14.21	14.29	14.36	8
3.8	14.44	14.52	14.59	14.67	14.75	14.82	14.90	14.98	15.05	15.13	8
3.9	15.21	15.29	15.37	15.44	15.52	15.60	15.68	15.76	15.84	15.92	8
4.0	16.00	16.08	16.16	16.24	16.32	16.40	16.48	16.56	16.65	16.73	8
4.1	16.81	16.89	16.97	17.06	17.14	17.22	17.31	17.39	17.47	17.56	8
4.2	17.64	17.72	17.81	17.89	17.98	18.06	18.15	18.23	18.32	18.40	9
4.3	18.49	18.58	18.66	18.75	18.84	18.92	19.01	19.10	19.18	19.27	9
4.4	19.36	19.45	19.54	19.62	19.71	19.80	19.89	19.98	20.07	20.16	9
4.5	20.25	20.34	20.43	20.52	20.61	20.70	20.79	20.88	20.98	21.07	9
4.6	21.16	21.25	21.34	21.44	21.53	21.62	21.72	21.81	21.90	22.00	9
4.7	22.09	22.18	22.28	22.37	22.47	22.56	22.66	22.75	22.85	22.94	10
4.8	23.04	23.14	23.23	23.33	23.43	23.52	23.62	23.72	23.81	23.91	10
4.9	24.01	24.11	24.21	24.30	24.40	24.50	24.60	24.70	24.80	24.90	10
5.0	25.00	25.10	25.20	25.30	25.40	25.50	25.60	25.70	25.81	25.91	10
5.1	26.01	26.11	26.21	26.32	26.42	26.52	26.63	26.73	26.83	26.94	10
5 2	27.04	27.14	27.25	27.35	27.46	27.56	27.67	27.77	27.88	27.98	11
5.3	28.09	28.20	28.30	28.41	28.42	28.62	28.73	28.84	28.94	29.05	11
5.4	29.16	29.27	29.38	29.48	29.59	29.70	29.81	29.92	30.03	30.14	11
n	0	1	2	3	4	5	6	7	8	9	Diff.

TABLE E. SQUARES OF NUMBERS (*Continued*)

n	0	1	2	3	4	5	6	7	8	9	Diff.
5.5	30.25	30.36	30.47	30.58	30.69	30.80	30.91	31.02	31.14	31.25	11
5.6	31.36	31.47	31.58	31.70	31.81	31.92	32.04	32.15	32.26	32.38	11
5.7	32.49	32.60	32.72	32.83	32.95	33.06	33.18	33.29	33.41	33.52	12
5.8	33.64	33.76	33.87	33.99	34.11	34.22	34.34	34.46	34.57	34.69	12
5.9	34.81	34.93	35.05	35.16	35.28	35.40	35.52	35.64	35.76	35.88	12
6.0	36.00	36.12	36.24	36.36	36.48	36.60	36.72	36.84	36.97	37.09	12
6.1	37.21	37.33	37.45	37.58	37.70	37.82	37.95	38.07	38.19	38.32	12
6.2	38.44	38.56	38.69	38.81	38.94	39.06	39.19	39.31	39.44	39.56	13
6.3	39.69	39.82	39.94	40.07	40.20	40.32	40.45	40.58	40.70	40.83	13
6.4	40.96	41.09	41.22	41.34	41.47	41.60	41.73	41.86	41.99	42.12	13
6.5	42.25	42.38	42.51	42.64	42.77	42.90	43.03	43.16	43.30	43.43	13
6.6	43.56	43.69	43.82	43.96	44.09	44.22	44.36	44.49	44.62	44.76	13
6.7	44.89	45.02	45.16	45.29	45.43	45.56	45.70	45.83	45.97	46.10	14
6.8	46.24	46.38	46.51	46.65	46.79	46.92	47.06	47.20	47.33	47.47	14
6.9	47.61	47.75	47.89	48.02	48.16	48.30	48.44	48.58	48.72	48.86	14
7.0	49.00	49.14	49.28	49.42	49.56	49.70	49.84	49.98	50.13	50.27	14
7.1	50.41	50.55	50.69	50.84	50.98	51.12	51.27	51.41	51.55	51.70	14
7.2	51.84	51.98	52.13	52.27	52.42	52.56	52.71	52.85	53.00	53.14	15
7.3	53.29	53.44	53.58	53.73	53.88	54.02	54.17	54.32	54.46	54.61	15
7.4	54.76	54.91	55.06	55.20	55.35	55.50	55.65	55.80	55.95	56.10	15
7.5	56.25	56.40	56.55	56.70	56.85	57.00	57.15	57.30	57.46	57.61	15
7.6	57.76	57.91	58.06	58.22	58.37	58.52	58.68	58.83	58.98	59.14	15
7.7	59.29	59.44	59.60	59.75	59.91	60.06	60.22	60.37	60.53	60.68	16
7.8	60.84	61.00	61.15	61.31	61.47	61.62	61.78	61.94	62.09	62.25	16
7.9	62.41	62.57	62.73	62.88	63.04	63.20	63.36	63.52	63.68	63.84	16
8 0	64.00	64.16	64.32	64.48	64.64	64.80	64.96	65.12	65.29	65.45	16
8.1	65.61	65.77	65.93	66.10	66.26	66.42	66.59	66.75	66.91	67.08	16
8.2	67.24	67.40	67.57	67.73	67.90	68.06	68.23	68.39	68.56	68.72	17
8.3	68.89	69.06	69.22	69.39	69.56	69.72	69.89	70.06	70.22	70.39	17
8.4	70.56	70.73	70.90	71.06	71.23	71.40	71.57	71.74	71.91	72.08	17
8.5	72.25	72.42	72.59	72.76	72.93	73.10	73.27	73.44	73.62	73.79	17
8.6	73.96	74.13	74.30	74.48	74.65	74.82	75.00	75.17	75.34	75.52	17
8.7	75.69	75.86	76.04	76.21	76.39	76.56	76.74	76.91	77.09	77.26	18
8.8	77.44	77.62	77.79	77.97	78.15	78.32	78.50	78.68	78.85	79.03	18
8.9	79.21	79.39	79.57	79.74	79.92	80.10	80.28	80.46	80.64	80.82	18
9.0	81.00	81.18	81.36	81.54	81.72	81.90	82.08	82.26	82.45	82.63	18
9.1	82.81	82.99	83.17	83.36	83.54	83.72	83.91	84.09	84.27	84.46	18
9.2	84.64	84.82	85.01	85.19	85.38	85.56	85.75	85.93	86.12	86.30	19
9.3	86.49	86.68	86.86	87.05	87.24	87.42	87.61	87.80	87.98	88.17	19
9.4	88.36	88.55	88.74	88.92	89.11	89.30	89.49	89.68	89.87	90.06	19
9 5	90.25	90.44	90.63	90.82	91.01	91.20	91.39	91.58	91.78	91.97	19
9.6	92.16	92.35	92.54	92.74	92.93	93.12	93.32	93.51	93.70	93.90	19
9.7	94.09	94.28	94.48	94.67	94.87	95.06	95.26	95.45	95.65	95.84	20
9.8	96.04	96.24	96.43	96.63	96.83	97.02	97.22	97.42	97.61	97.81	20
9.9	98.01	98.21	98.41	98.60	98.80	99.00	99.20	99.40	99.60	99.80	20
n	0	1	2	3	4	5	6	7	8	9	Diff.

Table F. Areas of Circles

d	0	1	2	3	4	5	6	7	8	9	Diff.
1.0	.7854	.8012	.8171	.8332	.8495	.8659	.8825	.8992	.9161	.9331	
1.1	.9503	.9677	.9852	1.003	1.021	1.039	1.057	1.075	1.094	1.112	
1.2	1.131	1.150	1.169	1.188	1.208	1.227	1.247	1.267	1.287	1.307	19
1.3	1.327	1.348	1.368	1.389	1.410	1.431	1.453	1.474	1.496	1.517	21
1.4	1.539	1.561	1.584	1.606	1.629	1.651	1.674	1.697	1.720	1.744	22
1.5	1.767	1.791	1.815	1.839	1.863	1.887	1.911	1.936	1.961	1.986	24
1.6	2.011	2.036	2.061	2.087	2.112	2.138	2.164	2.190	2.217	2.243	26
1.7	2.270	2.297	2.324	2.351	2.378	2.405	2.433	2.461	2.488	2.516	27
1.8	2.545	2.573	2.602	2.630	2.659	2.688	2.717	2.746	2.776	2.806	29
1.9	2.835	2.865	2.895	2.926	2.956	2.986	3.017	3.048	3.079	3.110	30
2.0	3.142	3.173	3.205	3.237	3.269	3.301	3.333	3.365	3.398	3.431	32
2.1	3.464	3.497	3.530	3.563	3.597	3.631	3.664	3.698	3.733	3.767	34
2.2	3.801	3.836	3.871	3.906	3.941	3.976	4.012	4.047	4.083	4.119	35
2.3	4.155	4.191	4.227	4.264	4.301	4.337	4.374	4.412	4.449	4.486	36
2.4	4.524	4.562	4.600	4.638	4.676	4.714	4.753	4.792	4.831	4.870	38
2.5	4.909	4.948	4.988	5.027	5.067	5.107	5.147	5.187	5.228	5.269	40
2.6	5.309	5.350	5.391	5.433	5.474	5.515	5.557	5.599	5.641	5.683	41
2.7	5.726	5.768	5.811	5.853	5.896	5.940	5.983	6.026	6.070	6.114	43
2.8	6.158	6.202	6.246	6.290	6.335	6.379	6.424	6.469	6.514	6.560	44
2.9	6.605	6.651	6.697	6.743	6.789	6.835	6.881	6.928	6.975	7.022	46
3.0	7.069	7.116	7.163	7.211	7.258	7.306	7.354	7.402	7.451	7.499	48
3.1	7.548	7.596	7.645	7.694	7.744	7.793	7.843	7.892	7.942	7.992	49
3.2	8.042	8.093	8.143	8.194	8.245	8.296	8.347	8.398	8.450	8.501	51
3.3	8.553	8.605	8.657	8.709	8.762	8.814	8.867	8.920	8.973	9.026	52
3.4	9.079	9.133	9.186	9.240	9.294	9.348	9.402	9.457	9.511	9.566	54
3.5	9.621	9.676	9.731	9.787	9.842	9.898	9.954	10.01	10.07	10.12	56
3.6	10.18	10.24	10.29	10.35	10.41	10.46	10.52	10.58	10.64	10.69	6
3.7	10.75	10.81	10.87	10.93	10.99	11.04	11.10	11.16	11.22	11.28	6
3.8	11.34	11.40	11.46	11.52	11.58	11.64	11.70	11.76	11.82	11.88	6
3.9	11.95	12.01	12.07	12.13	12.19	12.25	12.32	12.38	12.44	12.50	6
4.0	12.57	12.63	12.69	12.76	12.82	12.88	12.95	13.01	13.07	13.14	7
4.1	13.20	13.27	13.33	13.40	13.46	13.53	13.59	13.66	13.72	13.79	7
4.2	13.85	13.92	13.99	14.05	14.12	14.19	14.25	14.32	14.39	14.45	7
4.3	14.52	14.59	14.66	14.73	14.79	14.86	14.93	15.00	15.07	15.14	7
4.4	15.21	15.27	15.34	15.41	15.48	15.55	15.62	15.69	15.76	15.83	7
4.5	15.90	15.98	16.05	16.12	16.19	16.26	16.33	16.40	16.47	16.55	7
4.6	16.62	16.69	16.76	16.84	16.91	16.98	17.06	17.13	17.20	17.28	7
4.7	17.35	17.42	17.50	17.57	17.65	17.72	17.80	17.87	17.95	18.02	8
4.8	18.10	18.17	18.25	18.32	18.40	18.47	18.55	18.63	18.70	18.78	8
4.9	18.86	18.93	19.01	19.09	19.17	19.24	19.32	19.40	19.48	19.56	8
5.0	19.63	19.71	19.79	19.87	19.95	20.03	20.11	20.19	20.27	20.35	8
5.1	20.43	20.51	20.59	20.67	20.75	20.83	20.91	20.99	21.07	21.16	8
5.2	21.24	21.32	21.40	21.48	21.57	21.65	21.73	21.81	21.90	21.98	8
5.3	22.06	22.15	22.23	22.31	22.40	22.48	22.56	22.65	22.73	22.82	8
5.4	22.90	22.99	23.07	23.16	23.24	23.33	23.41	23.50	23.59	23.67	9
d	0	1	2	3	4	5	6	7	8	9	Diff.

TABLE F. AREAS OF CIRCLES (*Continued*)

d	0	1	2	3	4	5	6	7	8	9	Diff.
5.5	23.76	23.84	23.93	24.02	24.11	24.19	24.28	24.37	24.45	24.54	9
5.6	24.63	24.72	24.81	24.89	24.98	25.07	25.16	25.25	25.34	25.43	9
5.7	25.52	25.61	25.70	25.79	25.88	25.97	26.06	26.15	26.24	26.33	9
5.8	26.42	26.51	26.60	26.69	26.79	26.88	26.97	27.06	27.15	27.25	9
5.9	27.34	27.43	27.53	27.62	27.71	27.81	27.90	27.99	28.09	28.18	9
6.0	28.27	28.37	28.46	28.56	28.65	28.75	28.84	28.94	29.03	29.13	9
6.1	29.22	29.32	29.42	29.51	29.61	29.71	29.80	29.90	30.00	30.09	10
6.2	30.19	30.29	30.39	30.48	30.58	30.68	30.78	30.88	30.97	31.07	10
6.3	31.17	31.27	31.37	31.47	31.57	31.67	31.77	31.87	31.97	32.07	10
6.4	32.17	32.27	32.37	32.47	32.57	32.67	32.78	32.88	32.98	33.08	10
6.5	33.18	33.29	33.39	33.49	33.59	33.70	33.80	33.90	34.00	34.11	10
6.6	34.21	34.32	34.42	34.52	34.63	34.73	34.84	34.94	35.05	35.15	10
6.7	35.26	35.36	35.47	35.57	35.68	35.78	35.89	36.00	36.10	36.21	10
6.8	36.32	36.42	36.53	36.64	36.75	36.85	36.96	37.07	37.18	37.28	11
6.9	37.39	37.50	37.61	37.72	37.83	37.94	38.05	38.16	38.26	38.37	11
7.0	38.48	38.59	38.70	38.82	38.93	39.04	39.15	39.26	39.37	39.48	11
7.1	39.59	39.70	39.82	39.93	40.04	40.15	40.26	40.38	40.49	40.60	11
7.2	40.72	40.83	40.94	41.06	41.17	41.28	41.40	41.51	41.62	41.74	11
7.3	41.85	41.97	42.08	42.20	42.31	42.43	42.54	42.66	42.78	42.89	11
7.4	43.01	43.12	43.24	43.36	43.47	43.59	43.71	43.83	43.94	44.06	12
7.5	44.18	44.30	44.41	44.53	44.65	44.77	44.89	45.01	45.13	45.25	12
7.6	45.36	45.48	45.60	45.72	45.84	45.96	46.08	46.20	46.32	46.45	12
7.7	46.57	46.69	46.81	46.93	47.05	47.17	47.29	47.42	47.54	47.66	12
7.8	47.78	47.91	48.03	48.15	48.27	48.40	48.52	48.65	48.77	48.89	12
7.9	49.02	49.14	49.27	49.39	49.51	49.64	49.76	49.89	50.01	50.14	12
8.0	50.27	50.39	50.52	50.64	50.77	50.90	51.02	51.15	51.28	51.40	13
8.1	51.53	51.66	51.78	51.91	52.04	52.17	52.30	52.42	52.55	52.68	13
8.2	52.81	52.94	53.07	53.20	53.33	53.46	53.59	53.72	53.85	53.98	13
8.3	54.11	54.24	54.37	54.50	54.63	54.76	54.89	55.02	55.15	55.29	13
8.4	55.42	55.55	55.68	55.81	55.95	56.08	56.21	56.35	56.48	56.61	13
8.5	56.75	56.88	57.01	57.15	57.28	57.41	57.55	57.68	57.82	57.95	13
8.6	58.09	58.22	58.36	58.49	58.63	58.77	58.90	59.04	59.17	59.31	14
8.7	59.45	59.58	59.72	59.86	59.99	60.13	60.27	60.41	60.55	60.68	14
8.8	60.82	60.96	61.10	61.24	61.38	61.51	61.65	61.79	61.93	62.07	14
8.9	62.21	62.35	62.49	62.63	62.77	62.91	63.05	63.19	63.33	63.48	14
9.0	63.62	63.76	63.90	64.04	64.18	64.33	64.47	64.61	64.75	64.90	14
9.1	65.04	65.18	65.33	65.47	65.61	65.76	65.90	66.04	66.19	66.33	14
9.2	66.48	66.62	66.77	66.91	67.06	67.20	67.35	67.49	67.64	67.78	15
9.3	67.93	68.08	68.22	68.37	68.51	68.66	68.81	68.96	69.10	69.25	15
9.4	69.40	69.55	69.69	69.84	69.99	70.14	70.29	70.44	70.58	70.73	15
9.5	70.88	71.03	71.18	71.33	71.48	71.63	71.78	71.93	72.08	72.23	15
9.6	72.38	72.53	72.68	72.84	72.99	73.14	73.29	73.44	73.59	73.75	15
9.7	73.90	74.05	74.20	74.36	74.51	74.66	74.82	74.97	75.12	75.28	15
9.8	75.43	75.58	75.74	75.89	76.05	76.20	76.36	76.51	76.67	76.82	16
9.9	76.98	77.13	77.29	77.44	77.60	77.76	77.91	78.07	78.23	78.38	16
d	0	1	2	3	4	5	6	7	8	9	Diff.

TABLE G. TRIGONOMETRIC FUNCTIONS

Angle Deg.	Arc	Sin	Tan	Sec	Cosec	Cot	Cos	Coarc	
0	0.	0.	0.	1.	∞	∞	1.	1.5708	90
1	0.0175	0.0175	0.0175	1.0002	57.299	57.290	0.9998	.5533	89
2	.0349	.0349	.0349	1.0006	28.654	28.636	.9994	.5359	88
3	.0524	.0523	.0524	1.0014	19.107	19.081	.9986	.5184	87
4	.0698	.0698	.0699	1.0024	14.336	14.301	.9976	.5010	86
5	.0873	.0872	.0875	1.0038	11.474	11.430	.9962	.4835	85
6	0.1047	0.1045	0.1051	1.0055	9.5668	9.5144	0.9945	1.4661	84
7	.1222	.1219	.1228	1.0075	8.2055	8.1443	.9925	.4486	83
8	.1396	.1392	.1405	1.0098	7.1853	7.1154	.9903	.4312	82
9	.1571	.1564	.1584	1.0125	6.3925	6.3138	.9877	.4137	81
10	.1745	.1736	.1763	1.0154	5.7588	5.6713	.9848	.3963	80
11	0.1920	.01908	0.1944	1.0187	5.2408	5.1446	0.9816	1.3788	79
12	.2094	.2079	.2126	1.0223	4.8097	4.7046	.9781	.3614	78
13	.2269	.2250	.2309	1.0263	4.4454	4.3315	.9744	.3439	77
14	.2443	.2419	.2493	1.0306	4.1336	4.0108	.9703	.3265	76
15	.2618	.2588	.2679	1.0353	3.8637	3.7321	.9659	.3090	75
16	0.2793	0.2756	0.2867	1.0403	3.6280	3.4874	0.9613	1.2915	74
17	.2967	.2924	.3057	1.0457	3.4203	3.2709	.9563	.2741	73
18	.3142	.3090	.3249	1.0515	3.2361	3.0777	.9511	.2566	72
19	.3316	.3256	.3443	1.0576	3.0716	2.9042	.9455	.2392	71
20	.3491	.3420	.3640	1.0642	2.9238	2.7475	.9397	.2217	70
21	0.3665	0.3584	0.3839	1.0711	2.7904	2.6051	0.9336	1.2043	69
22	.3840	.3746	.4040	1.0785	2.6695	2.4751	.9272	.1868	68
23	.4014	.3907	.4245	1.0864	2.5593	2.3559	.9205	.1694	67
24	.4189	.4067	.4452	1.0946	2.4586	2.2460	.9135	.1519	66
25	.4363	.4226	.4663	1.1034	2.3662	2.1445	.9063	.1345	65
26	0.4538	0.4384	0.4877	1.1126	2.2812	2.0503	0.8988	1.1170	64
27	.4712	.4540	.5095	1.1223	2.2027	1.9626	.8910	.0996	63
28	.4887	.4695	.5317	1.1326	2.1301	1.8807	.8829	.0821	62
29	.5061	.4848	.5543	1.1434	2.0627	1.8040	.8746	.0647	61
30	.5236	.5000	.5774	1.1547	2.0000	1.7321	.8660	.0472	60
31	0.5411	0.5150	0.6009	1.1666	1.9416	1.6643	0.8572	1.0297	59
32	.5585	.5299	.6249	1.1792	1.8871	1.6003	.8480	1.0123	58
33	.5760	.5446	.6494	1.1924	1.8361	1.5399	.8387	0.9948	57
34	.5934	.5592	.6745	1.2062	1.7883	1.4826	.8290	.9774	56
35	.6109	.5736	.7002	1.2208	1.7434	1.4281	.8192	.9599	55
36	0.6283	0.5878	0.7265	1.2361	1.7013	1.3764	0.8089	0.9425	54
37	.6458	.6018	.7536	1.2521	1.6616	1.3270	.7986	.9250	53
38	.6632	.6157	.7813	1.2690	1.6243	1.2799	.7880	.9076	52
39	.6807	.6293	.8098	1.2868	1.5890	1.2349	.7771	.8901	51
40	.6981	.6428	.8391	1.3054	1.5557	1.1918	.7660	.8727	50
41	0.7156	0.6561	0.8693	1.3250	1.5243	1.1504	0.7547	0.8552	49
42	.7330	.6691	.9004	1.3456	1.4945	1.1106	.7431	.8378	48
43	.7505	.6820	.9325	1.3673	1.4663	1.0724	.7314	.8203	47
44	.7679	.6947	.9657	1.3902	1.4396	1.0355	.7193	.8029	46
45	.7854	.7071	1.	1.4142	1.4142	1.	.7071	.7854	45
	Coarc	Cos	Cot	Cosec	Sec	Tan	Sin	Arc	Angle Deg.

TABLE H. LOGARITHMS OF TRIGONOMETRIC FUNCTIONS

Angle Deg.	Log Arc	Log Sin	Log Tan	Log Sec	Log Cosec	Log Cot	Log Cos	Log Coarc	
0	$-\infty$	$-\infty$	$-\infty$	0.	∞	∞	0.	0.1961	90
1	$\bar{2}$.2419	$\bar{2}$.2419	$\bar{2}$.2419	0.0001	1.7581	1.7581	$\bar{1}$.9999	.1913	89
2	.5429	.5428	.5431	.0003	.4572	.4569	.9997	.1864	88
3	.7190	.7188	.7194	.0006	.2812	.2806	.9994	.1814	87
4	.8439	.8436	.8446	.0011	.1564	.1554	.9989	.1764	86
5	.9408	.9403	.9420	.0017	.0597	.0580	.9983	.1713	85
6	$\bar{1}$.0200	^{1}.0192	$\bar{1}$.0216	0.0024	0.9808	0.9784	$\bar{1}$.9976	0.1662	84
7	.0870	.0859	.0891	.0032	.9141	.9109	.9968	.1610	83
8	.1450	.1436	.1478	.0042	.8564	.8522	.9958	.1557	82
9	.1961	.1943	.1997	.0054	.8057	.8003	.9946	.1504	81
10	.2419	.2397	.2463	.0066	.7603	.7537	.9934	.1450	80
11	$\bar{1}$.2833	$\bar{1}$.2806	$\bar{1}$.2887	0.0081	0.7194	0.7113	$\bar{1}$.9919	0.1395	79
12	.3211	.3179	.3275	.0096	.6821	.6725	.9904	.1340	78
13	.3558	.3521	.3634	.0113	.6479	.6366	.9887	.1284	77
14	.3880	.3837	.3968	.0131	.6163	.6032	.9869	.1227	76
15	.4180	.4130	.4281	.0151	.5870	.5719	.9849	.1169	75
16	$\bar{1}$.4460	$\bar{1}$.4403	$\bar{1}$.4575	0.0172	0.5597	0.5425	$\bar{1}$.9828	0.1111	74
17	.4723	.4659	.4853	.0194	.5341	.5147	.9806	.1052	73
18	.4971	.4900	.5118	.0218	.5100	.4882	.9782	.0992	72
19	.5206	.5126	.5370	.0243	.4874	.4630	.9757	.0931	71
20	.5429	.5341	.5611	.0270	.4659	.4389	.9730	.0870	70
21	$\bar{1}$.5641	$\bar{1}$.5543	$\bar{1}$.5842	0.0298	0.4457	0.4158	$\bar{1}$.9702	0.0807	69
22	.5843	.5736	.6064	.0328	.4264	.3936	.9672	.0744	68
23	.6036	.5919	.6279	.0360	.4081	.3721	.9640	.0680	67
24	.6221	.6093	.6486	.0393	.3907	.3514	.9607	.0614	66
25	.6398	.6259	.6687	.0427	.3741	.3313	.9573	.0548	65
26	$\bar{1}$.6569	$\bar{1}$.6418	$\bar{1}$.6882	0.0463	0.3582	0.3118	$\bar{1}$.9537	0.0481	64
27	.6732	.6570	.7072	.0501	.3430	.2928	.9499	.0412	63
28	.6890	.6716	.7257	.0541	.3284	.2743	.9459	.0343	62
29	.7043	.6856	.7438	.0582	.3144	.2562	.9418	.0272	61
30	.7190	.6990	.7614	.0625	.3010	.2386	.9375	.0200	60
31	$\bar{1}$.7332	$\bar{1}$.7118	$\bar{1}$.7788	0.0669	0.2882	0.2212	$\bar{1}$.9331	0.0127	59
32	.7470	.7242	.7958	.0716	.2758	.2042	.9284	0.0053	58
33	.7604	.7361	.8125	.0764	.2639	.1875	.9236	$\bar{1}$.9978	57
34	.7734	.7476	.8290	.0814	.2524	.1710	.9186	.9901	56
35	.7859	.7586	.8452	.0866	.2414	.1548	.9134	.9822	55
36	$\bar{1}$.7982	$\bar{1}$.7692	$\bar{1}$.8613	0.0920	0.2308	0.1387	$\bar{1}$.9080	$\bar{1}$.9743	54
37	.8101	.7795	.8771	.0977	.2205	.1229	.9023	.9662	53
38	.8217	.7893	.8928	.1035	.2107	.1072	.8965	.9579	52
39	.8329	.7989	.9084	.1095	.2011	.0916	.8905	.9494	51
40	.8439	.8081	.9238	.1157	.1919	.0762	.8843	.9408	50
41	$\bar{1}$.8547	$\bar{1}$.8169	$\bar{1}$.9392	0.1222	0.1831	0.0608	$\bar{1}$.8778	$\bar{1}$.9321	49
42	.8651	.8255	.9544	.1289	.1745	.0456	.8711	.9231	48
43	.8753	.8338	.9697	.1359	.1662	.0303	.8641	.9140	47
44	.8853	.8418	.9848	.1431	.1582	.0152	.8569	.9046	46
45	.8951	.8495	0.	.1505	.1505	0.	.8495	.8951	45
	Log Coarc	Log Cos	Log Cot	Log Cosec	Log Sec	Log Tan	Log Sin	Log Arc	Angle Deg.

TABLE J. LOGARITHMS OF NUMBERS

n	0	1	2	3	4	5	6	7	8	9	Diff.
10	0000	0043	0086	0128	0170	0212	0253	0294	0334	0374	42
11	0414	0453	0492	0531	0569	0607	0645	0682	0719	0755	38
12	0792	0828	0864	0899	0934	0969	1004	1038	1072	1106	35
13	1139	1173	1206	1239	1271	1303	1335	1367	1399	1430	32
14	1461	1492	1523	1553	1584	1614	1644	1673	1703	1732	30
15	1761	1790	1818	1847	1875	1903	1931	1959	1987	2014	28
16	2041	2068	2095	2122	2148	2175	2201	2227	2253	2279	27
17	2304	2330	2355	2380	2405	2430	2455	2480	2504	2529	25
18	2553	2577	2601	2625	2648	2672	2695	2718	2742	2765	24
19	2788	2810	2833	2856	2878	2900	2923	2945	2967	2989	22
20	3010	3032	3054	3075	3096	3118	3139	3160	3181	3201	21
21	3222	3243	3263	3284	3304	3324	3345	3365	3385	3404	20
22	3424	3444	3464	3483	3502	3522	3541	3560	3579	3598	19
23	3617	3636	3655	3674	3692	3711	3729	3747	3766	3784	18
24	3802	3820	3838	3856	3874	3892	3909	3927	3945	3962	18
25	3979	3997	4014	4031	4048	4065	4082	4099	4116	4133	17
26	4150	4166	4183	4200	4216	4232	4249	4265	4281	4298	17
27	4314	4330	4346	4362	4378	4393	4409	4425	4440	4456	16
28	4472	4487	4502	4518	4533	4548	4564	4579	4594	4609	15
29	4624	4639	4654	4669	4683	4698	4713	4728	4742	4757	15
30	4771	4786	4800	4814	4829	4843	4857	4871	4886	4900	14
31	4914	4928	4942	4955	4969	4983	4997	5011	5024	5038	14
32	5051	5065	5079	5092	5105	5119	5132	5145	5159	5172	13
33	5185	5198	5211	5224	5237	5250	5263	5276	5289	5302	13
34	5315	5328	5340	5353	5366	5378	5391	5403	5416	5428	13
35	5441	5453	5465	5478	5490	5502	5514	5527	5539	5551	12
36	5563	5575	5587	5599	5611	5623	5635	5647	5658	5670	12
37	5682	5694	5705	5717	5729	5740	5752	5763	5775	5786	12
38	5798	5809	5821	5832	5843	5855	5866	5877	5888	5899	11
39	5911	5922	5933	5944	5955	5966	5977	5988	5999	6010	11
40	6021	6031	6042	6053	6064	6075	6085	6096	6107	6117	11
41	6128	6138	6149	6160	6170	6180	6191	6201	6212	6222	11
42	6232	6243	6253	6263	6274	6284	6294	6304	6314	6325	10
43	6335	6345	6355	6365	6375	6385	6395	6405	6415	6425	10
44	6435	6444	6454	6464	6474	6484	6493	6503	6513	6522	10
45	6532	6542	6551	6561	6571	6580	6590	6599	6609	6618	10
46	6628	6637	6646	6656	6665	6675	6684	6693	6702	6712	9
47	6721	6730	6739	6749	6758	6767	6776	6785	6794	6803	9
48	6812	6821	6830	6839	6848	6857	6866	6875	6884	6893	9
49	6902	6911	6920	6928	6937	6946	6955	6964	6972	6981	9
50	6990	6998	7007	7016	7024	7033	7042	7050	7059	7067	9
51	7076	7084	7093	7101	7110	7118	7126	7135	7143	7152	8
52	7160	7168	7177	7185	7193	7202	7210	7218	7226	7235	8
53	7243	7251	7259	7267	7275	7284	7292	7300	7308	7316	8
54	7324	7332	7340	7348	7356	7364	7372	7380	7388	7396	8
n	0	1	2	3	4	5	6	7	8	9	Diff.

Table J. Logarithms of Numbers (*Continued*)

n	0	1	2	3	4	5	6	7	8	9	Diff.
55	7404	7412	7419	7427	7435	7443	7451	7459	7466	7474	8
56	7482	7490	7497	7505	7513	7520	7528	7536	7543	7551	
57	7559	7566	7574	7582	7589	7597	7604	7612	7619	7627	
58	7634	7642	7649	7657	7664	7672	7679	7686	7694	7701	
59	7709	7716	7723	7731	7738	7745	7752	7760	7767	7774	
60	7782	7789	7796	7803	7810	7818	7825	7832	7839	7846	7
61	7853	7860	7868	7875	7882	7889	7896	7903	7910	7917	
62	7924	7931	7938	7945	7952	7959	7966	7973	7980	7987	
63	7993	8000	8007	8014	8021	8028	8035	8041	8048	8055	
64	8062	8069	8075	8082	8089	8096	8102	8109	8116	8122	
65	8129	8136	8142	8149	8156	8162	8169	8176	8182	8189	7
66	8195	8202	8209	8215	8222	8228	8235	8241	8248	8254	
67	8261	8267	8274	8280	8287	8293	8299	8306	8312	8319	
68	8325	8331	8338	8344	8351	8357	8363	8370	8376	8382	
69	8388	8395	8401	8407	8414	8420	8426	8432	8439	8445	
70	8451	8457	8463	8470	8476	8482	8488	8494	8500	8506	6
71	8513	8519	8525	8531	8537	8543	8549	8555	8561	8567	
72	8573	8579	8485	8591	8597	8603	8609	8615	8621	8627	
73	8633	8639	8645	8651	8657	8663	8669	8675	8681	8686	
74	8692	8698	8704	8710	8716	8722	8727	8733	8739	8745	
75	8751	8756	8762	8768	8774	8779	8785	8791	8797	8802	6
76	8808	8814	8820	8825	8831	8837	8842	8848	8854	8859	
77	8865	8871	8876	8882	8887	8893	8899	8904	8910	8915	
78	8921	8927	8932	8938	8943	8949	8954	8960	8965	8971	
79	8976	8982	8987	8993	8998	9004	9009	9015	9020	9025	
80	9031	9036	9042	9047	9053	9058	9063	9069	9074	9079	5
81	9085	9090	9096	9101	9106	9112	9117	9122	9128	9133	
82	9138	9143	9149	9154	9159	9165	9170	9175	9180	9186	
83	9191	9196	9201	9206	9212	9217	9222	9227	9232	9238	
84	9243	9248	9253	9258	9263	9269	9274	9279	9284	9289	
85	9294	9299	9304	9309	9315	9320	9325	9330	9335	9340	5
86	9345	9350	9355	9360	9365	9370	9375	9380	9385	9390	
87	9395	9400	9405	9410	9415	9420	9425	9430	9435	9440	
88	9445	9450	9455	9460	9465	9469	9474	9479	9484	9489	
89	9494	9499	9504	9509	9513	9518	9523	9528	9533	9538	
90	9542	9547	9552	9557	9562	9566	9571	9576	9581	9586	5
91	9590	9595	9600	9605	9609	9614	9619	9624	9628	9633	
92	9638	9643	9647	9652	9657	9661	9666	9671	9675	9680	
93	9685	9689	9694	9699	9703	9708	9713	9717	9722	9727	
94	9731	9736	9741	9745	9750	9754	9759	9763	9768	9773	
95	9777	9782	9786	9791	9795	9800	9805	9809	9814	9818	4
96	9823	9827	9832	9836	9841	9845	9850	9854	9859	9863	
97	9868	9872	9877	9881	9886	9890	9894	9899	9903	9908	
98	9912	9917	9921	9926	9930	9934	9939	9943	9948	9952	
99	9956	9961	9965	9969	9974	9978	9983	9987	9991	9996	
n	0	1	2	3	4	5	6	7	8	9	Diff.

Table K. Constants and their Logarithms

Name (Radius of circle or sphere = 1)	Symbol	Number	Logarithm
Area of circle	π	3.141 592 654	0.497 149 873
Circumference of circle	2π	6.283 185 307	0.798 179 868
Surface of sphere	4π	12.566 370 614	1.099 209 864
	$\frac{1}{6}\pi$	0.523 598 776	$\bar{1}$.718 998 622
Quadrant of circle	$\frac{1}{4}\pi$	0.785 398 163	$\bar{1}$.895 089 881
Area of semicircle	$\frac{1}{2}\pi$	1.570 796 327	0.196 119 877
Volume of sphere	$\frac{4}{3}\pi$	4.188 790 205	0.622 088 609
	π^2	9.869 604 401	0.994 299 745
	$\pi^{\frac{1}{2}}$	1.772 453 851	0.248 574 936
Degrees in a radian	$180/\pi$	57.295 779 513	1.758 122 632
Minutes in a radian	$10800/\pi$	3 437.746 771	3.536 273 883
Seconds in a radian	$648000/\pi$	206 264.806	5.314 425 133
	$1/\pi$	0.318 309 886	$\bar{1}$.502 850 127
	$1/\pi^{\frac{1}{2}}$	0.564 189 584	$\bar{1}$.751 425 064
	$1/\pi^2$	0.101 321 184	$\bar{1}$.005 700 255
Circumference/360	arc 1°	0.017 453 293	$\bar{2}$.241 877 368
	sin 1°	0.017 452 406	$\bar{2}$.241 855 318
Circumference/21600	arc 1′	0.000 290 888	4.463 726 117
	sin 1′	0.000 290 888	$\bar{4}$.463 726 111
Circumference/1296000	arc 1″	0.000 004 848	$\bar{6}$.685 574 867
	sin 1″	0.000 004 848	$\bar{6}$.685 574 867
Base Naperian system of logs	e	2.718 281 828	0.434 294 482
Modulus common system of logs	M	0.434 294 482	$\bar{1}$.637 784 311
Naperian log of 10	$1/M$	2.302 585 093	0.362 215 689
	hr	0.476 936 3	$\bar{1}$.678 460 4
Probable error constant	$hr\sqrt{2}$	0.674 489 7	$\bar{1}$.828 975 4

INDEX

(The numbers refer to pages.)